Cell and Molecular Biology

ERNEST J. DuPRAW

Associate Professor
University of Maryland School of Medicine
Baltimore, Maryland

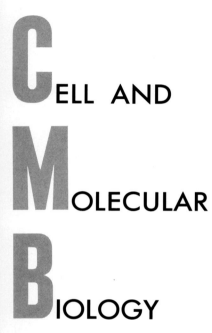

Cell and Molecular Biology

ACADEMIC PRESS

NEW YORK AND LONDON

ACADEMIC PRESS, INC.
111 Fifth Avenue, New York, New York 10003

United Kingdom Edition published by
ACADEMIC PRESS, INC. (LONDON) LTD.
Berkeley Square House, London W1X6BA

LIBRARY OF CONGRESS CATALOG CARD NUMBER: 68-18687

Fifth Printing, 1970

PRINTED IN THE UNITED STATES OF AMERICA

To my dearest people
Brian, Chris, Eric,
Marci, and Stephen

PREFACE

This textbook began as a series of lectures offered to senior under-graduates and graduate students in the University of California under the title "Cell Biology." Like the lectures, the book is organized to meet the logical requirements of teaching, i.e., the earlier chapters deal with those topics that are necessary for understanding the later chapters. The result has been to divide the subject roughly into two halves: Chapters 2 to 11 deal with the ways in which cells acquire, release, and dispose of energy, while Chapters 12 to 20 deal with the ways in which molecules, chromosomes, and cells replicate. Although these two sequences are by no means exclusive of one another, they do represent a genuine division in the way that cell biologists think about cells, at least in the present day. They also provide a convenient division of the material for courses that span two semesters or two academic quarters.

In organizing the available information, I have deliberately avoided the traditional patterns in which knowledge is segregated among sub-sciences, such as cytology, biochemistry, genetics, or cell physiology. Instead I have tried to arrange newer and older information meaning-fully to define a single, untraditional cell science that deals with the question "How are living cells organized to be alive?" A science so-defined is difficult to call by one name. The most appropriate terms, such as "cytology" and "cell biology," designate fields which traditionally have excluded some of the molecular data now required for the under-standing of cells. On the other hand, the more recent term "molecular biology," though it represents a movement of biochemically oriented disciplines toward a synthesis with the cell-level sciences, dismisses a great deal of older yet entirely significant literature. Perhaps the best thing that can be said is that cell biology and molecular biology are over-lapping fields, and that this text attempts to deal both with the overlap area and with as much data peculiar to each science as may be necessary for a meaningful discussion. The result is reflected in the bibliography in which references to the *Journal of Cell Biology* and the *Journal of Cell Science* mingle with those to the *Journal of Biological Chemistry* and the *Journal of Molecular Biology*.

Throughout the book special attention has been given to distinctions between such verbs as "to observe" and "to interpret"; in fact, the first chapter is largely devoted to an analysis of this distinction and the use of name-date references has been prompted by the key importance of the individual observer and the need to evaluate his observations in terms of contemporary techniques and ideas. Provision has also been made to use the bibliography as an author index by providing cross-references to the chapters in which each article is cited, and wherever possible, the availability of modern reprints for older references or English translations for non-English works has been noted.

The exact magnifications of the electron micrographs as they appear on the printed pages constitute some of the most important data of this text, and care has been taken to state these correctly in the figure legends. Using an accurate millimeter ruler and the given magnification, a student can estimate the sizes or distances of any objects in the illustrations by the simple formula

$$\text{size (in Å)} = \frac{\text{size (in mm)} \times 10^7}{\text{magnification}}$$

I am indebted for permissions to reproduce many electron micrographs and other illustrative materials, which were originally published as research contributions by scientists from England, Scotland, Germany, Austria, Switzerland, France, Japan, Israel, and Argentina, as well as from the United States. This is certainly a clear illustration of Bronowski's thesis (1965): "The dizzy progress of science, theoretical and practical, has depended on the existence of a fellowship of scientists which is free, uninhibited and communicative . . . The men and women who practise the sciences make a company of scholars which has been more lasting than any modern state . . ."

Though not every scientist will agree with the emphasis I have placed on conceptualization, I find myself very much in accord with Bronowski's thought, as expressed in his elegant little book "Science and Human Values" (1965): "Reality is not an exhibit for man's inspection. . . . There are no appearances to be photographed, no experiences to be copied, in which we do not take part. Science, like art, is not a copy of nature but a recreation of her. We re-make nature by the act of discovery, in the poem or in the theorem." I suppose this is the same thought that was expressed, somewhat more wryly, by Hermann Hesse: ". . . all attempts to make things comprehensible require the medium of theories, mythologies and lies; and a self-respecting author should not omit, at the close of an exposition, to dissipate these lies so far as may be in his power."

E. J. DuPraw

Baltimore, Maryland
March, 1968

CONTENTS

ix

1

HISTORICAL PERSPECTIVES

. . . I believe in perfect laws in a world of existing things, in so far as they are real, which I try to understand with wild speculation.

A. EINSTEIN *cited in* A. VALLENTIN *1954*

. . . (in 1861) the French protozoologist E. G. Balbiani was studying conjugation in some ciliate Protozoa. . . . Unfortunately, Balbiani totally misunderstood his own exquisite preparations. For him the macronucleus was the ovary and the micronucleus the "testicule" . . . The spindle fibres and the chromosomes in their metaphase were all too readily identified as a bundle of spermatozoa. Thanks in large part to this sad error, the discovery of the full sequence of changes during nuclear division was postponed to the following decade. Balbiani himself was then among those who made observations on the dividing nucleus, but only much later (1892) seems to have realised that he had already figured a dividing nucleus more than 30 years before.

A. HUGHES *1959*

At both the individual and historical levels, the progress of science depends on a peculiar interplay between observation and interpretation, fact and theory, reality and concept. There is in fact a kind of dialogue, in which the side of theory and conceptualization is at once more independent, more dominant, and more capricious than is usually recognized.

This interplay arises because ultimate physical realities are still very imperfectly known; consequently in contemporary thought they must be approximated by symbolic conceptions having greater or lesser theoretical content. In all important respects, such concepts stand for realities, and though they often grow very detailed and specific, their relationship to the physical world, in Einstein's words, is "not comparable to that of soup to beef, but more to that of the cloakroom ticket to the overcoat." Surprisingly enough, this substitution of concept for reality is not intuitively obvious, and each generation tends to accept its inherited conceptual system as a set of facts, believing in consequence that contemporary knowledge is much more advanced than it really is.

In historical perspective, the complex interplay between fact and theory is well illustrated by three centuries of attempts to prove or disprove that living matter can arise spontaneously from inanimate matter. Although this proposition has been alternately accepted and rejected again and again in past generations, it is still under serious investigation at the present time. The question was first tested experimentally in the 17th century by Redi (1688), who observed that the maggots and flies which appear in rotting meat do not arise *de novo*, but hatch from the eggs of parent insects. Redi stated his belief that spontaneous generation *never* occurs, yet his observations in themselves did not demonstrate this. The issue arose again during the 1780's in a famous controversy between two priests, Needham and Spallanzani. Both men carried out the same classic experiment, boiling and sealing flasks of broth to determine whether organisms would appear spontaneously; however they reached opposite conclusions, Needham claiming to have proved the theory and Spallanzani to have disproved it.

In the early 19th century, spontaneous generation at the cellular level became widely accepted, thanks in large part to the "cytoblast theory" of Schleiden and Schwann (1839). This theory, which was based on observations of nontypical, embryo-sac nuclei, asserted that the nucleolus "organizes" the nucleus from a structureless blastema, and that the nucleus (or cytoblast) develops into the cell. General acceptance of this concept made spontaneous generation seem plausible until the cytoblast theory itself was gradually replaced by Virchow's famous (and unprovable) dictum (1855): "All cells arise by the division of previously existing cells." At about that time by coincidence, a controversy arose between Pouchet and Pasteur which was very similar to the earlier dispute between Needham and Spallanzani and involved very similar "sealed flask" experiments. This time, however, Pasteur (1862) introduced the novel concept of airborne microorganisms, by which he was able to explain away apparent instances of spontaneous generation as the result of microbial contamination. Consequently for almost a century Pasteur's experiments were regarded as having disproved the theory of spontaneous generation.

On strictly logical grounds, nevertheless, no experiment can prove rigorously that life *never* arises spontaneously; it can only be demonstrated that certain types of organism do not appear under certain specified conditions within a specified time. The *conviction* that organisms do not arise spontaneously arises, not from observational proof, but from a particular concept of what organisms are, of the microscopic detail and intricacy of their construction—a concept which was established during the late 18th and early 19th centuries by new and startling discoveries at the microscope. Although Pasteur's experiments removed the last stumbling blocks, it was really this massive conceptual revision which made it suddenly unreasonable to postulate a genetic relationship between, for instance, a roundworm and a horsehair in a rain puddle. Thus relationships which appear to be properties of the objective world may be, in fact, merely properties of a particular set of conceptual approximations; when the concepts change, the relationships change.

In the contemporary era, a new "organism concept" has emerged which implies much less of a gulf between animate and inanimate, or between cell and molecule, than was current after Pasteur's work. This change has resulted primarily from an encounter between the concepts of biochemistry and those of morphology at the level of ultrastructure. Perhaps its most notable expression has been the development of various "cell-free systems," which reflect a basic conviction that major biological processes, such as muscle contraction and protein synthesis, can be made to occur in artificial, test-tube systems reconstructed from fragmented cells. Such systems were pioneered both by Hill (1937), who obtained light-induced evolution of oxygen and reduction of ferric salts by a suspension of isolated chloroplasts, and by Keilin and Hartree (1938), whose cell-free (mitochondrial) preparation was capable of carrying out the aerobic oxidation of succinic acid. A continuation of the same approach is recognizable in the contractile actomyosin fibers of Szent-Györgyi (1941–1942); the phosphorylating mitochondrial system of Lehninger and Kennedy (1948); Siekevitz's (1952) microsomal system, which incorporates amino acids into protein; the chloroplast system of

Arnon (1954), capable of photosynthesizing carbohydrates from carbon dioxide and water; the cell-free synthesis of RNA achieved by Ochoa (1956); Kornberg's system for cell-free synthesis of DNA (1956); and Nirenberg's system for RNA-dependent protein synthesis (1961). Still other systems, based on cell-free nuclei, nucleoli, cilia, mitotic spindles, and other components, will be discussed in later chapters. Implicit in these systems, and in the concept on which they are based, is the expectation that living matter itself will one day be brought into existence from its component molecules in the test tube.

If the history of the cell sciences is examined in detail (see Hughes, 1959; Sturtevant, 1965; Keilin, 1966) it appears that periods of net progress have resulted largely from two types of event; in the first place, from improvements in the techniques of observation, depending particularly on innovations in physical instruments; and secondly, but quite independently, from conceptual changes or insights, permitting more adequate interpretation and reinterpretation of new and old observations. When by good fortune these two types of event have occurred together, progress has been particularly rapid; yet one does not guarantee the other, and significant observations have often remained unnoticed for lack of an adequate interpretation, while brilliant theoretical insights have been ignored in the absence of techniques for obtaining supporting data. Sometimes the conceptual advance of one generation has clearly depended on a technical innovation during a previous generation; thus, Lavoisier could not recognize the nature of respiration (see Lavoisier and Laplace, 1780) until oxygen and carbon dioxide had been discovered in the 1770's; gas analysis, in turn, depended on the invention of the thermometer by Fahrenheit in 1714.

During the earliest period of cell biology, interpretations were generally scarce and many observations were recorded primarily as curiosities. As might be expected, progress during this period was associated largely with innovations in microscopy; for instance, the first compound microscope, which was introduced by Jansson and Jansson about 1590, led to the earliest published microscope drawings (Stelluti, 1625), representing a honey bee at a magnification of about 5×. Forty years later Robert Hooke attained magnifications of 30×, and in his book *Micrographia* (1665) depicted his famous discovery of "cells" in slices of cork. In the next decade, van Leeuwenhoek, a Dutch linen draper, began a long series of observations with single, homemade lenses which attained magnifications of 270×. Using little more than a precision magnifying glass, van Leeuwenhoek was actually able to describe human sperm cells (1677), the nuclei of blood corpuscles (1702), and single bacterial cells (1683). Nevertheless, almost a century later, the lack of unifying concepts is strikingly evident in the title of a 700-page book published in England by George Adams (1787): *Essays on the Microscope; containing a practical description of the most improved Microscopes: A General History of Insects, their transformations, peculiar habits, and Oeconomy; an account of the various species and singular properties of the Hydrae and Vorticellae: a description of Three Hundred and Seventy-Nine Animalcula, with a concise Catalogue of Interesting Objects: a view of the Organization of Timber, and the Configuration of Salts when under the Microscope.*

This era of preliminary observation did not give rise to serious theoretical interpretation until after 1800, when the concept began to dawn that "cells" might represent something fundamental in the organization of living matter. Curiously, these theoretical insights arose, at least partially, from erroneous observations made with faulty lenses, i.e., diffraction rings produced in the microscope were thought to be "globules" composing many kinds of tissues. The wide occurrence of such globules undoubtedly influenced Dutrochet (1824) when he arrived at the conclusion that ". . . the cell is truly the *pièce fondamentale* of the living organism" and ". . . all tissues, all animal (and plant) organs, are actually only a cellular tissue variously modified." Familiar as these generalizations sound now, the concept represented by "cell" was radically different in Dutrochet's time; it was the cell *wall* which was regarded as most important, and cells were believed to condense spontaneously from a structureless fluid. By contrast, the cell nucleus had hardly been noticed at all.

Just at the time when Dutrochet and others began to seek fundamental principles in microscopic structure, the physical techniques of microscopy also underwent a rapid improvement. Achromatic lenses were introduced in 1823, leading quickly to microscopes capable of 1 μ resolution (or a useful magnification of about 200×). The fortunate coincidence of these conceptual and technical advances introduced an era of very rapid progress in the 19th century, including Brown's description of the plant cell nucleus (1833), the discovery of the nucleolus by Schleiden and Schwann (1839), and Virchow's famous conception that all cells arise by the division of previously existing cells (1855). By 1873 Cleland could observe: "In the present day the protoplasmic element has assumed an enormous importance, casting the nucleus into shade, while the reign of cell walls has come to an end altogether." Further optical advances brought light microscopes to their theoretical limit in resolution (0.17 μ, or a useful magnification of about 1400×), first by the introduction of oil immersion lenses (1878) and later of apochromatic objectives (1886); simultaneously, chromosomes and the fundamental events of mitosis were discovered by Flemming (1880) and others, to be followed in the 1890's by a detailed elucidation of the complex events in meiosis. The same general trend toward improved microscope techniques has continued during the present century with the development of the phase contrast microscope (1934), the electron microscope (1938), and other equally sophisticated instruments.

Just as new techniques of observation lead ultimately to conceptual change, it is equally true that changing concepts imply new relationships and lead to novel observations. For instance, the problem of heredity could hardly be stated so long as the scientific world believed that familiar organisms congeal spontaneously from rain puddles and rotting meat. Similarly, the cytoblast theory of Schleiden and Schwann, in asserting that the nucleus develops into a cell, discouraged careful examination of the nucleus as an organelle distinct from the cell itself. Only after acceptance of Virchow's generalization that cells arise exclusively by the division of other cells could the mechanisms of cellular inheritance, and the role of the nucleus in them, be subjected to orderly investigation. Perhaps the first truly cellular conception of inheritance was Charles Darwin's "theory of pangenesis" (1868), which postulated that every cell in the body is represented by "gemmules" in the germ cells and that these gemmules are capable of developing into corresponding tissue cells in the embryo. One of the theoretical expectations of pangenesis was that several male elements would be involved in fertilization, and this provided unusual impact for the observations of Hertwig (1876) and Fol (1879) that only one spermatozoon enters the egg of nematodes and starfish.

The discovery of monospermy also influenced Nägeli in devising his "idioplasm theory" soon afterward (1884). Nägeli reasoned that, since father and mother have the same influence in the heredity of their offspring, and since the physical mass of material contributed by each is very dissimilar (i.e., one large egg and one small sperm), then it must follow that not all the material of the cell is active in heredity; he therefore postulated that there must be a special hereditary material (idioplasm), quantitatively the same in egg and sperm, which he imagined as extended in a network throughout the cell. Considering the information available to Nägeli, this was certainly a dubious theory, but it happened to coincide with the observations of several cytologists who were then investigating the behavior of certain peculiar, rod-shaped bodies in cell division. They recognized almost immediately that the chromosomes possessed just the properties postulated by Nägeli for the idioplasm; in this manner, Hertwig, Strasburger, Kölliker, and Weissmann arrived at the "chromatin theory of inheritance," which became the forerunner for Morgan's "theory of the gene" in the early 1900's, and more recently for the DNA theory of inheritance.

Although emphasis so far has been placed on the general *advance* of discovery in cell and molecular biology, it is clear from the record that periods of stasis or retreat have occurred as well. Albert Szent-Györgyi has illustrated graphically (Fig. 1-1) the twisted path of speculation followed by an individual investigator in the course of a creative discovery; at the social or historical level, progress follows a path no less twisted, but reinforced by the general inertia associated with social processes, and resulting in cycles of progress and retreat which occupy not days but decades. Often one research field is impeded as the price of rapid progress in another, involving what Amberson (1958) has called "fashion" in science:

> . . . in the world of science, fashion is a prevailing mode of thought or action determined by a recent innovation. A new technique or a seminal idea sweeps us toward renewed discovery, resulting in a wave of attention and emphasis, which can be construed as fashion without implying derogation. Yet in the wake of fashionable movements, difficult, even critical questions are neglected, which often escape attention through several succeeding waves.

That such waves of activity exist is very clear from the record. For instance, during the last part of the 19th century, the majority of significant advances concerned chromosomes and chromosome behavior; in the early 1900's, classical genetics was the fashion; during the 1930's, the analysis of aerobic and anaerobic metabolism reached a peak; and in the present day, the relationship between DNA, RNA, and protein synthesis is the prevailing line of research.

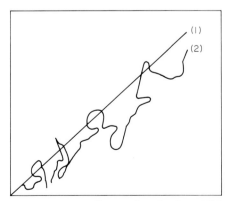

Fig. 1-1. Line (1) represents a sequence of research as finally published; line (2) represents the same research as actually carried out in the laboratory. From Szent-Györgyi (1960b).

Periods of actual retreat are often seen, in retrospect, to have been associated with interpretations that were inadequate for the observational data available. Such instances of conceptual retreat are particularly revealing, since they illustrate so uncomprisingly that an observation, however accurate, can never be more meaningful than the concepts that are available to interpret it. Indeed, relationships or possibilities not implicit in an existing concept literally cannot be discovered until, by speculative trial and error, the concept itself has been changed. A particularly clear instance is provided by Von Baer (1828), who believed that sperm cells are parasites (hence spermato*zoa*), despite the fact that Prévost and Dumas (1824) had already demonstrated experimentally that the sperm, rather than the seminal fluid, is the essential element in fertilization. Such was Von Baer's influence that some investigators of the period described gastrointestinal tracts in sperm cells, publishing illustrations which were less accurate than those of van Leeuwenhoek, published 150 years before! It remained for Kölliker (1841) to demonstrate that spermatozoa are actually differentiated tissue cells.

Another example is provided by the controversy in 1886 between Hoppe-Seyler, a leading biochemist of the day, and MacMunn, who had discovered a series of cell pigments capable of undergoing reversible oxidation-reduction changes (now known as the cytochromes). MacMunn correctly believed that these pigments must function in the basic processes of cell respiration, but he was severely criticized by Hoppe-Seyler, who maintained that they were merely the degradation products of hemoglobin. When MacMunn pointed out that the pigments occur even in organisms which do not possess hemoglobin, Hoppe-Seyler cut off the debate, and no further attention was given the cytochromes until 1925, when they were rediscovered by Keilin. Still a third example is that of Gregor Mendel (1865), whose classic analysis of genetic ratios was known to some of the leading scientists of his day, but could not be adequately interpreted until after the discovery of chromosomes and meiosis thirty years later. At that time (1900), genetic ratios were rediscovered independently in three different countries by Correns, Von Tchermak, and DeVries, and as Horowitz has remarked (1956): ". . . the development of genetics would have been the same even if (Mendel) had never lived."

In all these instances, the available observations implied much more than could be understood in terms of current theory; in other cases, however, it has been the techniques of observation that were inadequate to provide answers for theoretical questions being asked. A clear example of this is a famous controversy between Pasteur and Liebig during the 1850's, when Liebig and others maintained that it should be possible to obtain fermentation with a yeast extract in the absence of living yeast cells. At that time, no one was successful in supporting this theoretical expectation with experiments, and the technical problem was not solved until 1897 when the Buchner brothers half-accidentally observed carbon dioxide production in their medicinal yeast juice preparations. At the morphological level, a number of cell structures (e.g., mitochondria, the Golgi apparatus, and even the mitotic spindle) were thought to be artifacts by various eminent cytologists during the early 1900's; not until much later, in 1934, did the invention of the phase contrast microscope by Zernicke make it possible to confirm the existence of these structures directly in living, unstained cells.

Key technical innovations of this magnitude are almost always historical accidents, in the sense that the timing of their appearance is haphazard; yet such innovations are capable of reversing even direct observations made earlier with less sophisticated methods. A very instructive example is an experiment of E. B. Harvey (1946), still sometimes quoted, in which egg fragments obtained by centrifugation appeared under the light microscope to lack mitochondria; since these fragments later developed into larvae containing numerous mitochondria, it was concluded that the respiratory organelles form *de novo* in living cells. Although the electron microscope had been introduced in 1938, it was not until the early 1950's that instruments were developed for cutting ultrathin sections, making it possible to discover new structures, such as ribosomes and microtubules, and also to characterize known organelles, e.g., mitochondria by their "crista" substructure. At this time Lansing (1953) repeated Harvey's work and, using the electron microscope, found that egg fragments prepared by the same technique do, in fact, contain mitochondria, although these are not detectable with the light microscope. The *de novo* origin of mitochondria has therefore been discredited.

The examples that have been given illustrate a remarkably haphazard interplay between observation and interpretation, which has occurred at every stage in the development of cell and molecular biology, and certainly is occurring at the present time as well. It appears that the concepts and theories which become dominant in any given era depend to a considerable extent on historical accidents of discovery or of individual insight and persuasiveness. The arbitrariness of this process is the more disturbing because it rarely involves rigorous proofs; indeed, most conceptual revisions are too subtle to state as simple propositions, while those that can be stated are either logically unprovable (propositions containing "never" or "always") or hardly worth the proving. Even the most widely accepted principles ignore certain well-established exceptions: the cells of the insect blastoderm, for instance, do not really arise by cell division, nor are the mitotic chromosomes of the *Ascaris* embryo separated equally to the daughter cells.

Though the course of discovery is unpredictable, one of its most striking features nevertheless is a certain, unrelenting persistence. Early observations become the foundations for later interpretations, which lead to further observations in successive and intricate progressions, often spanning generations. In this process, many men carry out the observations that one man might wish to make, if it were possible—a social effort which ignores nationality and is achieved only through a persistent mutuality of interest. For example, in 1871 Miescher, using pus cells extracted from old surgical bandages, carried out a pioneer investigation of the chemical composition of cell nuclei, leading to the first description of nucleic acid (1874). Five years later, Flemming observed the longitudinal division of chromosomes, and soon afterward (1882) proposed a relationship between chromatin and nucleic acid. In the next decades the chromatin and gene theories of inheritance were developed, but not until 1924 was it found by Feulgen that two types of nucleic acid (DNA and RNA) occur side by side in many cells. This discovery paved the way for the observation of Avery and his co-workers that it is DNA which mediates inheritable transformations in bacteria (1944), and the finding of several investigators in 1948 that the amount of DNA per chromosome set is highly constant. In 1953 the concept of DNA as the hereditary material received new impetus from the theoretical model of the DNA molecule proposed by Watson and Crick, which made it possible to visualize molecular replication. Soon afterward, Kornberg (1956) was able to detect an apparent "replication" of DNA in a cell-free system, and since then it has been demonstrated that DNA carries information determining the amino acid sequence of proteins, and thereby determines specific properties of cells. This sequence of discovery, which is far from complete at the present time, spans ninety years and at least three generations of scientists.

If one inquires why it has not been possible to achieve greater directness, precision, and certainty in science, the answer lies in the extraordinary limitations of sense experience, which for scientist and philosopher alike are much more extreme than intuition tells us. Indeed, the points of contact between the human mind and the objective universe are no more than a few kinds of energy pattern, conveyed by neurons, whose sensitivity can be increased by sophisticated instruments but not changed in essential content. It is as though each individual were confined in a closed room, lacking even windows, so that information about the exterior world may be obtained only by inference from a few instruments measuring outside temperatures, pressures, and light fluxes. The comparison may seem exaggerated, yet persons who have been born blind and later gain their sight as adults do not immediately "see" tables, chairs, and people around them; the existence and identity of these objects must be inferred deliberately from the visual image by a long and extremely complex process (described in detail by J. Z. Young, 1951). Consider how little direct information is contained in the sense impression of a star—merely a point of light. Yet the astronomer has made much of this point of light, both by developing instruments to increase his sensitivity to its properties, and by postulating theoretical relationships which extend far beyond his direct observations.

Indeed, scientists are in the position of a primitive tribe which has undertaken to duplicate the Empire State Building, room for room, without ever seeing the original building or even a photograph. Their own working plans, of necessity, are only a crude approximation of the real thing, conceived on the basis of miscellaneous reports volunteered by interested travelers and often in apparent conflict on points of detail. In order to start the building at all, some information must be ignored as erroneous or impossible, and the first constructions are little more than large grass shacks. Increasing sophistication, combined with methodical accumulation of data, make it necessary to tear down the earlier replicas (each time after violent arguments), replacing them successively with more up-to-date versions. We may easily doubt that the version current after only 300 years of effort is a very adequate representation of the Empire State Building; yet, in the absence of clear knowledge to the contrary, the tribe must regard it as such (and ignore odd travelers' tales that cannot be made to fit).

Perhaps it may be said, then, that the function of concept and theory is to anticipate observations that cannot yet be made and relationships that cannot yet be detected; they must therefore remain liable to revision so long as there is the possibility of new knowledge. Theories are never so much proved as replaced, partially or entirely, with accurate and confirmed facts (supplemented with newer theories). It is for this reason that each generation owes to the next a clear distinction between what has been observed and what these observations have been taken to mean; in historical perspective it is only the well-defined observations which constitute a cumulative heritage. As Chesterton (1925) has remarked:

> What we know, in a sense in which we know nothing else, is that the trees and the grass did grow, and that a number of other extraordinary things do in fact happen; that queer creatures support themselves in the empty air by beating it with fans of various fantastic shapes; that other queer creatures steer themselves about alive under a load of mighty waters; that other queer creatures walk about on four legs, and that the queerest creature of all walks about on two. These are things and not theories; and compared with them evolution and the atom and even the solar system are merely theories.

At the present time, biologists of all specialties are sharing in a general sense of awakening or breakthrough, which has been occasioned primarily by advances in the cellular and molecular fields. These advances have altered many of the fundamental concepts, including even the concept of life, which are used in common by physiologists, morphologists, and behaviorists. Thus the discoveries of the molecular biologist have intruded on the thinking of the ecologist, and by outdating the general concepts of biology, have threatened to outdate the interconcept relationships investigated intensively within many different specialties. The new concepts, and the observations on which they are based, form the topics of the remaining chapters; they will be appraised primarily in terms of specific contributions made at specific points in time by specific individuals working with the limited techniques and concepts of their day. For what the history of cell biology teaches is that the direction of our thought in the present day is determined largely by the chance insights and discoveries of earlier investigators; that the best observations we can make are still severely limited by the physical techniques available; that there are among us contemporary Mendels and MacMunns, whose work must be ignored because it cannot yet be appreciated; and that the facts and theories which now engage our attention will be seen, in another era, to have overlooked the important questions entirely.

2

FREE ENERGY AND ENTROPY

The entropy concept . . . plays a role as important as that of the energy concept in every field of physics, chemistry and technology . . .

J. D. FAST *1962*

The loss, which is characteristic of an irreversible process, is *loss of information* . . . . Gain in entropy always means loss of information, and nothing more. It is a subjective concept, but we can express it in its least subjective form, as follows. If, on a page, we read the description of a physico-chemical system, together with certain data which help to specify the system, the entropy of the system is determined by these specifications. If any of the essential data are erased, the entropy becomes greater; if any essential data are added, the entropy becomes less.

G. N. LEWIS *1930*

Organisms, and the cells that compose them, are in all fundamental respects physical-chemical systems, and their activities occur in large part by the flow of chemical energy. Before considering the specific reactions involved in these energy transformations, it is logical to introduce the current conventions necessary to answer such questions as: Will a reaction occur spontaneously? Can the reaction accomplish biologically meaningful work? And precisely what is the maximum amount of work a given reaction can do?

In physical chemistry, such questions are generally answered for closed or defined reaction systems. Such closed systems, whether chemical or mechanical, are always defined in relation to some arbitrary process which the system is expected to accomplish and which, when accomplished, will be recognized as "work." That fraction of the system's energy which tends to carry out the work process (or reaction) is referred to as the *free energy;* however, in such systems there is always a large energy fraction which cannot be made to perform in the manner required of work, and this energy is regarded as unavailable or "lost to entropy." By definition the unavailable energy is associated with random (i.e., not work-ordered) processes, which are usually visualized as kinetic movements between and within molecules (heat). Consequently in analyzing the course of a reaction, three parcels of energy can be distinguished, i.e., the free energy driving the reaction, the unavailable energy associated with entropy, and the total energy (enthalpy). However the exact distribution of energy between the first two categories will depend on how "work" has been defined for the particular system.

The difficulty encountered in applying these concepts to living organisms is that the life process is neither a closed nor a defined reaction; although it can be divided into semiarbitrary but definable subreactions, the exact manner of definition may change with different investigators and it is usually unclear how closely a given test-tube system corresponds to an *in vivo* process. The usual basis for defining biological reaction systems is the isolation of a purified enzyme, which is able to catalyze some specific reaction *in vitro;* however, many enzymes are known to be altered or inactivated if they are separated from the structural orderliness of the intact cell. It should be borne in mind that the analysis of changes in free energy, entropy, and enthalpy, as applied to biological systems, always implies an isolated reaction proceeding under standard conditions *in vitro.*

Total Energy

As an example of an isolated, defined system, it is useful to imagine a flask in which two reactants, A + B, undergo a reaction to form the products, C + D (Fig. 2-1). Such a reaction will proceed until an equilibrium state is reached, when either A + B will have been entirely changed into C + D, or else the flask will contain some particular proportions of C and D relative to leftover amounts of A and B. The exact contents of the flask at equilibrium are determined not only by the chemical structures of A and B, but also by their initial concentrations, the temperature at which the reaction occurs, the pressure, and sometimes other factors.

Ordinarily when such a reaction occurs, it is accompanied by some change in the total energy, such that energy either leaves or enters the flask. Let us assume that it is possible to measure the total energy, or enthalpy (H), for the contents of the flask before the reaction begins and after the reaction is completed. If it should be found that the total energy at the end is less than that of the initial A + B, then obviously energy must leave the system during the reaction, and it will be observed that heat is given off from the flask (exothermic reaction). If, on the other hand, the total energy is greater at the end, then the reaction cannot occur unless energy enters the system, and it may be observed that the flask grows cooler (endothermic reaction); alternatively, it may be necessary to provide energy by warming the flask over a burner.

The *change* in enthalpy during the reaction (ΔH) corresponds to the energy which leaves or enters the system, and is known as the "heat

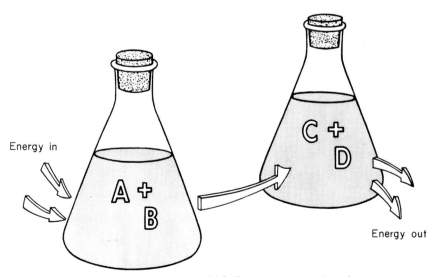

Fig. 2-1. An isolated reaction system, in which the reactants A + B undergo a reaction to form the products C + D. Energy entering or leaving the closed system is designated ΔH, the heat of reaction.

of reaction." For a reaction which goes to completion, ΔH is often estimated by combusting equivalent samples of (A + B) and (C + D), and measuring the number of calories produced in each case. The change in enthalpy is then calculated by subtracting the caloric output of the reactants (A + B) from that of the products (C + D); when this convention is followed, exothermic reactions necessarily show a negative ΔH, whereas endothermic reactions have a positive one. It is important to note that there exists a general tendency for reactions to go in the direction of minimum enthalpy (i.e., for the reaction to go "downhill" to a lower energy level).

Free Energy

Free energy (F) may be visualized as roughly similar to potential energy in a mechanical system—for instance, the potential energy of a large rock at the top of a hill. Just as the rock's energy depends on its position relative to the surface of the earth, so the free energy of a specific reaction system depends on the configuration of atoms in the molecules composing it. As will be seen later, these analogies are only approximate, since it is not meaningful to speak of the free energy of a particular molecule, but only of the change in free energy during a reaction.

The *change* in free energy, ΔF, is a measure of the tendency for a given reaction mixture to change in the direction of its equilibrium state (i.e., for a defined reaction to occur), and it is partly independent of changes in total energy. Since the free energy of a defined system also tends to a minimum, reaction mixtures which have a negative ΔF (subtracting $F_{products}$ from $F_{reactants}$) are likely to proceed spontaneously (exergonic reactions), whereas those with a positive ΔF (endergonic reactions) cannot occur spontaneously. One of the most useful properties of ΔF is that, for exergonic reactions, it equals the maximum amount of "work" which can be obtained from the system.

The value of ΔF is closely related to the energy distribution in the equilibrium state of the system, and it therefore varies with any factor that affects the equilibrium, including not only the molecular structure of the reactants and products, but their initial concentrations, the pH of the system, its temperature, the presence of charged ions, the occurrence and concentration of a specific enzyme, and, particularly for large molecules, the pressure. Strictly speaking, ΔF is a property of a particular, specified reaction mixture, and it cannot be determined for an intracellular reaction unless the conditions prevailing within the cell have been measured or estimated. However, as a basis for estimating ΔF

it is useful to determine the value of $\Delta F°$ for a specific reaction occurring under standard laboratory conditions.

Ordinarily $\Delta F°$ is calculated from the equilibrium constant of the reaction, which is given by

$$K = \frac{[C]\,[D]}{[A]\,[B]}$$

where [A], [B], etc., are the concentrations at equilibrium for a reaction mixture initially containing equimolar amounts of A, B, C, and D (at standard temperature and pressure). The relationship between $\Delta F°$ and K is then given by

$$\Delta F° = -RT \ln K$$

where T is the absolute temperature, R is the universal gas constant (1.98 calories/mole/degree absolute), and $\ln K$ is 2.3 log K. It will be seen that $\Delta F° = 0$ when $K = 1$ (i.e., no reaction), and is negative when $K > 1$ (spontaneous reaction to the right).

In estimating the actual ΔF from $\Delta F°$, it is possible to take into account the measured intracellular concentrations by means of the formula

$$\Delta F = \Delta F° + RT \ln \frac{[C]\,[D]}{[A]\,[B]}$$

It can be seen that if one or both of the products (C and D) is maintained in sufficiently low concentration, the term $\ln ([C]\,[D])/([A]\,[B])$ will be negative, and may render exergonic a reaction whose $\Delta F°$ is actually positive. This situation probably occurs frequently in cells, where the products of an endergonic reaction may be immediately used up in another, exergonic reaction. In that case, the $\Delta F°$ for the two "coupled" reactions, summed together, will be equal to the sum of the exergonic $\Delta F°$ (−) plus the endergonic one (+), and may therefore be negative (spontaneous) even though one of the reactions, considered alone, is nonspontaneous.

In reactions where H^+ is one of the products, pH becomes an important factor in determining ΔF, and its influence can be estimated by adding a pH term:

$$\Delta F = \Delta F° + RT \ln \frac{[C]\,[D]}{[A]\,[B]} - 2.3\,RT\,(\text{pH})$$

It is important to note at this point that the magnitude of ΔF does not reveal anything about the *rate* at which a given reaction will proceed. Rate theory will be dealt with in connection with enzyme activity in Chapter 12.

Unavailable Energy and Entropy

As noted previously, that energy of a defined system which does not contribute to the orderly "work" of the system must be associated, by definition, with disorderly or random events. The importance of this unavailable energy is that it tends to increase as the system carries out the work process, and the more of the total energy which becomes unavailable, the less reversible the process or reaction will be.

An interest in achieving some quantitative measurement of irreversibility first developed in connection with the efficiency of steam engines in the 1850's; the nature of the equations developed at that time led to defining the unavailable energy as

$$E_{unavailable} = TS$$

where T is the absolute temperature and S is a quantity called the *entropy*. It is important to realize at the outset that entropy cannot be visualized or otherwise grasped intuitively; it is a defined concept, but one which can be measured quantitatively and which has several important properties.

In the first place, entropy itself is not energy; its units are calories/mole/degree absolute, and it becomes an energy term only when it is multiplied by T. It may be helpful to recall that in a pressure-volume system, energy is given by

$$E = PV$$

where pressure (P) may be considered as an intensity factor, and volume (V) as a capacity factor. Analogously, the unavailable energy in a chemical system depends on temperature, as an intensity factor, and on entropy as a capacity factor. Like volume, entropy is an "extensive" property, which means that, for a given compound under standard conditions, two grams have twice the entropy of one gram.

From thermodynamic considerations, the entropy of a chemical system must be zero when the temperature is absolute zero, and the total entropy at any other temperature is given by the ratio between the energy required to bring the system up to that temperature, and the temperature itself (in degrees absolute). This ratio, as indicated above, varies directly with the mass of the system, but for a given mass it depends on the number of particles in the system and on their freedom of movement with respect to one another. Thus entropy is closely linked to the movement of electrons within atoms, to the vibrational and rotational movements of atoms within molecules, and to the translational movements of molecules relative to one another; the more freedom of kinetic motion within the system, the more energy can be absorbed for a given rise in temperature, and the greater will be the entropy. These relationships make it possible to distinguish between isomeric forms of the same molecule by measuring the entropy; for example, cyclic organic compounds generally have a lower entropy than their corresponding straight-chain isomers.

The entropy concept, as first developed, was based on the thermodynamics of steam engines and had no molecular basis. However, with the introduction of atomic theory in the late 19th century, it became possible to formulate a statistical concept of entropy, which is quite distinct from the older, thermodynamic definition. The behavior of enormous numbers of atoms or molecules can be accurately described and predicted in terms of the probabilities of alternative configurations available to them. For example, when a crystal of copper sulfate dissolves and diffuses uniformly throughout a flask of water, the process as a whole is the summation of probable movements by each of the many molecules making up the crystal. This kind of diffusion is also a highly irreversible process, which is understandable in terms of the low probability that all the molecules of copper sulfate will spontaneously reaggregate in one part of the flask.

This irreversibility can be related to a statistical expression for entropy, which was first formulated by Boltzmann in 1872:

$$S = k \ln g$$

where k is Boltzmann's constant (the gas constant divided by Avogadro's number) and g is the number of alternative configurations available to the particles in the system; the greater the number of configurations which are possible, the higher will be the entropy. In some systems the statistical value for entropy can be calculated and checked against empirical measurements of thermodynamic entropy. In general, excellent agreement is found between the two independent methods; however, the statistical entropy of some materials has a low residual value at absolute zero, leading to minor discrepancies with thermodynamic entropy.

Change in Entropy

As indicated previously, the change in entropy during a reaction (ΔS) is useful as a measure of the irreversibility of the reaction; the greater the entropy increase, the more energy ($T \Delta S$) becomes unavailable and the less reversible is the process. In practice, all isolated reactions are at least partially irreversible since, as stated by the second law of thermodynamics, the entropy of an isolated system tends to increase to a maximum; when maximum entropy is reached, no further "work" can be done by the system—a condition which, in chemical reactions, corresponds to a state of equilibrium.

It is instructive to consider the second law in terms of Boltzmann's statistical equation for entropy. When the entropy of a closed system increases, this must mean in molecular terms that it has changed to a state in which more alternative atomic arrangements are available than previously. On the assumption that each possible arrangement is equally probable, a state which permits more arrangements will be a more probable state. Thus, the second law says, in effect, that an isolated system will tend to change in the direction of its most probable molecular state; this most probable state corresponds to the condition of maximum entropy.

The probability concept of entropy and the second law of thermodynamics is closely involved with the concepts of "order" and "randomness," as well as with irreversibility. "Orderliness" in a system refers to certain very special configurations of matter, which can be recognized subjectively as differing from the majority of possible configurations, but only insofar as they satisfy our own arbitrary specifications. For instance, if we begin with a bag containing 50 pennies, and if we then shake it well and pour the pennies onto a table, we will recognize "order" if all 50 come up heads, or if they all come up tails, or if the coins fall in some special sequence, such as heads-tails-heads-tails, etc. In strictly physical terms there is nothing particularly special about any of these "orderly" sequences, and we know that no one of them is either more or less likely to occur than any given "random" sequence; nevertheless, we do not *expect* the orderly sequences to occur in an actual experiment. The reason is that there are so few sequences which we are willing to accept as "orderly," compared to the vast number that we prefer to call "random."

Energy systems which are defined in terms of a specific kind of work, or of a specific reaction, are *ipso facto* orderly systems, and they therefore represent more or less improbable arrangements of matter; likewise, "work" carried out by such systems can be considered as "orderly" energy, and nothing else. On the other hand, the number of "disorderly" arrangements possible to such a system may be incomparably greater, and the "disorderly" energy associated with them is that which we refer to entropy (i.e., heat). It should be seen from this that, for any defined system, an increase in entropy is conceptually inseparable from an increase in randomness, an increase in probability, and a decrease in reversibility. These relationships must hold for any defined system: for instance, if the Empire State Building should collapse, the process would represent a change from the present, highly ordered arrangement of its parts to some other arrangement, which would be a more probable and almost certainly a less orderly one; at the same time, the reduction of the Empire State Building to a pile of rubble would be associated with a large net increase in entropy, corresponding to a low expectation that the process would prove to be spontaneously reversible.

All these conceptions apply equally well at the molecular level. In functional protein molecules, for instance, the sequence of amino acids is highly specific, and therefore both orderly and improbable; the synthesis of such large, orderly molecules therefore necessarily involves a large decrease in entropy compared with the precursor system of randomly distributed amino acid molecules. For these reasons, the synthesis of specific proteins from amino acids is a highly reversible process requiring "work" (i.e., orderly input of external energy) to accomplish, and the breakdown of specific proteins to amino acids or carbon dioxide is a highly irreversible process which yields considerable energy. The same relationships must hold for all large, specific molecules.

The value of the entropy concept lies in the fact that, for a defined system, changes in entropy can be measured quantitatively. However, it should be borne in mind that living cells are not defined systems and that, however precisely ΔS is determined for a specified process, change in entropy remains primarily a subjective concept whose quantitative value depends on the way the process has been conceived and specified. This point is brought home especially well in the model situation known as "Gibbs' paradox." Suppose that a system is specified which consists of a closed container divided into two halves by a frictionless partition. If now we specify that the two sides of the container shall be filled with two different gases (e.g., neon and helium), and we then slide back the partition, we know that the two kinds of gas molecules will diffuse out to form a mixture filling the entire container. This mixing process is accompanied by an increase in entropy for the system, i.e., the new configurations of the gas molecules are more probable and also less "ordered" than the original ones, and the diffusion process is highly irreversible. If, then, another, identical system is specified, except that this time we require that the two sides of the container are to be filled with the same gas (e.g., helium only), now when the partition is removed the entropy of the system will not change, i.e., thermodynamically nothing happens. In comparing these two systems, it makes no difference whether the kinetic energy implicit in the random movement of molecules is exactly the same in the two cases; the increased entropy in the first case is due entirely to the fact that we have specified two kinds of molecules which initially are distributed in a relatively improbable manner. In a sense, the increasing entropy in this system represents nothing more than the loss of one of the original specifications for the system, i.e., the separation of the helium and neon. In exactly the same sense, a defined system capable of synthesizing protein molecules of very exact amino acid sequence would require an enormously greater entropy change (in a negative direction) than a system producing protein molecules of random amino acid sequences (even though the size of the protein molecules and the proportions of amino acids might be the same in both cases).

Clausius, who introduced the term entropy in the mid-19th century, believed that the trend to increased entropy was general throughout the universe, and that in consequence, the universe is gradually "running down," i.e., approaching maximum entropy when supposedly no further change will be possible. This idea is still sometimes encountered, but it ignores the fact that entropy has no meaning except relative to some defined process which involves large numbers of particles arranged in a specified or orderly manner. It is possible to speak of the sun's running down, but no one has yet been able to define a process which the universe at large is carrying out; therefore it is not possible to determine whether the universe is approaching, or perhaps has already reached, a condition of maximum entropy. Furthermore, maximum entropy in a system refers to a statistical equilibrium, or a condition of maximum probability, and it has no meaning relative to the behavior of individual particles; for instance, the particles in a colloidal suspension at maximum entropy show a great deal of activity under a microscope, in the form of Brownian movement.

Relationship between Total Energy, Free Energy, and Unavailable Energy

The fundamental relationship between the three "parcels" of energy in a defined system is given by the equation

$$\Delta H = \Delta F + T\,\Delta S$$

This states merely that the change in total energy (ΔH) must equal the sum of changes in available energy (ΔF) and unavailable energy ($T\,\Delta S$)— an intuitively reasonable relationship. If the equation is transposed, however, it takes a more interesting form:

$$\Delta F = \Delta H - T\,\Delta S$$

The relationship can now be stated as follows: the tendency of a reaction to occur (ΔF) depends on two factors; one is the tendency of the reaction to move toward a lower energy level (the more negative ΔH, the more negative ΔF, and the greater the tendency for the reaction to occur spontaneously); the other is the tendency of the reaction to move toward a state of higher entropy (the more positive ΔS, the more negative ΔF). In many spontaneous reactions, these two factors reinforce one another, so that ΔS has a positive value, and ΔF is therefore somewhat more negative than ΔH. For example, in the reaction given by

$$C_6H_{12}O_6 + 6\ O_2 \longrightarrow 6\ CO_2 + 6\ H_2O$$

$\Delta F°$ (maximum work obtainable) has been measured as -688 kcal/mole, while ΔH (heat of reaction) is only -673 kcal/mole. The difference between these two figures is due to the higher probability of the atomic configurations on the right side of the equation.

In some spontaneous reactions it is even possible for the tendency to increased entropy to overcome the tendency to a lower energy level; for instance, in the evaporation of water, water molecules spontaneously draw energy from the environment (notable in the cooling of the system) in order to move to a higher energy level—a change driven by the large increase in entropy in the gaseous state. In such a case, the entropy increase itself is responsible for any work produced in the reaction (i.e., negative ΔF); consequently it is clear that the free energy is not something which exists in the reactant molecules as a "packet" to be released. Rather, the free energy (or more properly, the change in free energy, ΔF) is, in the strictest sense, a property of the reaction as a whole.

Of somewhat greater biological interest are reactions in which the tendency to lower energy levels may overcome the tendency to higher entropy. For instance, at low temperatures the crystallization of water proceeds spontaneously, even though it involves a decrease in entropy; the reaction is spontaneous because it has a large negative ΔH (i.e., heat is given off and a lower energy level attained). In reactions which involve a balance between the tendency to higher entropy and the tendency to lower energy levels, the temperature at which the reaction is carried out becomes important. Higher temperatures favor increased entropy (due to the presence of T in the term, $T\ \Delta S$); lower temperatures favor the tendency to reduced energy levels.

Free Energy and Entropy in Biological Systems

These considerations are of particular importance for biological systems, since by and large, cells are composed of highly ordered, nonrandom arrangements of molecules, which are themselves synthesized as highly ordered, nonrandom combinations of precursor molecules. In no case do we have a full understanding of why the life process requires this degree of order; we simply observe that the order occurs, that when it is lost life is lost, and that the disintegration of living matter is a highly irreversible event. In the opposite direction, therefore, biological synthesis must involve converting precursor molecules of relatively high entropy into larger molecules and organelles of relatively low entropy; for this reason, it has sometimes been said that living organisms produce "negative entropy."

However, as will be seen in future chapters, the biological synthesis of low entropy protein and nucleic acid molecules is associated with the conversion of smaller "high energy" molecules to lower energy states. Living systems therefore follow a general "downhill" trend in energy level, which must be driven ultimately by radiant energy from the sun. If it is possible to regard all living things as parts of a single chemical reaction, then that reaction is an endothermic one, and so far as we know, an endergonic one as well (i.e., nonspontaneous). In the overall process, the more conspicuous decreases in entropy are compensated by entropy increases elsewhere in the system. It has been estimated by Rabinowitch that all life is driven by approximately 0.24% of the total sun energy reaching the earth; the overall life process may thus be regarded as a kind of energy quirk, in which a tiny fraction of the sun's energy is somewhat delayed in an otherwise rapid reduction to entropy.

In the analysis of specific biological processes, living systems present serious difficulties for the interpretation of free energy and entropy measurements based on test-tube biochemical reactions. For example, cells are "steady-state" systems, in which a controlled influx of matter and energy is balanced against a controlled outflow. The interpretation of such steady-state systems, as opposed to the closed systems of classical thermodynamics, is still in an early stage. We know that the organization of the cell is such that the availability of reactants (i.e., substrates), the disposition of products, and the occurrence of specific enzymes are all subject to precise control; as discussed previously, any or all of these factors can produce marked changes in the actual ΔF of any given reaction. The fact that living cells are constantly disposing of specific molecules in the form of CO_2 and water probably means that, for many processes, equilibrium is never reached, and under these circumstances, reactions that would hardly occur under test-tube conditions can be made to proceed at a steady rate.

Another difficulty is the fact that many intracellular reactions occur in association with membranes or other formed structures. It is entirely possible that such processes may be better understood in terms of semi-conductors and solid-state physics than within a framework of solvent-mediated chemical reactions. The importance of this distinction is especially apparent for those reactions in which water is a reactant or a product (hydrolysis and dehydration synthesis). Such reactions, when carried out in aqueous solution, may show a ΔF which is largely conditioned by the high concentration of water in the system (see page 17); on the other hand, the same reaction, occurring in the presence of limiting amounts of water, is likely to proceed spontaneously in an opposite direction. This point takes on added significance, since it is known that a localized, nonpolar (lipid) phase forms a part of many functional membranes, and it has been suggested that certain fundamental biological processes actually occur in a lipid, rather than in an aqueous, medium.

Perhaps the greatest difficulty is associated with the fact that many kinds of molecules in biological systems are present in extremely small numbers, or are compartmentalized into very small units. For instance, some bacteria contain only one or two extremely long molecules of DNA, which nevertheless specify amino acid sequences for most or all of the proteins of the cell. Entropy, free energy, and heat of reaction, on the other hand, are all statistical concepts, whose meaning at the level of single molecules is not always clear. Szent-Györgyi (1960b) has called attention to this problem by proposing a "submolecular biology," which is concerned with intramolecular events leading to transfer or trans-duction of energy within and between organelles. Although information pertinent to this subject is scanty, some principles of energy transfer at a submolecular level should be considered.

Energetics in Relation to Molecular Structure

In order to examine the energy structure of a molecule, as such, it is necessary to enter a different frame of reference from that which is used to describe the energetics of chemical reactions. This is the realm of quantum mechanics, which is based largely on the properties and kinetics of subatomic particles. For the purpose of this discussion, attention will be focused on the behavior of the negatively charged electrons which occupy fixed orbits around each positively charged atomic nucleus, and which determine the "valency" of an atom.

Individual atoms are able to absorb energy by the "excitation" of an orbital electron, which is regarded as moving to an outer orbit of higher energy level; if the electron later returns to a lower orbit, energy is reemitted, often in the form of light or other electromagnetic radiation. The unit of energy which can be absorbed or emitted when a single electron behaves in this way is known as a "quantum," and because of internal restrictions in the energy levels of the different orbits, its energy content may be characteristic for a given element. Since the quantum value of radiant energy is also directly related to its wavelength (the longer the wavelength the lower the quantum value), there is an intimate association between the electron structure of an atom and the wavelengths of radiation it will absorb or emit (i.e., its absorption spectrum and its fluorescence spectrum). These considerations will be of importance in discussing the absorption of light quanta in photosynthesis, and the identification of many organic compounds by spectrophotometry.

At the molecular level, energy changes always accompany the bonding of individual atoms to form a molecule. In polar bonds, electrons may be transferred from one atom to another, leading to a net positive charge on one, and a net negative charge on the other (ion formation). In nonpolar, or covalent, bonds (such as the C—C bond), electrons are shared between two atoms. In both cases, a bond can occur only if the total energy of the atoms is reduced when they enter the "bonded" state. Consequently, energy is given off when the bond is formed, and this energy must be returned before the bond can be broken—the greater the amount of energy, the more stable the bond. The quantity of energy involved in making and breaking chemical bonds is approximately characteristic for the specific pair of atoms involved (e.g., 80 kcal/mole for C—C), and it is therefore possible to calculate for a chemical reaction the energy required to break particular kinds and numbers of bonds in the reactants, and the energy produced when other kinds and numbers of bonds are formed in the products. The ΔH of the reaction then consists largely of the difference in total energy between the old bonds broken and the new bonds formed.

In the formation of polar bonds, and for other bond changes which involve the transfer of electrons, the atom receiving electrons is said to be "reduced," while the donor is "oxidized." The energy differential in such oxidation-reduction reactions corresponds to $\Delta F°$, and it can be calculated by the same law which governs the energy of batteries and other electric circuits:

$$\Delta F° = -nF(E_{0\,\text{receptor}} - E_{0\,\text{donor}})$$

where n is the number of electrons involved, F is the Faraday constant (23.068 kcal/V), and E_0 is the voltage potential, measured against a standard electrode, for an isomolar solution of the oxidized and reduced forms of the receptor, on the one hand, and the donor on the other. In chemical oxidation-reduction reactions, the number of electrons involved is usually two, and the energy change includes a molecular rearrangement. For example, when water is formed from elemental hydrogen and oxygen, two electrons are transferred to the oxygen from hydrogen, and two polar H—O bonds are formed:

$$H_2 + 1/2\ O_2 \longrightarrow H^+O^{2-}H^+ + \text{energy}$$

Since the oxidation-reduction potential of hydrogen (H_2/H^+) is -0.42 V, and the redox potential of oxygen (H_2O/O_2) is $+0.816$ V, the value of $\Delta F°$ for this reaction is:

$$\Delta F° = -2(23.068\ \text{kcal/V})1.236\ \text{V}$$

$$= -57\ \text{kcal/mole}$$

Energy can also be transferred between atoms and molecules by the passage of single electrons, without any molecular rearrangement or chemical reaction, as such. For example, iron ions can change reversibly from the ferric state (Fe^{+++}) to the ferrous state (Fe^{++}) by the addition of an electron. The amount of energy change for a single electron transfer can be calculated in the same manner as $\Delta F°$ for a chemical oxidation-reduction reaction, but the two types of transfer should be clearly distinguished. For example, the oxidation of cytochrome b ($E_0 = -0.04$ V) by cytochrome c ($E_0 = 0.25$ V) is a single electron event:

cytochrome b-Fe^{++} + cytochrome c-Fe^{+++} $\longrightarrow$

cytochrome b-Fe^{+++} + cytochrome c-Fe^{++}

The free energy change is given by

$$\Delta F° = -1(23.068\ \text{kcal/V})0.29\ \text{V}$$

$$= -6.7\ \text{kcal/mole}$$

Some large organic molecules are able to form complexes, composed of dissimilar molecules in close proximity, which are also able to transfer single electrons from a higher energy orbit of one to a lower energy orbit of the other. Characteristic quanta of energy are absorbed or emitted by such "charge transfer" complexes, in a manner analogous to quantum absorption in a single atom; however, the range of energy involved is usually much less. In some cases, a biological molecule that is known to participate in chemical (2 electron) oxidation-reduction reactions under test-tube conditions may actually function in the cell as part of a charge transfer complex, carrying out single electron transfers.

In organic molecules, the presence of numerous unsaturated covalent bonds and structural "rings" makes it possible for the bonds to shift their positions back and forth within the molecule, giving rise to slightly different, isomeric forms of the same compound. In these cases, the molecule is said to "resonate" between the various bond states, and the phenomenon is associated with bond energies higher than would be expected if resonance did not occur. The more resonance forms a molecule has, the more energetically stable it is; consequently, when molecules having fewer resonance forms react to produce molecules with more resonance forms, a "resonance energy" leaves the system as part of ΔH. In some reactions, the change in bond energy and the change in resonance energy may have the same sign (e.g., both exothermic), whereas in other reactions, they may have opposite signs and one must be subtracted from the other.

When the size of an organic molecule becomes sufficiently great, some of the electrons belonging to individual atoms may leave their atomic associations and move more or less freely around the molecule. These are known as π electrons, which may be imagined as forming an "electron cloud" of characteristic shape and position on the molecule. The migration of π electrons can be expected to leave some atoms with a net positive charge, while other atoms will acquire a net negative charge which accompanies the electrons. Such electron migration can set up electrostatic repulsions between neighboring atoms composing the molecule, altering the stability of particular bonds, and leading to specific redistribution of energy within the molecule. This effect will be found to play a major role in specific energy-transferring reactions to be considered in the next chapter.

3

THE BIOCHEMISTRY OF ENERGY TRANSFER

It is impossible for any simple bond-dissociation process to be energy-producing, and the concepts of "energy-rich" bonds and the storage of energy in bonds are physically meaningless.

Bond energies are always positive—energy is required to break a chemical bond.

R. J. GILLESPIE, G. A. MAW, AND
C. A. VERNON *1953*

Beginning in 1925, a number of biological compounds have been isolated and characterized which have two features in common: first, they are of universal or very widespread occurrence in the cells of animals, plants, and microorganisms; and second, they possess very special physical-chemical properties that enable them to transfer energy readily both among themselves and into the more specialized, energy-requiring systems. In their mode of energy transfer, these compounds sort themselves into two major classes:

1. Compounds in which energy transfer is associated with the transfer of an entire chemical unit from one compound to another (e.g., a phosphoryl radical).

2. Compounds in which energy transfer is associated with the transfer of electrons and protons only (oxidation-reduction reactions).

As will be seen, very dissimilar compounds may occur within the same class, while some very similar ones fall into different classes; consequently, these are more or less artificial groupings from a structural standpoint. With respect to function also, future investigation is likely to show that the actual mechanism of energy transfer at the submolecular level is much more similar in the two classes than we now realize. Nevertheless, at the present state of knowledge, it is more meaningful to treat the two groups separately.

Energy Transfer by Transferral of Chemical Groups

The compounds of the first class received attention in the late 1920's and 1930's through the pioneer work of Meyerhof, Lohmann, and others studying organic phosphates. As early as 1863, Liebig had recognized the importance of phosphates, and later Harden and Young (1906) had found that fermentation in cell-free yeast extracts is accompanied by the conversion of inorganic to organic phosphate. Nevertheless, it was only after the isolation of key compounds, such as phosphoarginine (Meyerhof and Lohmann, 1928), adenosine triphosphate (Lohmann, 1929), and phosphoenolpyruvate (Lohmann and Meyerhof, 1934) that the properties and significance of these materials could be understood.

During the 1930's Meyerhof investigated the free-energy changes (ΔF) and heats of reaction (ΔH) for the hydrolysis reactions of various organic phosphates:

$$\underset{\underset{O_-}{|}}{\overset{\overset{O}{\|}}{R-O+P-OH}} + HOH \rightleftharpoons ROH + \underset{\underset{O_-}{|}}{\overset{\overset{O}{\|}}{HO-P-OH}}$$

On the basis of these investigations, a special class of "high-energy" phosphates was defined, which seemed to be characterized by an unusually high $\Delta F°$ for hydrolysis together with surprising stability in aqueous solutions. The energy of these high-energy compounds has frequently been spoken of as if it resided in the P—O bond ruptured by the hydrolysis (termed an "energy-rich phosphate bond" by Lipmann in 1941); although the idea of releasing energy by breaking a chemical bond is antithetical to fundamental principles of physical chemistry, nevertheless the concepts of "high-energy" phosphates and formation of "energy-rich" bonds stimulated a great deal of research in this area. Two additional shortcomings have now become evident.

1. There is no special class of high-energy phosphates; rather the $\Delta F°$ for hydrolysis of the various phosphates takes the form of a graded series. Phosphates with higher $\Delta F°$'s tend to transfer the phosphoryl group

$$\begin{array}{c} O \\ \parallel \\ -P-OH \\ \mid \\ O_- \end{array}$$

to those with lower $\Delta F°$'s, in a manner very analogous to the transfer of electrons from compounds of high redox potential to those of low potential. This property has been called the "phosphoryl transfer potential" (Atkinson and Morton, 1960).

2. The physical chemistry of energy transfer, associated with transfer of the phosphoryl group, is not the same in all phosphates, nor even in all reactions of the same phosphate; in other words, there is no single device, "energy-rich bond" or otherwise, which "high-energy" phosphates have in common. This point will be developed further in considering the individual types of phosphate, and it will be of importance also in considering phosphates and other compounds which transfer energy in association with groups other than phosphoryl.

NUCLEOSIDE POLYPHOSPHATES

A nucleoside consists of a purine or pyrimidine base, joined to a ribose unit; adenosine, guanosine, inosine, cytidine, and uridine are the most important nucleosides, and they correspond to the nucleoside polyphosphates, adenosine triphosphate (ATP), adenosine diphosphate (ADP), and the corresponding tri- and diphosphates of the other nucleosides (GTP, GDP, ITP, IDP, CTP, CDP, UTP, UDP). Of these, ATP and ADP, whose basic structure was worked out by Lohmann (1932, 1935), are quite possibly the most important energy transformers which occur

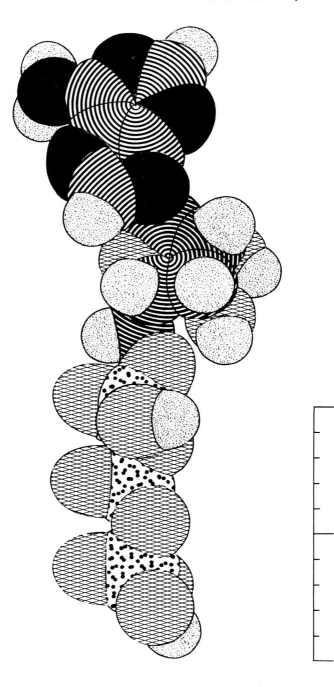

in biological systems (Fig. 3-1). For example, the phosphorylation of ADP to form ATP is a primary energy-storing event in both photosynthesis and oxidative metabolism; furthermore, there is good evidence that ATP constitutes the immediate energy source in such essential biological phenomena as protein synthesis, cell division, muscle contraction, amoeboid movement, flagellary and ciliary movement, active transport, and bioluminescence.

Energy is transferred to and from ATP in two major types of reaction: first, by phosphorylation reactions of the type

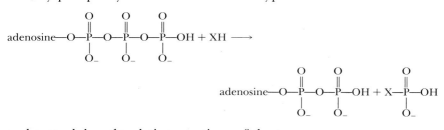

and second, by adenylating reactions of the type

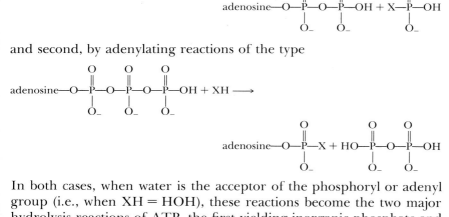

In both cases, when water is the acceptor of the phosphoryl or adenyl group (i.e., when XH = HOH), these reactions become the two major hydrolysis reactions of ATP, the first yielding inorganic phosphate and the second releasing pyrophosphate.

With respect to the first type of reaction, the $\Delta F°$ for hydrolysis of the terminal phosphate in ATP was first determined by Meyerhof and Lohmann (1932) and for many years was considered to be in the range -10 to -12 kcal/mole (as compared with -2 kcal/mole for hydrolysis of "energy-poor" phosphates, such as adenosine monophosphate). During the 1950's, however, many laboratories undertook to redetermine

---

Fig. 3-1. An ATP molecule with triphosphate chain in an extended configuration. The scale indicates 10 Angstrom units. Structural formula is:

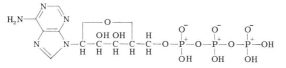

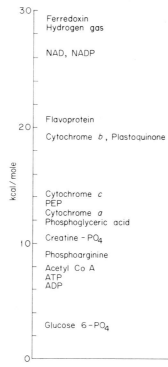

Fig. 3-2. The relative energy levels of some common phosphoryl- and electron-carriers. The base line for phosphoryl carriers is the transfer of phosphoryl to water (hydrolysis), whereas the base line for electron carriers is the transfer of one electron to molecular oxygen.

this value, and it became apparent that the earlier measurements had been somewhat too high. The exact published values of $\Delta F°$ for hydrolysis of ATP vary considerably, due to variations in the buffer systems used, in the concentration and type of enzyme employed to catalyze the hydrolysis, and in the presence or absence of Mg^{++}. The range is approximately -6 to -9 kcal/mole, and Huennekens and Whiteley (1960) in their general review accept the figure -7 kcal/mole for $\Delta F°$ at pH 7.0, 25°C, excess Mg^{++}, and catalytic quantities of enzyme. The ΔH for the reaction has been determined by Podolsky and Morales (1956) as -4.7 kcal/mole (the difference presumably depending on an entropy increase).

The relationship between $\Delta F°$ for hydrolysis, and the ability of ATP to transfer a phosphoryl group with an associated release of energy, is illustrated by the reactions used by Atkinson *et al.* (1959) to measure the ΔF for ATP hydrolysis:

$$\begin{array}{lll}
\text{galactose} + \text{ATP} & \rightleftharpoons \text{galactose 1-phosphate} + \text{ADP} & \Delta F = -1.9 \text{ kcal/mole} \\
\text{galactose 1-phosphate} + H_2O & \rightleftharpoons \text{galactose} + P_i & \Delta F = -5.0 \text{ kcal/mole} \\
\hline
\text{ATP} + H_2O & \rightleftharpoons \text{ADP} + P_i & \Delta F = -6.9 \text{ kcal/mole}
\end{array}$$

It can be seen that water acts as an ultimate acceptor for the phosphoryl group, and that the $\Delta F°$ for hydrolysis is a kind of energetic "distance" between any given organic phosphate and the "zero energy" of inorganic phosphate. Phosphates with a higher $\Delta F°$ for hydrolysis can transfer phosphoryl with a release of "free energy" to those with lower $\Delta F°$'s (Fig. 3-2). In this "phosphoryl transfer potential" series, ATP has an intermediate position, which makes it ideally suited to act as both a donor and acceptor—receiving phosphoryl from higher compounds such as phosphoenolpyruvate ($\Delta F° = -12.8$ kcal/mole) and using it to phosphorylate lower compounds such as glucose 6-phosphate ($\Delta F° = -3.3$ kcal/mole). This intermediate position also permits ATP to participate in many phosphorylation reactions which involve small energy differentials, and which can therefore be readily reversed by slight changes in concentration or other factors (as in the storage and recovery of energy in phosphocreatine). It should be noted that ATP itself is usually present only in small amounts (e.g., 5×10^{-6} mole/gm in skeletal muscle).

Compounds phosphorylated by ATP may be regarded as "activated," inasmuch as they thereby become able to act as phosphoryl donors themselves. Since their ultimate hydrolysis to inorganic phosphate is exergonic, it may be "coupled" to any of several endergonic reactions, making them energetically feasible (see page 17). For example, the bonding of acetate to coenzyme A is energetically unfavorable, but theoretically it could be made much more favorable if it could be coupled to ATP hydrolysis:

$$\begin{array}{lll}
\text{acetate} + \text{CoA} & \rightleftharpoons \text{acetyl-CoA} + H_2O & \Delta F = +7.5 \text{ kcal/mole} \\
\text{ATP} + H_2O & \rightleftharpoons \text{ADP} + P_i & \Delta F = -7.0 \text{ kcal/mole} \\
\hline
\text{acetate} + \text{CoA} + \text{ATP} & \rightleftharpoons \text{acetyl-CoA} + \text{ADP} + P_i & \Delta F = +0.5 \text{ kcal/mole}
\end{array}$$

This coupling is actually accomplished in bacteria by the phosphorylation of the acetate and subsequent transferral to CoA:

$$\begin{array}{lll}
\text{acetate} + \text{ATP} & \rightleftharpoons \text{acetyl phosphate} + \text{ADP} & \Delta F = +3.1 \text{ kcal/mole} \\
\text{acetyl phosphate} + \text{CoA} & \rightleftharpoons \text{acetyl-CoA} + P_i & \Delta F = -2.6 \text{ kcal/mole} \\
\hline
\text{acetate} + \text{CoA} + \text{ATP} & \rightleftharpoons \text{acetyl-CoA} + \text{ADP} + P_i & \Delta F = +0.5 \text{ kcal/mole}
\end{array}$$

The exchange of phosphoryl between ATP and the other nucleoside polyphosphates occurs quite freely:

$$\text{ATP} + \text{XDP} \rightleftharpoons \text{ADP} + \text{XTP}$$

For the inosine polyphosphates, the equilibrium constant of this reaction is very close to 1, so that $\Delta F° = 0$ and the $\Delta F°$ for hydrolysis of ITP must therefore be about the same as that for ATP. The other nucleoside polyphosphates participate in RNA synthesis and in certain other reactions to be discussed later.

In the second type of ATP hydrolysis, leading to release of pyrophosphate instead of orthophosphate, $\Delta F°$ has been determined at about -8 kcal/mole:

$$\text{ATP} + \text{H}_2\text{O} \rightleftharpoons \text{AMP} + \text{PP} \qquad \Delta F° = -8 \text{ kcal/mole}$$

Although transfer of pyrophosphate to other compounds is not very common, this hydrolysis constitutes an energy baseline for adenylation reactions, which are important in the synthesis of protein, RNA, NAD, FAD, and other biologically active compounds. The interchangeability of phosphorylation and adenylation is shown by the fact that in animals, unlike bacteria, the bonding of acetate to CoA is thought to be coupled with ATP hydrolysis by means of an adenylation reaction:

$$\begin{array}{l} \text{acetate} + \text{ATP} \rightleftharpoons \text{acetyl adenylate} + \text{PP} \\ \underline{\text{acetyl adenylate} + \text{CoA} \rightleftharpoons \text{acetyl-CoA} + \text{AMP}} \\ \text{acetate} + \text{CoA} + \text{ATP} \rightleftharpoons \text{acetyl-CoA} + \text{AMP} + \text{PP} \qquad \Delta F° = -0.6 \text{ kcal/mole} \end{array}$$

It is significant that inorganic pyrophosphate, which is a product of all adenylation reactions, itself has a high free energy of hydrolysis

$$\text{PP} + \text{H}_2\text{O} \rightleftharpoons 2 \text{ P}_i \qquad \Delta F° = -6.6 \text{ kcal/mole}$$

In some systems this energy can be recovered by ATP:

$$\text{ADP} + \text{PP} \rightleftharpoons \text{ATP} + \text{P}_i$$

In fact, bacteria seem to employ both inorganic pyrophosphate and acetyl phosphate as important phosphoryl storage compounds.

The terminal phosphoryl of ADP is also available to phosphorylate other compounds, and its position in the "phosphoryl transfer potential" series may be determined from the reaction

$$\text{ATP} + \text{AMP} \xrightleftharpoons[\text{kinase}]{\text{adenylate}} 2 \text{ ADP} \qquad \Delta F° = -0.6 \text{ kcal/mole}$$

In this reaction, the terminal phosphoryl of ATP becomes the terminal phosphoryl of ADP, and therefore the $\Delta F°$ for the reaction must represent the difference in $\Delta F°$ for hydrolysis between ADP and ATP. On this basis, the value of $\Delta F°$ for terminal hydrolysis of ADP can be estimated as about -6.4 kcal/mole ($-7.0 + 0.6$). This calculation is of special interest since the terminal phosphoryl of ADP represents the same phosphorus which is separated from ATP in pyrophosphate hydrolysis (where $\Delta F°$ is -8 kcal/mole). This suggests that the structure of the entire molecule is involved in determining the free energy of hydrolysis, and raises the broader question of the submolecular basis for "high energy" in ATP and other phosphates.

MOLECULAR STRUCTURE IN RELATION TO HIGH FREE ENERGY OF HYDROLYSIS

It was explained in the preceding chapter that changes in bonds and bond energies, together with differences in resonance energy, constitute a large part of the ΔH (and thereby $\Delta F°$) for any chemical reaction. Furthermore, in phosphate hydrolysis the $\Delta F°$ for ionization of the inorganic phosphate residue is part of $\Delta F°$ for the overall reaction; since H^+ is a product of this ionization, the free energy of hydrolysis is very sensitive to pH and to the particular type of buffer system used. Since the bond and resonance changes, as well as heat of ionization, might be expected to be roughly equivalent in hydrolysis of both "high" and "low" energy phosphates, we are entitled to ask why some phosphates have a significantly higher $\Delta F°$ for hydrolysis than others.

This question has been investigated by Pullman and Pullman (1960), who calculated the electron structure of various phosphates, using the techniques of quantum mechanics. They found that phosphates with relatively high free energies of hydrolysis tend to show an unusual distribution of π electrons, such that the molecule contains chains of adjacent atoms, all bearing a positive charge. In ATP, for instance, a chain of six positively charged atoms occurs:

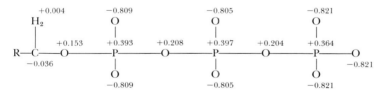

The unusual distribution of charges in "high energy" phosphates has two effects, which vary in relative importance from one compound to another, but which together are sufficient to account for the higher $\Delta F°$ values.

1. Some of the phosphates show special restrictions in the resonance of their bond electrons (opposing resonance), so that upon hydrolysis there is a disproportionate increase in resonance stability, accompanied by a release of energy (see page 28). In ATP this effect accounts for 3.2 kcal/mole of $\Delta F°$ for hydrolysis, while in ADP it is 2.6 kcal/mole and in

carboxylphosphates (e.g., acetyl phosphate and 1,3-diphosphoglycer-aldehyde), 5.6 kcal/mole.

2. The adjacent positive charges, together with adjacent negative charges on the oxygen atoms, lead to strong electrostatic repulsions. The net contribution to $\Delta F°$ from this effect is calculated as 2 kcal/mole in ATP and 1.4 kcal/mole in ADP; in all other types of phosphates studied, this effect is negative (i.e., there is a net attraction), amounting to about -0.7 kcal/mole in carboxylphosphates.

Since the "extra" energy of ATP (as compared with a low-energy phosphate) amounts to only 4 or 5 kilocalories/mole, it is apparent that opposing resonance and electrostatic repulsion together are sufficient to account for it.

It must not be forgotten that the actual value of ΔF (as opposed to $\Delta F°$) is a property of the reaction as a whole, and in some cases, special side reactions accompanying the hydrolysis can also contribute to the overall energy change. This is especially notable in the carboxyphosphates, where the ionization of the carboxylic acid after hydrolysis has a ΔF of its own (depending on pH) which at standard conditions can contribute -3.2 kcal/mole to the total free energy of hydrolysis. In this category should also be included the notable effects of Mg^{++} concentration on $\Delta F°$ for hydrolysis of ATP. ATP has a notable tendency to form a chelate with divalent ions, such that the pyrophosphate bridge folds back in the direction of the adenine group. As reported by Burton (1959), ADP does not bind magnesium as strongly as ATP, and consequently, the presence of Mg^{++} in the reaction

$$ATP + H_2O \; \rightleftharpoons \; ADP + P_i$$

shifts the equilibrium toward the left; Burton has calculated that $\Delta F°$ for hydrolysis of ATP is -8.6 kcal/mole in the absence of Mg^{++}, as compared with -7.0 kcal/mole when it is present.

Phosphoenolpyruvate (PEP)

Phosphoenolpyruvate (Fig. 3-3) has the highest phosphoryl transfer potential of any naturally occurring phosphate (ca. -12.4 kcal/mole), and it is also of interest because the factors leading to its high $\Delta F°$ are quite different from those which contribute to the "high energy" of ATP and carboxylphosphates.

Lohmann and Meyerhof (1934) first isolated this compound and showed that it is an important intermediate in fermentation. Its $\Delta F°$ for hydrolysis has been estimated from the ΔF for the reaction:

$$PEP + ADP \; \rightleftharpoons \; ATP + pyruvate$$

which is approximately -5.3 kcal/mole in the presence of Mg^{++}. Meyerhof and Schultz (1935) measured the ΔH for hydrolysis of PEP as -8.5 kcal/mole, which when compared to a $\Delta F°$ of -12.4 kcal/mole, would indicate a fairly large entropy increase during the reaction.

The unusually high $\Delta F°$ for hydrolysis in this case seems to be due to a particularly large lowering of bond energies accompanying the tautomerization of enol pyruvate to keto pyruvate (after removal of the phosphate group).

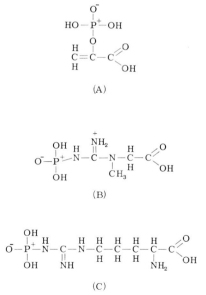

Oesper (1950) has estimated that the keto form is approximately -18 kcal/mole more stable than the enol form with respect to bond energies, and Pullman and Pullman (1960) estimate that the keto form is about $+10$ kcal/mole less stable than the enol form with respect to resonance energy; consequently, a net energy change of -8 kcal/mole would be expected as "heat of tautomerization" alone. Factors such as opposing resonance and electrostatic repulsion, on the other hand, seem to be of minor importance in the hydrolysis of phosphoenolpyruvate.

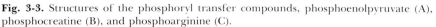

Fig. 3-3. Structures of the phosphoryl transfer compounds, phosphoenolpyruvate (A), phosphocreatine (B), and phosphoarginine (C).

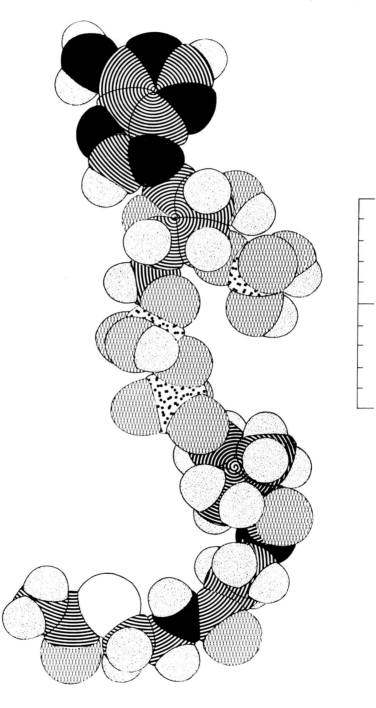

PHOSPHAGENS

The term "phosphagen" has been applied to phosphocreatine and phosphoarginine (Fig. 3-3), as well as to some related organic phosphates that appear to function primarily in the storage of phosphoryl energy. These materials are able to accept phosphoryl from ATP during periods of rapid energy intake (i.e., high ATP concentration), returning it to ATP later when energy is being expended (low ATP concentration), and they are often present in larger amounts than ATP itself (phosphocreatine/ATP = ca. 4 in vertebrate skeletal muscle).

Phosphocreatine was first isolated by Fiske and SubbaRow (1927), and Noda *et al.* (1954) made a thorough study of ΔF for the reaction:

$$\text{creatine phosphate} + \text{ADP} \rightleftharpoons \text{creatine} + \text{ATP}$$

The value of ΔF is -2.8 kcal/mole at pH 7.4, but it becomes zero or slightly positive (i.e., the reaction reverses) at higher pH, and it also varies with the concentration of Mg^{++}. From these data, $\Delta F°$ for hydrolysis of phosphocreatine has been estimated at about -10.5 kcal/mole.

Phosphoarginine, the other major compound of this type, was first isolated by Meyerhof and Lohmann (1928), and ΔF for the comparable phosphoryl transfer with ATP was studied by Griffiths *et al.* (1957). In this case, too, the value of ΔF varies with pH and Mg^{++} concentration, the range being from -0.9 to $+1.2$ kcal/mole; $\Delta F°$ for hydrolysis is estimated at -9 kcal/mole. It is of interest that phosphoarginine has not been found in vertebrates.

The basis for the high energy of hydrolysis in phosphagens seems to depend on several factors, including both opposing resonance and the ΔF for neutralization of the basic amino group which characterizes creatine and arginine. It is also noteworthy that hydrolysis of these substances involves rupture of a P—N bond, rather than the P—O bond which characterizes most organic phosphates (Fig. 3-3).

ACETYL- AND SUCCINYL-CoA (FIG. 3-4)

It has already been emphasized that energy is commonly transferred, not only in association with the phosphoryl group, but with the adenyl

---

Fig. 3-4. An acetyl-CoA molecule, with the acetyl group at the lower end of a flexible carbon-nitrogen chain. The scale indicates 10 Angstrom units. Structural formula is:

group as well. However, both phosphoryl and adenyl energy can also be interchanged in certain instances with carboxyl esters of coenzyme A, and these compounds also show high $\Delta F°$ values for hydrolysis. Consequently, they make up a special group of "high energy" molecules, whose energy is transferred in association with acetyl, succinyl, and other acyl esters, rather than with phosphoryl.

Acetyl coenzyme A (Fig. 3-4) was first isolated by Lynen and Reichert (1951) and has since been found to be an important intermediary in the oxidation of pyruvic acid. It is of interest that CoA itself consists of an adenyl group, which is bound to pantothenic acid; in essence, the molecule acts as a reversible carrier of acetate, succinate, and other carboxylic acids, which are bound in a thioester linkage at the sulfhydryl end of the pantothenic acid. The interchangeability of energy between acetate as a phosphoryl carrier and CoA as an acetate carrier is evident in the reaction:

$$\text{acetyl phosphate} + \text{CoA} \rightleftharpoons \text{acetyl CoA} + \text{P}_i$$

where $\Delta F = -2.6$ kcal/mole. It is also of interest that in some bacteria CoA can act as a phosphoryl carrier as well.

The $\Delta F°$ for hydrolysis of acetyl-CoA is about -8 kcal/mole, making it about equivalent to ATP hydrolysis. This value appears to be due in part to opposing resonance and in part to ΔF for ionization of the carboxylic acid which is released upon hydrolysis (a relationship very similar to that in the carboxyl phosphates). The reactions of acetyl- and succinyl-CoA will be discussed in greater detail during the general discussion of oxidative metabolism in Chapter 6.

Energy Transfer by Oxidation-Reduction

It has already been pointed out that energy changes accompany the transfer of electrons from one molecule to another, and this process is known to be an important mechanism in intracellular energy transfer. In many ways the storage or release of biological energy by electron transfer is analogous to similar energy changes accompanying phosphoryl or adenyl transfer: i.e., any given molecule is characterized by an "electron transfer potential," such that compounds of more negative potential tend to transfer electrons to those of more positive potential with an associated release of energy. Furthermore, just as water is the ultimate acceptor for the phosphoryl group, molecular oxygen is the ultimate acceptor for electrons, thereby establishing the energetic "zero point" for this type of reaction (Fig. 3-2). Electron transfer potential, however, is usually measured in volts, and $\Delta F°$ for chemical oxidation-reductions is calculated from the formula discussed in Chapter 2:

$$\Delta F° = -nF \ (E_{0 \text{ acceptor}} - E_{0 \text{ donor}})$$

It should be kept in mind that the actual ΔF for an oxidation-reduction reaction (as opposed to $\Delta F°$) depends on the initial concentrations of electron donor and acceptor compounds, as in other chemical equilibria.

Major advances in understanding the role of oxidation-reduction in biological processes date from 1925, when Keilin rediscovered a type of cellular pigment first reported by MacMunn in 1886 (see Chapter 1). This class of pigments, which Keilin named "cytochrome," consists of iron porphyrin (heme)-containing proteins which have characteristic absorption spectra in the visible range, and which in many organisms impart an easily detectable (brownish) color to the cells. Keilin found that in a suspension of living yeast or in the thorax of a live wax moth at least three characteristic absorption peaks could be detected under anaerobic (reducing) conditions; these peaks became smaller or disappeared under aerobic (oxidizing) conditions, but the appearance or disappearance of the absorption peaks was entirely reversible. Since almost the same absorption peaks were detectable across a wide range of animals, plants, and microorganisms, Keilin proposed (as had MacMunn before him) that this class of pigment plays a fundamental role in the utilization of oxygen by cells. By 1930 Keilin had found that at least three different compounds are responsible for the three absorption peaks and he had isolated the one responsible for peak "c" at 550 mμ, which he called cytochrome c; cytochromes a and b showed characteristic absorption peaks at 605 mμ and 562 mμ, respectively.

During the early 1930's, two other classes of compound capable of reversible oxidation-reduction were discovered and analyzed by Warburg and Christian—the pyridine nucleotides and the flavoproteins. By 1936 Theorell could postulate that the three classes of compound might form an oxidation-reduction chain, such that pyridine nucleotide could accept protons and electrons from substrate materials and transfer them to flavoprotein, which could in turn transfer the electrons to cytochrome c (an event already demonstrated *in vitro*), and that the cytochromes would ultimately transfer them to atmospheric oxygen, reducing it to H_2O. This concept was further elaborated and supported by the work of Ball (1938), and Ball and Ramsdell (1939), who determined the values of E_0 for the three cytochromes and pyridine nucleotide, demonstrating that such a stepwise electron transfer is energetically feasible. It was not until 1955, however, that Chance and Williams suc-

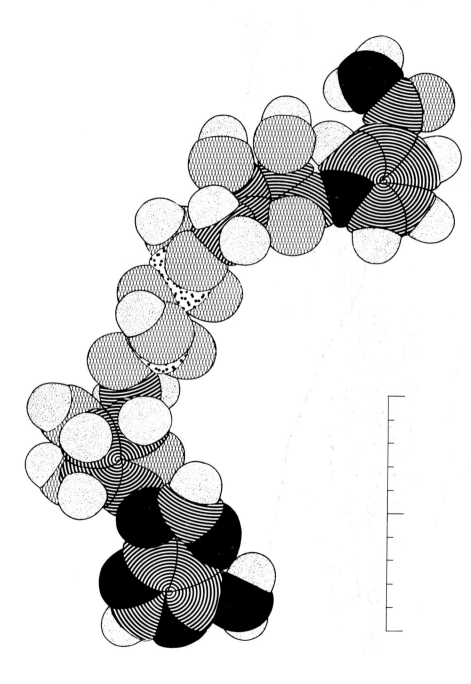

ceeded in observing the sequential transfer of electrons among these substances in living cells, finding that the actual sequence of transfer is essentially the same as the sequence of E_0 values.

PYRIDINE NUCLEOTIDES

Two pyridine nucleotides of major importance are known: the first of these was isolated by Harden and Young in 1906 as a dialyzable, heat-resistant cofactor in cell-free fermentation. Warburg referred to it as "coenzyme I" until its structure was worked out, when it came to be called diphosphopyridine nucleotide (DPN); however, it has now been officially renamed nicotinamide-adenine dinucleotide (NAD; see Fig. 3-5). The second pyridine nucleotide was isolated as "coenzyme II" by Warburg and Christian (1931), was known for many years as triphosphopyridine nucleotide (TPN), and is now termed nicotinamide-adenine dinucleotide phosphate (NADP; Fig 3-6). In 1935 Warburg found that both compounds consist of an adenyl group (AMP) bound to nicotinamide mononucleotide. In fact, NAD is synthesized in a typical adenylation reaction for which $\Delta F°$ is very close to zero:

$$\text{nicotinamide mononucleotide} + \text{ATP} \rightleftharpoons \text{NAD} + \text{PP}$$

and NADP is synthesized from NAD in a phosphorylation reaction:

$$\text{NAD} + \text{ATP} \rightleftharpoons \text{NADP} + \text{ADP}$$

A. Kornberg, who discovered the latter reaction, determined the position of the phosphoryl in NADP during the early 1950's, placing it at the 2'-carbon of the ribose.

E_0 for the two pyridine nucleotides is approximately the same, and has been determined as -0.32 V; consequently, these compounds can accept electrons from many substrates, such as isocitrate ($E_0 = -0.48$ V) and molecular hydrogen ($E_0 = -0.42$ V). Of great importance, furthermore, is the fact that the pyridine nucleotides are hydrogen carriers as well as electron carriers; Fisher *et al.* (1953) used radioactive-labeled hydrogen to demonstrate that protons (H^+) removed from substrate molecules actually became part of NADH during its reduction, and

Fig. 3-5. An NAD (or DPN) molecule in an oxidized state, with the potential electron-carrying end uppermost. The scale indicates 10 Angstrom units. Structural formula is:

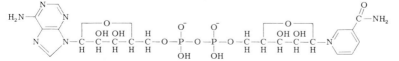

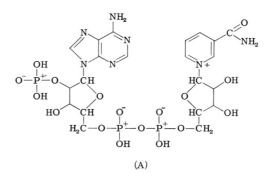

(A)

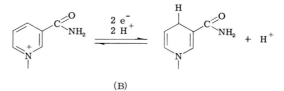

(B)

Fig. 3-6 (A) Structure of NADP (or TPN); (B) Generalized reaction by which a pyridine nucleotide carries two electrons and one proton.

Pullman *et al.* (1954) showed that this hydrogen is added specifically at the pyridine ring (Fig. 3-6B).

The oxidation-reduction of pyridine nucleotides involves a molecular rearrangement, i.e., it is a chemical reaction in which a transfer of two electrons occurs (see Chapter 2). In this type of reaction, the number of protons (H^+) removed from the substrate is the same as the number of electrons; however, the NADH molecule actually carries only one proton (and two electrons), while the second proton accompanies the reaction in solution.

Since E_0 is very similar in the two pyridine nucleotides, electrons and protons (and energy) are freely exchangeable between them:

$$NADH + NADP \rightleftharpoons NAD + NADPH$$

Their oxidation or reduction can be monitored spectrophotometrically by the disappearance of an absorption peak at 340 mμ (in the ultraviolet), which is characteristic for the reduced form.

NAD is the hydrogen acceptor for many dehydrogenase enzymes, and two moles of NAD actually form a structural part of the enzyme phosphoglyceraldehyde dehydrogenase; however, most NAD functions in unbound form. In many animal cells, NADP occurs side-by-side with NAD, and NADP also acts as a hydrogen acceptor for an isocitrate dehydrogenase; nevertheless, the most prominent role of NADP occurs in photosynthetic cells, where its reduction to NADPH is a primary event in the conversion of radiant energy to chemical energy (and where it acts as a reducing agent for the conversion of CO_2 into carbohydrates). Klingenberg *et al.* (1959) have determined the ratio of NADP/NAD for the mitochondria of various rat tissues, finding values of 1.7 for liver, 0.24 for heart, 0.19 for kidney, and 0.15 for brain. They also found that most of the NAD occurs in oxidized form, whereas most of the NADP is in its reduced form.

FLAVOPROTEINS

The first flavoprotein was isolated also by Warburg and Christian (1932), who referred to their discovery as "yellow enzyme" (from its color in solution). Yellow enzyme attracted attention because it catalyzed the oxidation of NADPH by O_2, and it was soon found that purified preparations of yellow enzyme could be reversibly reduced by NADPH and oxidized by cytochrome c or molecular oxygen (although the oxidation proceeds at a very slow rate); its E_0, which was determined in 1936 as -0.06 V, is also intermediate between pyridine nucleotide and the cytochromes.

Theorell (1934) showed that yellow enzyme could be separated by dialysis into a white protein moiety and a yellow "coenzyme" fraction, the latter being identified soon after as the monophosphate of the vitamin riboflavin (flavin mononucleotide or FMN). Neither the protein alone nor FMN alone could catalyze the oxidation of NADPH, but if the two were remixed, activity was restored. In subsequent years, many different flavoprotein enzymes have been found and studied, some of which catalyze the oxidative degradation of amino acids, pyruvic acid, succinic acid, and fatty acids.

Many of the flavoproteins require as coenzyme, not FMN, but its adenylation product, flavine adenine dinucleotide (FAD) (Fig. 3-7); this is formed in the reaction:

$$\text{FMN} + \text{ATP} \rightleftharpoons \text{FAD} + \text{PP}$$

In fact, it is now understood that the ability of flavoproteins to catalyze substrate oxidations depends on the activity of FMN or FAD as intermediate hydrogen and electron carriers, according to the two-electron reaction shown in Fig. 3-7B. E_0 for riboflavin alone (as distinguished from flavoprotein) is -0.20 V; $\Delta F°$ for the two electron reaction

$$\text{NADH} + \text{H}^+ + \text{FAD-protein} \rightleftharpoons \text{NAD} + \text{FADH}_2\text{-protein}$$

can be calculated by the method previously described:

$$\Delta F° = -2\ (23.068)\ 0.26\ \text{V} = -12\ \text{kcal/mole}$$

It is noteworthy that this value exceeds $\Delta F°$ for hydrolysis of ATP, and

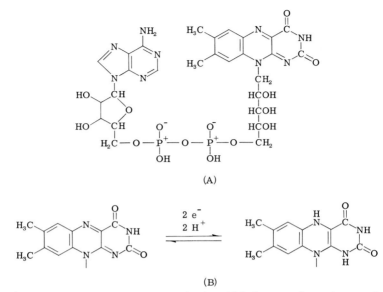

(A)

(B)

Fig. 3-7. (A) Structure of FAD; (B) Reaction by which flavoprotein carries two electrons and two protons.

in fact there is evidence that in living cells the oxidation of NADH by flavoprotein supplies energy for the reversal of ATP hydrolysis (see Chapter 6). Since reduced riboflavin lacks the characteristic yellow color, its oxidation or reduction can be monitored spectrophotometrically.

Although both FMN and FAD can function in 2-electron oxidation-reductions as outlined above, many flavoproteins serve to link 2-electron oxidations with single-electron reductions. For instance, Masters *et al.* (1965) have found evidence that in one NADP-cytochrome *c* reductase a single-electron cycling occurs between FADH and FADH₂. Furthermore many of the flavoprotein enzymes contain nonheme iron atoms, which seem to play a role in single-electron transfers (see below). Flavoproteins can also form charge transfer complexes (Chapter 2) that are capable of transferring energy in single electron events. Consequently, the mechanisms of energy transfer involving flavoproteins have proved to be complex and difficult to unravel.

Attempts to isolate a single flavoprotein as a primary NADH dehydrogenase have proved difficult because of alterations in the properties of the enzyme during preparation, e.g., by fragmentation into subunits, or by conversion of FAD to FMN. A flavoprotein capable of rapidly reducing cytochrome *c in vitro* at the expense of NADH was first isolated by Mahler *et al.* (1952), and contained a coenzyme similar to FAD; in addition, the enzyme contained four iron atoms that were necessary for the cytochrome reduction but not the NADH oxidation. Using more refined methods of preparation, Singer (1963, 1965) later purified an NADH dehydrogenase of molecular weight about 500,000, which contains 1 mole of FMN together with at least 16 nonheme iron atoms. Although the enzyme shows high substrate specificity in removing electrons from NADH, and also exhibits an electron paramagnetic resonance (EPR) characteristic of mitochondrial respiration, its natural electron acceptor is evidently not a cytochrome. The enzyme acquires cytochrome reductase activity only after it has been fragmented to subunits of about 80,000 molecular weight.

CYTOCHROMES

As already described, the three primary cytochromes (*a*, *b*, and *c*) were discovered and characterized by Keilin, using spectrophotometric techniques, during the late 1920's and early 1930's. Spectrum analysis has continued to be the most productive method for analyzing the cytochromes, since most of them (except cytochrome *c*) are firmly bound to insoluble components of the cell, and are known to undergo alterations in their biological properties when purified, or solubilized with emulsifying agents such as bile salts.

Since Keilin's original discoveries, twenty or more additional cytochromes have been found, most of them much more restricted in distribution than the first three. All the cytochromes are proteins containing an iron porphyrin (heme-hemin) group (Fig. 3-8), and, except for the

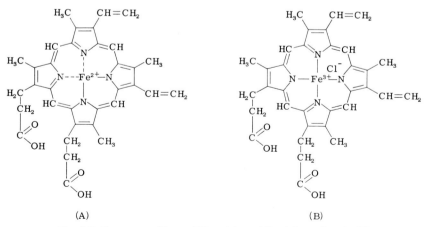

(A)   (B)

Fig. 3-8. Structure of heme (A) and its oxidized form, hemin (B).

cytochrome *a* complex, they are not sensitive to carbon monoxide or cyanide. Most of the cytochromes show three absorption maxima: one in the violet (γ band at 415–452 mμ) which is characteristic of the porphyrin group and is not so sensitive to oxidation; one in the green (β band at 521–530 mμ); and a more specific peak in the longer wavelengths (α band = 603 mμ for cytochrome *a*, 563 mμ for cytochrome *b*, and 550 mμ for cytochrome *c*). The α and β peaks disappear upon oxidation and reappear under reducing conditions; since this behavior is characteristic of the oxidation of ferrous iron (Fe^{++}) in the heme group to ferric iron (Fe^{+++}) in the hemin group, the cytochromes are regarded as simple electron carriers in which oxidation or reduction is a single electron event (not involving a chemical rearrangement). Reduced cytochromes are sometimes referred to as ferrocytochromes, as compared with the corresponding oxidized ferricytochromes.

The oxidation-reduction sequence for the three primary cytochromes was first postulated by Ball (1938) on the basis of his E_0 measurements:

$$\text{H}_2 \longrightarrow \text{Cyt } b \longrightarrow \text{Cyt } c \longrightarrow \text{Cyt } a \longrightarrow \text{O}_2$$
$$-0.42 \text{ V} \quad\quad 0.00 \text{ V} \quad\quad +0.26 \text{ V} \quad\quad +0.29 \text{ V} \quad\quad +0.82 \text{ V}$$

Since the E_0 values for pyridine nucleotides and flavoproteins are intermediate between substrate-H_2 and cytochrome *b*, these two components can also be regarded as part of the "electron transport chain." Chance and Williams (1955), using rapid flow spectrophotometry, were able to confirm that this is the actual order in which these components are oxidized when oxygen is made available to cells in a reducing atmosphere; they observed, for example, that all the cytochrome *c* becomes oxidized before any of the cytochrome *b* or flavoprotein. However, it is not yet clear how the two-electron chemical oxidation-reductions of NAD and FAD are coordinated with the one-electron oxidation-reductions of the cytochromes.

Cytochrome a

Simultaneously with Keilin's (1925) pioneer work on the cytochromes, Warburg became interested in characterizing the primary compound in cells responsible for accepting molecular oxygen and reducing it to water. This compound, whose most characteristic property would be autoxidation, was called the "*Atmungsferment*." Warburg found that it was inhibited by carbon monoxide in the dark, but that this inhibition could be reversed by photodissociation of the enzyme–carbon monoxide complex in the light; by 1929 he was able to publish the light absorption curve (action spectrum) for this photodissociation, and from the action spectrum he concluded that the *Atmungsferment* contained iron and was probably a heme protein of molecular weight about 70,000.

Some years later, Keilin and Hartree (1938) undertook to investigate an enzyme system capable of catalyzing the oxidation of cytochrome c by molecular O_2 (which they called cytochrome oxidase); they found that this system was also subject to photoreversible inhibition by carbon monoxide. Shortly thereafter, Keilin and Hartree (1939) discovered that *part* of the material responsible for the cytochrome a absorption band at 603 mμ was also sensitive to carbon monoxide, that the absorption maxima of this material, when complexed to CO, corresponded closely with the absorption peaks found by Warburg for the *Atmungsferment*, and that this fraction of cytochrome a was autoxidizable. Consequently, Keilin and Hartree defined this fraction as cytochrome a_3 (retaining the term cytochrome a for the material not sensitive to CO), and summarized impressive evidence that cytochrome a_3, Warburg's *Atmungsferment*, and cytochrome oxidase were all the same material. Although confusion is still encountered with this terminology, Keilin and Hartree's conclusion has been confirmed in its essential aspects: atmospheric oxygen is reduced in cells by a single system which when it is regarded as an electron carrier is called "cytochrome a_3," and when it is regarded as an enzyme system is still often referred to as "cytochrome oxidase."

Intriguing relationships exist between cytochrome a_3, which forms a complex with carbon monoxide, and cytochrome a, which does not. As was recognized by Keilin and Hartree twenty-five years ago, these two materials are extremely similar, if not interconvertible. Chance has found that the ratio of a_3 to a approximates $1:1$ in mitochondria from a wide range of species. Furthermore, attempts to separate a and a_3 have not been successful; only one "cytochrome a protein" has been isolated, which accounts for the total absorption of a and a_3 combined. This protein in the monomeric form has a molecular weight of 66,000–70,000 (as predicted by Warburg), contains one heme group, but is inactive; the active form may be a pentamer or hexamer of the 70,000 molecular weight unit. Cytochromes a and a_3 have a distinctive type of porphyrin group, which does not show a β absorption band in the green; consequently they appear greenish in color, unlike the other cytochromes, which are reddish. Cytochrome a also contains one atom of bound copper per iron-porphyrin; the position and function of the copper is not known, but in other oxidases copper acts as a carrier of molecular oxygen.

Cytochrome c

Cytochrome c has been distinctive from the beginning because it is easily
extracted by acid or salt, and it resists denaturation; consequently, it
could be purified by Keilin as early as 1930, it was crystallized in 1956,
and it has been examined in monomolecular form in the electron microscope by Levin (1962). This cytochrome is a very basic protein (isoelectric
pH $= 10.5$) of relatively low molecular weight (about 13,000), containing one heme group; the molecule, as seen in the electron microscope,
is prism-shaped and measures about 39×28 Å; however, there is evidence that oxidation or reduction of cytochrome c leads to changes in
the three-dimensional configuration of the molecule.

In 1940, Yakushiji and Okunuki found that the cytochrome c absorption peak at 550 mμ could be separated into two components, one of
which has its true peak at 553 mμ. This observation has led to the recognition of a new cytochrome, usually called cytochrome c_1 (or cytochrome
e). All of its three absorption peaks lie close to those of cytochrome c, suggesting that the two have structural similarities. Unlike cytochrome c
however, c_1 is tightly bound to insoluble cell components, the monomer
has a molecular weight of 51,000–55,000, and it shows a strong tendency
to polymerize. Cytochrome c_1 is reduced by cytochrome b ($E_0 = 0.0$ V)
and oxidized by cytochrome c ($E_0 = 0.26$ V) *in vitro;* it is therefore
thought to participate between these two components in the electron
transport chain. Although its E_0 value has apparently not been measured, it is expected to lie close to that of cytochrome c.

Cytochrome b

Cytochrome b was first purified in 1956 by Sekuzu and Okunuki, who
found that the monomer has a molecular weight of about 28,000. Like
cytochromes a and c_1 (but unlike cytochrome c), it has a strong tendency
to polymerize spontaneously and to form stoichiometric complexes with
the "structural protein" of Criddle *et al.* (1962). It is of some theoretical
interest that E_0 for the monomer is -0.34 V, much lower than that of
mitochondrial cytochrome b, but a $1:1$ complex between cytochrome b
and structural protein shows the typical E_0 (0.0 V). Since cytochrome
b represents the point of contact between the cytochrome chain and
various flavoproteins, the mechanisms of energy transfer in which it is
involved are complex and have not yet been completely unraveled.

Beginning with the work of Hill and Scarisbrick (1951), a variety of
cytochromes showing b-type absorption maxima have been isolated from
plants. For instance, cytochrome b_6 is thought to be involved in electron
transport during photosynthesis. Montague and Morton (1960) have

also crystallized a cytochrome b_2 from yeast; this protein contains *both* heme and flavin in 1:1 proportion and functions as a yeast lactic dehydrogenase. It is also associated with a uniform, low molecular weight DNA component which is necessary for crystallization, but not for enzymatic activity.

Many of the plant *b*-type cytochromes have the intriguing property of being autoxidizable in the presence of atmospheric oxygen; correspondingly, the concentration of cytochrome *a* (cytochrome oxidase) in many plants is remarkably low. Since the autoxidizable *b*-cytochromes are not inhibited by carbon monoxide or cyanide, they can act as terminal oxidases in the presence of these cytochrome oxidase inhibitors, and they support a cyanide-resistant respiration. In the extreme case of *Arum* spadix, no cytochrome *a* has been detected at all and cyanide has no detectable effect on respiration, but there is present a unique cytochrome b_7 (α band = 560 mμ; $E_0 = -0.03$). Another autoxidizable cytochrome b_3 ($E_0 = +0.04$ V) is, like cytochrome *c*, easily extractable and of general occurrence in plants.

Cytochrome f and the Role of Cytochromes in Photosynthesis

Hill and Scarisbrick (1951) also discovered an easily extracted cytochrome having an α absorption maximum at 555 mμ, molecular weight about 110,000, and E_0 of +0.365 V, which they named cytochrome *f*. Soon after, Davenport (1952) found that cytochrome *f* is localized in chloroplasts, and Davenport and Hill (1952) showed that, in plants where the ratio of photosynthesis to respiration is about 10, the ratio of cytochrome *f* to cytochrome b_3 and *c* is about the same. Consequently, they proposed that cytochrome *f* plays a role in photosynthesis.

Spectral analysis of cytochromes in green cells is difficult because their absorption peaks are masked by those of chlorophyll. However Lundegardh (1954) was able to show that in *Chlorella* and wheat cytochrome *f* is primarily in the oxidized form during illumination, and primarily reduced in the dark; cytochromes *c* and *b* in his preparations did not show this effect. In photosynthetic bacteria also, Duysens (1954) was able to detect marked differences in the visible absorption spectra indicating that a compound like cytochrome *f* (or possibly cytochrome *c*) is reversibly oxidized during photosynthesis. Kamen has found evidence, in fact, that the processes of oxidative metabolism and photosynthesis may compete for the same cytochrome chain in some facultatively photosynthetic bacteria. Still other evidence, to be discussed in the next chapter, has made it clear that electron transfer is a primary event in photosynthesis, in which cytochromes undoubtedly play a part.

As Hill has pointed out, E_0 for cytochrome *f* (+0.365 V) is about half-way between that of chloroplasts (-0.03 V) and E_0 for oxygen (0.82 V). Chloroplasts are also known to contain a modified form of cytochrome b (cytochrome b_6), but they are lacking in cytochrome c and cytochrome oxidase. In the absence of terminal oxidases, cytochrome f apparently cannot discharge electrons to oxygen, and this fact may play an important role in diverting electrons into the reduction of carbon dioxide and the formation of carbohydrates.

Nonheme Iron Proteins

Recently a class of electron carriers has been recognized which lacks flavin or heme groups, but which contains nonheme iron. The earliest of these compounds to be discovered was ferredoxin, a type of protein first found by Mortenson *et al.* (1962) in the bacterium *Clostridium* and subsequently shown to be localized in the chloroplasts of spinach leaves by Tagawa and Arnon (1962; ferredoxin:chlorophyll = 1:400). According to Tanaka *et al.* (1965), *Clostridium* ferredoxins are low molecular weight proteins (mol. wt. 5800) which have 55 amino acid residues, of which eight are sulfur-containing cysteines; each molecule contains seven atoms of nonheme iron in a characteristic linkage with sulfide ions on the cysteine residues. Like the cytochromes, the ferredoxins undergo single-electron oxidation-reductions, which can be followed spectrographically by changes in the absorption peaks of the brown oxidized form (390, 300, 280 mμ), as compared with the pale yellow reduced form (260 mμ).

The ferredoxins have very acid isoelectric points (pH 3.7) and are the most electronegative of any naturally occurring electron carriers ($E_0 = -0.417$ V in bacteria and -0.432 V in spinach, compared with -0.42 V for molecular hydrogen gas). In fact, ferredoxin in the presence of a hydrogenase is able to accept electrons from molecular hydrogen, or conversely to release hydrogen gas from water by transferring electrons to protons (H^+) in solution. There is evidence, to be discussed in the next chapter, that ferredoxin acts as a primary electron transfer agent in the various bacterial reactions involving molecular hydrogen, in nitrogen fixation, and in photosynthesis, where it appears to act as the primary acceptor of excited electrons from chlorophyll. The low value of E_0 would indicate that ferredoxin functions at the head of the electron transfer chain, accepting electrons from substrates (or from excited chlorophyll) and passing them on to pyridine nucleotide; in support of this concept, Shin *et al.* (1963) have crystallized a flavoprotein from spinach chloroplasts which catalyzes the reduction of NADP by reduced ferredoxin. It is of interest that this single-electron oxidation is coupled with the two-electron reduction of pyridine nucleotide by a flavoprotein, just as another flavoprotein couples oxidation of pyridine nucleotide to the single-electron reductions of the cytochromes.

Still another nonheme iron protein has recently been isolated by Rieske (1965), which occurs in mitochondria as a functional complex with cytochrome b and cytochrome c_1. The molecular weight of this protein is about 26,000, and each molecule contains two atoms of nonheme iron. The oxidized protein is reddish in color, with absorption peaks at 575 and 460 mμ, while the reduced form has peaks at 380, 420, and 515 mμ. Evidence from electron charge analysis indicates that this protein, like the cytochromes, functions as an electron carrier in respiration.

SUBSTITUTED QUINONES

A number of nonprotein compounds which contain the quinone ring are also thought to function during electron transport in both oxidative metabolism and photosynthesis. These compounds are known to undergo reversible oxidation-reduction changes according to the mechanism shown in Fig. 3-9. Substituted quinones have been found to be associated with the better-known electron carriers, such as the cytochromes. One of their more interesting properties is that they are primarily lipid-soluble, leading to the suggestion that they function in

Quinone   Quinol

	R_1 = Isoprenoid chain	R_2	R_3	R_4
CoQ$_{6-10}$	$\left[\text{CH}_2-\text{CH}=\overset{\overset{\text{CH}_3}{\mid}}{\text{C}}-\text{CH}_2\right]_{6-10}\text{H}$	CH_3	OCH_3	OCH_3
Plastoquinone	$\left[\text{CH}_2-\text{CH}=\overset{\overset{\text{CH}_3}{\mid}}{\text{C}}-\text{CH}_2\right]_{9}\text{H}$	H	CH_3	CH_3
Vitamin K$_2$	$\left[\text{CH}_2-\text{CH}=\overset{\overset{\text{CH}_3}{\mid}}{\text{C}}-\text{CH}_2\right]_{4-7}\text{H}$	CH_3	$\text{HC}\overset{\text{H}}{\underset{}{\diagdown}}\text{C}-\text{C}\overset{\text{H}}{\diagup}\text{CH}$	

Fig. 3-9. Structures of the isoprenoid quinones, Coenzyme Q, plastoquinone, and vitamin K. The upper figure shows the reversible reduction of the quinone ring.

lipid-phase reactions; however, the possible mechanisms and energetics of such reactions are still highly speculative.

One type of substituted quinone, termed coenzyme Q, was isolated as a respiratory coenzyme by several laboratories in 1957–1958. Coenzyme Q actually represents a class of quinones which vary in the length of one isoprenoid side chain (Fig. 3-9); depending on the number of isoprenoid units in the chain, these molecules are designated as coenzyme Q_6 through Q_{10}, and (since they are widely distributed) the term "ubiquinone" is often used by those who enjoy a pun. These coenzymes are present in many parts of the cell (including nuclei), and in the respiratory organelles they are even more abundant than the cytochromes. D. E. Green has demonstrated that coenzyme Q is reduced to its quinol by NADH and reoxidized to quinone by cytochrome oxidase. It has also been found that electron transport is impaired by extraction of coenzyme Q, an effect which is reversed when the coenzyme is added back; consequently it appears that this compound forms an integral part of the respiratory chain. Experimental evidence, to be discussed in a later section, indicates that it occupies a place between flavoprotein and cytochrome b. Clayton and Sistrom (1964) also cite evidence that the reduction of CoQ is a feature of *photosynthesis* in certain bacteria.

Another class of quinone-containing compounds is represented by vitamin K_1 (phylloquinone), which is localized in the chloroplasts of green plants, and by the vitamin K_2 series, which occurs in bacteria. The various K vitamins are also distinguished by variations in the length of an isoprenoid side chain (Fig. 3-9), and there is experimental evidence that they play a role in electron transport during photosynthesis. A somewhat similar compound, plastoquinone (Fig. 3-9), was isolated by Kofler in 1946 and later found to be localized in chloroplasts. Arnon and Horton (1963) have shown that plastoquinone is intimately involved in the release of oxygen during photosynthesis, and it has also been observed that plastoquinone is reduced by illuminated chloroplasts and reoxidized in the dark (E_0 = about 0.0 V).

Interrelationships between Electron Transfer and Phosphoryl Transfer

The concept that energy is released from substrates by a sequential reduction-oxidation of an electron carrier chain was first introduced in the mid-1930's, and it opened the way to two further questions: first, how is the free energy of an oxidation-reduction reaction put to effective biological use; and second, what is the relationship between oxidation-reduction reactions and the newly discovered class of high-energy phosphates? It is now clear that these two questions have in large part a single answer; i.e., most of the energy released in the electron transport chain is conserved and used by means of a mechanism that "couples" oxidation-reduction to the phosphorylation of ADP:

cytochrome-Fe^{++} + H^+ + O_2 + ADP + phosphate $\longrightarrow$

$$\text{cytochrome-}Fe^{+++} + ATP + H_2O$$

Belitzer and Tsibakowa (1939) were the first to suggest that each step in the electron transport chain might be coupled with a phosphorylation, and using minced muscle they attempted to measure the number of moles of phosphocreatine produced per atom of oxygen consumed; this ratio of organic phosphate formed to oxygen consumed (P/O ratio), Belitzer found to be 2. Since 1939, P/O ratios for different systems have been measured frequently, and have been found to depend somewhat on the substrate used as energy source. However, for those oxidations involving the entire respiratory chain from NADH to oxygen, the maximum P/O ratio is about 3. In other words, under ideal conditions three molecules of ATP are formed for every *two* electrons transferred from NADH to oxygen (oxidative phosphorylation).

It is of interest to examine the energy relationships of these coupled reactions. $\Delta F°$ for the oxidation of NADH by atmospheric oxygen is easily calculated as:

$$\Delta F° = -2 \ (23.068 \text{ kcal/volt}) \ [0.82 \text{ V} - (-0.32 \text{ V})] = -52 \text{ kcal}$$

Since the phosphorylation of ADP is the reverse of ATP hydrolysis, its $\Delta F° = +7.0$ kcal/mole. Three phosphorylations therefore represent a conservation of at least 21 kcal of the 52 kcal theoretically available (i.e., 40%). As pointed out by Lehninger (1964), the remaining 31 kcal are not necessarily lost to entropy, but may be conserved by the cell in undefined ways, e.g., through intracellular control of precursor concentrations, ion transport, and other processes which are still poorly understood.

It is now known that phosphorylation of ADP is also a primary event associated with electron transport in photosynthesis (photophosphorylation). Since the process requires light but not oxygen, it is distinct from oxidative phosphorylation. Both ferredoxin and plastoquinone are known to be intimately involved in photophosphorylation, and it seems likely that the special plant cytochromes function in this process as well. Further details will be discussed in the next chapter, but it is worth noting that coupled phosphorylation seems to be a general property of the electron transfer chain in both respiration and photosynthesis. The possible mechanisms by which this coupling is achieved, and the mechanisms by which the energy of ATP is used in energy-requiring biological processes (e.g., muscle contraction) will be the subject of future chapters.

4

PHOTOSYNTHESIS AS A REACTION

What drives life is . . . a little electric current, kept up by the sunshine.

A. SZENT-GYÖRGYI *1960*

The concept that heat is a form of energy, and that energy is converted but never created or destroyed, was not established until the 1840's by Joule, Mayer, and others. Thereafter biology came face to face with an astonishing fact: essentially all biological activities including those of animals are driven by the radiant energy of the sun, captured and converted into chemical energy during photosynthesis. Although the term "photosynthesis" as such was not introduced until 1898, Mayer himself (1845) clearly pointed out the role of green plants in energy conversion.

For many years, photosynthesis was represented by the reverse of the equation for the burning of glucose:

$$6\ CO_2 + 6\ H_2O \xrightarrow[\text{chlorophyll}]{\text{light}} C_6H_{12}O_6 + 6\ O_2$$

This equation offers almost no insight into the mechanisms of photosynthesis as they are now known, but it is an accurate description of the precursor-product stoichiometry that characterizes most autotrophs. It is of interest to explore the energetic and molecular significance of this equation on a planetary scale; for example, the total radiant sun energy reaching the earth per unit area per unit time is a constant, equal to about 1.35×10^6 ergs/cm^2/sec (Abetti, 1957). The greater part of this energy never enters the biosphere, but is changed to heat by absorption in the atmosphere or through evaporation of ocean water and is eventually reradiated into space. Rabinowitch (1945) has estimated that only 0.24% of the radiant energy reaching the earth is ultimately converted into biological substrates; energetically speaking, therefore, photosynthesis (and indeed all biological activity) is hardly more than a minor quirk in the energy economy of the solar system. Chemically speaking, on the other hand, photosynthesis is the dominant chemical process on earth. Rabinowitch has estimated that, in effect, plants "renew all the oxygen in the air in a little over two thousand years, and decompose all the water in the oceans in about two million years." Even more startling, they would use up all the available carbon in 300 to 400 years if it were not replenished by animal respiration and decay (the carbon dioxide in the atmosphere, excluding dissolved carbonates, would be sufficient for only 10 years!).

The assembly of the first crude empirical equation for photosynthesis spanned 200 years or more. It was Van Helmont who concluded in 1648 that water is a major precursor in plant growth, when he discovered that a tree grown in a carefully weighed bucket of earth removed only tiny amounts of the earth itself. The roles of oxygen, carbon dioxide, and light were discovered much later, during the 1770's and 80's, in the flurry of activity that accompanied the discovery of the gases themselves.

For instance, the evolution of oxygen by plants was first detected by Priestly (1772), and reported in the words: "I flatter myself that I have accidentally hit upon a method of restoring air which has been injured by the burning of candles, and that I have discovered at least one of the restoratives which nature employs for this purpose. It is vegetation." In 1779 Ingen-Housz discovered that sunlight is necessary for this reaction, titling his paper: "Experiments upon Vegetables, discovering their great power of purifying the common air in Sunshine and injuring it in the Shade and at Night." In the same period, Senebier (1782) discovered that CO_2 is used up by plants in the light. The necessity for chlorophyll in this process was not demonstrated until 1837 by Dutrochet, at the time that chlorophyll was demonstrated to be localized in the chloroplast. Finally, in the 1860's, carbohydrate was shown to be a primary product of photosynthesis.

A more detailed dissection of the photosynthetic process did not begin until 1930, and at first it centered on the question of whether the free oxygen produced by plants comes from carbon dioxide or from water. During most of the 19th century it was generally assumed that the oxygen is split from CO_2, which is then "hydrated" to carbohydrate:

$$CO_2 + H_2O \longrightarrow C(H_2O)_n + O_2$$

This was a natural assumption, since in the stoichiometric equation, there seem to be insufficient oxygen atoms in the water to account for the total free oxygen produced. However, Van Niel in 1931 found this concept inadequate to explain the stoichiometry of photosynthesis in various specialized bacteria which do not produce oxygen, and where hydrogen gas or hydrogen sulfide is used as substrate. He proposed that the general equation for photosynthesis should be:

$$CO_2 + 2 H_2X \longrightarrow CH_2O + H_2O + 2 X$$

This equation would establish a basic similarity between photosynthesis in which hydrogen sulfide is used up and elemental sulfur given off (X = sulfur), and the common photosynthesis of green plants in which water is used up and elemental oxygen is given off (X = oxygen). As suggested by Thunberg in 1923, photosynthesis may be viewed as an oxidation-reduction reaction, in which CO_2 is reduced at the expense of an electron donor, which may be water, hydrogen sulfide, molecular hydrogen (X = nothing), or even a compound like sodium thiosulfate which does not contain hydrogen. A notable consequence of Van Niel's equation is that the free oxygen must come from water rather than from carbon dioxide, and this brilliant prediction was confirmed by Ruben et al. (1941) in a tracer experiment using water labeled with heavy oxygen (H_2 ^{18}O); all the oxygen produced during photosynthesis in such an experiment comes from the labeled water, and it may be concluded that water participates primarily as a proton and electron donor.

The next major advance was the recognition that two separate events occur in photosynthesis, one requiring light (the light reaction) and one not (the dark reaction). Although this had been suggested much earlier on thermodynamic grounds, the distinction between light and dark reactions was supported and reemphasized by Emerson and Arnold (1932), who investigated the quantum efficiency of photosynthesis in plants exposed to light flashes of differing duration. They found that efficiency is higher when dark periods alternate with light flashes than when plants are continuously illuminated, and they therefore concluded that essential photosynthetic reactions occur which do not require light.

The distinction between light and dark reactions was further clarified in 1937 when Hill demonstrated that a suspension of dried chloroplasts could use light energy to evolve oxygen and reduce ferric salts (Fe^{+++}) without the necessity to form carbohydrate. This experiment, interpreted in terms of Van Niel's hypothesis, indicated that the light reaction involves a liberation of oxygen and a "reducing principle" from water:

$$HOH \xrightarrow{\text{light}} O_2 + XH_2$$

while the dark reaction involves the expenditure of the reducing principle to reduce carbon dioxide to carbohydrate:

$$XH_2 + CO_2 \longrightarrow (CH_2O)_n \quad \text{carbohydrate}$$

This general interpretation was greatly supported when Ruben *et al.* (1939), using radioactive-labeled carbon dioxide ($^{11}CO_2$), demonstrated the fixation of carbon dioxide by barley and *Chlorella* in the dark.

As a result of this line of reasoning, the essential energy-trapping event in photosynthesis has often been considered to be a "photolysis" of water molecules, in which light quanta bring about a reaction similar to electrolysis of water:

$$2 H_2O \xrightarrow{4 e^-} 2 H_2 + O_2$$

Although it is true that water is normally decomposed in photosynthesis, the concept of photolysis as the fundamental event is no longer strictly acceptable. It has become clear in recent years that the primary photosynthetic trap is intimately involved with electron transfer and coupled phosphorylation, and that even in higher plants it does not necessarily involve the release of molecular oxygen from water.

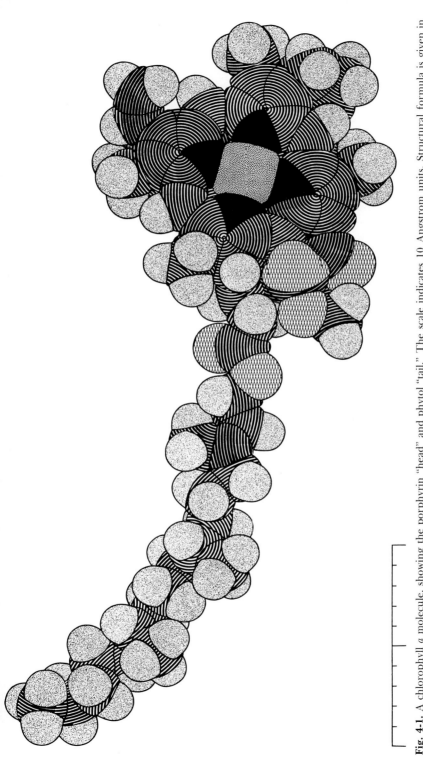

Fig. 4-1. A chlorophyll *a* molecule, showing the porphyrin "head" and phytol "tail." The scale indicates 10 Angstrom units. Structural formula is given in Fig. 4-2C.

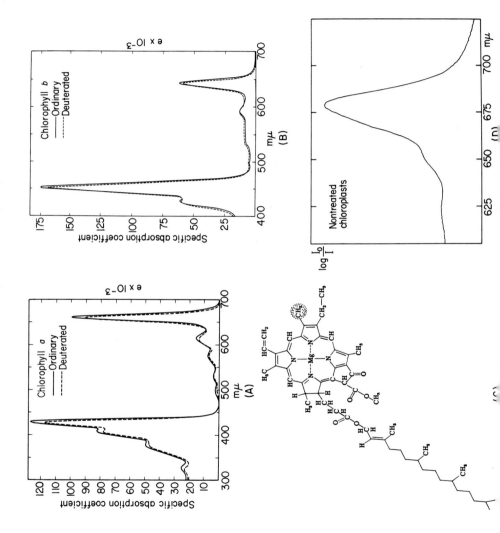

The Light Reactions

A common denominator in photosynthesis, and therefore a key to the mechanism of transforming light energy, is the absorption of light by chlorophyll molecules. Chlorophyll *a*, whose structure was worked out by Willstätter between 1905 and 1913 (Fig. 4-1) and which has recently been synthesized *in toto* (Woodward, 1960), occurs in all photosynthetic organisms except bacteria; photosynthetic bacteria contain a closely related *bacteriochlorophyll*. Other modified chlorophylls are common, including protochlorophyll (which develops in plants grown in the dark and converts to chlorophyll *a* in the light), and chlorophyll *b*, which occurs in most green plants together with chlorophyll *a* (1 chlorophyll *b* to 2 or 3 chlorophyll *a*).

Like the cytochromes (and hemoglobin), protochlorophyll is based on a porphyrin ring which is complexed with a metal—in this case, magnesium instead of iron. Chlorophylls *a* and *b* are based on "dihydroporphin," and are therefore two hydrogen atoms more reduced than protochlorophyll, while bacteriochlorophyll is based on a "tetrahydroporphin," and occupies an even more reduced level. In addition to the magnesium-complexed pyrrole ring, the chlorophylls contain a long-chain phytol group, which forms a flexible, lipophilic and easily removable tail on the molecule (Fig. 4-1). Chlorophylls *a* and *b* both show two major absorption peaks in the visible spectrum—one in the blue-violet and one in the red (Fig. 4-2), which seem to be due primarily to the hydrogenated porphyrin (chlorin) ring rather than to the magnesium or the phytol. The low absorption in the green is, of course, responsible for the characteristic color of chlorophyll *a* (blue-green) and *b* (yellow-green), as well as of chlorin. Slight but significant differences occur in the exact positions of absorption maxima between chlorophylls *a* and *b*, the red peak of chlorophyll *a* being shifted toward the longer wavelengths and the blue-violet peak toward the shorter wavelengths. During the last part of the 19th century it was established (following a violent controversy) that a general correspondence exists between the light energy which is transformed during photosynthesis and the wavelengths (or quantum values) absorbed by chlorophyll. Plants kept in monochromatic green light, for instance, do not grow well, whereas the wavelengths which are used most efficiently approximate the absorption maxima of the chlorophyll molecule. Although more accurate measurements in recent years have revealed significant discrepancies between

Fig. 4-2. (A) and (B) Absorption spectra of chlorophylls *a* and *b*. From Strain and Svec (1966). (C) Structure of chlorophyll *a*; chlorophyll *b* differs by the oxidation of one methyl group (stipple) to an aldehyde. (D) Absorption spectrum of isolated chloroplasts. From Thomas and Bartels (1966).

the absorption spectrum of chlorophyll and the "action spectrum" of photosynthesis, there is no reason to doubt that light absorption by chlorophyll is the primary path of energy capture in photosynthesis. These discrepancies do indicate, however, that more than one photochemical reaction occurs in the process (Fig. 4-2D).

The characteristic quantum absorption of chlorophyll represents an excitation of orbital electrons (see page 25) and is directly reversible; thus, when chlorophyll or chloroplasts are irradiated, they return energy in a characteristic red fluorescence. These facts led to early speculation that the primary event in photosynthesis could be an oxidation of chlorophyll, in which light-excited electrons are removed from chlorophyll by a suitable oxidizing agent and are eventually channeled into the reduction of carbon dioxide. A photoreduction of ferric ions (Fe^{+++}) and hemoglobin by an illuminated suspension of chloroplasts was clearly demonstrated in the Hill reaction (1937), and at about the same time Rabinowitch and Weiss (1937) demonstrated that chlorophyll itself can be reversibly oxidized by ferric chloride (the solution changing from green to yellow). During the 1950's, this line of reasoning led directly to work by Hill and his colleagues which revealed the presence of special cytochromes in chloroplasts (page 53), and implicated electron transport as a primary event in photosynthesis. Vishniac and Ochoa (1952) were also successful in showing that pyridine nucleotides can be reduced in the Hill reaction (replacing ferric ion as electron acceptors), and by mixing chloroplasts and mitochondria they also obtained ATP synthesis at the expense of light energy. More recently, Krasnovsky (1960) has demonstrated that an illuminated chlorophyll *solution* can mediate electron transfer from ascorbate to pyridine nucleotide.

However, the major breakthrough in the analysis of photosynthesis was achieved by Arnon *et al.* (1954), who became the first to demonstrate that *isolated* chloroplasts can carry out the complete scheme of photosynthesis, including not only the release of oxygen and reduction of pyridine nucleotides, but the "fixing" of CO_2 as sugar and starch. At the same time they found that chloroplasts alone, in the absence of the respiratory electron transport chain, can carry out the phosphorylation of ADP to form ATP. The possibility of such a photosynthetic phosphorylation, analogous to respiratory phosphorylation, had been suggested by Ruben as early as 1943, but the experiments of Vishniac and Ochoa (1952) had suggested that this might occur through the respiratory chain itself, by oxidation of some photosynthetic product (e.g., reduced pyridine nucleotide) with coupled phosphorylation. However, Arnon *et al.* (1958) confirmed that photophosphorylation, in marked contrast to oxidative phosphorylation, requires light but not oxygen and is closely associated with chlorophyll-containing elements; they also established that the reaction is independent of carbon dioxide fixation, pyridine nucleotide reduction, or oxygen production, requiring no substrates except ADP and inorganic phosphate and yielding no product but ATP and water:

$$\text{ADP} + \text{phosphate} \xrightarrow[\text{chlorophyll}]{\text{light}} \text{ATP} + H_2O$$

This direct conversion of light quanta into chemical energy by the chlorophyll-mediated synthesis of ATP has now been demonstrated in algae and bacteria as well as in other higher plants, and it appears to be the most fundamental of the photosynthetic reactions. Arnon has called it "cyclic photophosphorylation," in order to distinguish it from other processes to be discussed later.

After the discovery of ferredoxin in 1962 (Chapter 3) it was found that photoreduction of ferredoxin accompanies cyclic photophosphorylation, and in fact under certain conditions the amount of ATP produced is proportional to the amount of ferredoxin added. Whatley and Horton (1963) also discovered that extraction of plastoquinone (Chapter 3) blocks phosphorylation, but that the effect is reversed when plastoquinone is added back. Other evidence suggests that vitamin K is involved in the electron transport system as well. Using these and other facts, Arnon *et al.* (1965) have proposed that the basic mechanism of cyclic photophosphorylation follows the scheme illustrated in Fig. 4-3A. The

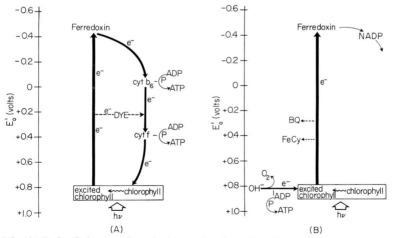

Fig. 4-3. (A) Path of electron flow during cyclic photophosphorylation, as postulated by Arnon *et al.* (1965); (B) Path of electron flow during noncyclic photophosphorylation in plants, as postulated by Arnon *et al.* (1965). From ferredoxin the electrons flow to an electron "sink" provided by NADP and the reduction of CO_2 to carbohydrate.

primary event is the quantum excitation of electrons in chlorophyll, in effect lifting them to a more negative E_0 value; these higher energy electrons can then flow to ferredoxin ($E_0 = -.432$ V), and back down to chlorophyll by way of an electron transport chain which probably includes cytochromes f and b_6, plastoquinone and vitamin K. In the course of the sequential oxidation-reductions, ATP is formed through coupled phosphorylations of unknown mechanism, but in a manner analogous to those which occur in oxidative phosphorylation (see Chapter 6).

In 1958 Arnon *et al.* established that a second mechanism exists which is noncyclic in form and which normally couples the photophosphorylation of ADP specifically to the reduction of NADP (not NAD) and to the production of oxygen. The most characteristic feature of this noncyclic process is that the excited electrons do not return to chlorophyll, but flow via NADP into an electron sink, generally the reduction of CO_2 to carbohydrate (Fig. 4-3B); new electrons must therefore be drawn to chlorophyll from an exogenous electron donor, which in green plants is believed to be the OH^- ions normally present in the aqueous environment. Removal of electrons from hydroxyl ions releases molecular oxygen as an excretion product, according to a stoichiometry which is mimicked in the Hill reaction (with ferricyanide as electron acceptor):

$$4 \text{ Fe}^{+++} + 4 \text{ OH}^- \longrightarrow 4 \text{ Fe}^{++} + 2 \text{ H}_2\text{O} + \text{O}_2$$

Originally the stoichiometry of noncyclic photophosphorylation was reported to be:

$$2 \text{ NADP} + 2 \text{ H}_2\text{O} + 2 \text{ ADP} + 2 \text{ P}_i \longrightarrow 2 \text{ NADPH} + 2 \text{ H}^+ + 2 \text{ ATP} + \text{O}_2$$

However it has since been recognized that ferredoxin is also an intermediate in the noncyclic flow of electrons to NADP, and that the reduction of ferredoxin precedes the reduction of NADP:

$$4 \text{ ferredoxin}_{\text{oxid.}} + 4 \text{ H}_2\text{O} + 2 \text{ ADP} + 2 \text{ P}_i \longrightarrow$$
$$4 \text{ ferredoxin}_{\text{red.}} + 2 \text{ H}_2\text{O} + 2 \text{ ATP} + 4\text{H}^+ + \text{O}_2$$

From reduced ferredoxin the electrons are evidently transferred to NADP by a flavoprotein enzyme which Shin *et al.* (1963) have crystallized from chloroplasts (ferredoxin-NADP reductase). Since a close stoichiometric linkage between ADP phosphorylation and O_2 production is unexpected, this discovery has been taken to mean that the phosphorylation site is coupled specifically with electron flow from OH^- to chlorophyll (Fig. 4-3B).

The electron flow theories of cyclic and noncylic photophosphorylation are strongly supported by the fact that a suspension of chloroplasts carrying out noncyclic phosphorylation (i.e., producing oxygen, reduced ferredoxin or NADPH, and ATP) can be switched to cyclic phosphorylation (producing ATP only) by the addition of vitamin K or FMN, and can be switched back to the noncyclic scheme by the further addition of ferricyanide. Noncyclic phosphorylation always occurs when electrons are drawn away from the system into an electron sink (e.g., CO_2, NADP, ferredoxin, ferric ions, etc.), and it requires the presence of some substrate as electron donor (hydroxyl ions, etc.). The significance of ferredoxin as the most electronegative of naturally-occurring electron carriers has also been dramatically illustrated by Tagawa and Arnon (1962), who demonstrated that isolated spinach. chloroplasts, in the presence of ferredoxin and a hydrogenase, can reduce protons (H^+) to release molecular *hydrogen gas* from water with coupled phosphorylation of ATP; in this process, H^+ replaces NADP as the electron acceptor (Fig. 4-4A). Even more startling, the reaction is reversed in a hydrogen atmosphere, and isolated chloroplasts (with added hydrogenase) are

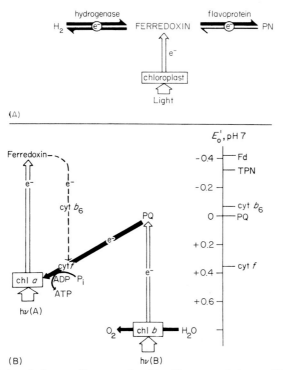

Fig. 4-4. (A) Paths of electron flow postulated by Tagawa and Arnon (1962), explaining how ferredoxin is able to reduce pyridine nucleotides (PN) using electrons from excited chlorophyll, or alternatively from molecular hydrogen (in the presence of a hydrogenase). The flow can also be reversed to release molecular hydrogen from protons in solution. (B) Scheme illustrating a possible linkage between two separate light reactions, one involving a transfer of electrons from chlorophyll *b* to plastoquinone (PQ), and the other an electron lift from chlorophyll *a* to ferredoxin. From Arnon *et al.* (1964).

then able to carry out photosynthesis in the absence of light! The latter reaction is explained by the ability of ferredoxin ($E_0 = -0.43$ V) to capture electrons from molecular hydrogen ($E_0 = -0.42$), and to transfer them by way of NADP for the reduction of carbon dioxide (Fig. 4-4A). In effect, hydrogen gas replaces light and chlorophyll in the photosynthetic reaction.

In 1961 Losada, Whatley and Arnon further dissected noncyclic photophosphorylation into two separate light-driven reactions. By using indophenol dyes to alter the normal paths of electron flow, they could demonstrate two independent events: 1) a light-driven reaction in which NADP reduction is coupled with ADP phosphorylation but without the production of oxygen; and 2) a light-driven reaction in which oxygen is produced without ATP production. The first reaction occurs if reduced indophenol dye is used as an electron donor and if the participation of water is prevented by omitting chloride ion from the reaction mixture; under these conditions the dye is oxidized in the light and reduced in the dark. The second reaction occurs if ferric ions and chloride are added to the mixture in addition to the indophenol, and under these conditions the dye is reduced in the light and oxidized in the dark (by the ferric ions). It appears that photophosphorylation depends on an electron flow sequence which, when it is interrupted by ferric ion alone ($E_0 = 0.77$ V) still leads to phosphorylation, but when it is interrupted by indophenol ($E_0 = 0.217$) does not. This electron transport chain, with its coupled phosphorylation, is thus bracketed by indophenol and ferricyanide, and may be common to both the cyclic and noncyclic mechanisms.

As first suggested by Van Niel and reemphasized by these experiments of Arnon's, the participation of water is not an essential characteristic of photosynthesis. When water acts as electron donor, oxygen is produced as an excretion product, but other suitable electron donors can replace water in the process, either naturally (e.g., hydrogen gas in bacterial photosynthesis) or experimentally (as in Arnon's indophenol experiments). Tagawa, Tsujimoto, and Arnon (1963) have also discovered that monochromatic light at 708 mμ (absorbed by chlorophyll a but not chlorophyll b) leads primarily to cyclic photophosphorylation, whereas light at 663 mμ (absorbed by both chlorophylls) supports mainly noncyclic phosphorylation; this indicates that chlorophyll b is required for the oxygen-producing noncyclic scheme, but not for the cyclic process. The action spectrum for oxygen evolution is also more characteristic of chlorophyll b, whereas that for phosphorylation and reduction of NADP is similar to chlorophyll a. Finally, Arnon, Whatley, and Horton (1962) have shown that the photoreduction of NADP by the oxidation of *water* has a very characteristic requirement for plastoquinone (as well as chloride ion), and plastoquinone is also required for the indophenol-catalyzed production of oxygen without coupled ATP synthesis. These data taken together indicate that the use of water as a reducing agent in photosynthesis requires a special system, which includes chlorophyll b (lacking in bacteria), plastoquinone and chloride ion.

Since both plastoquinone and ferredoxin participate in cyclic as well as noncyclic photophosphorylation, Arnon et al. (1964) postulated that the two light reactions of the noncyclic scheme may represent a linkage between a "chlorophyll a-ferredoxin" system and a "chlorophyll b-plastoquinone" system. Light excitation of chlorophyll b would raise electrons from the energy level of hydroxyl ions ($E_0 = 0.82$ V) to the level of plastoquinone ($E_0 = $ ca 0.0 V), while excitation of chlorophyll a would raise them to the much higher energy level of ferredoxin ($E_0 = -0.43$ V); in the noncyclic process, the electrons would then flow to NADP and the carbohydrate sink, whereas in cyclic phosphorylation, only electrons from chlorophyll a would reach ferredoxin and these would return to chlorophyll a by way of plastoquinone (Fig. 4-4B). The linkage between the two light reactions would presumably occur by a "downhill" electron flow from plastoquinone to chlorophyll a, possibly by way of cytochrome f; this part of the sequence, which would be common to both the cyclic and noncyclic schemes, might also be the part bracketed by indophenol and ferricyanide. Although his two-step scheme was subsequently disavowed by Arnon and his collaborators (1965) on the basis of experiments with desaspidin, a new inhibitor, other laboratories have obtained inconclusive results with desaspidin. Consequently many workers in the field continue to accept a model which postulates two successive light-driven reactions during noncyclic photophosphorylation (Fig. 4-4B).

Other linked photoreactions are known to occur during photosynthesis which involve light absorption by special "accessory pigments," which are capable of capturing energy from regions of the spectrum not absorbed by chlorophyll. For instance, Emerson and Lewis (1943) carried out a quantitative analysis of light absorption relative to photosynthetic yield at various wavelengths in Chlorella and found evidence that carotenoid pigments are about half as efficient as chlorophyll in capturing quantum energy for photosynthesis. Brown algae (seaweeds) and diatoms are characterized by the pigment, fucoxanthin, which has also been shown by Dutton and Manning (1941) and others to contribute markedly in light absorption for photosynthesis. Similarly, the red algae and the blue-green algae contain characteristic phycobilin pigments, which in some red algae may function more efficiently as light absorbers for photosynthesis than chlorophyll (Haxo and Blinks, 1950). Although the exact mechanisms by which such accessory pigments function in photosynthesis is not known, it has been demonstrated in all these instances that light of wavelengths absorbed only by the accessory pigment leads to fluorescence characteristic of chlorophyll; it therefore seems likely that the energy is transferred directly to the chlorophyll molecule, which functions as the unique entry to the electron transport mechanisms of photosynthesis.

The Dark Reactions

As mentioned previously, Ruben *et al.* (1939) succeeded in demonstrating that barley and *Chlorella* are able to reduce isotopically labeled carbon dioxide in the dark; however, at about the same time, it was found that CO_2 fixation is carried out by many *nonphotosynthetic* cells, including "propionic acid" bacteria, the roots of higher plants, and even rat liver. One mechanism for CO_2 fixation in animals is by the carboxylation of phosphoenolpyruvate:

$$PEP + CO_2 + GDP \; \overset{Mg^{++}}{\rightleftharpoons} \; oxaloacetate + GTP$$

Consequently, the difficulty was not to find a mechanism able to account for CO_2 fixation, but to determine the actual mechanisms of fixation and reduction that are coupled to the light reactions of photosynthesis.

Ruben in 1943 directed attention to the possible role of phosphorylated intermediates in carbon dioxide reduction. He suggested that, following a process of CO_2 fixation by the carboxylation of some intermediate compound, a carboxyl phosphate might be formed which could be reduced more easily than the nonphosphorylated molecule. This set the stage for a fundamental breakthrough by Calvin and Benson (1948), who succeeded in showing that $^{14}CO_2$ is *first* taken up during photosynthesis by the 3-carbon, phosphorylated molecule, phosphoglyceric acid (PGA); the labeled carbon is very rapidly distributed among various 5-, 6-, and 7-carbon sugars, so that the detection of PGA as the primary product requires very short "pulse" exposures to labeled CO_2, followed by rapid fixation and chromatographic fractionation.

Despite the discovery of the primary product, it was still uncertain what compound functions as the actual acceptor of carbon dioxide in photosynthesis, and what relationship exists between this primary acceptor and PGA. Calvin's group made two key observations which led to the ultimate solution of these questions: first, when photosynthesizing plants are deprived of light, PGA increases while ribulose diphosphate (a five-carbon phosphorylated sugar) decreases; second, when photosynthesizing plants are deprived of carbon dioxide, ribulose diphosphate increases while PGA decreases. These two data suggest that PGA is formed at the expense of RiDP (in the first case), and that the process requires CO_2 (in the second case). It has now been firmly established that the primary mechanism of carbon dioxide fixation in photosynthesis involves a condensation of ribulose diphosphate (5 C) with carbon dioxide (1 C), together with a simultaneous hydration and split to form two molecules of PGA (2 × 3 C):

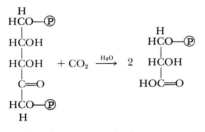

This reaction, which is slightly exergonic, is catalyzed by the enzyme carboxydismutase (mol. wt. 550,000), which has been purified by Horecker from spinach leaves, and which makes up 5–10% of the soluble protein (see Fig. 5-4).

These brilliant advances left one problem still to be solved: How is energy from the light reaction coupled to regenerate ribulose diphosphate for use in the "dark" condensation reaction? Calvin answered this question by a theoretical perception which has since been experimentally confirmed: the regeneration of ribulose diphosphate proceeds by the reversal of several well-known reactions previously found to occur during the anaerobic fermentation of glucose, and they involve the identical enzymes of the glycolytic pathway (see Chapter 6). Specifically, phosphoglyceric acid is first reduced to phosphoglyceraldehyde (PGAL) in a reaction requiring 1 mole of NADPH, 1 mole of ATP, and the enzyme phosphoglyceraldehyde dehydrogenase:

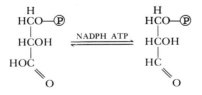

The phosphoglyceraldehyde is then converted to ribulose monophosphate through a series of reactions mediated largely by the enzyme aldolase and referred to collectively as the pentose shunt. This includes four basic reactions: (1) condensation of two PGAL (3 C) to form one hexose monophosphate (6 C); (2) condensation of one hexose monophosphate (6 C) with one PGAL (3 C) to form one ribulose monophosphate (5 C) and one tetrose monophosphate (4 C); (3) condensation of one tetrose monophosphate (4 C) and one PGAL (3 C) to form one 7-carbon sugar (sedoheptulose) monophosphate; (4) condensation of one sedoheptulose monophosphate (7 C) and one PGAL to form two ribulose monophosphate (2 × 5 C).

The net result of the pentose shunt is that five molecules of PGAL (5 × 3 C) are transformed into three molecules of ribulose monophosphate (3 × 5 C), according to the flow chart:

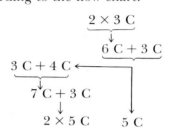

Finally, in the overall scheme, the regeneration of ribulose diphosphate is completed by the phosphorylation of ribulose monophosphate at the expense of one molecule of ATP.

This cyclic series of reactions, driven entirely by ATP and NADPH, is often referred to as the Calvin cycle, and it constitutes the primary link between the products of cyclic and noncyclic photophosphorylation (light reactions) and the reduction of carbon dioxide to carbohydrate during photosynthesis (Fig. 4-5). The complete sequence has been demonstrated *in vitro* by Racker (1955), who obtained the synthesis of hexose phosphate from CO_2 in the dark using a mixture of the necessary enzymes with ATP and NADPH as energy sources. As Calvin has pointed out (1959, 1963), all the enzymes involved are known to occur also in nonphotosynthetic cells, including carboxydismutase, which is found in the bacterium, *Escherichia coli.* Consequently, it seems likely that the coupling of photophosphorylation to the reduction of carbon dioxide was a secondary event in evolution.

It is of some interest to consider the stoichiometry of the carbon reduction process in relation to the classic equation of photosynthesis (page 60). In order to make this comparison, it is necessary to assume that the Calvin cycle "goes around" six times, binding six molecules of carbon dioxide, using up six molecules of ribulose diphosphate, and producing twelve molecules of PGAL at the expense of twelve ATP's and twelve NADPH's. Of the twelve molecules of PGAL, ten must be

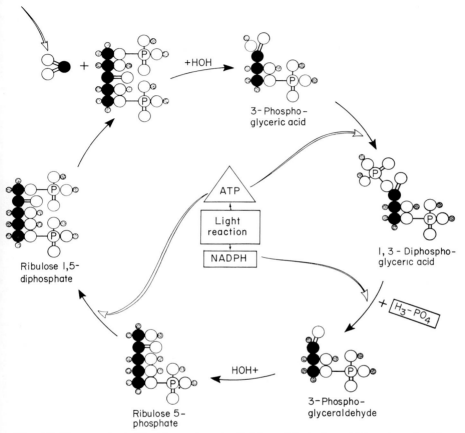

Fig. 4-5. Photosynthetic "dark" reactions (or Calvin cycle), during which carbon dioxide is fixed by condensing with ribulose diphosphate. ATP and NADPH from the "light" reactions contribute to the reduction of phosphoglyceric acid to phosphoglyceraldehyde. Black circles are carbon, white circles oxygen, and stippled circles hydrogen.

used to replace the six ribulose diphosphate (10×3 C $= 6 \times 5$ C)—a step requiring six more ATP's. The remaining two PGAL's represent a net synthesis equivalent to one glucose molecule. The stoichiometry for these various steps is:

$$6 \ CO_2 + 12 \ NADPH + 12 \ H^+ + 18 \ AT\textcircled{P} + 12 \ H_2O \longrightarrow$$
$$C_6H_{12}O_6 + 12 \ NADP + 18 \ ADPH + 18 \ \textcircled{P}OH$$

In order to provide this amount of reduced NADP, 24 electrons must be transferred from hydroxyl ions to NADP in noncyclic photophosphorylation:

$$12 \text{ NADP} + 24 \text{ H}_2\text{O} + 12 \text{ ADPH} + 12 \text{ (P)OH} \xrightarrow[\text{light}]{24 \text{ e}^-}$$
$$12 \text{ NADPH} + 12 \text{ H}^+ + 12 \text{ AT(P)} + 24 \text{ H}_2\text{O} + 6 \text{ O}_2$$

Since only 12 molecules of ATP are produced in the balanced noncyclic scheme, the remaining 6 ATP's may be synthesized in cyclic photophosphorylation:

$$6 \text{ ADPH} + 6 \text{ (P)OH} \xrightarrow{\text{light}} 6 \text{ AT(P)} + 6 \text{ H}_2\text{O}$$

If now these three equations are summed together, it will be found that all terms cancel out except the classic ones:

$$6 \text{ CO}_2 + 6 \text{ H}_2\text{O} \xrightarrow{\text{light}} \text{C}_6\text{H}_{12}\text{O}_6 + 6 \text{ O}_2$$

It should be kept in mind that extra ATP required for carbon dioxide reduction may also be formed by oxidative phosphorylation, using NADPH from the noncyclic scheme as substrate; in this case the stoichiometry would be somewhat different.

Energy Requirements for Photosynthesis

The minimum number of light quanta used per molecule of carbon dioxide reduced to carbohydrate during photosynthesis has been the subject of intensive investigation. A theoretical minimum may easily be calculated from the $\Delta F°$ of the reaction:

$$\text{C}_6\text{H}_{12}\text{O}_6 + 6 \text{ O}_2 \longrightarrow 6 \text{ CO}_2 + 6 \text{ H}_2\text{O}$$

Since $\Delta F°$ for this reaction is -688 kcal/mole, the reverse reaction must require at least 688 kcal for fixation of six moles of carbon dioxide, or 115 kcal per mole of carbon; the equivalent quantum energy of red light used in photosynthesis is about 43 kcal per "mole quantum" (einstein), and therefore the theoretical minimum would be three quanta per molecule of carbon dioxide ($3 \times 43 > 115$).

It is not to be expected, however, that photosynthesis can proceed with such near-perfect efficiency. A more sophisticated calculation can be made on the basis of the requirements for NADPH and ATP in the Calvin cycle, which were given in the stoichiometric equation on page 75. The fixation of six CO_2's requires 12 NADPH and 18 ATP, or 2 NADPH + 3 ATP per carbon dioxide. The energy required for reduction of NADPH (52 kcal/mole) and phosphorylation of ATP (7 kcal/mole) has been discussed previously (Chapter 3); the energy requirement in the Calvin cycle (2 NADPH + 3 ATP) is therefore equal to at least 125 kcal per mole of CO_2, which would suggest a minimum quantum requirement of 4 ($4 \times 43 > 125$ plus entropy).

A still more sophisticated estimate may be based on the energy requirements for raising one electron from the E_0 of hydroxyl ion (0.82 V) to that of ferredoxin (-0.43 V); this requirement may be calculated by the basic equation for redox reactions (Chapter 3) and is equal to:

$$\Delta F^\circ = -1(23.068)[0.82 - (-0.43)] = 29 \text{ kcal/mole}$$

On the assumption that one quantum can "lift" one electron from hydroxyl ion to ferredoxin, 4 quanta would be required for the reduction of 2 NADPH and phosphorylation of 2 ATP; however, this falls short of the energy requirement in the Calvin cycle by one ATP, and it appears that 5 quanta per carbon dioxide would be the minimum necessary to support reduction to carbohydrate.

Various attempts have been made to measure the quantum efficiency of photosynthesis empirically. The results obtained vary widely and approach a maximum only in light of low intensity, or with flashing light alternated with intermittent dark periods. The most reliable early estimates were in the order of 10 ± 2 quanta per O_2, including both *in vivo* measurements and measurements from the Hill reaction (isolated chloroplasts). However, more recently Warburg and Ostendorf (1963) have reported an empirical measurement of 5.5 quanta per CO_2, corresponding well with the theoretical minimum. Under *natural* conditions, employing CO_2 at an atmospheric concentration of 0.03% and very intense light, the supply of CO_2 probably becomes rate limiting, and it appears that the conversion of visible radiation by plants in nature has a very low average efficiency (in the order of 2% of the radiation absorbed). Emerson and Arnold (1932) in their flashing light experiments found that, under conditions of maximum efficiency, only one O_2 molecule is released for every 2000–2500 chlorophyll molecules present; the conclusion, that not all chlorophyll molecules are equivalent in photosynthesis, has been supported by more recent evidence to be discussed in the next chapter, and brings us to the question of the structural requirements for photosynthesis.

5

CHLOROPLASTS AND
OTHER PHOTOSYNTHETIC ORGANELLES

The morphologist, on the one hand, strives to elucidate the structure of protoplasm down to its finest details; the biochemist, on the other, with his apparently ruder yet still more searching methods, seeks to determine the chemical functions of the same protoplasm; broadly speaking, they are only dealing with two different sides of the same thing.

F. HOFMEISTER *1901*

In all photosynthetic cells, both chlorophyll and the primary energy-trapping reactions are closely associated with insoluble structural elements. Despite the great diversity and range of complexity in these photosynthetic structures, they generally include conspicuous formed membranes or lamellae; except in green bacteria, purple bacteria, and blue-green algae, these lamellae are contained in a characteristic plastid, the chloroplast. The necessity for insoluble or lamellar structure is not entirely clear, since Krasnovsky (1960) has shown that chlorophyll in solution can convert light energy to the energy of reduced pyridine nucleotides. However, since *oxidative* phosphorylation also exhibits a dependence on membraneous organization, it seems likely that the structural requirement in photosynthesis is related to the mechanics of photophosphorylation (Chapter 4).

The simplest system known to carry out photophosphorylation is that found in the green sulfur bacterium *Chlorobium*. This cell contains characteristic chlorobium vesicles about 300–400 Å wide and up to 1500 Å long. A homogeneous ultracentrifuge fraction consisting of vesicles about 150 Å in diameter has been isolated from *Chlorobium* by Fuller (1963), who estimates the molecular weight of each particle as about 1.5×10^6. Such particles are thought to contain only about 100 chlorophyll molecules and one or two molecules of cytochrome, yet they are able to carry out a light-dependent phosphorylation of ATP *in vitro*.

In most photosynthetic bacteria, bacteriochlorophyll is associated with "chromatophores," consisting of a unit membrane surrounding an area of low electron density. The number and size of chromatophores vary, not only from species to species but also within a species depending on light conditions; however, they range from as low as 200 Å to about 1000 Å. The extensively studied chromatophores of purple bacteria are about 600 Å in diameter and are enclosed in a 70 Å membrane; as first demonstrated by Frenkel (1954), isolated chromatophores can carry out photophosphorylation, but unlike chloroplasts, they do not seem to function independently in carbon dioxide reduction.

In some types of purple bacteria, the photosynthetic pigments are associated with loosely-arranged cytoplasmic lamellae, and this condition is the rule in blue-green algae. These membrane sheets seem to represent an organization intermediate between bacterial chromatophores and the chloroplasts of other algae and higher plants. Such an interpretation is consistent with the fact that blue-green algae are intermediate between bacteria and higher organisms in many other respects, including the organization of their genetic material.

79

The Biology of Chloroplasts

In higher plants and algae, chlorophyll is localized in large, well-defined and conspicuous plastids, which have received the attention of cytologists since the early 1800's. Typically the chloroplasts of higher plants number 20–40 per cell, they are biconvex or lens-shaped, and their usual dimensions are in the order of 5 μ in diameter by 3 μ in thickness. Nevertheless, many algae contain only one, or very few, chloroplasts exhibiting exotic forms, e.g., netlike, star-shaped, spiral ribbon, or bell-shaped. The percent composition of whole, isolated chloroplasts varies from species to species, but Kirk and Tilney-Bassett (1967) give the general ranges:

Protein	50–69%
Lipid	21–34%
Chlorophyll	5–8%
Carotenoids	0.7–1.1%
RNA	1.0–7.5%
DNA	0.02–0.1%

The high lipid content of chloroplasts is probably correlated with their abundant internal membranes.

Although in some species the chloroplasts move actively around the cell, in most higher plants they occupy relatively fixed positions along the cell wall. Even in these cells, however, the chloroplasts retain the ability to reorient relative to the direction of the light, either by swinging from profile to full-face or by changing shape. In these reactions it has been demonstrated that each chloroplast moves independently, and that changes in chloroplast orientation have a very large influence on the efficiency of conversion of light energy. In *Mougeotia,* Haupt (1964) found that light at the blue end of the spectrum induces chloroplast movement from full-face to profile, whereas red light induces the opposite movement; these changes seem to require ATP phosphorylation, which can be either oxidative or photosynthetic.

It has been discovered by Itoh *et al.* (1963) that *isolated* spinach chloroplasts undergo changes in shape and marked volume decreases during photophosphorylation; within 10 minutes after the beginning of illumination, the chloroplasts contract to 51–78% of their "dark" volume. This effect, which is totally reversible, has been confirmed by Packer *et al.* (1963; Packer, 1966), who showed that whole cells of the photosynthetic bacterium *Rhodospirillum* exhibit similar structural changes during photophosphorylation. Packer (1966) has also found that chloroplast contraction can be brought about in the dark by addition of ATP, and that this reaction persists in glycerol-extracted "chloroplast models" which have lost up to 85% of their protein. The probable molecular basis for this chloroplast contraction has been discovered by Ohnishi (1964), who isolated two chloroplast proteins having the properties of actin and myosin (the contractile proteins of muscle; see Chapter 8). "Chloroactin" comprises 2–4% of the total chloroplast protein and forms a complex with myosin from rabbit muscle; "chloromyosin" has ATPase activity, makes up 5–10% of the total chloroplast protein, and forms a complex with rabbit actin. Chloroactin and chloromyosin together show ATP-induced viscosity changes characteristic of muscle actomyosin. It is not certain at present whether chloroplast shrinkage also involves osmotic changes conditioned by an ATP-dependent ion pump mechanism (Packer, 1966).

The absorption maxima of whole chloroplasts do not coincide exactly with those of chlorophyll-carotenoid extracts, and it therefore appears that chlorophyll is not present in the form of a simple solution. On the other hand, it seems unlikely that all the chlorophyll is bound to protein, since the ratio of porphyrin to protein in chloroplasts is much higher than in pure heme-protein compounds like hemoglobin and cytochrome. There is spectroscopic evidence, to be discussed later, that about 5% of the chlorophyll differs from the rest in its orientation, and it is probable that some part of the total chlorophyll is present as a chlorophyll-protein compound. Criddle and Park (1964; Criddle, 1966) have isolated a "structural protein" from spinach chloroplasts, which is insoluble under physiological conditions but forms 1:1 complexes with chlorophyll. This protein closely resembles another structural protein first found in mitochondria, and it has a similar molecular weight (ca. 25,000); in spinach chloroplasts this structural protein accounts for about 40% of the total chloroplast protein. The chloroplasts of brown algae (seaweeds, etc.) are brown rather than green, which is thought to be due to the presence of the carotenoid accessory pigment fucoxanthin; in this case too, the chloroplast color evidently depends on the formation of a pigment complex, since there is actually not enough fucoxanthin present to mask the chlorophyll, and heating changes the chloroplasts from brown to green.

In most higher plant cells, chlorophyll appears to be concentrated in specific bodies within the chloroplast; these were discovered by Meyer (1883), who called them "grana" to distinguish them from the lighter "stroma" in which they are embedded. The existence of grana was considered doubtful during the early years of the 20th century, until Heitz (1932) published clear photographs of them; since then their reality has been amply confirmed by electron microscopy. In corn leaves, the

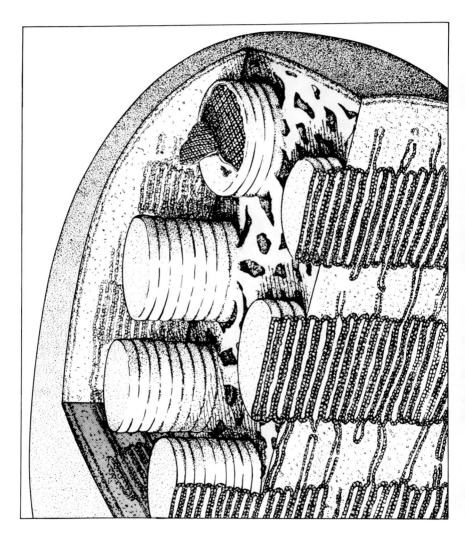

border parenchyma cells of the vascular bundles have chloroplasts which lack grana, resembling algal chloroplasts in this respect; at the same time, chloroplasts elsewhere in the same leaf contain typical grana. When grana occur, it is not clear whether all the chlorophyll is confined to them or whether some chlorophyll occurs in the stroma as well.

Fine Structure of Chloroplasts

By the early 1950's thin-sectioning had reached a generally useful level of sophistication, and the first significant publications on the ultrastructure of chloroplasts, mitochondria, Golgi apparatus, and many other cell organelles date from this period. As in the development of optical lenses during the 19th century, the resolution achieved with biological material in the electron microscope has steadily improved (largely by improvements in fixation and embedding); with improved resolution has come the ability to establish a synthesis between molecular and higher orders of structure. A technical point of special significance is the widespread use of osmium tetroxide for fixation or postfixation of sectioned material; certain structures and materials tend to bind osmium (i.e., they are osmiophilic), and electron scattering by the osmium atoms makes them appear as dark lines or bodies in electron micrographs.

The earliest thin-section preparations of chloroplasts, by Steinmann (1952), Wolken and Palade (1952), and others, served to confirm that chloroplasts have a highly lamellar (or layered) structure in both higher plants and algae. This result had been expected on the basis of analyses with X-rays and polarized light, as well as from earlier electron microscopy of unsectioned chloroplasts. The thickness of the lamellae, which in sections appeared as parallel osmiophilic lines, was measured as 70 Å by both Steinmann (1952) and Cohen and Bowler (1953), although Wolken and Palade (1952) reported much greater values. In addition, Cohen and Bowler were able to distinguish grana in the chloroplasts of tobacco, reporting lamellae present in both the grana and stroma.

Steinmann and Sjöstrand (1955) published the first accurate comparison of grana and stroma lamellae, finding that the grana consist of stacks of dark osmiophilic membranes about 65 Å thick, in regular alternation with light (osmiophobic) layers of the same thickness; the stroma lamellae, on the other hand, are only about 30 Å thick, but are

---

Fig. 5-1. An interpretation of chloroplast ultrastructure. Quantasome particles are organized into grana lamellae, which form closed disks. Each stack of disks is a granum, and the entire plastid is surrounded by two unit membranes.

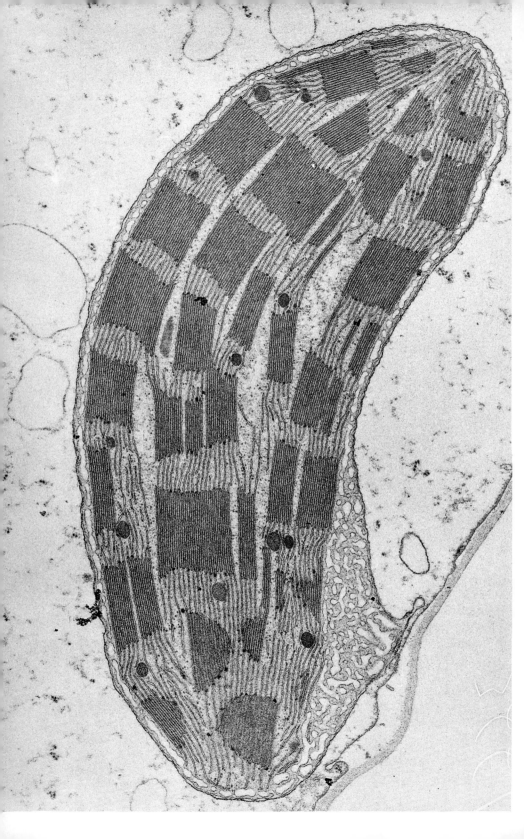

often present in equal numbers and show continuities with the grana lamellae. Steinmann and Sjöstrand referred to each osmiophilic layer in the granum as a "disk," associating these with earlier whole-mount preparations in which chloroplast fragments were seen to contain objects (grana) resembling piles of coins. They noted, however, that the disks are connected in pairs at their rims, forming closed sacs which swell in hypotonic solutions (Fig. 5-1).

The basic arrangement of parts, as described by Steinmann and Sjöstrand for the chloroplasts of higher plants, is now well established (Fig. 5-2). The entire chloroplast is enclosed by two concentric "unit membranes," each approximately 50 Å thick, which are semipermeable (e.g., sucrose penetrates slightly or not at all). Internally the chloroplast is filled with a hydrophilic matrix, the stroma, in which are embedded 40–80 cylindrical grana measuring 0.25–0.8 μ in diameter and of varying depths. Each granum, in turn, is composed of about 5–25 disk-shaped compartments, each of which contains an enclosed space or "loculus" whose contents are separated from the stroma. The grana, finally, are interconnected by a system of intergranal membranes (stroma lamellae), which appear to be about half as thick as the granal partitions and, at least in some cases, are continuous with them. Beyond these basic features, there exists considerable variation in the exact manner of interconnection between grana and stroma lamellae. Grana are lacking in the chloroplasts of algae and of some higher plant tissues, which are usually filled with uniform lamellae traversing the entire chloroplast.

Various details of membrane relationships in the chloroplasts of higher plants cannot be settled until the precise localization of different macromolecules is determined, and this goal has not yet been reached. One of the early controversies was whether layers of stroma penetrate between the closed compartments of the granum; such alternating layers of stroma were indicated, for instance, by both Steinmann and Sjöstrand (1955) and Von Wettstein (1959), whereas Weier and Thompson (1962) maintained that the granum is a structural unit, which is not penetrated by the stroma and in which all of the light, osmiophobic layers are closed loculi (or thylakoids). Careful analysis of swollen grana by Weier et al. (1963) has now established that the latter organization is the most typical one, although alternating bands of stroma apparently occur in some species.

The fact that granal compartments are stacked adjacently bears also on the structural basis for the greater thickness of grana partitions com-

Fig. 5-2. Thin-section of a maize chloroplast, showing grana and stroma lamellae. 32,000×. From Shumway and Weier (1967).

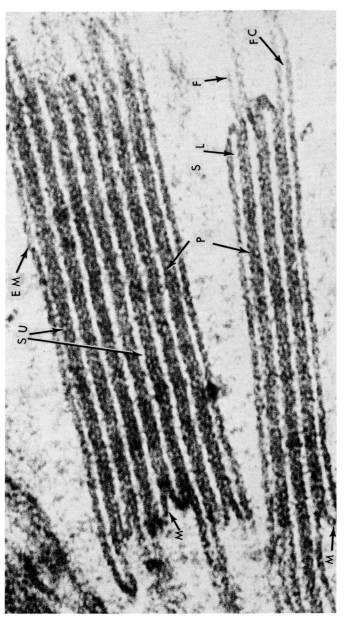

Fig. 5-3. High resolution micrograph of grana lamellae from *Phaseolus vulgaris.* The membranes are composed of spheroids having light centers and dark rims. Partitions (P) contain two closely-appressed layers of particles, whereas the end membranes (EM), margins (M) and stroma lamellae (F) contain but a single layer. The membranes delimit several types of space, including loculi (L), fret channels (FC) and the stroma (S). 250,000×. From Weier and Benson (1966).

pared with stroma lamellae. Hodge (1959) interpreted this greater thickness as due to the presence of chlorophyll in the grana membranes and its presumed absence in stroma lamellae [according to Rabinowitch (1951), the heads of chlorophyll molecules measure $15.6 \times 15.5 \times 3.7$ Å and would align themselves at a water interface into a monomolecular layer 12.8 Å thick; see Fig. 4-1]. However Weier *et al.* (1963) found that the grana lamellae separating adjacent compartments are approximately twice as thick as the lateral margins of the compartments, and also twice the thickness of the outer membrane enclosing the terminal compartments of each granum (Fig. 5-3); consequently, they suggested that the double thickness is due to the fusion of two contiguous membranes enclosing adjacent loculi. This interpretation has been beautifully supported by Weier *et al.* (1965), using the newly introduced glutaraldehyde fixation; they demonstrated that each thick grana lamella is superficially five-layered (three 40 Å osmiophilic layers enclosing two 17 Å light osmiophobic layers). Furthermore, their high-resolution micrographs indicate that this five-layered effect is due to the presence of spherical units or macromolecules, which are arranged as two layers in the grana partitions but only one layer in the marginal membranes and stroma lamellae (Fig. 5-3). The apparent dimensions of the grana lamella vary somewhat with the fixative used, but after $KMnO_4$ fixation Weier *et al.* (1965) measured the double partitions of the grana as 159 Å thick, and the single stroma lamellae as 89 Å thick. The globular subunits themselves are composed of a light osmiophobic core about 33–37 Å in diameter, surrounded by an osmiophilic rim estimated to be 20–28 Å wide (Weier and Benson, 1966). Such dimensions would be consistent with an interpretation of each globular unit as a single protein molecule. This work indicates that the increased thickness of grana partitions is due to the fusion of two single membranes, and does not necessarily imply a specific localization of chlorophyll into grana.

The exact manner in which stroma lamellae and grana lamellae fuse is also a problem of long standing. The interpretations both of Steinmann and Sjöstrand (1955) and of Von Wettstein (1959) implied that the number of stroma lamellae would be approximately equal to the number of grana lamellae. They differed in that Wettstein recognized a continuity between the loculi of two or more grana which he believed to be interconnected through a channel bounded by two stroma lamellae; the entire structure, including two or more loculi and connecting channels would amount to a modified and flattened cisterna traversing the entire chloroplast. Steinmann and Sjöstrand, on the other hand, indicated that each loculus would be a closed unit. Weier and Thomson (1962) have confirmed that both these arrangements occur, together with a number of other fusion patterns (Fig. 5-3); it is a general rule, however, that a loculus never opens directly to the stroma. Weier has pointed out that the number of stroma lamellae is often many fewer than the number of grana lamellae, and he visualizes the stroma lamellae as forming a "fretwork" of anastomosing channels (Fig. 5-1). In general, grana and stroma membranes may be regarded as separating the interior of the chloroplast into at least three types of space: (1) the stroma; (2) the grana loculi; and (3) the "fret channels" traversing the stroma. Unfortunately the significance of these spaces is still largely unknown, although Von Wettstein (1959) and others have observed differences in the visible contents of the fret channels and the stroma.

A slightly different concept of lamellar structure has been advanced by Menke (1966), largely on the basis of low-angle X-ray diffraction data. Menke has proposed that, in addition to each layer of particles composing the wall of a granum compartment (or thylakoid), there exists a subjacent layer of lipid. In a sense, the particulate elements of the chloroplast might be imagined as embedded in a continuous lipid layer. Such a scheme would conform well with electron micrographs of intact chloroplasts prepared by freezing in liquid nitrogen, fracturing, and platinum shadowing of the fractured membrane surfaces (Fig. 5-4). According to Branton and Park (1967), chloroplasts prepared in this way show three types of membrane face: surfaces in which the membrane shows densely packed 100–130 Å particles; apposed surfaces in which 160–200 Å particles are more sparsely embedded in a continuous smooth phase; and surfaces with few discrete particles but a generally rough texture (Fig. 5-4A). The relationship between the structure of such fractured lamellae, the thin-sectioned lamellae studied by Weier and his collaborators, and torn thylakoids to be described in the next section, is not yet settled (Weier et al., 1966).

Functional Organization of Chloroplasts

When plants are kept in the dark their total chlorophyll content decreases, a phenomenon that is associated with a general decrease in the amount of intrachloroplast membrane; likewise, light-induced chlorophyll synthesis is accompanied by increases in chloroplast membrane. Fractionated and centrifuged chloroplast preparations can be separated into (1) a green, insoluble pellet containing morphologically recognizable lamellae and almost all the chlorophyll; and (2) a colorless supernatant. The functional significance of these observations was clarified by Trebst et al. (1958), who showed that the photosynthetic light reactions ac-

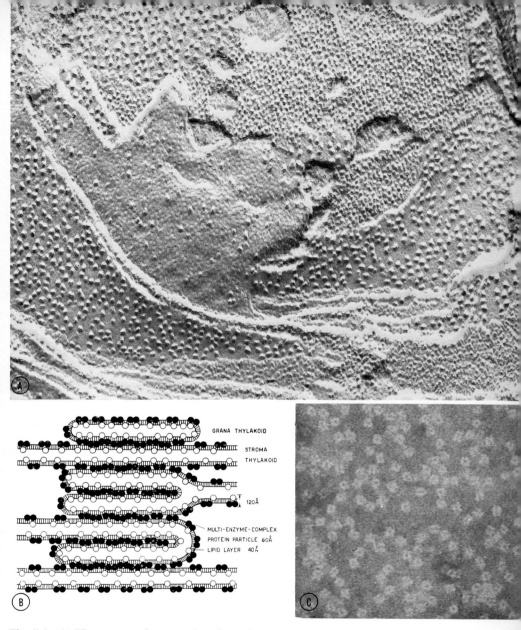

Fig. 5-4. (A) Three types of granum lamella surface, as revealed by freeze-etching. One surface has small, closely packed particles, and another has large, more widely distributed particles. 90,000×. From Branton and Park (1967). (B) An interpretation of granum structure taking account of freeze-etch images. From Muhlethaler (1966). (C) Molecules of carboxydismutase, the enzyme which catalyzes the condensation of CO_2 and ribulose diphosphate. Each particle measures about 80×110 Å. 200,000×. From Park (1966).

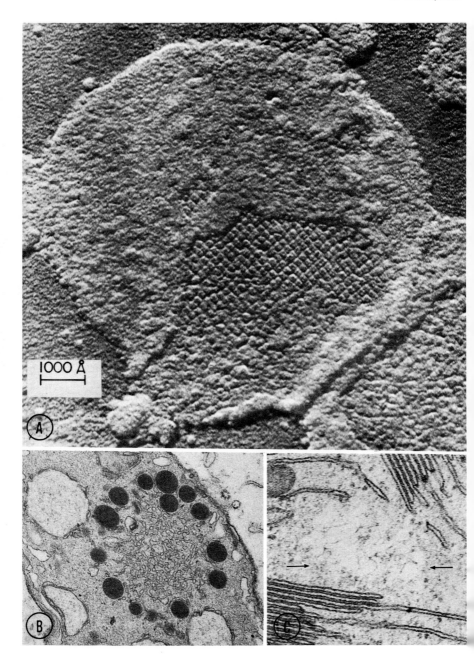

company the green, insoluble pellet, whereas the dark reactions are carried out by soluble enzymes from the supernatant. The evidence is now very strong that in intact chloroplasts, the light reactions are mediated by the chlorophyll-containing lamellae, whereas the dark reactions (CO_2 fixation and reduction) are catalyzed by soluble enzymes in the stroma.

Park and Pon (1961) carried out a combined electron microscope and biochemical analysis of the phosphorylating lamella fraction (green pellet), which led them to conclude that chlorophyll is evenly distributed in the lamellae (including both grana and stroma lamellae) and that the unit of phosphorylation is an ellipsoid particle with axes of about 200×100 Å. According to Sauer and Calvin (1962), aggregates containing as few as 3–8 of these particles and measuring 500×100 Å are able to support CO_2 fixation when combined with the supernatant fraction. Although so far only aggregates of particles show photosynthetic activity, Park and Pon (1963) have called each ellipsoid a "quantasome," and it is presumed that quantasomes in higher plants are equivalent to photophosphorylating particles of similar size which have been isolated from bacteria.

More recently, Park and Biggins (1964) have reported units measuring $185 \times 155 \times 100$ Å, each of which seems to be composed of 4 subunits (Fig. 5-5); the larger units are regarded as quantasomes, whereas the subunits may correspond to the 80–90 Å spheres found by Weier *et al.* (1965) in thin-sectioned chloroplasts. The quantasomes themselves seem to occur in at least three different arrangements in the lamellae of spinach chloroplasts. From their dimensions, the molecular weight of one quantasome may be estimated at about 2×10^6. Lichtenthaler and Park (1963) have reviewed data on the composition of isolated lamellae from spinach chloroplasts, and from these gross chemical analyses, Park (1966) has speculated about the molecular organization of the individual quantasome. Assuming that the quantasomes are identical, each one would contain about half lipid and half protein (by weight), including the molecules listed in Table 5-1. It should be emphasized that these calculations are for an "average" quantasome, and that in fact there may be several types; little evidence exists on this point.

Fig. 5-5. (A) An isolated disk from a spinach chloroplast, showing a paracrystalline array of particles (quantasomes) on the inner surface. Each particle has four subunits. 120,000×. From Park and Biggins (1964). (B) An abnormal maize plastid, showing replacement of grana by a latticelike structure. 31,000×. From L. K. Shumway, by permission. (C) A presumed DNA-containing region from a maize chloroplast. 67,000×. From L. K. Shumway, by permission.

Table 5-1

MOLECULAR INVENTORY OF A QUANTASOME[a]

Moles per quantasome		Total molecular weight
Lipid		
230 Chlorophylls		206,400
160 chlorophyll *a*	143,000	
70 chlorophyll *b*	63,400	
48 Carotenoids		27,400
14 β-carotene	7,600	
22 lutein	12,600	
6 violaxanthin	3,600	
6 neoxanthin	3,600	
46 Quinone compounds		31,800
16 plastoquinone A	12,000	
8 plastoquinone B	9,000	
6 plastoquinone C	3,000	
8–10 α-tocopherol	3,800	
4 α-tocopherylquinone	2,000	
4 vitamin K_1	2,000	
116 Phospholipids (phosphatidyl glycerols)		90,800
114 Digalactosyl diglyceride		134,000
346 Monogalactosyl diglyceride		268,000
48 Sulfolipid		41,000
? Sterols		15,000
Unidentified lipids		175,000
	Total lipid:	990,000
Protein		
9380 Nitrogen atoms as protein		928,000
2 Manganese		110
12 Iron including 1 as cytochrome b_6 and 1 as cytochrome *f*		672
6 Copper		218
	Total protein:	930,000
Total lipid plus protein:		1,920,000

[a] Estimated from the chemical composition of isolated chloroplast membranes and based on a quantasome molecular weight of about 2×10^6. From Park (1966).

Additional details are suggested by the work of Sauer and Calvin (1962), who analyzed the light absorption properties of quantasome preparations and found that the absorption spectrum of isolated quantasomes is identical to that of entire chloroplasts (but different from pigment extracts). Their data indicate that about 5% of the chlorophyll is absorbing light at 695 mμ, rather than at the 678 mμ peak characteristic of chlorophyll in solution. This and other data are interpreted to mean that 11–12 of the 230 chlorophyll molecules are oriented parallel to the quantasome axis, and since the quantum energy at 695 mμ is slightly less than at 678 mμ, these oriented molecules can act as an energy trap, accepting and channeling energy in a "downhill" transfer from the nonoriented chlorophyll (and carotenoid) molecules. This concept helps to explain the presence of so many pigment molecules in a physical-chemical unit which supposedly carries out the conversion of individual light quanta.

It seems clear from these investigations that the conspicuous lamellae of chloroplasts are composed of many thousands of chlorophyll-containing units, each of which is capable of carrying out the conversion of light energy to the phosphoryl energy of ATP. These units are identical or of very few kinds, and are organized as replicate arrays, which in the aggregate constitute the lamellae. This model of lamella structure has broad theoretical significance for the interpretation of biological membranes in general. For many years, membranes have been regarded as composed of monomolecular protein and lipid layers, a model which was the basis of Hodge's (1959) suggestion that grana lamellae contain an additional layer of chlorophyll oriented between the lipid and protein "sandwich." However high resolution electron microscopy, as carried out by Weier *et al.* (1965) and Park and Branton, strongly suggests that chloroplast lamellae are composed of oriented supramolecular particles (rather than layers); similar data are accumulating with respect to other biological membranes as well (to be discussed in later chapters). Since in chloroplasts the membranes themselves are composed of units which carry out photophosphorylation, Nobel and Packer's (1965) discovery that isolated spinach chloroplasts actively accumulate both calcium and phosphate ions is particularly significant. This ion uptake is light dependent and requires photophosphorylation in the presence of ATP; similar energy-dependent ion accumulation (active transport) is a general property of the plasma membrane, nuclear envelope and other biological membranes.

Analysis of chloroplast structure has brought biology to a level where microscopic structure merges with the atomic structure of molecules, and where the analysis of function merges with the principles of physical chemistry. At this level, both structure and function are inseparable properties of the atomic configurations of single molecules, and are hardly distinguishable. For instance, in physical-chemical terms it is understandable that the photosynthetic dark reactions, which are of a thermochemical nature and occur in solution in the chloroplast stroma, do not require a highly ordered structural arrangement. By contrast, photophosphorylation is known to depend on a separation of positive and negative charges into specific pathways of electron flow (or circuits); thus, excited electrons from chlorophyll must flow to ferredoxin, plastoquinone and cytochromes in order to bring about phosphorylation. If these electrons are diverted to the wrong acceptors (such as indophenol) or are permitted to give up their energy in fluorescence, ATP is not formed. The quantasome may thus be imagined as a tiny photoelectric cell coupled to a storage battery; light energy generates a flow of electrons, which in turn is converted to stored chemical energy. Such circuitry may be expected to depend on highly restricted, orderly (and low entropy) arrangements of macromolecules; such orderly arrays of molecules when resolved in the electron microscope are recognizable as a system of membranes (or lamellae).

Tollin (1960) has, in fact, attempted to simulate the structural-functional relationships of the chloroplast lamellae by means of a physical-chemical "model." In this model, a very thin layer of pigment is covered by a second thin layer of oxidizing agent (quinones), the combined thickness of the two layers being about 1 μ; Tollin then measures the potential difference across the layers in the dark and during illumination. He has found that light in the wavelength of the pigment absorption maximum increases the potential difference across the layers, and that the presence of the quinone as an electron acceptor has the effect of increasing the quantum yield, as well as the lifetime of the charge carriers. In fact, some of his models are capable of producing small amounts of work at the expense of light energy. Faludi-Daniel and Galmiche (1963) have examined the supramolecular structure-function relationship within the chloroplast itself by studying CO_2 fixation in barley mutants whose chloroplast structure is strikingly altered. The plastids of the mutant, xantha-3, for instance, do not contain grana or a lamellar structure at all, although the usual pigments are present in association with "globules"; in this mutant, CO_2 fixation is estimated at only 50% relative to nonmutant, grana-containing chloroplasts under the same conditions.

The Origin of Chloroplasts

It has been known for many years that chloroplasts, particularly in algae and simpler plants, are capable of multiplying by fission. For instance it was stated by E. B. Wilson (1925):

> The classical work of Schimper and of Meyer (1883) led them to the conclusion that plastids are never formed *de novo* but always by growth and division of pre-existing plastids. . . . The fact is now generally admitted that differentiated forms of plastids, in particular the chloroplasts, multiply in this manner.

Many unicellular algae contain only one chloroplast, which divides when the cell itself undergoes division, and the same situation occurs in some multicellular plants such as liverworts and ferns (Granick, 1961). Von Wettstein (1959) has described the changes in fine structure during division of plastids in the seaweed *Fucus,* and the length of the chloroplast division cycle was measured by Reinhard (1933) as approximately 8 hours in moss leaves. Chloroplast division has also been recorded cine-micrographically by Green (1964), who found a division cycle of 18 hours in the alga *Nitella.* In algae which contain one, or very few, chloroplasts and where the division of chloroplasts is as orderly as the division of chromosomes, the question arises whether sexual fusion of chloroplast-containing gametes leads to "chloroplast diploid" cells. Several classical studies have shown that this actually occurs, and that there is a corresponding "chloroplast reduction" process (analogous to meiotic reduction), in which the plastids contributed by the male cell degenerate.

Plastid reproduction by fission implies that daughter plastids can undergo a growth process. In fact, several careful studies with the electron microscope have provided direct evidence for such plastid growth. In *Fucus,* Von Wettstein (1959) observed that the number of lamellae per chloroplast increases from about 8 in younger plants up to 18 in older plants; similarly, Kaja (1955) found that moss chloroplasts increase in diameter from about 2 μ in younger cells to 7 μ in older cells, whereas the number of grana per chloroplast increases from about 5 up to as many as 80. In higher plants and in some algae, the division of plastids appears to be confined to early growth stages, and the young plastids may lack internal lamellae entirely; such undifferentiated plastids are referred to as *proplastids.* According to Kirk and Tilney-Bassett (1967), proplastids appear as colorless vesicles about 0.7–1.5 μ in diameter, they are surrounded by two concentric membranes, and there are 7–20 in an average meristematic cell.

The stages by which proplastids differentiate into mature chloroplasts containing lamellae and grana, have been inferred from electron micrographs by Von Wettstein (1959, 1961), Ben-Shaul (1964), and others. The proplastid buds off closed vesicles from the inside membrane of the two limiting membranes, and these orient into layers; contact between vesicles occupying the same level leads to fusion and the development of very long, flattened cisternae traversing the entire chloroplast. Finally, the long flattened cisternae differentiate into grana and stroma lamellae, a process which seems to involve a joining of adjacent membranes vertically at their "outer" surfaces in the grana regions. The intracisternal spaces thus give rise to both the loculi of the grana and the "fret channels" which connect the loculi of different grana. During the entire process, the inside of the vesicles or cisternae is always kept separate from the surrounding stroma. It is interesting that Stanier (1963) has found evidence that the chromatophores of some photosynthetic bacteria also arise by budding from a preexisting membrane, in this case the limiting plasma membrane of the bacterial cell.

The above sequence of proplastid differentiation is altered when plants are grown in the dark or if they contain specific genetic mutations. In the dark synthesis of chlorophyll is blocked at the protochlorophyll stage, and although vesicles are budded from the inner proplastid membrane, they do not orient into layers; rather they accumulate in the center of the developing chloroplast and fuse into a complex system of tubules. After sufficient time, these tubules establish a highly ordered pattern, reminiscent of a crystal. In some of the barley mutants studied by von Wettstein, development appears to be blocked at specific points in the sequence of light or dark differentiation; for instance, the mutant chloroplasts may fail to develop typical grana, but become filled with vesicles instead. Proplastids are also thought to be capable of differentiating into other specialized forms of plastid, which function in starch storage or as chromoplasts in flowers; in some species, even mature chloroplasts can undergo such structural alterations. These relationships in higher plants are summarized in the following scheme:

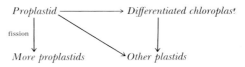

Although there is little doubt that chloroplasts do undergo processes of fission, growth, and differentiation, the degree of independence in chloroplast inheritance is still under investigation. As indicated above, chloroplast characters are clearly influenced by nuclear genes, and in maize over 50 different loci are known which affect them. Kirk (1966) has summarized evidence that the synthesis of chlorophyll, carotenoids, and some photosynthetic electron carriers depends on nuclear genes. At the same time, there are many recorded instances in which single "abnormal" plastids are able to perpetuate their own characteristics independently of Mendelian factors. Renner (1936), in a classical analysis, was able to recombine the chloroplasts of one species with the cytoplasm and nuclei of another species, and found that the plastids maintained their species characteristics. Furthermore Sager (1964) has found an extensive nonchromosomal inheritance affecting chloroplast characters in the green alga *Chlamydomonas*.

These instances of "chloroplast inheritance" have become more understandable in light of recent demonstrations that chloroplasts contain both DNA and the necessary mechanisms for synthesizing specific RNA's and proteins from a DNA template (Chapters 13 and 14). Evidence for the occurrence of DNA in chloroplasts was reported by Stocking and Gifford (1959), who observed radioactivity in the large spiral chloroplast of the alga *Spirogyra* after incorporation of tritium-labeled thymidine (a specific DNA precursor). Later Ris and Plaut (1962) used specific Feulgen staining and DNase to demonstrate visible accumulations of DNA in the chloroplasts of the alga *Chlamydomonas*. In spinach and beet leaves, as well as in the green algae *Chlorella* and *Chlamydomonas*, Sager and Ishida (1963) and Chun *et al.* (1963) found a minor DNA component with a characteristic low density in the analytical ultracentrifuge; this component was concentrated in the chloroplast fraction but absent from the nuclear fraction. It has now been generally accepted that characteristic chloroplast DNA's (or chloroplast chromosomes) occur in the photosynthetic organelles of algae and higher plants. According to Brawerman (1966) this DNA differs from nuclear DNA either by a much lower GC content (about 24–27% GC in green algae), or sometimes by a greater GC content (in most higher plants). The amount of DNA per chloroplast varies slightly from species to species in the range 2 to 5×10^{-15} g, slightly less than the DNA content of a typical bacterium (*E. coli*). DNA regions resembling bacterial nucleoids have also been identified in thin-sectioned chloroplasts by electron microscopy (Gunning, 1965; see Fig. 5-5C). It is not yet known whether all the DNA of a given chloroplast is in one continuous piece, although Ray and Hanawalt (1965) have found DNA helices of 20 to 40×10^6 molecular weight (10–20 μ of Watson-Crick helix). Since chloroplasts also contain a DNA-dependent RNA polymerase (Chapter 13), it appears that specific RNA's are synthesized from chloroplast DNA as a template (Kirk, 1966).

That isolated chloroplasts can incorporate labeled amino acids into protein was first reported by Stephenson and Zamecnik (1956), a discovery which in retrospect seems reasonable since the chloroplasts of higher plants sometimes account for 70–80% of total leaf proteins. Heber (1962) has shown that photosynthesizing spinach chloroplasts can use labeled CO_2 to synthesize proteins both *in vivo* and *in vitro*. With whole cells, Heber found that labeled proteins appear in the chloroplast fraction about 2 minutes before they can be found in the cytoplasmic fraction; he also reported that the rate of incorporation is highest for the insoluble fraction (i.e., the lamellae) both in isolated chloroplasts and in the chloroplasts of whole cells. The discovery of protein synthesis in chloroplasts set the stage for Lyttleton's (1962) isolation of chloroplast ribosomes (Chapter 14), which are estimated to make up 3–7% of the chloroplast dry mass. As summarized by Brawerman (1966), several authors have found that such chloroplast ribosomes are smaller than cytoplasmic ribosomes from the same cells (sedimentation coefficient = 60–66 S, versus 70–76 S for cytoplasmic ribosomes); their base composition is also distinctive for a higher A + U and lower C content than the cytoplasmic particles. App and Jagendorf (1963) have demonstrated that isolated chloroplast ribosomes are able to carry out cell-free protein synthesis; concomitantly, a messenger RNA fraction has been isolated from chloroplasts by Brawerman (1966). Finally it is estimated that 15–40% of the amino acid-activating (adenylating) enzymes of some cells occur in their chloroplasts (for details of the protein synthesizing mechanisms, see Chapter 14).

The evidence for independent mechanisms of inheritance in chloroplasts has reached its highest level of sophistication with the unicellular green alga, *Euglena* (which can survive and multiply either autotrophically or heterotrophically). In one of the earliest studies, Lwoff (1950) used a species (*E. mesnili*) which could synthesize chlorophyll in the dark; over a period of months, however, Lwoff observed a gradual reduction in the average number of chloroplasts contained by successive generations of dark-grown cells. Eventually some cells were produced which seemed to lack chloroplasts entirely. From these experiments, it was concluded that the cells had "outgrown" their chloroplasts and that the rate of multiplication of chloroplasts is at least partly independent of the rate of multiplication of entire cells. Brawerman and Chargaff (1960) discovered a similar relationship in *Euglena gracilis* after a temperature shock; cells which were permitted to multiply rapidly became irreversibly bleached, whereas cells prevented from dividing regained their normal ability to produce chloroplasts. They concluded that *Euglena* contains an autonomously replicating factor which is necessary for chloroplast formation; however, this factor is distinct from the chloroplasts themselves, since it can multiply in the absence of chloroplast increases.

More recent experiments have employed strains of *Euglena* which cannot synthesize chlorophyll in the dark; consequently, dark-grown cells lack typical chloroplasts but they contain proplastids which can differentiate into chloroplasts in the light. Ben-Shaul (1964) has followed the course of this differentiation at the fine-structural level and has found evidence that vesicles bud off from the inner proplastid membrane (as in higher plants); these vesicles then fuse together in groups of four, establishing cisternae, and later the *proplastids* fuse together in groups of three to produce mature chloroplasts. According to Pogo and Pogo (1964), the entire process is accompanied by considerable net synthesis of chlorophyll, RNA, and protein.

Lyman *et al.* (1961) showed that differentiation of the proplastids in *Euglena* can be blocked by irradiation with ultraviolet light (as well as by streptomycin or high temperature), and the action spectrum for this effect shows peaks at 260 and 280 mμ, indicating that the inactivation directly involves nucleoprotein molecules. Subsequently, Gibor and Granick (1962) found that irradiation of the nucleus alone does not produce bleaching, but irradiation of the cytoplasm alone (using a "doughnut beam" of ultraviolet light) is as effective as total cell irradiation. These experiments therefore demonstrate a requirement for nucleoprotein localized in the cytoplasm and not replaceable from nuclear DNA. That DNA and RNA are specifically involved has been shown in experiments by Pogo and Pogo (1964), who found that proplastid differentiation, together with synthesis of chlorophyll, RNA, and protein, are blocked in *Euglena* by actinomycin D (which specifically affects DNA-dependent RNA synthesis). Similarly, Ray and Hanawalt (1965) found that mutant *Euglena* which lack the ability to form chloroplasts also lack the characteristic, low density chloroplast DNA.

At present the exact interrelations between nuclear DNA, chloroplast DNA, and the chloroplast's mechanisms for specific RNA and protein synthesis have not been completely elucidated. The fact that chloroplasts incorporate thymidine-^{3}H indicates that their DNA replicates *in situ*. However, nuclear DNA clearly plays a determining role in the synthesis of chlorophyll, carotenoids, and the photosynthetic electron carriers (Kirk, 1966). It is possible that chloroplast DNA determines nothing more than the synthesis of chloroplast ribosomes, and that specific chloroplast proteins are then dictated by messenger RNA's made in the nucleus (Chapter 14). The fact that chloroplast structure can vary considerably from tissue to tissue in the same leaf also implies a differentiation process which is coordinated with the overall differentiation of the cell; however, the exact mechanisms of coordination between nuclear DNA and chloroplast DNA are almost unknown.

It has been pointed out that chloroplasts have many of the characteristics of autonomous microorganisms or symbionts living in the cells of green plants. In particular, they have the capacity to divide and differentiate, they are able to trap and make use of energy from the environment, and most significantly they contain distinctive species of DNA and RNA, the fundamental genetic materials. Ris and Plaut (1962) have suggested that chloroplasts as organelles may be descended from symbiotic (autotrophic) microorganisms. However this theory does not accord well with the apparent phylogenetic sequence represented in the photosynthetic organelles of bacteria (simple vesicles), blue-green algae (free lamellae), higher algae (chloroplast-enclosed lamellae), and the more advanced plants (grana-containing chloroplasts). Kirk (1966) has also pointed out that nuclear genes are evidently responsible for enzymes required in the synthesis of the photosynthetic pigments and associated electron transport system; under the symbiont theory, coding for such proteins would be expected to reside in the chloroplast DNA.

6

ENERGY-RELEASING PROCESSES

Like acrobats performing their complicated exercises high above the circus crowd,
the molecules of proteins, carbohydrates,
fats, vitamins, enzymes, and other constituents of the living organisms combine,
exchange, or dissociate in the midst of
an ocean of oxygen which continuously
threatens them with breakdown and ex-
tinction. . . . Every day, almost a billion
tons of organic compounds are destroyed
by oxidation. . . . At this rate of destruc-
tion, all organic matter now present on this
globe will be consumed in the next ten or
twenty years; . . .

E. I. Rabinowitch *1945*

Respiration is therefore a combustion, certainly very slow, but nevertheless entirely
similar to that of charcoal.

A. L. Lavoisier and P. Laplace *1780*

Just as the biochemistry of photosynthesis could not be understood until the discovery of carbon dioxide and oxygen, so the analysis of reactions which release biological energy from organic substrates (food) also depended on an understanding of the relationship between oxygen and combustion. It was more than an accident that the same decade saw Priestly and Ingen-Housz's pioneer studies of gas exchange in plants, and Lavoisier's discovery that combustion is a chemical reaction between a substrate and atmospheric oxygen. In 1780 Lavoisier came to the further startling conclusion that animal respiration is also a form of combustion, in which organic material is "burned" with the same products (and energy yield) as if it had burned in a fire. Glucose, for instance, burns readily, giving off carbon dioxide and water according to the stoichiometry:

$$C_6H_{12}O_6 + 6\ O_2 \longrightarrow 6\ CO_2 + 6\ H_2O \qquad \Delta F^\circ = -688\ kcal/mole$$

In a similar manner an animal may consume sugar and inhale oxygen, exhaling carbon dioxide and water vapor, together with heat and other forms of energy according to the same equation. Ingen-Housz's discovery (1779) that plants, too, "injure the air" in the absence of light provided a clue that respiration occurs in plant cells as well. Although combustion in living cells is a slower and highly controlled process, it is not confined to stored food materials. Oxidation is the inescapable fate of aerobic organisms, including their essential structural materials; the half-life of an average liver protein is only 5–6 days.

During the 19th century the realization developed that certain types of biological energy release can occur in the absence of oxygen; this was most apparent in the ancient art of wine-making, in which yeast cells transform sugar into alcohol and carbon dioxide under anaerobic conditions. Enough energy is derived from this anaerobic process to support the cells' own growth and reproduction. The classic experiments of Pasteur, carried out on behalf of the French wine-makers, laid the groundwork for an eventual understanding of both anaerobic fermentation and aerobic respiration; nevertheless, detailed analysis of the reactions depended on the discovery of cell-free fermentation by Buchner (1897) and the introduction of a second system, the anaerobic contraction of muscle, by Fletcher and Hopkins (1907) and Meyerhof. In the muscle system, glycogen is used as substrate and lactic acid is produced anaerobically (instead of alcohol); however, many of the intermediate transformations are identical to those of yeast, and comparison of the two systems by Meyerhof and others in the 1920's and 1930's led to the isolation of various specific enzymes catalyzing the intermediate reactions.

102

Anaerobic Glycolysis

The first stages in the enzymatic degradation of carbohydrates require, not oxygen, but donors and acceptors of hydrogen and the phosphoryl group (i.e., ATP, ADP, NAD, NADH). In Fig. 6-1, the biochemical changes leading from glucose to alcohol or lactic acid are portrayed in three sequences: first, the phosphorylation of the carbohydrate and its degradation to phosphoglyceraldehyde; second the oxidation of phosphoglyceraldehyde to phosphoglyceric acid, followed by dehydration and dephosphorylation to pyruvic acid; and third, the reduction of pyruvic acid to lactic acid or (after decarboxylation) to alcohol.

The first reaction in Fig. 6-1, involving phosphorylation of glucose to glucose 6-phosphate, is catalyzed by a class of enzymes known as hexokinases, the first of which was isolated by Meyerhof in 1927 (mol. wt. 96,000). Hexokinase was detected initially as a factor necessary for fermentation of glucose, which disappeared from muscle extracts after aging, but could be replaced from yeast extracts. As in many intermediate steps of fermentation, alternative pathways exist; for instance, aged muscle extracts *can* catalyze the fermentation of glycogen, which gives rise to glucose 6-phosphate in two reactions catalyzed by the enzymes, glycogen phosphorylase (which employs inorganic phosphate instead of ATP as phosphoryl donor) and phosphoglucomutase (which catalyzes an isomerization of glucose 1-phosphate to glucose 6-phosphate). After the formation of glucose 6-phosphate, the enzyme phosphoglucoisomerase (isolated by Lohmann in 1933) brings about an isomerization to fructose 6-phosphate (Fig. 6-1), and phosphofructokinase (isolated in 1936) then catalyzes a phosphorylation to fructose 1,6-diphosphate at the expense of ATP.

The splitting of fructose 1,6-diphosphate to form phosphodihydroxyacetone and 3-phosphoglyceraldehyde (Fig. 6-1) is catalyzed by the enzyme aldolase (mol. wt. 150,000), which was discovered by Meyerhof and Lohmann in 1934. This reaction deserves special notice since the same enzyme catalyzes the reverse reaction during photosynthesis, i.e., a condensation of two trioses to form hexose; in fact the equilibrium constant of the reaction favors the hexose ($\Delta F°$ for splitting $= +5$ kcal/mole). In the condensation reaction, aldolase is specific for phosphodihydroxyacetone, but a number of short-chain carbohydrates will serve as partners, including tetroses (4-carbon sugars) which condense with trioses to form sedoheptuloses (7-carbon sugars). The latter reaction occurs in the phosphate shunt when ribulose phosphate is regenerated for carbon dioxide fixation (Calvin cycle; see Chapter 4). Aldolase commonly occurs together with the enzyme triosephosphate isomerase (isolated by Meyer-

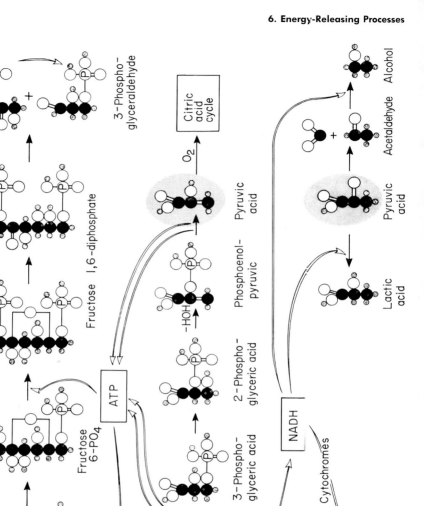

hof in 1935), which isomerizes phosphodihydroxyacetone to 3-phospho-glyceraldehyde (PGAL); consequently, the second series of reactions in Fig. 6-1 may be dealt with on the assumption that each glucose molecule has yielded two molecules of PGAL.

The next step in anaerobic glycolysis is the oxidation of PGAL to 3-phosphoglyceric acid (PGA). It should be recalled that PGA is the primary product of CO_2 fixation in photosynthesis (Chapter 4) and that its reduction to PGAL in the Calvin cycle requires an input of energy from NADPH and ATP (formed in the light reactions). In anaerobic glycolysis these reactions are reversed, returning NADH and ATP as products. The energy-yielding events are catalyzed by the enzyme phosphoglyceraldehyde dehydrogenase, and lead to the intermediate product, 1,3-diphosphoglyceric acid; however, the final phosphorylation of ADP involves a phosphoryl transfer, dephosphorylating the glyceryl diphosphate to glyceryl monophosphate, which is catalyzed by phosphoglyceryl kinase (Fig. 6-1).

This coupling of ATP formation with oxidation of PGAL was first demonstrated by Warburg, and helped to establish the biological importance of ATP. The mechanics of the reaction have since been closely investigated by Racker (1965) and others as a possible analogy to the coupling of phosphorylation with oxidation-reduction in the electron transport chain (oxidative and photophosphorylation). Cohn (1953) used isotopically labeled oxygen to show that the essential event is a binding of inorganic phosphate to PGAL by formation of a C—O bond, followed by removal of the phosphoryl by rupture of the P—O bond; thus, ^{18}O from the inorganic phosphate remains behind, constituting the additional oxygen in the oxidation of aldehyde (CHO) to acid (COOH; see below). At the same time, inorganic phosphate of low phosphoryl transfer potential becomes the terminal phosphoryl of ATP, with much higher transfer potential. The associated dehydrogenation involves reduction of NAD at the expense of electrons from PGAL and protons accompanying ADP and the inorganic phosphate. Phosphoglyceraldehyde dehydrogenase, which catalyzes these changes, contains free SH groups as well as two tightly bound molecules of NAD, and is thought to form a complex with the phosphoglyceryl comparable to the complex of acetyl with coenzyme A (Fig. 3-4). Thus the overall reaction series is visualized as:

Fig. 6-1. The sequence of reactions involved in anaerobic glycolysis. One molecule of glucose yields two molecules of pyruvic acid, which may then be oxidized through the citric acid cycle (in presence of O_2) or reduced to lactic acid (in muscle) or alcohol (in yeast). Black circles are carbon, white circles oxygen, and stippled circles hydrogen.

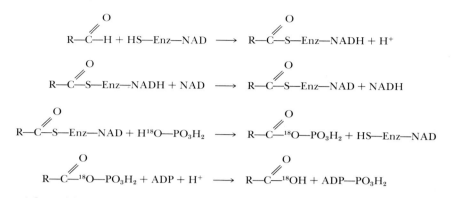

After this series of energy-yielding reactions, the 3-phosphoglyceric acid can be isomerized to 2-phosphoglyceric acid by the enzyme phosphoglyceromutase (mol. wt. 112,000); 2-phosphoglyceric acid is then capable of being dehydrated by enolase to form the high-energy compound phosphoenolpyruvate (PEP; see Chapter 3). Subsequent transphosphorylation to ADP by phosphopyruvate kinase yields the important product pyruvic acid. It is a significant fact, discovered by Pette *et al.* (1962), that the activity ratios of the five enzymes triosephosphate isomerase, phosphoglyceraldehyde dehydrogenase, phosphoglyceryl kinase, phosphoglyceromutase, and enolase appear to be essentially constant across a wide range of species and tissues. Although the reactions catalyzed by these enzymes are usually discussed as a linked progression, they are thought to be coupled only by their common products and reactants: Pette's data suggest that these reactions are much more tightly coupled, perhaps through coordinated synthesis of the respective enzymes.

It is possible to estimate the change in free energy during degradation of glucose to pyruvate by comparing the respective free energies of combustion. $\Delta F°$ for the burning of glucose is -688 kcal/mole, and for the burning of pyruvate the value for 2 moles (comparable to 1 mole of glucose) is -546 kcal; consequently, the overall reaction involves the release of 142 kcal/mole of glucose, or 21% (142/688) of the energy available from combustion of the glucose molecule. In the scheme illustrated in Fig. 6-1, 2 moles of ATP are required to phosphorylate the glucose, and these phosphoryl groups are returned to ATP during the dephosphorylation of phosphoenolpyruvate to pyruvate. *Net* energy capture occurs only during the oxidation of PGAL to PGA, and this amounts to 2 moles of ATP and 2 moles of NADH per glucose molecule. Substituting the energy equivalents for these molecules (ATP = 7 kcal/mole; NADH = 52 kcal/mole) reveals that about 118 of the 142 kcal available are retained as high-energy compounds. The remainder is not necessarily lost to entropy, but may accomplish biologically useful work of a still undefined nature (e.g., in intracellular transport).

The entire series of reactions leading from glucose to pyruvic acid occurs under either aerobic or anaerobic conditions, but the further transformation of pyruvate can follow one of several pathways, depending on the presence of oxygen and specific enzymes. In the absence of oxygen, pyruvate acts as an acceptor for the electrons and protons of NADH produced in the oxidation of PGAL (Fig. 6-1); however, the exact product of pyruvate reduction depends on the particular enzyme system that is present. In muscle preparations, pyruvic acid is reduced to lactic acid by the enzyme lactic dehydrogenase; in yeast preparations, on the other hand, pyruvate decarboxylase catalyzes decarboxylation of pyruvate to form CO_2 and acetaldehyde, and the acetaldehyde is then reduced to alcohol by alcohol dehydrogenase. In both cases, the *net* energy yield for degradation of glucose under anaerobic conditions is diminished because NADH is lost in its reoxidation by pyruvate, and the accumulating reduction products (lactic acid and alcohol) are inaccessible for biological purposes. Consequently, the energy yield for one mole of glucose under anaerobic conditions is only 2 moles of ATP, or 14 kcal; correspondingly, the difference in $\Delta F°$ for combustion of glucose versus lactic acid is only -47 kcal, and for glucose versus alcohol it is -56 kcal. Nevertheless, many cells are able to maintain themselves, and even to carry on growth and reproduction, using this restricted anaerobic source of energy. There is even some reason to believe that the pathway of anaerobic glycolysis may be the most primitive of all energy-trapping systems, and may have constituted the only energy source of the first, emerging life forms.

Aerobic Processes

As early as 1911 it was observed that the substrates most rapidly oxidized aerobically by ground frog muscle preparations are di- and tricarboxylic acids, especially succinate, fumarate, malate, and citrate. Later Martius and Knoop (1937) showed that pyruvic acid can condense *in vitro* with dicarboxylic oxaloacetic acid to form tricarboxylic citric acid; this key observation led Krebs and Johnson (1937) to suggest that the citric acid might then regenerate oxaloacetic by decarboxylation (to CO_2), in essence establishing a cycle in which pyruvate would be used up, CO_2 given off, and succinic, fumaric, and malic acids would constitute intermediate products. Subsequent research has confirmed and elucidated this cycle, which is now variously known as the Krebs cycle, citric acid cycle, TCA or tricarboxylic acid cycle.

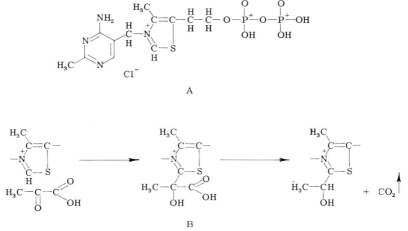

Fig. 6-2. (A) Structure of thiamine pyrophosphate (or cocarboxylase). (B) The action of TPP in the pyruvic decarboxylase reaction.

The initial condensation of pyruvate with oxaloacetate to form citrate and CO_2 was further elucidated by Stern and Ochoa (1949), who showed that *two* reactions are involved:

$$\text{pyruvate} + \text{CoA—SH} + \text{NAD} \rightleftharpoons \text{acetyl—S—CoA} + \text{NADH} + \text{H}^+ + CO_2$$
$$\underline{\text{acetyl—S—CoA} + \text{oxaloacetate} + H_2O \rightleftharpoons \text{citrate} + \text{CoA—SH}}$$
$$\text{pyruvate} + \text{oxaloacetate} + H_2O + \text{NAD} \rightleftharpoons \text{citrate} + \text{NADH} + \text{H}^+ + CO_2$$

The first of these reactions is catalyzed by the pyruvate oxidase complex, and is similar to the anaerobic decarboxylation of pyruvate to form acetaldehyde and carbon dioxide. Both decarboxylations require the cofactors, Mg^{++} and thiamine pyrophosphate (TPP or cocarboxylase), whose structure was worked out by Lohmann and Schuster in 1937 (see Fig. 6-2). Decarboxylation occurs after pyruvate binds to a specific carbon of the thiazole ring in TPP, as shown in Fig. 6-2. In the anaerobic pyruvic decarboxylase reaction, free acetaldehyde is then split from the complex and is usually reduced to alcohol; in the aerobic pyruvate oxidase reaction, on the other hand, a further oxidation occurs, which requires the additional cofactors lipoic acid (Fig. 6-3) and coenzyme A (see Chapter 3). First the acetyl group is transferred to lipoic acid, with reduction of one sulfur group, as shown in Fig. 6-3. Next the acetyl group is transferred from lipoic acid to CoA, forming acetyl-CoA and reducing the other sulfur atom of lipoic acid (Fig. 6-3). Finally, the reduced lipoic acid is reoxidized by NAD, a reaction catalyzed by the flavoprotein α-lipoyl dehydrogenase. Since the energy of acetyl-CoA can be transferred directly to ATP, it is evident that lipoic acid acts as a coupling molecule between an oxidation-reduction reac-

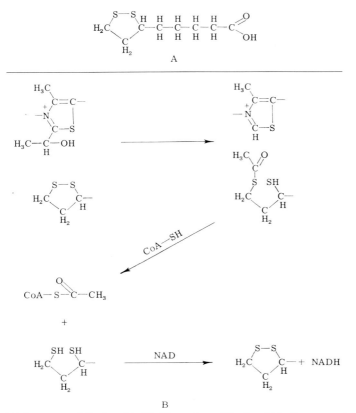

Fig. 6-3. (A) Structure of lipoic acid. (B) The action of lipoic acid in the pyruvate oxidase reaction.

tion and a (potential) phosphorylation; in this respect it resembles phosphoglyceraldehyde dehydrogenase which, like lipoic acid, contains active sulfhydryl groups. For the overall degradation of pyruvate to acetyl-CoA and CO_2, $\Delta F°$ is -62.3 kcal/mole, of which 52 kcal are conserved in NADH. The catalyst pyruvate oxidase includes at least three enzymes, which are organized as a structural complex having a molecular weight of 4×10^6.

The second reaction, in which acetyl-CoA condenses with oxaloacetate to form citric acid, constitutes the primary entrance to the citric acid cycle for fatty acids as well as carbohydrates. As early as 1904, Knoop found evidence that fatty acids are degraded by successive removal of 2-carbon units (β oxidation), and in 1952, Green and Lynen independently succeeded in isolating five enzymes which in combination carry out this β oxidation. In the overall scheme, coenzyme A acts as carrier for the intact fatty acid, which then undergoes successive oxidations

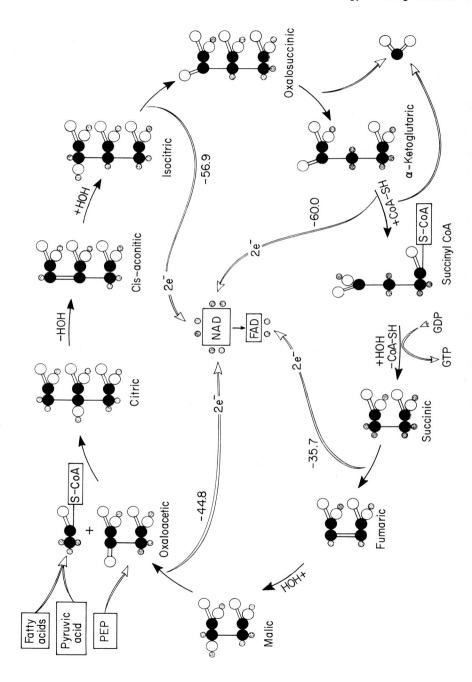

(reducing NAD and FAD), and finally is fractured at the β carbon, yielding acetyl-CoA. Successive repetitions of these events lead to complete degradation of the residual fatty acid chain into two-carbon acetyl-CoA units.

The condensation of acetyl-CoA (2 C) with oxaloacetate (4 C) to form citric acid (6 C) is catalyzed by so-called "condensing enzyme" and is slightly exergonic ($\Delta F° = -7.8$ kcal/mole). After condensation, the reactions of the citric acid cycle lead to regeneration of oxaloacetic acid by two decarboxylations and four dehydrogenations (Fig. 6-4); since acetic acid itself contains only two atoms of oxygen and four of hydrogen, the remaining oxygen and protons are provided from two molecules of water.

The first step after the condensation reaction is an isomerization of citric acid to isocitrate (Fig. 6-4), which is catalyzed by the enzyme aconitase. *Cis*-aconitic acid is usually regarded as an intermediate in this isomerization although there is some evidence that the true intermediate is a charged ion; in any case, the overall reaction is slightly endergonic (1.6 kcal/mole). Isocitrate is then dehydrogenated and decarboxylated to α-ketoglutaric acid in a reaction which is catalyzed by isocitric dehydrogenase, and which under aerobic conditions is strongly exergonic ($\Delta F° = -56.9$ kcal/mole). Since the enzyme also accepts oxalosuccinic acid as substrate, oxalosuccinate is presumably an intermediate; however, it remains bound in the enzyme complex and cannot be detected as a free product. Two different isocitric dehydrogenases occur, a mitochondrial one that requires NAD as specific hydrogen acceptor and a cytoplasmic one that requires NADP.

Next, α-ketoglutaric acid is dehydrogenated and decarboxylated by α-ketoglutaric dehydrogenase; this reaction yields succinyl-CoA and is also strongly exergonic ($\Delta F° = -60.0$ kcal/mole). The reaction requires lipoic acid and thiamine pyrophosphate as cofactors, uses NAD as hydrogen acceptor, and is entirely homologous with the pyruvic oxidase reaction discussed above (in which pyruvic acid is dehydrogenated and decarboxylated to yield *acetyl*-CoA). The succinyl-CoA produced in this step is hydrolyzed to succinate and CoA in a reaction catalyzed by succinic thiokinase and coupled to the phosphorylation of GDP (a substrate-level phosphorylation, equivalent to the production of 1 mole of ATP; see Fig. 6-4).

Succinate is next dehydrogenated by the flavoprotein enzyme succinic

Fig. 6-4. Reactions of the citric acid cycle (or Krebs cycle), during which the acetyl group of acetyl-CoA is oxidized to carbon dioxide. The major energy-yielding steps are four dehydrogenase reactions, coupled with electron flow to NAD and FAD. Black circles are carbon, white circles oxygen, and stippled circles hydrogen.

dehydrogenase (mol. wt. 200,000), producing fumaric acid in a mildly exergonic reaction ($\Delta F^\circ = -35.7$ kcal/mole). This is the only one of the four dehydrogenations in the citric acid cycle which does not use pyridine nucleotides as hydrogen acceptors; in this case the acceptor is the enzyme's own FAD and the electrons subsequently flow to cytochrome b. The fumaric acid is next hydrated to malic acid by fumarase (mol. wt. 200,000; $\Delta F^\circ = -0.9$ kcal/mole), and the malic acid is then dehydrogenated by malic dehydrogenase to regenerate oxaloacetic acid ($\Delta F^\circ = -44.8$ kcal/mole). It should be noted that the activity ratios of succinic dehydrogenase and malic dehydrogenase, together with pyruvate oxidase, cytochrome a, cytochrome c, and glutamate oxaloacetate transaminase, have been found to be approximately constant across a wide range of cell types (Pette et al., 1962); this interrelated group of enzymes is comparable to the previously mentioned "constant proportion group" which occurs in anaerobic glycolysis.

To summarize the oxidative processes, transformations catalyzed by pyruvate oxidase and the citric acid cycle enzymes result in the degradation of one molecule of pyruvic acid (3 C), with the release of three molecules of carbon dioxide (3 × 1 C), four molecules of reduced pyridine nucleotide, one molecule of reduced FAD, and one molecule of ATP (substrate-level phosphorylation). The overall ΔF° for combustion of 1 mole of pyruvic acid is -273 kcal, but in the citric acid cycle this large packet of energy is released in five smaller dehydrogenation steps having ΔF° values of -62.3, -56.9, -60.0, -35.7, and -44.8, respectively. The reduced pyridine nucleotide and FAD are reoxidized through the cytochrome system with the formation of water and coupled phosphorylation (to be discussed in the next section). It can be assumed that each mole of reduced pyridine nucleotide from the oxidative processes leads to phosphorylation of three moles of ATP (Chapter 3), each mole of reduced FAD leads to phosphorylation of two moles of ATP, and each mole of NADH from anaerobic glycolysis leads to phosphorylation of two moles of ATP; the overall energy recovery from glucose metabolism may then be expressed in ATP units (see tabulation).

1 glucose $\longrightarrow$	2 pyruvic acid	6 ATP
2 pyruvate $\longrightarrow$	2 acetyl-CoA	6
2 acetyl-CoA $\longrightarrow$	2 α-ketoglutaric	6
2 α-ketoglutaric $\longrightarrow$	2 succinyl-CoA	6
2 succinyl-CoA $\longrightarrow$	2 succinate	2
2 succinate $\longrightarrow$	2 fumaric	4
2 fumaric $\longrightarrow$	2 oxaloacetic	6
		36 ATP $= \dfrac{252}{688} = 37\%$

It should not be assumed that the remaining 63% of glucose energy is lost to entropy; Lehninger (1964) has emphasized that in living cells much of this energy may actually be converted into other forms of biologically useful work, such as intracellular transport. There is strong evidence that this is so in the case of NADH from anaerobic glycolysis, which is usually estimated to yield only 2 ATP units compared with 3 ATP units for NADH from the citric acid cycle. The remaining ATP equivalent can be accounted for as energy expended in transport to the cytochrome chain.

The citric acid cycle can be entered by pathways other than through acetyl-CoA condensation. For example, the hydrolysis of protein yields amino acids, and deamination of the amino acid glutamate produces α-ketoglutaric acid directly; similarly, deamination of aspartic acid yields oxaloacetic acid, while alanine is converted by deamination to pyruvate. Phosphoenolpyruvate can also be carboxylated by the enzymes, PEP carboxylase or PEP carboxykinase, to form oxaloacetic acid directly (see page 72); pyruvate can be carboxylated by malic enzyme to yield malic acid (a reaction requiring NADPH). Still another pathway involves the fragmentation of isocitrate into succinate and glyoxylate, followed by condensation of acetyl-CoA with glyoxylate to form malic acid. Further details of these reactions can be found in biochemistry texts.

It should also be noted that the entire pathway from glucose to pyruvic acid and through the citric acid cycle can be bypassed by means of the aerobic pentose shunt reactions. In the pathways of photosynthetic carbon dioxide fixation, the pentose sugar ribulose phosphate undergoes phosphorylation, carboxylation, fragmentation, and reduction to produce two molecules of phosphoglyceraldehyde; later reactions can form either hexose or pentose from PGAL (Chapter 4). In many nonphotosynthetic cells, the effect of these reactions is approximately reversed, leading to decarboxylation of glucose 6-phosphate to form ribulose phosphate, and reorganization of the ribulose through phosphoglyceraldehyde to form hexose. Consequently, it is possible for six molecules of glucose 6-phosphate to become reorganized into five molecules of glucose 6-phosphate plus six carbon dioxide molecules (each CO_2 incorporating the C-1 carbon from a different hexose). The energy yield from these conversions is 12 moles of NADPH, equivalent to 24–36 moles of ATP, and the scheme totally bypasses pyruvic acid and the citric acid cycle. Evidence indicates that this mechanism is an important source of energy in leukocytes, mammary glands, and mature leaf tissue.

OXIDATION OF NADH WITH COUPLED PHOSPHORYLATION

Regardless of the pathways by which biological substrates are metabolized, a nearly universal feature is the transfer of electrons and hydrogen to pyridine nucleotides. The release of energy from reduced pyridine nucleotides, in turn, involves the transfer of these electrons to atmospheric oxygen, with formation of polar bonds between the oxygen and hydrogen:

$$NADH + H^+ + 1/2\ O_2 \longrightarrow NAD + H_2O \qquad \Delta F° = -52\ kcal/mole$$

During the 1930's it was understood that flavoproteins and cytochromes are intermediates in this oxidation (see Chapter 3), i.e., electrons from reduced NADH are not transferred directly to oxygen, but flow "downhill" through a graded series of oxidation-reduction reactions. Only the terminal member of this "electron transport chain" reacts with atmospheric oxygen, and this is the famous, autoxidizable *"Atmungsferment"* of Warburg or "cytochrome oxidase" of Keilin (Chapter 3). The standard free energy change for each intermediate electron transfer between NADH and O_2 is determined by the E_0 values of the particular electron donor and acceptor involved; E_0 for most of the cytochromes and NAD was first determined by Ball (1938, 1939), and it was postulated that the sequence of intermediate oxidation-reductions is the same as the sequence of E_0 values (although for coupled reactions this is not necessarily so, because the real ΔF depends on the concentrations of the reactants). Nevertheless, Chance and Williams (1956) confirmed by direct spectrophotometry of living cells that, after total reduction of the chain, the electron carriers are in fact reoxidized sequentially in the order of their E_0 values:

Substrate $\longrightarrow$ NAD $\longrightarrow$ FAD protein $\longrightarrow$ CoQ $\longrightarrow$ Cyt b $\longrightarrow$

$\qquad\qquad\quad$ −0.32 V $\qquad\qquad$ 0.0 V $\qquad\qquad\qquad\qquad$ +0.04 V

Cyt c_1 $\longrightarrow$ Cyt c $\longrightarrow$ Cyt a $\longrightarrow$ Cyt a_3 $\longrightarrow$ O_2

$\qquad\qquad$ +0.26 V $\qquad$ +0.29 V $\qquad\qquad\qquad$ +0.82 V

For example, under the conditions of Chance's experiment, all the cytochrome c becomes reoxidized before any of the cytochrome b. Chance and Williams (1955) also determined that, at maximum respiration rates (abundant substrate, oxygen, and ADP), the percentage reduction of the carriers shows a gradient:

NAD	FADprotein	cyt b	cyt c	cyt a	
53%	20%	16%	6%	<4%	reduced

This gradient is markedly influenced by the concentrations of ADP, ATP, and phosphate—that is, by the ratio $[ATP]/([ADP][P_i])$ (see page 17).

A relationship between respiration and phosphorylation was first discovered by Kalckar (1937), who showed that oxidation of pyruvic acid in muscle preparations can be energetically coupled with the phosphorylation of hexose (at the expense of inorganic phosphate); this "oxidative phosphorylation" was shown to be distinct from the anaerobic phosphorylations that occur in glycolysis. Thus:

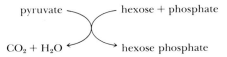

pyruvate ⟶ hexose + phosphate

$CO_2 + H_2O$ ⟷ hexose phosphate

Following further development of the electron transport concept by Ball (1938), Belitzer and Tsibakowa (1939) proposed on theoretical grounds that each step in the electron transport chain might be coupled with a phosphorylation, and they were the first to measure the ratio of phosphorus esterified to oxygen consumed (P/O ratio). Belitzer found a P/O ratio of at least 2; subsequently Ochoa (1943), correcting for loss of some observable phosphorylation by residual ATPase activity, concluded that the P/O ratio must be 3. Much more detailed evidence has now confirmed that the oxidation of one mole of NADH by the electron transport chain is ordinarily coupled with the phosphorylation of 3 moles of ADP; the ATP formed in this way is the major energy product of substrate oxidation. However, phosphorylation is not a requirement for electron transport, since a number of reagents are known (most notably 2,4-dinitrophenol) which "uncouple" phosphorylation without impairing the pathway of oxidation.

Considerable effort has been directed toward discovering which of the several intermediate oxidation-reduction reactions are coupled with ATP phosphorylation. Since ΔF° for phosphorylation is +7 kcal/mole, some of the reactions are unlikely on energetic grounds; for instance, the oxidation of cytochrome c ($E_0 = 0.26$ V) by cytochrome a ($E = 0.29$ V) yields only:

$$\Delta F^\circ = -1 \ (23.068 \ \text{kcal/volt}) \ 0.03 \ \text{V}$$
$$= -0.7 \ \text{kcal/mole}$$

On the other hand, the oxidation of NADH by flavoprotein has a ΔF° of -12 kcal/mole (see Chapter 3), and in this case a coupled phosphorylation would certainly be energetically feasible. It should be understood that this type of calculation yields only tentative conclusions, since the actual ΔF values depend on the concentrations of oxidized and reduced reactants; furthermore, since the various electron transport steps are coupled together by the flow of electrons, even highly improbable endergonic reactions could be driven by neighboring exergonic steps.

Experimental isolation of reactions with coupled phosphorylations has proved difficult, since the capacity for oxidative phosphorylation depends on intact structural units and does not survive in solution (Chapter 7). However, Nielsen and Lehninger (1954) were able to establish that oxidation of pure reduced cytochrome c by atmospheric oxygen in rat liver preparations is accompanied by phosphorylation with a P/O ratio of 0.8; by contrast, oxidation of substrate (β-hydroxybutyrate) by oxidized cytochrome c has a P/O ratio approaching 2. These two experiments indicate that one phosphorylation site is between cytochrome c and oxygen, while two sites lie between cytochrome c and substrate. More precise localizations are suggested by the spectrophotometric analysis of Chance and Williams (1955), who found that a deficiency of ADP inhibits electron transfer at three points in the chain: (1) between NADH and flavoprotein (site I); (2) between cytochrome b and cytochrome c (site II); and (3) between cytochrome c and oxygen (site III).

More recently Green and his collaborators have shown that the electron transport chain can be isolated in the form of four multienzyme complexes. These include: (1) an NADH dehydrogenase–CoQ reductase complex; (2) a CoQ oxidase–cytochrome c reductase complex (including cytochrome b); and (3) a cytochrome oxidase complex (cytochromes a and a_3). The fourth complex is a succinic dehydrogenase–CoQ reductase, which catalyzes the dehydrogenation of succinic acid in the Krebs cycle and couples it *in situ* with electron transport to cytochrome b (and CoQ). Green has speculated that each of these four complexes *in vivo* may carry out a single coupled phosphorylation, a possibility that will be discussed further in the next chapter.

THE MECHANISM OF COUPLED PHOSPHORYLATION

Coupling of ADP phosphorylation with oxidation-reduction reactions occurs not only in oxidative phosphorylation, but also in photosynthetic phosphorylation (Chapter 4) and in substrate level phosphorylation (e.g., the oxidation of phosphoglyceraldehyde during anaerobic glycolysis, and of α-ketoglutaric acid in the Krebs cycle). Although it is not known whether the basic mechanism of coupling is the same in all these instances, the two substrate-level phosphorylations proceed on very similar principles, and they are by far the best understood; consequently they have served as models for speculation in the other two cases.

On theoretical grounds, the coupling of any two reactions requires an intermediate compound common to both (see Chapter 3); in theory therefore, the simplest mechanism of coupled phosphorylation would proceed by phosphorylation of an electron carrier, with subsequent phosphoryl transfer to ADP:

$$AH + B + phosphate \longrightarrow A\text{-}phosphate + BH$$
$$A\text{-}phosphate + ADP \longrightarrow ATP + A$$

Evidence that this simplest mechanism occurs has been found by Griffiths and Chaplain (1962), who reported the discovery of a labile phosphoryl-NAD (not NADP) which is formed during the oxidation of succinate by a heart muscle preparation; this compound, whose formation requires electron transport, was also shown to form ATP in the presence of ADP and phosphate. Further evidence supporting a simple coupling mechanism is based on the fact that, in both oxidative and photophosphorylation, quinol-quinones such as plastoquinone and coenzyme Q appear to function as electron carriers; that quinol phosphates can act as coupling intermediates has been suggested by Wieland and Patterman (1959), who showed that the oxidation of quinol phosphate leads to the formation of high-energy pyrophosphate:

$$HO-\underset{}{\bigcirc}-O-PO_3H_2 + P_i \longrightarrow O=\underset{}{\bigcirc}=O + PP$$

Wieland has also demonstrated that oxidation of ^{32}P-labeled coenzyme Q-phosphate by an appropriate cell fraction leads to formation of ^{32}P-labeled ATP with a P/O ratio between 1 and 2. With regard to phosphorylation coupled with cytochrome oxidation, Calvin (1963) has suggested that ferrous iron–phosphate intermediates may occur, and this suggestion is supported by Barltrop's observation that the oxidation of ferrous ion by hydrogen peroxide in the presence of orthophosphate leads to the generation of high-energy pyrophosphate.

Whether or not these simple mechanisms occur, the mechanics of substrate-level phosphorylation are known to be considerably more complex. The oxidation of PGAL, for instance, is thought to proceed by formation of an acyl thioester, followed by oxidation of the thioester by NAD, substitution of inorganic phosphate at the thioester bond, and finally transfer of phosphoryl to ATP (see page 106). In the oxidation of α-ketoglutaric acid, although entirely different cofactors are involved, very similar steps occur: the decarboxylated substrate forms an acyl thioester linkage, first with lipoic acid and then with coenzyme A, leading to the reduction of lipoic acid; the lipoic acid is then reoxidized by NAD while inorganic phosphate is substituted at the thioester bond of the acyl-CoA; finally phosphoryl is transferred to ATP via GTP. Extensive analysis of oxidative phosphorylation, using specific inhibitors, isotopic tracers, and kinetic measurements, indicates that coupling of phosphorylation here too involves a complex set of intermediate reactions. For instance, phosphorylation may be uncoupled by 2,4-dinitrophenol without impairing electron transport, whereas a number of partial intermediate reactions of phosphorylation (e.g., exchange of ^{32}P between ATP and inorganic phosphate; reversible incorporation of labeled ADP into ATP) can be detected in the absence of net electron transport. These facts indicate that in oxidative phosphorylation the electron carriers themselves are not the phosphorylated intermediates.

In photophosphorylation too, Hind and Jagendorf (1963) have shown that the phosphorylation process itself involves both "light" and "dark" reactions; the light reaction does not require phosphate or ADP, but results in accumulation of a labile intermediate (presumably non-phosphorylated) compound; in the dark this compound can supply energy for phosphorylation of ATP. Although the half-life of the intermediate is less than a second, enough can accumulate to phosphorylate one ATP for every 15 chlorophyll molecules.

Lehninger (1965), Racker (1965), and others have postulated various complex schemes for oxidative phosphorylation, most of which are heavily based on the known mechanisms of substrate-level phosphorylation. In one such scheme, the following reaction series is visualized:

$$AH_2 + I \rightleftharpoons AH_2\text{-}I$$
$$AH_2\text{-}I + B \rightleftharpoons A\text{-}I + BH_2$$
$$A\text{-}I + phosphate \rightleftharpoons I\text{-}phosphate + A$$
$$I\text{-}phosphate + ADP \rightleftharpoons ATP + I$$

In this hypothetical scheme of oxidative phosphorylation, A and B represent two successive members of the electron transport chain, and I is an unknown intermediate. However, nearly the same equations can represent the known mechanisms of substrate-level phosphorylation; in this case, the compound $AH_2\text{-}I$ stands for reduced acyl-thioester, and compound B represents NAD.

There have been extensive efforts to isolate the hypothetical compound I, which is responsible for coupling phosphorylation with electron transport. Pinchot and Hormanski (1962) discovered a soluble, heat-labile fraction (protein) which is necessary for phosphorylation, and is apparently bound to the electron transport structure by means of a polynucleotide molecule. During oxidation of NADH, this soluble protein forms a covalent linkage with NAD; if the NAD-protein complex is then incubated with ADP and phosphate, ATP is formed and NAD released. A similar factor which forms a complex with cytochrome c during electron transport has been found by D. E. Green, and this complex has also been shown to mediate phosphorylation of ADP. Analogous behavior characterizes the high-energy intermediate detected in photophosphorylation by Hind and Jagendorf (see above).

Since the mechanisms of oxidative phosphorylation are not yet definitely known, it is not known whether the same type of coupling system operates at all three phosphorylation sites. Although all the sites are uncoupled by 2,4-dinitrophenol, they differ in pH sensitivity and in other respects; furthermore, the NADH-flavoprotein site is thought to involve a 2-electron reaction, whereas the cytochrome sites apparently carry out single-electron oxidation-reductions. The energetics of $\Delta F°$ values would suggest that the reduction of two cytochrome molecules might be coupled to the phosphorylation of one ADP molecule, but it is not clear how this might be accomplished. (A related problem is the mechanism by which cytochrome oxidase carries out the reduction of one molecule of atmospheric oxygen, O_2, requiring the transfer of 4 electrons.) The role of lipid-phase reactions in coupled phosphorylation also remains to be elucidated; Slater (1962) has shown that the activity of dinitrophenol derivatives in uncoupling phosphorylation increases with their lipid solubility, and it is also well known that coenzyme Q, which appears to function as an electron carrier in the chain, is relatively insoluble in water. The energetics of phosphorylation would be drastically altered in a nonaqueous medium (since water is a product of the reaction), and the new equilibrium would be expected to favor ATP formation (see Chapter 3).

Bioluminescence

The emission of light by living organisms is achieved through a great variety of biochemical mechanisms, but in most or all instances these mechanisms (1) depend on electron flow; (2) are coupled with one or more of the familiar high-energy intermediates NAD, FMN, or ATP; and (3) involve the reduction of molecular oxygen by electrons derived from a specialized substrate. In these respects, bioluminescence reactions can be regarded as similar in kind to the oxidative reactions already discussed.

Considered at the level of the whole organism, bioluminescence is an exciting and beautiful phenomenon which attracted scientific attention as early as 1668 (when Boyle found that the light from putrifying wood or fish disappears in the absence of air). Luminescence is apparently lacking in land vertebrates (amphibians, reptiles, birds, mammals) and in higher plants, but otherwise it occurs willy-nilly from bacteria to fishes; curiously the effect shows very little phylogenetic trend, often being present in one species and lacking in other closely related species. The luminescence is more or less continuous in bacteria, fungi, and a few other forms, whereas in most higher animals light emission occurs as a flash, or a series of flashes, of less than a second's duration. The light is always colored, most often in the blues and greens, but occasionally in the yellow, orange, and red. A few forms are able to emit different colors from different light organs on the same individual: for instance the "railroad worm" of Brazil (an insect larva) has green lights on the sides and a red light on the head; similarly, a so-called "automobile bug" exists which has green "parking lights" and a yellow or orange "headlight."

The biological function of the luminescence is also variable. In many cases the lights serve as sexual stimuli or mating cues; in other species, luminescence is employed to confuse predators or to attract prey; in still other instances the light may actually be used as an aid to vision. A fascinating example of the latter type occurs in the deep-sea fish *Photoblepharon*, which has evolved a light organ immediately beneath each eye; in this fish light is produced continuously by symbiotic bacteria "cultured" in the light organ, while the fish itself is able to control light emission by a special mask or shade arrangement!

LUCIFERIN–LUCIFERASE REACTIONS

Dubois (1887) was the first to carry out a significant experimental analysis of bioluminescence. In a pioneer investigation with fireflies and molluscs, he found that the luminescent effect could be obtained *in vitro* by extracting the light organs in cold water; such aqueous extracts would glow for a time and then be extinguished. Two additional properties of the reaction were that it was abolished by heat, but that a "dark" hot water extract was able to restore luminescence in an "old" cold water extract. These results indicated that luminescence requires at least two factors, one a heat-sensitive enzyme and the other its heat-stable substrate. Dubois therefore named the substrate luciferin (present in hot water extracts) and the enzyme luciferase (surviving in cold water extracts). Since Dubois's time it has been found that a luciferin–luciferase type reaction is responsible for bioluminescence in at least eleven different kinds of organism. However the chemical nature of the two compounds differs considerably in different phyla, so that cross-reactions generally cannot be obtained. In addition to luciferin and luciferase, oxygen and various other molecules are usually required.

Perhaps the simplest of the luciferin-luciferase mechanisms has been found in the ostracod crustacean *Cypridina*. This organism luminesces by a straightforward oxidation of reduced luciferin according to the scheme:

$$H_2\text{-luciferin} + 1/2\ O_2 \xrightarrow{\text{luciferase}} \text{luciferin} + H_2O + \text{light}$$

The luciferin, which behaves as a high-energy oxidation-reduction intermediate, has been crystallized by Shimomura *et al.* (1957), and its structural formula has been worked out by Hirata *et al.* (1959) (Fig. 6-5).

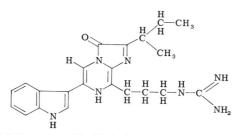

Fig. 6-5. Structure of luciferin from the crustacean, *Cypridina.*

The *Cypridina* luciferase has also been considerably purified by Shimomura *et al.* (1961), who have estimated the molecular weight of the enzyme to be 48,500–53,000 and the isoelectric point to be pH 4.34. Light emitted during the oxidation of *Cypridina* luciferin has an emission maximum at about 465 mμ (blue), while the reaction itself shows a pH optimum at 7.3. It is of interest that the ratio of light quanta emitted to molecules of luciferin oxidized is only about 0.29, indicating a relatively low efficiency.

Sie *et al.* (1961) have found that certain luminescent fish seem to possess a luciferin–luciferase system virtually identical to that of *Cypridina.* The fish luciferin reacts perfectly well with the crustacean luciferase, and the emission spectrum of the reaction is also virtually the same for all combinations between fish and crustacean. A related but not identical reaction also occurs in the dinoflagellates *Noctiluca* and *Gonyaulax.* These marine protozoans often occur in huge numbers, producing a luminescent glow when they are disturbed by fish, ships, or wave action; the effect, as of "burning seas," was a marvel to early mariners until the development of microscopy revealed the presence of protozoans in enormous numbers. Available evidence indicates that the luminescent reaction in these organisms is also a simple oxidation of reduced luciferin, but the chemical nature of the luciferin is not known and it does not cross-react with *Cypridina* luciferase. DeSa *et al.* (1963) have reported that the actual sources of light in *Gonyaulax* are tiny crystalline bodies about 0.3–0.6 μ long, which they have named "scintillons."

In fireflies and certain other organisms, ATP is required for luminescence in addition to a reduced luciferin and luciferase. This reaction has been extensively analyzed by McElroy and his collaborators, who have shown that two steps are involved:

$$\text{luciferase} + \text{H}_2\text{-luciferin} + \text{ATP} \underset{}{\overset{\text{Mg}^{++}}{\rightleftharpoons}} \text{luciferase–H}_2\text{-luciferyl adenylate} + \text{PP}$$

$$\text{luciferase–H}_2\text{-luciferyl adenylate} + \text{O}_2 \rightleftharpoons \text{luciferase–luciferyl adenylate} + \text{H}_2\text{O} + \text{light}$$

$$\text{luciferase} + \text{H}_2\text{-luciferin} + \text{ATP} \rightleftharpoons \text{luciferase–luciferyl adenylate} + \text{H}_2\text{O} + \text{PP} + \text{light}$$

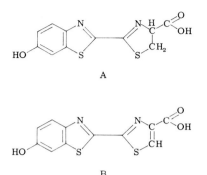

A

B

Fig. 6-6. Structures of reduced (A) and oxidized (B) luciferin from the firefly, *Pyrophorus*.

The luciferin of this system was first crystallized by Bitler and McElroy (1957), and its structural formula has been confirmed in a total synthesis by White *et al.* (1961); the reduced and oxidized forms have the structures shown in Fig. 6-6. Firefly luciferase has also been crystallized by Green and McElroy (1956), who found that the molecular weight of the enzyme is about 100,000, the isoelectric point about pH 6.2–6.3, and the pH optimum of the reaction about 7.8. It is obvious that both the luciferin and luciferase of fireflies are chemically unlike the corresponding compounds in *Cypridina*, and they differ also in their highly specific requirement for ATP; neither ADP, GTP, UTP, ITP, pyrophosphate, acetyl phosphate or phosphocreatine will serve to activate the firefly luminescence. In fact, this reaction has been widely used as an assay technique for detecting small amounts of ATP photometrically. In the presence of ATP the firefly system emits one light quantum (photon) for every molecule of luciferin oxidized (Seliger and McElroy, 1960). An ATP-dependent bioluminescence has also been found in the sea anemone *Renilla*, but this system differs in emission spectrum and other features from that of fireflies.

Thanks to the successful chemical characterization of firefly luciferin and luciferase, a fairly sophisticated molecular analysis of the reaction has been possible. Seliger and McElroy were able to demonstrate that synthetic luciferyl adenylate can react with luciferase to produce light in the absence of ATP; this indicates that the role of ATP in the native reaction is to adenylate luciferin, in a manner analogous to the activation of amino acids for protein synthesis (Chapter 14). The site of the adenyl linkage has been tentatively established as the luciferin carboxyl group (Fig. 6-6). Subsequently the same authors (1962) found that luciferyl adenylate will luminesce nonenzymatically (i.e., in the absence of luciferase) on addition of solid KOH, provided that the system is stabilized by solution in (nonaqueous) dimethyl sulfoxide. From these results they have concluded that the action of luciferase (like KOH) is to remove a proton, making it possible for oxygen to attack the luciferyl adenylate molecule. The fact that the enzyme reaction proceeds in two steps was demonstrated by contrasting the reactions of d- and l-stereoisomers of luciferin; the l-isomer can form luciferyl adenylate and complex with luciferase, but it cannot react with oxygen to emit light.

Some variation occurs in the color of light emitted by different species of firefly, the emission maximum ranging from 543 to 582 mμ (green to bright yellow). Since cross-reactions between the luciferin of one firefly and the luciferase of another are practical, Seliger and McElroy (1964) have been able to show that, in hybrid reactions, it is the enzyme which determines the color of light emitted; by contrast, the various firefly luciferins appear to be structurally identical. Further evidence for the influence of enzyme configuration on the color of light emitted has been obtained by varying the pH of the reaction *in vitro* (recall that the isoelectric point of firefly luciferase is about pH 6.3). Above pH 6.5 the *in vivo* emission spectrum is obtained, while at lower pH's there is a shift toward a low-intensity emission maximum at 616 mμ (in the red). It appears that the actual source of energy for light emission in fireflies is luciferyl adenylate, but that the light-emitting molecule is the luciferase–luciferyl adenylate complex.

BIOLUMINESCENCE REACTIONS THAT DIFFER FROM LUCIFERIN–LUCIFERASE SYSTEMS

Luminescence in a number of species is now known to be produced either in the absence of a special "luciferin" substrate, or in the absence of a specific enzyme. Of these systems, the best known is that of luminescent bacteria, which typically emit light continuously in the presence of oxygen and appropriate metabolic substrates. The bacterial system was not obtained *in vitro* until 1951, when it was found that luminescence requires an enzyme (luciferase) plus reduced flavin mononucleotide (FMNH$_2$) and a long-chain aldehyde. The exact fate of the aldehyde is still unknown, so that the reaction can only be approximated as:

$$\text{FMNH}_2 + \text{R}\overset{\displaystyle\text{O}}{\overset{\|}{-\text{CH}}} + 1/2\ \text{O}_2 \xrightarrow{\text{luciferase}} \text{FMN} + \text{H}_2\text{O} + \text{products} + \text{light}$$

However, it is clear that the source of reduced FMNH$_2$ for this reaction is the ordinary metabolic oxidation of substrates via the Krebs cycle. When the available substrates are used up (such as glucose), luminescence quickly ceases; in this respect bacterial luminescence is clearly different from that in luciferin–luciferase systems, where luciferin is "stockpiled" as a specific substrate and light emission is a form of activity which appears only at specific times. By contrast, luminescence in bacteria is a metabolic phenomenon, which provides a means for the cell to bypass the cytochrome chain but which has no clear adaptive significance. Although the emission spectrum varies somewhat from one species to another, the maximum is usually in the region 465–490 $m\mu$. Some purification of bacterial luciferase has been achieved, and the molecular weight has been estimated by ultracentrifugation as about 85,000.

The role of the aldehyde in bacterial luminescence is a highly intriguing one. It was found very early that no specific aldehyde is required, but that the intensity of light emitted increases with the length of the aldehyde carbon chain. Later Cormier and Totter (1957) showed that the aldehyde is used up in the reaction and that only saturated aldehydes are acceptable. In a limiting reaction the total light produced is proportional to the amount of aldehyde present, one quantum being emitted for about 20 molecules of aldehyde expended. More recently Hastings and Gibson (1963) have succeeded in showing that several steps are involved in the overall reaction, and that the aldehyde participates at a relatively late stage. The first step involves the reduction of luciferase at the expense of $FMNH_2$; the reduced enzyme then reacts with oxygen to form a "reduced enzyme–oxygen" complex. This latter intermediate has been isolated and shown to emit light in the total absence of aldehyde. However under these conditions the amount of light produced is comparatively slight, attaining a maximum of about one photon per three molecules of $FMNH_2$ oxidized; in the presence of aldehyde, on the other hand, this intermediate produces much more light in a reaction which is essentially anaerobic, i.e., this final stage does not require atmospheric oxygen.

Many fungi also exhibit continuous, or metabolic, light emission. Although it has been shown that fungal luminescence requires neither $FMNH_2$ nor a long-chain aldehyde, there is a requirement for NADH or NADPH. Through these compounds, then, light emission in fungi is closely linked with substrate oxidation in a manner fundamentally similar to the coupling in bacterial systems. Whether electron flow in the luminescence reaction of fungi also involves a specific luciferin, such as *Cypridina* luciferin (which would be reduced by the NADH), remains to be determined.

In two genera of jellyfish, *Aequorea* and *Halistaurea,* Shimomura et al. (1963) have recently demonstrated an altogether unique mechanism of bioluminescence which does not require oxygen at all; the intensity of light production is identical in pure oxygen, pure hydrogen or in a vacuum. This luminescence depends on a specific protein in each genus which has the property of emitting light on exposure to calcium ions. Since the intensity of light production falls off with time according to the kinetics of a first-order reaction, it appears that these two proteins (aequorin and halistaurin) do not function as enzymes. Furthermore, from an analysis of the luminescent emission spectrum, together with the absorption and fluorescence spectra of the purified proteins, Shimomura has concluded that both compounds contain an NADH group which changes to NAD in the course of the reaction. Presumably light production is brought about by an intramolecular rearrangement, which results in a change in the energy state of the molecule together with emission of light quanta. Since the emission spectrum is very similar to the fluorescence spectrum of NADH, it is likely that this cofactor is the actual emitting component. Aequorin has been estimated to have a total molecular weight of about 35,000.

7

MITOCHONDRIA AND RELATED ORGANELLES

> . . . mitochondria (can) be visualized as microscopic power plants where the energy of molecular oxygen is ultimately transferred and utilized.
>
> A. CLAUDE *1948*

Just as the enzymes, pigments and structural requirements for photosynthesis are localized in chloroplasts, so the machinery for the oxidative reactions of the citric acid and fatty acid cycles, together with electron transport and coupled phosphorylation, are localized in mitochondria. Historically speaking this localization was not nearly so evident in the case of mitochondria as with chloroplasts; the general appearance of mitochondria, as viewed with the light microscope, is one of tiny, nondescript granules or threads, and in fact their reality as cell organelles was in serious question during the first part of the 20th century. It was not until 1948 that the significance of mitochondria as sites of cellular respiration was clearly demonstrated.

The mitochondria of muscle cells are particularly prominent, and under the term "sarcosomes" they received the early attention of Kölliker and other cytologists during the last half of the 19th century. It was Benda (1897) who introduced the term "mitochondrion" to designate threadlike granules which he found in many cells and which he believed to constitute part of the hereditary mechanism. About the same time, Michaelis (1900) found that the mitochondria can be stained specifically *in vivo* by the oxidation-reduction indicator Janus green B, and Lewis and Lewis (1914) later made extensive observations of mitochondria in living cells, emphasizing their sensitivity to metabolic conditions. Unfortunately, the situation was confused by cytologists who maintained that these objects were symbiotic bacteria or artifacts. Meves (1918) believed like Benda that mitochondria form part of the hereditary mechanism, and he reported that they differentiate into muscle and nerve fibrils as well as into the basal bodies of cilia. In 1934, Bensley and Hoerr became the first to isolate mitochondria in bulk by differential centrifugation of a tissue homogenate; although they carried out no physiological experiments, their work served to pioneer a new approach.

The actual significance of mitochondria was discovered not by cytologists, but by biochemists and physiologists. As early as 1912, Kingsbury suggested that mitochondria might be sites of cellular oxidation, and about the same time Warburg (1913) noted that most of the oxygen uptake by liver extracts was associated with large granules. Attempts by many investigators to isolate the reactions involved in substrate oxidation invariably showed that these reactions are tightly bound to insoluble components of the cell. The first successful cell-free system of this type was an insoluble preparation, isolated from heart muscle by Keilin and Hartree (1938), which was able to carry out the aerobic oxidation of succinic acid (succinoxidase activity). Later Green *et al.* (1948) developed a cell-free "cyclophorase" system from rabbit kidney, which contained the entire citric acid cycle together with the cytochrome chain, and was capable of catalyzing the oxidation of pyruvic acid to CO_2 and water. (Neither of these systems, however, was able to carry out coupled phosphorylation.)

The association of respiratory activity specifically with mitochondria was first demonstrated by Hogeboom *et al.* (1948), building on the earlier work of Claude (1941). The key to their success was the use of sucrose solution instead of isotonic NaCl as an isolation medium—a technical advance which permitted them to obtain a bulk centrifugation fraction that not only showed succinoxidase activity, but also contained rod-shaped particles stainable with Janus green B. Soon afterward Lehninger and Kennedy (1948), using the technique of Hogeboom *et al.*, reported that the mitochondrial fraction catalyzes all the reactions of the citric acid cycle, fatty acid oxidation, and, of even greater significance, coupled phosphorylation. The development of this cell-free mitochondrial system was an achievement entirely comparable with Arnon's demonstration of photosynthesis by isolated chloroplasts (see Arnon *et al.*, 1954), and in a similar manner it opened the way for detailed analysis of mitochondrial composition, physiology, and functional organization.

The mitochondria of many cells are filamentous or threadlike bodies, 0.2–1 μ in diameter and perhaps 3–10 μ in length; a typical cell may average 300–800 mitochondria. In rat liver, these organelles account for as much as 35% of the total protein and 22% of the cytoplasmic volume; according to Michejda (1964), the sarcosomes of insect flight muscle may constitute as much as one-third of the total muscle volume. On the other hand, some algal cells are known which contain only a single mitochondrion.

Within a given cell, considerable variation occurs in the length of mitochondria, the shorter ones being spherical with diameters about the same as the width of the filamentous ones. Lewis and Lewis (1914) observed that living mitochondria change shape frequently, that filaments may fragment into several spheres, and that such changes are reversible, the spheres fusing again into filaments. Such fragmentation and fusion phenomena have been amply confirmed and even filmed, thanks to the introduction of the phase contrast microscope in 1934. In highly differentiated cells, mitochondria may occur with exotic forms, e.g., the helical mitochondria of spermatozoa, saclike or stellate sarcosomes in muscle, and ring-shaped forms which occur surrounding lipid droplets in pancreatic cells.

Typically the mitochondria of living cells are in motion, their movements appearing either random or orderly depending on the type of cell and environmental circumstances. Individual mitochondria often exhibit sudden, independent changes in velocity or direction (saltatory movement), so that like chloroplasts they move autonomously. Nevertheless, in many cells the distribution of mitochondria is closely restricted, and highly oriented patterns may be found; for example, in renal tubule cells they are oriented near the plasma membrane and perpendicular to it, while in other cells they may be concentrated near the nuclear envelope, or conversely, excluded from a peripheral zone surrounding the envelope. In muscle cells, the sarcosomes are more or less fixed in position and closely packed between the muscle fibrils; in some types of muscle a very regular pattern is seen, with two or three sarcosomes to a sarcomere. In other instances, the pattern of distribution may change within the same cell at different stages of the life cycle.

The gross chemical composition of isolated mitochondria has been determined in many laboratories; it varies somewhat with the tissue and species. On the average, mitochondria are about three-fourths protein and one-fourth lipid by dry weight, with small amounts of RNA and DNA. Two to five percent of the lipid is cholesterol, 50–93% is phospholipid, and the rest consists of triglycerides and free fatty acids; the high phosphatide content is a general characteristic of highly membranous structures. The specific enzymes associated with isolated mitochondria have also been thoroughly studied for many species: these include pyruvate oxidase, all the enzymes of the citric acid cycle, those catalyzing β-oxidation of fatty acids, all the components of the electron transport chain, and the enzymes of coupled phosphorylation, both known and unknown. In addition, mitochondria contain a number of subsidiary enzymes, including adenylate kinase, β-hydroxybutyrate dehydrogenase, α-glycerophosphate dehydrogenase, and other enzymes that catalyze transamination of amino acids as well as synthesis of proteins, phosphatides, and, in some mitochondria, fatty acids. Altogether mitochondria have been shown to contain upward of 70 different enzymes and 14 coenzymes; however, it should be noted that they do not contain the enzymes of anaerobic glycolysis, which occur in solution in the extramitochondrial cytoplasm.

The protein fraction includes a "mitochondrial structural protein" discovered by Criddle *et al.* (1962) and an actomyosin-like protein isolated by Ohnishi and Ohnishi (1962). The structural protein is immunologically similar in yeast, *Neurospora,* and beef mitochondria, it has a molecular weight in the range 22,000–23,000, and it self-polymerizes to form insoluble aggregates at physiological pH's. Further details will be given in a later section.

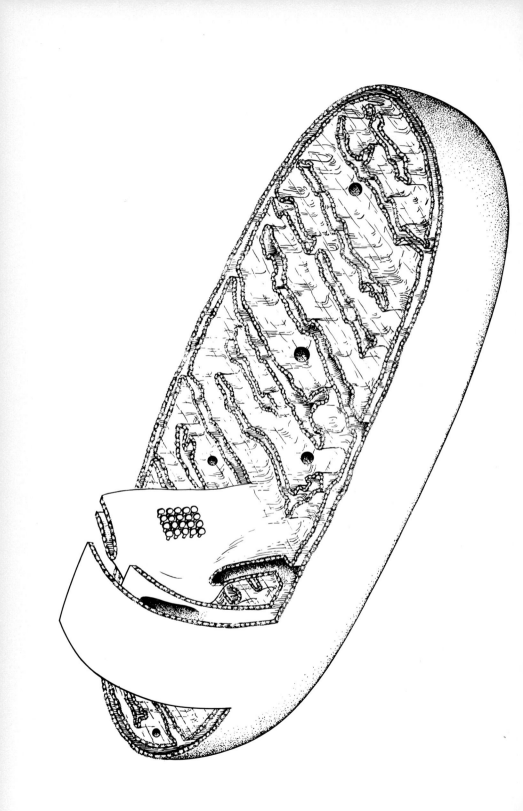

Fine Structure of Mitochondria

Successful electron microscopy of mitochondria, as of many cell organ-elles, depended on the introduction of refined thin-sectioning tech-niques during the early 1950's. Consequently, the first full-scale study was that of Palade (1952), who observed that each mitochondrion is surrounded by two concentric membranes, the inner membrane being highly convoluted into folds or transverse septa, which he named "cristae." In this early study, each membrane appeared as a simple, osmiophilic line without notable substructure; the width of the outer line or membrane was 70 Å, the inner membrane was 50–70 Å wide, and the total width of a crista (including an 80–100 Å osmiophobic internal space) was 180–200 Å (Fig. 7-1). Soon afterward, Sjöstrand and Hanzon (1954) published a somewhat different interpretation of mitochondrial structure. Although the general appearance and dimensions of corre-sponding parts in Sjöstrand's micrographs were approximately the same as in Palade's, Sjöstrand did not find continuities between the internal septa (or cristae) and the inner osmiophilic line surrounding the mito-chondrion as a whole. Partly because of this difference, he was led to interpret *two* osmiophilic lines together with the osmiophobic space between them as a *single* membrane. In his work, and that of his stu-dents, the "inner membrane" was the same as the cristae of Palade and had a dimension of 160–210 Å; the "outer membrane" comprised both the outer and inner membrane of Palade (minus the cristae) and mea-sured 140–180 Å in width.

More refined techniques have now revealed that *each* osmiophilic line of Palade has a substructure (to be described), and electron micros-copy of artificially swollen mitochondria has made it clear that each 70 Å line behaves like a separate membrane (Novikoff, 1957). The inner of the two membranes separates the contents of the mitochondrion into at least two spaces, an innermost "matrix" and the intracristal space, whose contents sometimes show a distinctly different density (Fig. 7-2). Sjöst-rand's student Andersson-Cedergren (1959) also confirmed by careful analysis of serial sections that the cristae do have continuities with the inner membrane; however, these continuities are much more common in some tissues than in others. More recently Hackenbrock (1966) has discovered that isolated mouse liver mitochondria can alternate between two entirely different ultrastructural states. One of these, the classic

---

Fig. 7-1. An interpretation of mitochondrial ultrastructure. The cristae are folds of an inner membrane composed of spheroid subunits; a relatively unfolded outer membrane encloses the inner membrane and matrix. Polyplike particles line the cristae surfaces in regular arrays.

crista organization of Palade (Fig. 7-1), changes reversibly in response to ADP concentration; the matrix loses volume, becoming very electron dark, while the intracristal spaces gain volume, become electron light, and no longer resemble cristae. Other variations are known: for instance, mitochondria from motor end plates show tubular rather than platelike cristae; the cristae of mammalian neurons are longitudinal rather than transverse; even more exotic spiral, branched, or triangular semicrystalline cristae occur (Fig. 7-3B).

High resolution electron microscopy has revealed that each mitochondrial membrane, which in earlier micrographs appeared as a simple osmiophilic line, actually possesses a complex substructure; unfortunately this substructure shows a strikingly different appearance depending on the method of preparation. Three major kinds of organization have been described. The first of these was originally found in osmium-fixed material, and showed the membrane as a "sandwich" structure consisting of two osmiophilic sheets (17–25 Å wide) separated by a 25 Å osmiophobic sheet (Fig. 7-2). A similar "unit membrane" appearance is seen in the surface or plasma membrane of the cell (Fig. 10-3A), which long ago was postulated by Danielli and Davson (1935) to consist of a bimolecular layer of lipid between two monomolecular layers of protein (Chapter 10). The triple-layered plasma membrane structure seen in electron micrographs generally supports Danielli and Davson's hypothesis (since nonpolar lipids are osmiophobic and polar proteins are osmiophilic), and by extension each mitochondrial membrane has also been interpreted as a phospholipid layer enclosed by two protein layers.

However, higher resolution electron micrographs by Sjöstrand (1963) revealed a second type of substructure in both osmium and permanganate-fixed mitochondria. In these micrographs (Fig. 7-2), the three-layered "sandwich" clearly includes osmiophilic crossbars, and the presence of such crossbars led Sjöstrand to reinterpret the mitochondrial membranes as consisting of arrays of spherical units; each unit is 40–45 Å in diameter and consists of an osmiophobic core surrounded by an osmiophilic cortex. In some micrographs, Sjöstrand finds clear evidence of such spherical units arranged in a highly regular pattern (Fig. 7-2). It is of interest that these spherical mitochondrial units resemble the spherical units found in chloroplast lamellae by Weier *et al.* (1965). Since both mitochondrial membranes and chloroplast la-

Fig. 7-2. Thin-section of two mouse kidney mitochondria, showing spheroid subunits composing the outer and inner membranes. The intracrista spaces contain material which differs in density from the general mitochondrial matrix. 160,000×. From Sjöstrand (1963).

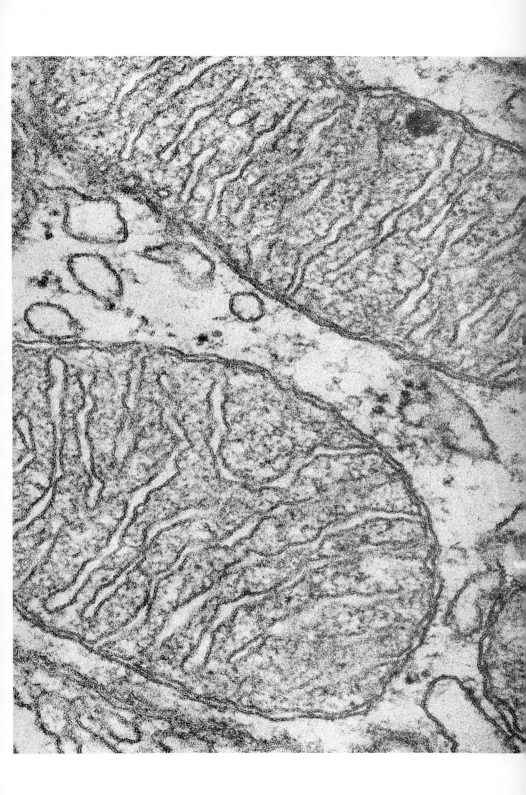

mellae carry out phosphorylation, the resemblance may be more than accidental.

Still a third type of substructure has been found by Parsons, Smith, and others in mitochondria prepared by negative staining, e.g., with phosphotungstic acid. After this type of preparation, the crista membranes appear to be covered with a "fur" of 75–100 Å spheres, each attached to the membrane by a 45–50 Å neck and distributed regularly at 100–110 Å intervals (Fig. 7-3). It has been estimated that there are about 4000 of these polyplike protrusions per square micron of membrane, or approximately 10,000–100,000 in a single beef heart mitochondrion. According to Racker *et al.* (1965), the spheroid heads, which protrude into the matrix between the cristae (Fig. 7-3), are the sites of ATPase activity. Parsons (1963) has also found that, after negative staining, the *outer* mitochondrial membrane in rat liver appears to contain distinctive, hollow cylindrical particles 60 Å in diameter and 60 Å long, with a 20 Å central space.

Although the details of mitochondrial substructure are not yet settled, it seems clear that the membranes are composed of numerous subunits having macromolecular dimensions. This concept is strongly supported by high-resolution analysis of mitochondrial transformations during spermatogenesis. In the spermatocytes of many organisms, mitochondria undergo striking fusions or rearrangements, often producing a single large mitochondrial mass near the nucleus (known to early cytologists as the "Nebenkern"; Butschli, 1871). André (1962) has shown that, in spermatocytes of the snail *Testacella,* the mitochondria spontaneously disintegrate as membraneous organelles, after which their components reassemble into a long, cylindrical crystalline configuration surrounding the filaments of the sperm flagellum. In this process, the visible mitochondrial subunits have the appearance of hollow rodlets about 90 Å in diameter, and they are arranged in their crystalline pattern approximately as rectangles, with center-to-center spacings of 110 Å in one dimension and 170 Å in the other. André has also shown that this mitochondrial crystal possesses a very concentrated oxidative activity.

Functional Organization of Mitochondria

A comparison of mitochondrial structure from one tissue to another has shown that, by and large, those tissues with high oxygen consumption and ATP requirements (e.g., heart and insect flight muscle) possess mitochondria with very extensively developed cristae. This general correlation became understandable when Devlin and Lehninger (1956)

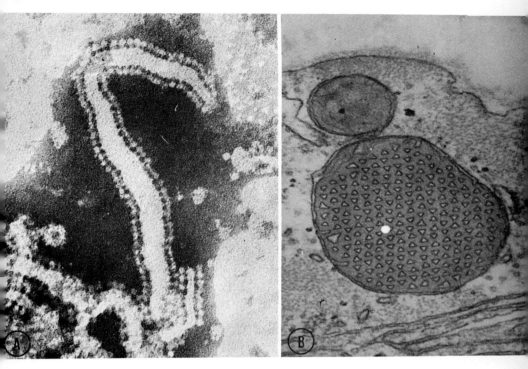

Fig. 7-3. (A) Polyplike particles attached to the crista surfaces of an adult honey bee. 230,000×. From Chance and Parsons (1963). (B) Atypical prismatic cristae found in hamster brain. 60,000×. From Blinzinger *et al.* (1965).

and Cooper and Lehninger (1956) succeeded in isolating a sedimentable (insoluble membrane) fraction by centrifugation of digitonin-treated liver mitochondria; membrane fragments as small as 1/3000 of the whole mitochondrion (mol. wt. 50×10^6) were able to carry out oxidative phosphorylation coupled to the oxidation of β-hydroxybutyrate:

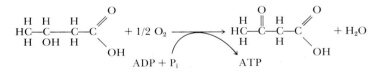

The oxidation requires only β-hydroxybutyrate dehydrogenase and the electron transport chain, and it has been shown to support a P/O ratio of 2.8, indicating that the entire transport chain with its three phosphorylation sites is present in the membrane fragments. By contrast, such fragments do not contain the citric acid cycle enzymes or those catalyzing β oxidization of fatty acids (most of which are soluble enzymes).

From such fractionations it is inferred that the fatty acid and citric acid cycle enzymes (except succinic dehydrogenase) are present in the mitochondrial matrix between the cristae, whereas the cytochrome chain (including succinic dehydrogenase; see below) and the enzymes of coupled phosphorylation are firmly bound to the membranes (especially the cristae).

This interpretation has been supported more directly by Barrnett and Palade (1957) and others, who have demonstrated succinic dehydrogenase activity in the cristae of thin-sectioned mitochondria by electron cytochemical techniques. Similar methods employed by Scarpelli *et al.* (1962) indicate that NADH dehydrogenase activity is more generally distributed in the mitochondrion and is somewhat concentrated in the peripheral membranes. Most recently McConnell *et al.* (1966) have reported that a purified preparation of cytochrome oxidase is able to form artificial membranes *in vitro*. According to Lehninger, 60–90% of mitochondrial dry weight is associated with the membrane fraction, and of this, 60–65% is protein and the rest lipid (including almost all the lipid of the mitochondrion). The enzymes of the electron transport chain make up as much as 25–30% of the membrane protein.

These data require that in electron micrographs of the 70 Å crista membranes, one must be viewing directly the cytochromes, flavoproteins, and other functional molecules composing the electron transport chain (the dimensions of a cytochrome c molecule are about 39×28 Å). Since very small membrane fragments carry out both electron transport and coupled phosphorylation, it can also be concluded that mitochondria contain several thousand replicate units, which may be visualized as composing the membranes like the bricks of a wall. Support for this concept is provided by the fact that the electron carriers seem to be in simple molar ratios to one another; for instance, Chance and Hess (1959) reported that the concentrations of cytochromes a, a_3, b, c, c_1 and flavoprotein (as determined spectrophotometrically for isolated rat heart and rat liver mitochondria) show very nearly a $1:1:1:1:1:4$ ratio. Lehninger *et al.* (1958) also determined that digitonin fragments from rat liver mitochondria have a ratio of 1 Cyt $a:1$ Cyt $a_3:0.7$ Cyt $b:1.8$ Cyt c. In beef heart mitochondria, D. E. Green and his associates have found ratios of $6(a + a_3):3b:2c:1c_1:1$ succinic dehydrogenase FAD:1 NADH dehydrogenase FAD. Klingenberg and Pette (1962) have measured a fairly constant ratio of 6 to 12 moles NAD per mole of cytochrome c in a wide variety of mitochondria. These data suggest that the electron transport chain may be organized into units, each of which contains one or very few molecules of each electron carrier; such hypothetical units have been called "oxysomes" by Chance *et al.* (1963), in analogy with the quantasomes of the chloroplast. The number of oxysomes in one mitochondrion is estimated to be of the order of 10,000 or more.

Criddle *et al.* (1962) have also isolated a homogeneous "structural protein" (mol. wt. 22,000), which makes up about 50–60% of the mitochondrial membrane proteins. This component shows a striking tendency to polymerize and to form complexes in $1:1$ or $2:1$ ratio specifically with pure cytochromes a, b, and c_1, myoglobin, ATP, and NADH. Structural protein also combines with phospholipids and can bring about complexing between cytochromes a and c_1. Since Fleischer *et al.* (1967) have been able to extract up to 92% of mitochondrial phospholipid without destroying the basic mitochondrial organization, it appears that structural protein may play a key role in holding the respiratory chain in its membraneous configuration. Woodward and Munkres (1966) have also shown that mitochondrial structural protein in *Neurospora* forms complexes with and influences the activity of the respiratory enzyme malate dehydrogenase; mutations affecting the amino acid composition of this structural protein are inherited through the cytoplasm, presumably in association with mitochondrial DNA (to be discussed).

Still further details about the functional units of mitochondria have been obtained by analysis of "electron transport particles" (ETP), which were first isolated from beef heart sarcosomes by Crane *et al.* (1956); the ETP's catalyze oxidation of NADH and succinate but without coupled phosphorylation. Native ETP contains some structural protein and about 30% lipid; it has been separated into four complexes that are the smallest operational units so far isolated from mitochondria. Complex I (mol. wt. 786,000) catalyzes the oxidation of NADH coupled to reduction of coenzyme Q, and it contains 1 mole of flavin (presumably as NADH dehydrogenase), 20% lipid, 3 moles of coenzyme Q (lipid soluble), and 16 atoms of nonheme iron. Complex II (mol. wt. 250,000) is similar to complex I, but catalyzes the oxidation of succinate coupled to reduction of coenzyme Q; it contains 1 mole of flavin (as succinic dehydrogenase), 1 mole of cytochrome b, lipid, coenzyme Q, and nonheme iron. Complex III (mol. wt. 285,000) catalyzes the oxidation of coenzyme Q coupled to the reduction of cytochrome c; this complex, which is red in color, contains two moles of cytochrome b, one mole of cytochrome c_1, 1 mole of nonheme iron protein (recently purified by Rieske, 1965), and lipid. Finally, complex IV (mol. wt. 615,000) contains cytochromes a and a_3 (cytochrome oxidase) and exhibits their characteristic green color.

These various complexes can recombine with one another in $1:1:1:1$ ratio, reestablishing the entire chain of electron transfer from NADH or succinate to oxygen; however, since coenzyme Q and cytochrome c are not structurally bound, they must be added back to the preparation for effective oxidation. The total molecular weight of the native ETP is estimated at about 2×10^6, including about 30% lipid (it has been shown that phospholipid is required for activity within each complex). Although the ETP and its subunits do not carry out coupled phosphorylation, it is worth noting that each complex corresponds approximately to a part of the electron transport chain believed to contain one of the three phosphorylation sites; Green has suggested that, in the intact mitochondrion, each complex carries out a different phosphorylation.

Attempts to correlate these functional complexes with visible particles seen in electron micrographs of mitochondrial membranes have not yet been successful. At one time Green and his colleagues postulated that the knob-like structures seen on the crista membranes after negative staining (Fig. 7-3A) might represent "elementary particles"; each elementary particle was postulated to contain all the components of the intact electron transport chain, together with the enzymes of coupled oxidative phosphorylation. Since the knobs themselves are much too small (75–100 Å) to include all the necessary macromolecules, the elementary particle was extended in hypothetical terms to include a brick-like section of the crista membrane; the imaginary base piece, together with the observed neck and knob, were then said to correspond respectively with complexes I, II, III, and IV of the electron transport particle. Almost immediately this concept was severely criticized by Chance and Parsons (1963) and by Racker et al. (1965), whose evidence has led to a general abandonment of the elementary particle concept. Chance and Parsons (1963) examined negative-stained preparations of *Ascaris* mitochondria, which are deficient in cytochromes a and c_1, as well as preparations of mitochondria from emerging honeybees, which are deficient in cytochrome c; they found that the individual knobs in both cases seem to be unreduced in size, but that there is some decrease in the number of particles. They therefore concluded that the enzymes of electron transport and coupled phosphorylation are distributed among several particles in the membranes, which they referred to as a "distributed oxysome." Racker et al. (1965) prepared submitochondrial particles by sonic oscillation, and found that treatment with trypsin and urea removes the knobs from the crista membranes, while at the same time the particles' ATPase activity and capacity for coupled phosphorylation is eliminated. Since the same treatment does not affect electron transport from NADH, they concluded that the knobs cannot constitute an essential part of the electron transport chain. However, they may correspond to a protein factor which is involved in the coupling of ADP phosphorylation with electron transport, and which under certain conditions acts as an ATPase.

Although the detailed relationships are still not settled, it seems clear that the functional molecules which carry out electron transport and oxidative phosphorylation are arranged as replicate, highly ordered assemblies, which in the aggregate constitute the visible internal membranes of the mitochondrion. It may be recalled that the functional molecules which carry out photophosphorylation are also arranged as replicate assemblies constituting the lamellae of the chloroplast. In most bacteria no specialized cytoplasmic bodies or mitochondria-like particles have been found as sites of respiratory enzymes; instead, as demonstrated by Weibull *et al.* (1959), the electron transport chain is localized in the cell's plasma membrane. This intimate relationship between electron flow, coupled phosphorylation and a lamellar or membranous structural organization is not yet fully understood, but it amounts to a general principle in the functional design of plants, animals, and microorganisms.

Mitochondrial Permeability and Transport

As early as 1888, Kölliker teased out the sarcosomes of muscle, showed that they swell in hypotonic medium (water), and concluded that they possess a semipermeable membrane. The same observation is easily carried out with suspensions of isolated mitochondria, which in general behave like ideal osmometers (permeable to water but impermeable to many ions and larger molecules; see Chapter 10). Since the essential function of mitochondria involves taking up various substrates together with oxygen, while releasing carbon dioxide, water, and phosphoryl energy, the permeability of the mitochondrial membranes to these and other materials has been carefully investigated. Particular interest attaches to the results, since of all the membranes in the cell the mitochondrial membranes are particularly well characterized, especially in regard to their protein components. Unfortunately, no attempt has been made in many studies to distinguish the permeability properties of the external and internal membranes, although there is evidence that the two differ in some important respects.

Lehninger (1951), Van den Bergh and Slater (1962), and others have found that mitochondria in the *absence* of energy expenditure (e.g., at low temperatures) are surprisingly impermeable to NADH (formed outside the mitochondrion by phosphoglyceraldehyde dehydrogenase), NADPH (formed by extramitochondrial isocitric dehydrogenase), ATP, ADP, AMP, inorganic phosphate, citrate, isocitrate, α-ketoglutarate, and succinate. On the other hand, pyruvate, malate, phosphodihydroxyacetone, and α-glycerophosphate appear to penetrate more readily. Although a general low permeability of mitochondria might be predicted in order to prevent indiscriminate oxidation of essential cell components, their impermeability to substrates like NADH, citric acid cycle intermediates, and ATP, is unexpected and requires some explanation. In particular, a low passive permeability to the reactants and product of phosphorylation

$$ADP + P_i \rightleftharpoons ATP + H_2O$$

implies an efficient mechanism for transporting phosphoryl energy across the membrane without transfer of ADP and ATP themselves.

Siekevitz and Potter (1955) have suggested that phosphoryl transfer could be accomplished by adenylate kinase molecules, which occur in the mitochondrial membrane and might catalyze the transfer of phosphoryl from intramitochondrial ATP to extramitochondrial AMP by the reaction:

$$ATP_{inside} + AMP_{outside} \xrightleftharpoons[\text{kinase}]{\text{adenylate}} ADP_{inside} + ADP_{outside}$$

The energy loss in this process would be only the difference between $\Delta F°$ for hydrolysis of the terminal phosphoryl in ATP and the terminal phosphoryl in ADP (i.e., -0.6 kcal/mole), plus the energy necessary to transport inorganic phosphate back into the mitochondrion (see below).

The mechanism by which extramitochondrial NADH from glycolysis is reoxidized through the intramitochondrial respiratory chain has been investigated by Estabrook and Sacktor (1958). They found that in insect muscle, the electrons of NADH are carried into the mitochondrion by α-glycerophosphate. First, NADH in the cytoplasm reduces phosphodihydroxyacetone to α-glycerophosphate (via cytoplasmic α-glycerophosphate dehydrogenase), the latter then diffuses into the mitochondrion and is reoxidized to phosphodihydroxyacetone (by mitochondrial α-glycerophosphate dehydrogenase):

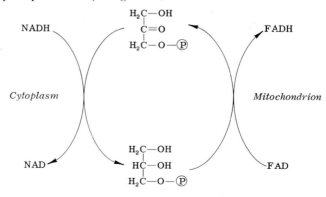

Since the E_0 value of α-glycerophosphate is much less negative than that of NADH, the equivalent of one phosphorylation is sacrificed for the sake of this transport; consequently, glycolytic NADH leads to P/O ratios approaching 2, whereas citric acid cycle NADH leads to ratios approaching 3.

Many biological membranes, including the plasma membrane, nuclear envelope and mitochondrial membranes, have the capacity to accumulate specific ions or molecules by the expenditure of energy (active transport; see Chapter 11). Even though the passive permeability of mitochondria to phosphate ions is fairly low, metabolically active mitochondria have been found to accumulate massive amounts of inorganic phosphate from the medium (Brierley *et al.*, 1962). In Brierley's system, phosphate uptake is accompanied by uptake of Mg^{++} (or Mn^{++}) in a ratio of $1.5:1$, suggesting formation of the salt, $Mg_3(PO_4)_2$; furthermore, the amount of material accumulated would correspond to an intramitochondrial concentration of $1\ M$, far exceeding the solubility of the salt and indicating that magnesium phosphate crystallizes out inside the mitochondrion. The ion uptake requires electron transport, is inhibited by 2,4-dinitrophenol, and is reduced to about 20% of maximum under conditions favoring ADP phosphorylation; consequently it appears to compete with coupled phosphorylation for part of the mechanism which draws on the energy of electron transport.

Vasington and Murphy (1962) have also found a massive calcium ion uptake in rat kidney mitochondria, and Lehninger *et al.* (1963) have observed that calcium uptake by rat liver mitochondria is accompanied by phosphate accumulation showing a Ca/P ratio of 1.7; this indicates formation of the salt hydroxylapatite $[Ca_3(PO_4)_2]_3 \cdot Ca(OH)_2$. The intramitochondrial concentration of calcium may increase as much as 1000 times; in fact, almost all the calcium available in the medium can be taken up in this way. Greenawalt *et al.* (1964) found that such "calcium loaded" mitochondria sediment more rapidly in a sucrose gradient, and in electron micrographs they are seen to contain characteristic osmiophilic granules (which presumably account for the supersaturation of the salt).

A very important feature of phosphate accumulation in the presence of calcium is that it proceeds with a stoichiometry comparable to that of phosphorylation itself, i.e., the P/O ratios for "phosphate-accumulated" approach 3 as a maximum and are correspondingly reduced if the substrate bypasses one or more phosphorylation sites. Phosphate uptake and coupled ADP phosphorylation also behave as if they are competing processes, e.g., addition of calcium ion abolishes (or uncouples) oxidative phosphorylation. These facts support the suggestion of Brierley *et al.*

(1962) and Lehninger (1964) that active accumulation of ions by metabolizing mitochondria is a modification of oxidative phosphorylation, in which calcium (or other ions) act as phosphate acceptors instead of ADP. If this phenomenon is indeed a "calcium phosphorylation," it would suggest that the enzymes of oxidative phosphorylation, which compose the mitochondrial membranes, capture phosphate on the extramitochondrial side of the membrane in order to phosphorylate ADP or calcium on the intramitochondrial side. In ordinary ADP phosphorylation, no net accumulation of phosphate would be detectable, since phosphoryl would immediately be transferred back to extramitochondrial AMP by the adenylate kinase reaction (see above); however, in calcium phosphorylation, the product is evidently retained in the mitochondrion as a precipitate. This hypothesis provides an interesting link between active ion transport and the functional molecules which compose the mitochondrial membranes. It also suggests that energy used to transport phosphate into the mitochondrion in this way may account for part of the difference between the free energy of pyruvate and the ATP energy produced during pyruvate oxidation in the citric acid cycle; although this energy is often said to be "lost to entropy," Lehninger (1964) has emphasized that it may actually bring about unsuspected, biologically useful effects (such as phosphate transport).

As a result of phosphate uptake (H_3PO_4) and phosphoryl output (H_2PO_3), water would be transported into the mitochondrion (assuming that all reactions are accompanied by sufficient protons to confer electrical neutrality). Water is also formed inside the mitochondrion by transfer of substrate protons and electrons to oxygen. This accumulation of water represents a large amount of osmotic work, and also accounts for much of the free energy of pyruvate. It is not known whether this osmotic work is harnassed to any biologically important process, but Mitchell (1961) has pointed out that restrictions on the movement of either protons or hydroxyl ions across the membranes would result in a separation of charges, permitting the mitochondrion to perform electrical work in the manner of a tiny battery. In fact, he has proposed that such a mechanism could drive coupled phosphorylation. Evidence that mitochondria can bring about a separation of protons and hydroxyl ions in this way has been found by Brierley et al. (1962), who observed that during active accumulation of phosphate, the mitochondria become more alkaline and at the same time release one mole of acid into the medium for every mole of phosphate bound.

As has been noted, mitochondria are osmotically sensitive objects which swell in hypotonic media; however, a second type of swelling, which occurs in *iso*tonic media and depends on oxidative phosphorylation, has been discovered by Raaflaub (1953), Lehninger (1960), and others. This metabolism-dependent swelling may increase mitochondrial volume by 4 or 5 times, resulting in an uncoupling of phosphorylation, generally increased membrane permeability or "leakage," and loss of mitochondrial contents such as ATP (although all the effects are reversible). Such swelling is observable in metabolizing mitochondria in the absence of ADP, and it is greatly accelerated by inorganic phosphate, calcium ions, or thyroxine among other agents. The immediate cause of swelling is an influx of water from the medium, accompanying a sudden penetration of sucrose, KCl, or NaCl (which are added to the medium in large amounts in order to establish isotonicity); this phenomenon therefore represents a change in the permeability characteristics of the mitochondrial membranes. Since it also depends on the oxidation-reduction state of the electron transport chain, metabolic swelling provides further evidence that the electron carriers form an important structural part of the membranes, and suggests that their oxidation state directly influences membrane permeability (the cytochrome c molecule is known to undergo changes in shape with oxidation-reduction). It is not yet clear whether metabolic swelling is associated with active ion transport; osmotic penetration of water would be expected to accompany net ion uptake, and, like ion uptake, swelling is prevented by the absence of substrate or oxygen and by the uncoupling of phosphorylation by 2,4-dinitrophenol.

Experimental work with such swollen mitochondria by Lehninger (1960) has revealed still another phenomenon, which is the reversal of swelling by an active contraction; in the absence of metabolic activity, mitochondrial contraction can be brought about specifically by the addition of ATP. This contraction is relatively rapid, and Lehninger (1959) has calculated that as many as 2400 molecules of water may be extruded for each ATP molecule hydrolyzed; furthermore, contraction is not inhibited by 2,4-dinitrophenol or by the absence of respiration. It therefore does not seem to represent an osmotic mechanism, i.e., a reversal of metabolic swelling, but rather a mechanical event similar to muscle contraction. This interpretation has received strong confirmation from Ohnishi and Ohnishi (1962), who succeeded in extracting a specific mitochondrial protein, constituting 5–6% of the total membrane protein and having the characteristics of actomyosin (the contractile protein of striated muscle; see Chapter 8). Like muscle actomyosin, this mitochondrial protein has ATPase activity, its solutions show decreased viscosity upon addition of ATP, and it dissociates into separate actin and myosin moieties. More recently, Blair et al. (1964) have reported strong similarities between contractile protein from heart muscle mitochondria and heart actomyosin itself. It has been suggested that the mitochondrial contractile mechanism may be located in the outer mitochondrial membrane, or in the space between the two membranes, but this has not yet been demonstrated. As mentioned in Chapter 5, chloroplasts also contain a contractile protein and undergo ATP-induced volume changes.

Neubert *et al.* (1962), Vignais *et al.* (1963), and others have shown that several other specific molecules are required for mitochondrial contraction; these include long-chain unsaturated fatty acids (oleate) and α-glycerophosphate, both of which appear to be synthesized into phosphatidic acid and cardiolipin synchronously with mitochondrial contraction. Phosphatidyl inositol is also a required factor, as well as the enzymes catalase and glutathione peroxidase. However, the exact mechanisms of the phenomenon are not yet understood.

Ion accumulation, swelling and active contraction have all been discovered and analyzed in suspensions of isolated mitochondria, and it has not been clearly demonstrated that they occur or are of physiological significance in living cells. However, since osmiophilic granules characteristic of "calcium loaded" mitochondria have been found in osteoblasts, it seems likely that this mechanism of calcium phosphate accumulation plays a role in bone deposition. It is also known that mitochondria in kidney tubule cells, which are active in water transport, orient themselves near the plasma membrane and perpendicular to it; this suggests that alternate swelling and contraction of mitochondria could act as a water pump in these cells. Lehninger (1964) has postulated a control mechanism in which contraction, induced by high levels of cytoplasmic ATP, would restrict the permeability of mitochondria to respiratory substrates, slowing up phosphorylation, whereas low levels of cytoplasmic ATP would lead to swelling, increased penetration of substrate, and more active phosphorylation. Further investigations may confirm that such mechanisms play an important part in the economy of the cell.

Mitochondrial Work and the Energy Equivalent of ATP

Since ATP plays a role in virtually all major biological phenomena, it would be useful in many disciplines to know the amount of energy which can be provided by a single ATP molecule, or by a gram molecular weight of ATP. Unfortunately, as was explained in Chapter 2, free energy is not a property of an individual molecule or compound, but of a given reaction mixture; therefore, a single universal value for ATP does not exist. A kind of standard value is provided by the free energy of hydrolysis for ATP under standard conditions, which for some 20 years was thought to be -12 kcal/mole; more sophisticated techniques have since revealed that the figure is considerably lower, close to -7 kcal/mole (see Chapter 3). Because this discovery did not fit well with the prevailing concepts of "high-energy phosphate" and the "energy-rich phosphate bond," many authors suggested that the "true" ΔF for hydrolysis of ATP must be higher under the nonstandard conditions inside the cell. On the assumption that the ratio [ATP]/[ADP] is close to unity, a lower phosphate concentration would result in a higher free energy of hydrolysis (Chapter 3), which could approach or exceed the earlier (erroneous) figure of -12 kcal/mole. A few authors have therefore continued to regard the value of an ATP "high-energy bond" as 12 kcal, while others have compromised and accepted intermediate values of 9 or 10 kcal/mole. Nevertheless, it is certainly erroneous to compare ΔF for hydrolysis of ATP under (presumed) *physiological* conditions with $\Delta F°$ for other reactions under *standard* conditions. This practice is most common in calculations of biological efficiency when, for example, the value of NADH may be taken as 52 kcal (standard free energy of oxidation), and compared with 36 kcal "stored" during three coupled phosphorylations. Such comparisons are never more than approximate, but in carrying them out the standard $\Delta F°$ for hydrolysis of ATP should be used (-7 kcal/mole).

The actual energy relationships can be visualized best if ATP is regarded, not as an energy source, but as an energy carrier; the distinction is analogous to the difference between closed test-tube systems, and the open, or steady-state, systems of living cells. Specifically, the standard free energy of hydrolysis for ATP represents the maximum amount of work that can be done by a closed, standard solution of ATP, ADP, and phosphate when it spontaneously moves to equilibrium; in this concept, the hydrolysis reaction is regarded as an energy *source*. In living cells, on the other hand, special mechanisms are present which divert environmental energy (from light or substrates) to reverse ATP hydrolysis, and this creates a situation in which the system never really approaches equilibrium. A simple example might be visualized as a flask which is absorbing light and emitting heat and in which equal numbers of ADP molecules are undergoing endergonic photophosphorylation and exergonic hydrolysis side by side in solution. In such a system, the ratios of ATP, ADP, and phosphate will remain constant, no matter how far from test-tube equilibrium they may be at any given moment. It follows that the ATP in the flask does not produce any work at all (i.e., there is no net reaction); what does occur is a flow of energy from one part of the environment, through the ATP–ADP system, to

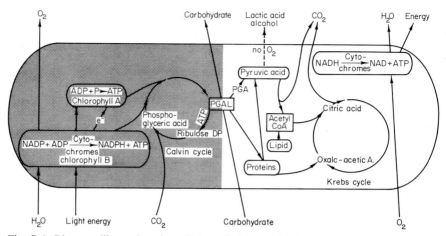

Fig. 7-4. Diagram illustrating the relation of photosynthetic reactions (left) to the reactions of oxidative and anaerobic metabolism (right).

another part of the environment. Essentially the same phenomenon occurs in living systems, with the proviso that the energy flow (i.e., ATP hydrolysis) is coupled to mechanisms that perpetuate the system. Since the actual energy source is external, the total energy flux is more or less independent of the number of ATP molecules, and it becomes essentially meaningless to ask how much energy is supplied by each one.

In Fig. 7-4 are summarized the major relationships between energy capture in photosynthesis and energy release in anaerobic and aerobic metabolism. The oval boundary delimits a generalized "living system" (or the biosphere), within which all the photosynthetic reactions are confined to the left side of the diagram, while the degradative processes are shown on the right. Energy and materials required as input from the environment are shown below the "cell"; energy and materials released to the environment are shown above it. This diagram emphasizes that energy flows *through* the system, entering as light and leaving in various forms which eventually become heat, while the system itself approximates a constant or "steady" state. In a very similar manner, matter also flows through the system in the form of carbon dioxide, water (and nitrates, not shown).

ATP and reduced pyridine nucleotides act as energy carriers in the first and last stages of this energy flow; however, interposed between the initial phosphorylations of photosynthesis and the final hydrolysis of, for example, muscle contraction, is an elaborate network of synthesis and degradation, in which energy is also transferred to and among many types of macromolecule. These reactions serve to maintain the structural requirements for the energy flow (and they may or may not lead to some net storage or increase in the energy and matter of the system). The specific kinds and rates of these intermediary reactions are subject to genetic control, which thereby determines approximately the state which will be kept steady in the face of changing environmental conditions (i.e., the phenotype of the organism).

Although for such a system the total energy flux is independent of the number of ATP molecules, it is valid to inquire how much energy is carried through the system by each phosphorylation-hydrolysis event. In the simplest case, i.e., the hypothetical ADP–ATP *solution*, an average value would be given by the total energy flux divided by the number of phosphorylations (which would equal ΔF for hydrolysis at the steady-state concentrations of ATP, ADP, and phosphate in the solution); this means that the total energy flux when it enters the steady-state system is broken up into "packets," and the size of the packets is a direct function of the ratio $[ATP]/([ADP][P_i])$ in the flask. The flask is therefore a kind of energy transducer, and this ratio represents its functional constant. It is apparent that the value of an ATP energy packet need not be the same in every flask, and it might also be different at different times in the same flask (the steady-state concentrations being easily altered by temporary discrepancies in the ratio of phosphorylation to hydrolysis). Also, the size of ATP energy packets might vary in different parts of the same flask without affecting the average ATP value as a function of the average concentrations.

It might be tempting to conclude that the "physiological" free energy for hydrolysis, while it does not guarantee the energy value of any given ATP molecule, is at least a true average value and a closer approximation than the standard free energy. Unfortunately the situation is more complex than that. The following question may be posed: In a steady-state ATP–ADP system, is it possible to change the size of the ATP energy "packet" (i.e., the average ΔF for phosphorylation-hydrolysis) without varying the average concentrations of ATP, ADP, and phosphate? Referring to the hypothetical flask with its intermingled phosphorylation and hydrolysis, what modifications would make the average ΔF independent of the average reactant concentrations? Only two conditions are necessary: (1) The distribution of molecules must be restricted in such a way that the flask contains two compartments, one with a higher-than-average ΔF value and the other with a lower-than-average value. (2) Phosphorylation must occur primarily in one compartment and hydrolysis in the other, i.e., the two processes must be physically separate, but linked by a transport system. Under these conditions, which are almost certainly met in typical cells, *the average*

*energy carried per ATP molecule is determined entirely by the reactant con-
centrations at the site of phosphorylation,* and is quite independent of the
steady-state ATP, ADP, and phosphate concentrations averaged over
the entire flask.

Imagine a flask containing a small compartment rich in ATP but low
in ADP and phosphate (and therefore characterized by a relatively
high ΔF for hydrolysis); if the phosphorylation mechanism is localized
entirely in this compartment, then every phosphorylation will require
relatively greater external energy, i.e., the total energy flux will be
broken up into fewer ATP packets, each of which will have relatively
high energy "value." After phosphorylation, the ATP will tend to diffuse
along its concentration gradient to the second compartment, where
ATP is relatively low, ADP and phosphate are high, and ΔF for hydrolysis is relatively less. In this compartment the ATP is hydrolyzed (with
coupled reactions), and the ADP and phosphate then diffuse back into
the phosphorylation compartment (again following the concentration
gradients).

If this flask were suddenly frozen, the average concentrations of
ATP, ADP, and phosphate measured, and the ΔF for hydrolysis calculated in the context of a closed thermodynamic system, the value of
each ATP molecule would appear to be relatively low (due to a much
greater volume of the low ΔF compartment). Furthermore, the total
ATP energy available in the hydrolysis compartment would seem to be
much less than the original energy input, indicating a large loss to
entropy (and a relatively inefficient machine). However these conclusions would not be accurate, since the total energy passing through the
system per phosphorylation-hydrolysis cycle is actually relatively high,
and is determined by the conditions (never measured) at the phosphorylation site. Furthermore, the lower ATP energy at the hydrolysis sites
compared with the phosphorylation site is not lost to entropy, but
actually drives the transport mechanism (in this case, a diffusion gradient) by which ADP and phosphate are supplied to the phosphorylation
reaction and ATP is supplied to the hydrolysis mechanisms. As indicated
in this model, the true energy equivalent of an ATP molecule can never
be determined without reference to the energy involved in transporting
ATP, ADP, and phosphate (+ water) to regions of higher or lower phosphoryl potential.

The inescapable conclusion from this model is that the "physiological"
energy value of an ATP molecule (i.e., of one phosphorylation-hydrolysis
cycle) cannot be estimated from measurements of average ATP, ADP,
and phosphate concentration; rather, this value depends on the still-
unknown reaction conditions at the sites of oxidative and photophos-

phorylation, and it is masked or distorted by energy expenditures in intracellular transport phenomena (which are also poorly known). Undoubtedly, the physiological value of ATP varies widely from one cell type to another (e.g., autotrophic and heterotrophic cells), and even in the same cell depending both on the form in which energy is presented (e.g., light flux, different substrates), and the types of phosphorylation, hydrolysis, and transport mechanism that are available. It has already been noted that active phosphate transport into the mitochondrion probably occurs at the expense of NADH energy usually thought to be lost to entropy; this energy of phosphate transfer necessarily becomes a part of the physiological energy packet transported through the cell by each ATP phosphorylation-hydrolysis cycle. Exact calculations for living cells are complicated by the likelihood that some metabolically important energy flux occurs which is more or less independent of the ATP–ADP system (e.g., as NADPH or "incubation" heat).

In short, present information about energy flow *in vivo* is so rudimentary that it is almost meaningless to speak of a physiological energy value for ATP. Nevertheless, progress in analyzing cell mechanisms is often achieved by isolating specific reactions or processes as closed *in vitro* systems. In characterizing or comparing such test-tube reactions, the *standard* $\Delta F°$ is usually the most appropriate value to work with (since it was introduced for this purpose). For the hydrolysis of ATP in the presence of Mg^{++}, this value is -7 kcal/mole.

The Origin of Mitochondria

Over fifty years ago, Lewis and Lewis (1914) observed that mitochondria *in vivo* have the ability to fragment, as well as to fuse. Such spontaneous mitochondrial fragmentation is apparently a frequent and normal event, which has since been reported and even filmed many times. Provided that mitochondria also have a capacity for independent growth, it is clear that a process of repeated mitochondrial growth and fragmentation would suffice to account for the multiplication of these organelles.

Such a process clearly occurs in some unicellular organisms which contain only one mitochondrion; in these cases, the single mitochondrion undergoes growth and division synchronously with the mitotic replication of the whole cell. However, in the cells of higher organisms the mitochondria do not divide during mitosis, but are distributed more or less randomly to the daughter cells; in some instances, they clump together to form an organized mass surrounding the spindle, a process that may facilitate an approximate halving of their numbers. During interphase the number of mitochondria in each daughter cell increases again. Frédéric (1958) has photographed an entire cell life cycle under the phase contrast microscope, using time-lapse techniques, and has observed directly that this mitochondrial increase occurs by gradual lengthening and fragmentation (or division) of the original mitochondria.

Direct experimental evidence for synthetic activity in mitochondria has also been found. For instance, Roodyn (1962) observed incorporation of amino acids into membrane proteins having succinoxidase activity, as well as into structural protein. Submitochondrial particles have been reported by Kroon (1963) to incorporate amino acid even more rapidly than intact mitochondria, and soluble amino acid activating enzymes (which play an essential role in cytoplasmic protein synthesis) have been found in isolated mitochondria by Truman and Korner (1962). In addition to protein synthesis, mitochondrial preparations can also carry on active synthesis of fatty acids and of phospholipids such as lecithin and inositol phosphatide. In oocytes, Ward (1962) has shown that the lipoprotein yolk platelets are formed inside typical mitochondria.

The concept of mitochondrial growth and division has received further support from an *in vivo* experiment by Luck (1963), using carbon-14 labeled choline with a "cholineless" mutant of the fungus *Neurospora*. Choline is a general component of cell membranes, including mitochondrial membranes, and Luck began by labeling all choline-containing parts of the cell. The cells were then transferred to non-radioactive choline for the duration of three "doubling cycles," after which the distribution of radioactivity among the mitochondria was determined by autoradiography. In this experiment, the concentration of radioactive choline (per unit cytochrome oxidase) in the isolated mitochondrial fraction was reduced linearly as the total protoplasmic mass increased (Fig. 7-5); this indicates that labeled nonmitochondrial membranes did not contribute material to the mitochondria (and vice versa). Furthermore the label was randomly distributed among all the mitochondria of the daughter cells, excluding the possibility that mitochondria were formed *de novo* (since that would lead to unlabeled "new" mitochondria intermingled with labeled "old" mitochondria). The simplest interpretation for the pattern of radioactivity found by Luck is that the mitochondria increase by an addition of precursors to old mitochondria (i.e., growth), followed by random division or fragmentation.

Although it seems well established that mitochondria do grow and divide (or fragment), their degree of independence in this process is not entirely clear. Early evidence for an independent cytoplasmic inheritance affecting mitochondria was found by Ephrussi (1950) in yeast. Ephrussi could obtain natural or induced mutants which lacked cytochrome oxidase, cytochrome *b*, and oxidative substrate metabolism, and which bred true during vegetative reproduction; these mutants showed non-Mendelian patterns of inheritance during sexual reproduction, such that the mutation disappeared after mixing of mutant cytoplasm with "wild-type" cytoplasm. From this and other observations, Ephrussi concluded that synthesis of cytochrome oxidase and cytochrome *b* in yeast requires cytoplasmic particles that exhibit an independent genetic continuity. Later Raut (1954) found that this type of respiratory mutation could be induced by ultraviolet radiation at 254 mμ, indicating participation of a nucleic acid.

These early investigations have now been clarified by the discovery

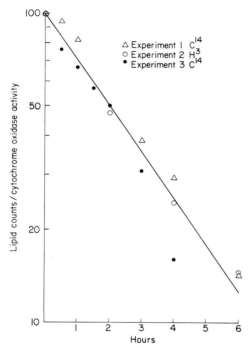

Fig. 7-5. The relative labeling of *Neurospora* mitochondria, originally fully labeled with radioactive choline, decreases inversely with the increase in dry mass during growth. The line in this graph shows the theoretical values expected if the choline is conserved in the mitochondrial membranes, and if choline from other cell membranes does not enter the mitochondrial fraction. Observed points are in good agreement with this expectation. From Luck (1963).

that typical mitochondria contain DNA, that some mitochondrial mutations cause changes in the amino acid sequence of the mitochondrial structural protein, and that the cytoplasmic (or non-Mendelian) inheritance of such mutations can be accounted for by the special properties of mitochondrial DNA. One of the earliest reports of mitochondrial DNA was that of Nass and Nass (1963), who observed fibrous, DNase-sensitive regions in thin-sectioned chick mitochondria examined with the electron microscope. Confirmation was provided by Luck and Reich (1964), who isolated a low density mitochondrial DNA from *Neurospora* by biochemical techniques; in the same mitochondria, they also demonstrated a DNA-dependent RNA polymerase activity. Data summarized by Granick and Gibor (1967) shows that the mitochondrial DNA's of yeast and *Neurospora* are of lower density than nuclear DNA, whereas in mammals the mitochondrial DNA is of the same or higher density. The amount of DNA in an average beef heart mitochondrion corresponds to a DNA helix of 3×10^7 molecular weight, only about 1/100 the size of a bacterial chromosome (*E. coli*). Furthermore this DNA occurs as several separate molecules, since Nass (1966) and others have now established that mitochondrial DNA occurs as closed rings (Fig. 7-6) with circumferences in the range of 5–6 μ (corresponding to a DNA molecular weight of only 10–12×10^6). Dawid and Wolstenholme (1967) have also shown that these circular mitochondrial DNA's are locked in super-coiled configurations.

Strong evidence has been obtained that in fungi such as yeast and *Neurospora,* mitochondrial DNA replicates *in situ* independently of nuclear DNA, and that mitochondrial DNA functions to specify amino acid sequences in some but not all mitochondrial proteins; in these respects this DNA behaves as a kind of mitochondrial chromosome. For example Corneo *et al.* (1966) have shown by ^{15}N labeling that yeast mitochondrial DNA replicates semiconservatively (like nuclear DNA; Chapter 13), and Wintersberger (1966) has found the enzyme of replication (DNA polymerase) in isolated yeast mitochondria. In both yeast and *Neurospora,* synthesis of mitochondrial DNA proceeds with different kinetics and from a different precursor pool than synthesis of nuclear DNA. Some respiratory mutants of yeast appear to have lost their mitochondrial DNA, while in other mutants (*Neurospora*), the pattern of inheritance of mitochondrial DNA parallels the uniparental (maternal) inheritance that characterizes the mutation itself (Reich and Luck, 1966). Woodward and Munkres (1966) have found that in two cytoplasmic mutants of *Neurospora,* the mitochondrial structural protein differs from wild-type in at least one amino acid residue; when such mutant structural proteins are complexed with nonmutant malate dehydrogenase, they have the effect of lowering the oxidative activity of the enzyme in a way that may account for the *in vivo* phenotypes. Yeast cytochrome b_2 also contains a small DNA component of about 10,000–20,000 molecular weight, which exhibits a characteristic base composition (Montague and Morton, 1960). In higher organisms there is very little information about the origin and function of mitochondrial DNA; however Weiss and Pillai (1965) have shown that the mitochondria of mammalian neurons originate in the vicinity of the nucleus, and are then gradually transported toward the distal end of the axon without any marked increase in numbers.

Even though it may be found that multiplication of mitochondria occurs in most cells by growth and division of previously existing mitochondria, this would not exclude the possibility that other modes of origin exist. For instance, normal yeast cells grown anaerobically lack mitochondria, as well as cytochromes *a* and *b*, but in aerobic cultures they possess typical mitochondria. Linnane *et al.* (1962) have shown that anaerobic yeasts contain a special system of disconnected membranes or lamellae, which under aerobic conditions seem to orient and undergo

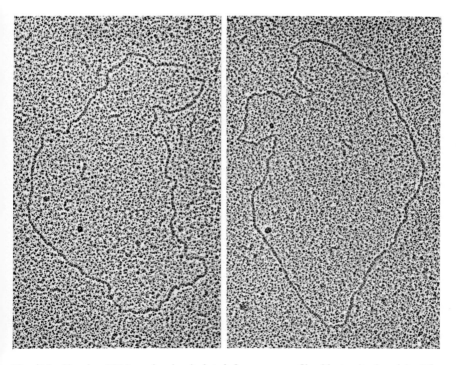

Fig. 7-6. Circular DNA molecules isolated from mouse fibroblast mitochondria. The circumference of each molecule is about 5 μ. 45,000×. From Nass (1966).

a fusion process to form recognizable mitochondria (compare with the reverse events observed in spermatogenesis by André, 1962). The formation of mitochondria in yeast would seem to be closely associated with the synthesis of cytochromes *a* and *b*, which behave like inducible enzymes since their formation is stimulated by exposure of the cells to an oxygen "substrate."

Electron micrographs sometimes show continuities between mitochondrial membranes and other membrane systems of the cell. The significance of these continuities is hard to assess, but it has often been suggested that they represent "budding" of mitochondria from the nuclear envelope, the endoplasmic reticulum, the Golgi apparatus, or the plasma membrane. In view of the evidence discussed in previous paragraphs, these interpretations seem unlikely; such membrane-to-membrane contacts may well represent transport phenomena or physiologically important processes other than genesis of mitochondria.

Similarity between Mitochondria and Chloroplasts

Throughout the preceding discussion of mitochondrial structure and function, a remarkable resemblance to chloroplast organization has been noted. Both chloroplasts and mitochondria are highly membraneous organelles enclosed by two semipermeable membranes, both contain a very similar structural protein and an actomyosin-like contractile protein, and both show ATP-dependent contraction. Both organelles appear to have the capacity for independent growth and division, including the presence of characteristic DNA's and RNA; both carry out phosphorylation of ADP coupled to electron transport phenomena; in both cases pyridine nucleotides, cytochromes, and quinones function as electron carriers, and electron transport can be coupled to active uptake of calcium and phosphate ions. The phosphorylation sites in both cases are localized in the internal membranes, which appear to be made up largely of fundamental phosphorylating units in replicate array; and as emphasized by Park and Pon (1963), there appears to be a similarity in size (mol. wt. about 2×10^6) and organization between the quantasome of the chloroplast and oxysome of the mitochondrion.

This similarity at all levels of organization has led to various hypotheses that chloroplasts might develop from mitochondria, or that both chloroplasts and mitochondria might develop by differentiation of a common proplastid. Although there is strong evidence for differentiation of chloroplasts from proplastids in *Euglena* and higher plants, no relationship has been found between these proplastids and mitochondria; proplastids often contain starch, which is not ordinarily present in mitochondria. Consequently an ontogenetic relationship between chloroplasts and mitochondria remains to be demonstrated, if it exists.

Nevertheless, it is possible that some phylogenetic relationship exists, such that one organelle may have evolved from the other, or both may have evolved from a common ancestral particle. This concept takes its most imaginative form in the hypothesis that the ancestral chloroplast or mitochondrion was a symbiotic microorganism. In the symbiote theory, the host cell is conceived as an anaerobe maintaining itself with energy from glycolysis (which is an extramitochondrial process) and the parasite is imagined as an autotrophic microorganism; the anaerobe–autotroph complex, once established, has the selective advantage of being able to capture energy either from substrates or from light. Subsequent modification of the autotrophic particles could lead to the oxidative capabilities associated with mitochondria. The symbiote theory receives some support from the fact that both chloroplasts and mitochondria contain all the mechanisms necessary to trap and convert energy from their environments, and they are apparently able to use this energy in self-replicative mechanisms, such as the synthesis of macromolecules and a more or less orderly division process. The low permeability and active transport capabilities of both mitochondrial and chloroplast membranes is also suggestive, especially when considered with the fact that in bacteria, oxidative and photophosphorylation are associated with the plasma membrane of the cell. It is interesting that some cells show an inhibition of respiration by glycolysis and vice versa (Pasteur and Crabtree effects), suggesting active competition for ADP or phosphate between the intramitochondrial and extramitochondrial processes.

8

MUSCLE CELLS AND CONTRACTILITY

Our surprise at the behavior of muscle is
. . . [due] to our failure so far to develop
. . . the study of the mechano-chemistry of
long [molecules] with chemically reactant
side groups.

J. R. PLATT *1961*

Previous chapters have described the mechanisms by which cells convert environmental energy into the chemical energy of phosphoryl compounds; this and following chapters will consider the wide variety of ways in which phosphoryl energy can be transformed to mechanical, electrical, bioluminescent, or nonphosphoryl biochemical energy—forms of energy which are required for the maintenance, growth, and reproduction of living matter. In most of these transformations, there is good evidence that ATP is intimately involved, and this has been established most firmly and in the greatest detail for the chemical-mechanical transductions of muscle. Indeed, ATP was first discovered in muscle by Lohmann (1929) during the analysis of anaerobic glycolysis as a primary energy source for contraction. The unique cytochemical-ultrastructural organization of striated muscle has also permitted special insights concerning energy transformations at a molecular level. This advanced state of understanding with respect to contractility in muscle will provide a basis for later discussion of contractile systems which are less well understood.

The gross appearance of muscle cells, as seen under the light microscope, is highly variable and includes cells that are conspicuously "striated" or cross-banded (but which vary widely in the details of banding), cells that show bands only during contraction, cells which show a diagonal or diamondlike pattern, cells which lack cross bands but have conspicuous longitudinal bands (sometimes in the form of coils or helices), and cells which appear to be entirely "smooth" or without resolvable differentiations. Despite this variability in gross morphology, all types of muscle have important functional properties in common and all show striking biochemical similarities. Examination of muscle fine structure also indicates that the contractile elements of all muscle cells are based on filamentous protein aggregates whose basic units are usually unresolvable with the light microscope. The variability in gross morphology of muscle cells seems to be due primarily to differences in the arrangement of these unresolvable filaments, which in the era of light microscopy probably received more emphasis than it deserved. For instance, in some molluscs the heart is striated while in others it is smooth; similarly, though Annelida, Onychophora, and Arthropoda have many structural features in common, most annelid and onychophoran muscles are smooth (including the locomotor muscles), while most arthropod muscles are striated (including the gut muscles). In scallops the adductor muscles contain two parts, one of which is striated and the other smooth. Finally, during the embryonic differentiation of striated muscles, their ability to contract often precedes the development of visible striations.

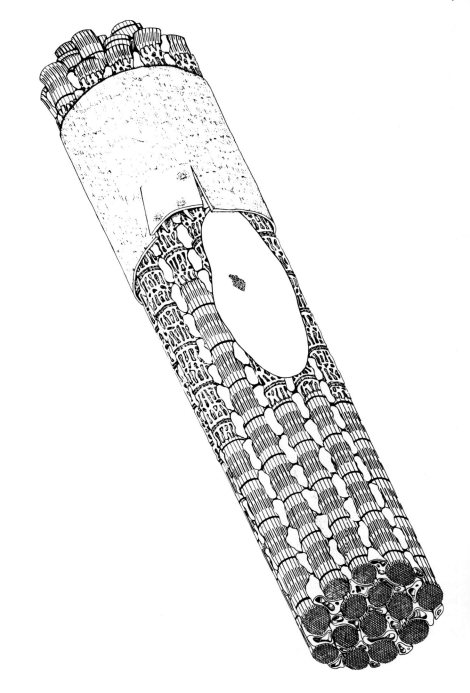

Muscle Ultrastructure

From a comparative analysis of muscle ultrastructure, three general classes of muscle cell are recognizable: (1) those in which the protein filaments are arranged in highly ordered, transverse arrays; (2) those in which the filaments are in orderly longitudinal or oblique arrays; and (3) those in which the filaments are in more or less random, longitudinal orientations.

Transverse Arrays

This class includes the most thoroughly studied types of muscle, particularly the striated skeletal and heart muscles of vertebrates. In skeletal muscle the cellular units are actually multiple structures (muscle fibers), which are formed by the fusion of several embryonic cells (myoblasts); each fiber is extremely long, roughly cylindrical in shape, and contains many peripherally located nuclei capable of replicating by amitosis (Fig. 8-1). Although the composite nature of such striated fibers was long a matter of controversy, Wilde (1958) has shown that intermingled myoblasts from chick and mouse embryos produce skeletal fibers containing nuclei from both species. Unlike skeletal fibers, vertebrate heart muscle contains recognizable uninucleate units, which Sjöstrand has shown are equivalent to single cells; although these cells are very intimately associated, they are set off from one another by transverse or oblique "intercalary disks" representing thickenings of the plasma membranes.

Mature skeletal fibers are highly variable in length and diameter, not only from one species to another, but within the same muscle. It is well known that the growth of a muscle from embryo to adult (including muscle development in athletes) occurs by increases in the diameters of existing fibers, rather than by increased numbers of fibers. Commonly the diameters vary from 10 to 100 μ, while the length of a single fiber in human sartorius muscle can exceed 34 cm.

As seen in Fig. 8-1, an individual skeletal fiber contains several parallel, longitudinal striated cylinders, or myofibrils, which are approximately 1–2 μ in diameter. The myofibrils are the actual contractile elements and are separated from one another by mitochondria, sarcoplasm, and sarcoplasmic reticulum (an extensive system of closed vesicles or lamellae bounded by single unit membranes: Porter and Palade, 1957).

Fig. 8-1. A dissected skeletal muscle fiber, showing cylindrical myofibrils surrounded by sarcosomes (mitochondria) and enclosed in a sarcolemma. Individual myofibrils are organized as a series of sarcomeres 2–3 μ in length. A nucleus is seen in a typical position just beneath the sarcolemma.

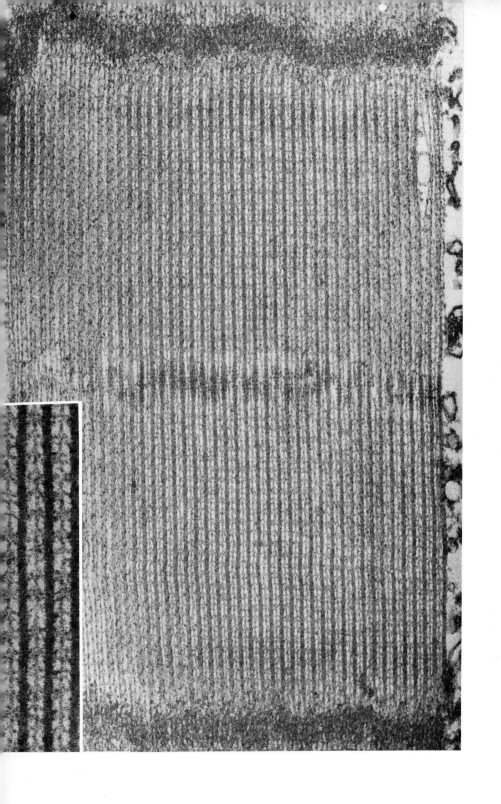

In cross section each myofibril shows a striking, hexagonal paracrystalline organization, whereas lengthwise the cross striations of all the myofibrils lie in register and are responsible for the cross-banded appearance of the muscle fiber as a whole. At higher magnification it can be seen that the striations of each myofibril divide it into tandem units, or *sarcomeres*, arranged end-to-end along the fibril; each sarcomere is separated from the next by a dense line or plate known as the Z line. As first described by Huxley and Hanson (1954), a single sarcomere contains two kinds of very fine filament, each occupying its own distinct morphological regions; at the two ends of the sarcomere, attached to the Z lines, are parallel, hexagonal arrays of "thin filaments" about 50–70 Å in diameter, while at the center of the sarcomere there are "thick filaments" about 110 Å in diameter, with a center-to-center spacing of 450 Å. The two kinds of filament overlap to a greater or lesser extent, producing two denser zones to either side of the mid-plane, where fine bridges connect the thick filaments with the intermingled thin filaments (Fig. 8-2).

When whole striated fibers are examined in the light microscope with plane polarized light, the entire thick filament region at the center of the sarcomere is anisotropic, i.e., it passes polarized light more rapidly in a longitudinal plane than in a transverse plane; consequently this region is called the A band. By contrast, the regions occupied exclusively by thin filaments do not show anisotropy, and they are therefore referred to as I bands (for isotropic). At lower resolutions the I bands of adjacent sarcomeres may appear to be continuous, so that A and I bands alternate regularly along the whole length of the fiber, A-I-A-I-A-I, etc.; nevertheless, it is usually possible to detect the fine Z line at the midpoint of each "duplex" I region. The center of the A band is also frequently divided by a light zone (where overlap does not occur), and this is referred to as the H zone.

As Fig. 8-1 shows, the entire muscle fiber is covered by a cell membrane, or sarcolemma, whereas the myofibrils within the fiber have no membranes. Ordinarily each striated fiber receives an axon branch from a motor neuron, which comes into close contact with the sarcolemma at a specialized motor end plate. It has long been known that the nerve impulse is propagated to all parts of the muscle fiber as an action potential associated with the sarcolemma. Recently Porter and Franzini-Armstrong (1964) discovered that the sarcolemma also sends out deep invaginations which penetrate each myofibril at the Z lines. It appears,

---

Fig. 8-2. Thin-section of an insect sarcomere, showing thick and thin filaments in overlapping array. The sarcomere is bounded at either end by two Z lines. Note numerous bridges connecting thick and thin filaments. 79,000×. Inset: The bridges are arranged in chevronlike groups with a periodicity of 380 Å. 150,000×. From M. Reedy, by permission.

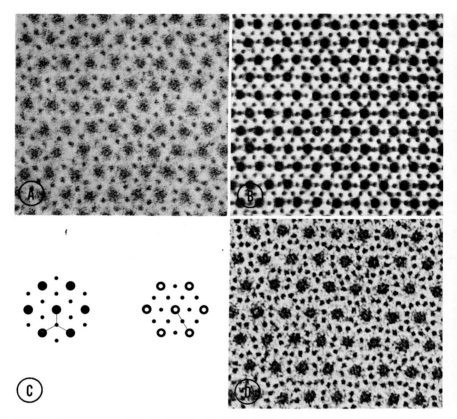

Fig. 8-3. (A) Cross-sectioned rabbit skeletal muscle, showing one thin filament for every three thick filaments. 182,000×. From H. E. Huxley (1966). (B) Cross-sectioned insect flight muscle, showing one thin filament for every two thick filaments. 122,000×. From M. Reedy, by permission. (C) Diagram contrasting the differences between vertebrate skeletal muscle and insect flight muscle. (D) Cross-sectioned cockroach femoral muscle, showing approximately two thin filaments for every two thick filaments. 150,000×. From Hagopian (1966).

therefore, that the contraction of all the myofibrils in the fiber is coordinated by the sarcolemma, which transmits motor impulses from the enervating neuron directly to each sarcomere.

Although the same basic organization is found in striated fibers across a wide range of animals, considerable variation occurs in such details as sarcomere dimensions, abundance of mitochondria, and amount of sarcoplasmic reticulum. In some instances, these variations can be correlated with functional differences; for example, the abundance of mitochondria seems to be related to constancy of activity, being greater in steadily active muscles (e.g., heart) and less in intermittent (but powerful) muscles. The development of sarcoplasmic reticulum, on the other hand, is related to the rapidity of the contraction-relaxation cycle, being greater in rapidly contracting muscles and less in slower muscles. Contraction-relaxation cycles as short as 0.00045 second have been observed in the flight muscles of gnats, whereas this cycle requires about 0.1 second in frog gastrocnemius.

With respect to sarcomere dimensions, overall lengths occur as great as 15 μ, but typical sarcomeres in vertebrate fibers are about 2–3 μ long. The proportions of I to A regions are also variable, and in fact both the length of the I band and the total sarcomere length decrease proportionately during contraction of the sarcomere. When I-band length is compared in striated fibers from different muscles at rest, this dimension seems to be correlated with the percent shortening which is normal for the particular fiber. Insect flight muscles shorten very little (bumble bee flight muscle fibers usually achieve only 88% of resting length), and these sarcomeres have unusually short I bands; typical vertebrate skeletal fibers, on the other hand, often shorten to 57% of their resting length, and correspondingly the I bands in rabbit psoas muscle measure 2.24 μ at full stretch (compared to 1.5 μ for the A bands). There is also some variability in the cross-sectional pattern of thick and thin filaments in the region of overlap. In vertebrate muscle each thin filament is about equidistant from three thick filaments, while each thick filament is surrounded by six thin filaments (Fig. 8-3A); the consequence of this geometry is that there are exactly twice as many thin filaments as thick ones. In insect flight muscle, on the other hand, each thin filament is equidistant from only two thick filaments, and the thick filaments also show a "hollow" center of low electron density, i.e., the centers are osmiophobic (Fig. 8-3B). In the walking muscles of cockroaches, Hagopian (1966) has found that each thick filament is surrounded by about twelve thin ones (Fig. 8-3D).

Longitudinal or Oblique Arrays

In classical light microscopy, muscle cells lacking transverse striations were regarded as belonging to a single class of "smooth" muscle; electron microscopy, however, has revealed several different types of smooth muscle, some of which very much resemble striated muscle in containing two types of filament in overlapping arrays. These muscle cells differ most conspicuously in that the arrays are not oriented as transverse sarcomeres with Z line boundaries, but lie in semicontinuous, oblique or longitudinal units.

The locomotor muscles of annelids and some molluscs are of a type known as "helical smooth"; this type of muscle can contract to 35% of its resting length, and in the light microscope helical smooth fibers seem to contain longitudinal fibrils running obliquely in parallel helices (giving the cell a barber-pole effect). Hanson and Lowy (1960) have shown that these helical bands, in the pharynx retractor of the snail *Helix* and in the mantle muscles of squids, contain thick and thin filaments linked together by cross bridges (as in striated sarcomeres). More recently Hanson and Lowy (1961) have found a similar organization in the so-called "paramyosin" muscle which closes the shell of the oyster; in this case each thick filament is surrounded by 12 thin filaments, and each thin filament tends to be equidistant between two thick filaments. When seen in longitudinal section, thick and thin filaments alternate in overlapping, diamond-shaped arrays, and the authors regard the thick filament regions as equivalent to A bands in striated muscle.

Random Longitudinal Orientations

Various types of "smooth muscle" occur in vertebrates and most other organisms, which show little specialized structure under the light microscope, and even by electron microscopy seem to lack any organization based on two types of filament in overlapping arrays. Cells of this type typically line the digestive and reproductive tracts of vertebrates. They are relatively small (50–250 μ long), spindle-shaped, and uninucleate. The smooth cells of rabbit uterus muscle do contain myofibrils about 0.5–1 μ in diameter, which like skeletal myofibrils are abundantly surrounded by mitochondria; however, these uterine myofibrils are anisotropic throughout their lengths and appear to be packed with more or less uniform, longitudinal filaments. Muscle cells from the digestive tract lack even myofibrils, but contain very fine, longitudinal filaments distributed throughout the cytoplasm. The contraction of this type of muscle is notable for its slowness and for the extreme degree of shortening that is possible under physiological conditions (particularly as compared with the much more rapid but less extreme contraction of striated muscle in the same organism).

Generalized Properties of Muscle Cells

Regardless of the particular way in which the contractile elements are organized, all muscle cells appear to share certain physiological and biochemical properties; this fact in itself suggests that the mechanisms of contractility may be basically similar in most or all cells. Some of the more important common physiological properties are the following:

1. It seems that all muscles produce their greatest force when they are at or near resting length; the shorter the muscle becomes in the contraction cycle, the less force it is able to exert. Furthermore when muscle fibers are stretched beyond their normal resting length, the force they can develop becomes progressively less.

2. In all types of muscle, the force that can be produced decreases as the velocity of contraction increases (and inversely, the velocity of contraction decreases as the weight on the muscle increases). When the weight or force becomes great enough, the velocity of contraction falls to zero and the length of the muscle does not change (although force is being produced); such a contraction is said to be isometric. During isometric contractions, the tension developed by a muscle is at a maximum (as velocity reaches a minimum). For most vertebrate muscles this maximum tension is in the order of 3–4 kg/cm^2 (cross-sectional area of muscle), but the paramyosin adductors of clams and other shellfish develop about twice this force. At the other extreme with zero tension (i.e., an unloaded muscle), the velocity of contraction reaches a maximum, and this varies from about 1 to 10 muscle lengths per second. For a typical vertebrate muscle, the velocity of contraction at half maximum load is about 1.8 μ/sec. The interrelationship between velocity and force in muscle is particularly intriguing because, if the contraction is viewed as a chemical reaction, it means that the rate of the reaction is influenced in a "feedback" manner by the amount of energy to be expended. An exact quantitative relationship between force and velocity in contraction has been expressed by Hill (1938) in the so-called "Hill equation":

$$(P + a)v = (P_0 - P)b$$

Here P is the tension developed, v is the velocity of contraction, P_0 is the isometric tension, and a and b are constants.

3. It is also a general property of muscle that the total quantity of energy the muscle expends in lifting a weight through a constant distance becomes greater as the weight increases. This is another remarkable feedback property, since it implies a mechanism whereby the muscle knows when more energy is required and is able to release just the right amount to match the demand. As suggested by Podolsky (1960), muscle contraction resembles an electrochemical reaction in this respect, e.g., the energy released by an automobile battery is greater during the high demands of starting the engine than during the more modest requirements when the engine is running.

4. If the weight on a muscle is suddenly released and then caught again, the force developed by the muscle falls briefly to zero, then recovers. This phenomenon implies that tension is transmitted through

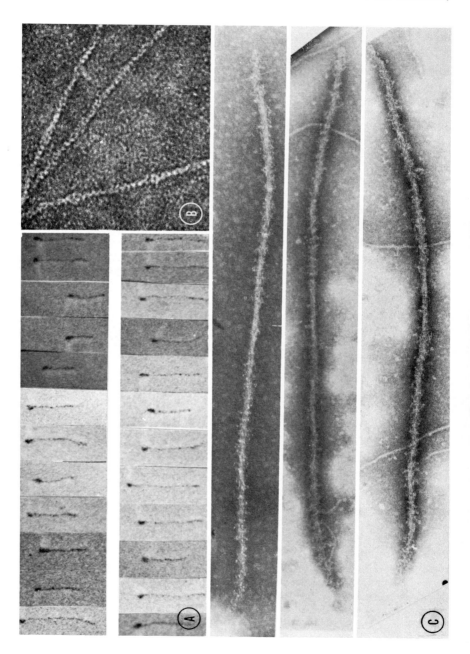

an elastic component, which is linked in series to the contractile mechanism (and is perhaps a part of it).

5. The well-known hardness or mechanical rigidity of a contracted muscle is also a property common to all kinds of muscle.

These and other physiological similarities among the different muscle types find a common denominator at the biochemical level in the occurrence of the three muscle proteins—actin, myosin and tropomyosin—which are universally present in muscle cells. Kuhne in the mid-1800's was the first to extract a characteristic muscle protein, which he named myosin. However, because of the complex and variable association now known to occur between actin and myosin, no consistent concept of the muscle proteins could be worked out until the isolation of actin by Straub (1942). Subsequently the third protein, tropomyosin, was isolated and characterized by Bailey (1948). These three proteins account for the following percentages of total protein and myofibril protein in rabbit muscle:

Protein	Percent of total protein	Percent of myofibril protein
Myosin	34	54
Actin	14–20	20–25
Tropomyosin	6–10	11

The remaining 30–40% of total protein is largely accounted for by components of the sarcoplasm, including the oxygen carrier myoglobin and the enzymes of anaerobic glycolysis. Szent-Györgyi (1960a) has pointed out that all the fibrous muscle proteins are characterized by high percentages of charged amino acid residues, the anionic groups being slightly in excess to give isoelectric points in the acid range (between pH 5 and 6).

MYOSIN

Individual myosin molecules, as visualized in the electron microscope by Huxley (1963) and Zobel and Carlson (1963), are tadpole-shaped objects with an overall length of 1520 ± 260 Å (Fig. 8-4A). The head piece accounts for about 150–250 Å of the total length and is about 40 Å in diameter, while the tail makes up the rest of the length and is about

Fig. 8-4. (A) Individual myosin molecules, each consisting of a globular "head" and an alpha-helical "tail." 90,000×. From Huxley (1963). (B) F-actin filaments, showing G-actin monomers in two, helically wound chains. Ca. 280,000×. From Hanson and Lowy (1963). (C) Isolated thick filaments from vertebrate sarcomeres, showing regularly spaced bridges which may correspond to the heads of single myosin molecules. 90,000×. From Huxley (1963).

15–20 Å in diameter. Measurements of the molecular weight vary considerably, but the most usual value is in the vicinity of 470,000. The myosin molecule also has a strong tendency to bind calcium and magnesium ions, as well as ATP; in the absence of Ca^{++} or Mg^{++} the isoelectric point is about pH 5.4, whereas in their presence it is shifted to pH 9.6. Pure myosin is insoluble in ion-free water, but is solubilized and extracted in 0.6 M KCl or other salt solutions.

In the literature prior to 1942, the term "myosin" usually refers to a complex between myosin (as it is understood now) and the protein actin (which had not yet been isolated). Nevertheless it was in this period that the ATPase activity of myosin was discovered by Engelhardt and Ljubimova (1939), and Weber (1935) demonstrated myosin's property of forming fibers when a myosin-salt solution is squirted into pure water. The discovery that myosin catalyzes the dephosphorylation of ATP provided an early suggestion that ATP is an immediate energy source in muscle contraction, but it is now known that ITP, UTP, CTP, and GTP are also catalytically hydrolyzed by myosin. The ATPase activity is markedly sensitive to various ions, being stimulated by Ca^{++} and inhibited by Mg^{++}. Nanninga and Mommaerts (1960) have shown that prior to hydrolysis, ATP is firmly bound to myosin in a 1:1 molar ratio, and that the free energy of binding is relatively high (in the order of -10 kcal/ mole). Since ATPase activity is inhibited in intact, relaxed muscles, it is likely that in this state each myosin molecule is associated with one bound ATP molecule.

Szent-Györgyi (1953) found that brief digestion with trypsin would separate pure myosin into two fractions of different molecular weights and differing sedimentation rates in the ultracentrifuge. The heavy fraction (heavy meromyosin) was water soluble (unlike intact myosin) and was found to have all the ATPase activity as well as the actin-binding property of myosin; Huxley (1963) has shown by electron microscopy that this fraction contains the "head" of the myosin molecule, together with part of the tail. The "light meromyosin" fraction, which contains headless tails, has the typical solubility characteristics of intact myosin, forms gels in water, but lacks ATPase or actin-binding activity. Apparently the effect of trypsin is to break the myosin molecule into two or more fragments, probably at specific peptide linkages. The molecular weights and lengths reported for the meromyosins have been somewhat variable, and it is possible that the exact sites of breakage and the number of fragments produced vary with experimental conditions. At the submolecular level, X-ray diffraction analysis of light meromyosin indicates that it is composed of two polypeptide chains in parallel, which are secondarily coiled or twisted around one another (Lowey and Cohen, 1962); the periodicity of the double chain is about 420 Å.

ACTIN

Actin was first isolated and its properties determined by Straub (1942). The monomeric form, which is known as G-actin, has a molecular weight in the order of 70,000, it is soluble in ion-free water, and it contains 1 mole of bound ATP together with 1 mole of bound calcium per mole of actin. Electron microscopy by Hanson and Lowy (1963) indicates that G-actin is an approximately spherical molecule with a diameter of about 56 Å, and X-ray diffraction analysis suggests that only about 30% of the polypeptide chain is in an α-helical configuration (compared to over 90% for light meromyosin). G-actin has no ATPase activity.

In weak salt solutions (0.1 M KCl) G-actin polymerizes to form F-actin, which shows molecular weights in the order of 1.5 to 3×10^6 and is highly insoluble in water. This polymerization is accompanied by dephosphorylation of the bound ATP, releasing inorganic phosphate to solution in 1:1 stoichiometry with the polymerized G-actin units. Both X-ray diffraction analysis and electron microscopy of F-actin (Hanson and Lowy, 1963; Huxley, 1963) show that the monomers are linked to form two helical chains twisted around each other (Fig. 8-4B). Each chain contains approximately 13 G-actin units per turn, and the cross-over points of the two chains therefore occur every 350 Å (two cross-over points per turn; 2×350 Å = approximately 13×56 Å); the diameter of the actin double helix is about 70–80 Å. It is of interest that X-ray diffraction analysis of whole muscle has revealed a universally occurring 400 Å periodicity which is associated with the presence of actin; however, no such periodicity occurs in isolated F-actin. Huxley has suggested that *in vivo* the F-actin helix may have a periodicity of 400 Å instead of the 350 Å measured *in vitro*.

Since the bound ADP and Ca^{++} in F-actin do not exchange with free molecules in solution (as they do in G-actin) and since agents which remove ADP or Ca^{++} bring about depolymerization of the F-actin chain, it appears that these two constituents are involved in bonding the G-actin units together. The addition of ATP to a suspension of F-actin also brings about reversible depolymerization. The fact that actin is in the polymerized form in intact muscle accounts for earlier difficulties in extracting it. The current procedure for preparing actin involves prior removal of myosin with 0.6 M KCl in the presence of pyrophosphate and Mg^{++} (to prevent actin depolymerization), followed by depolymerization and extraction of the actin with potassium iodide.

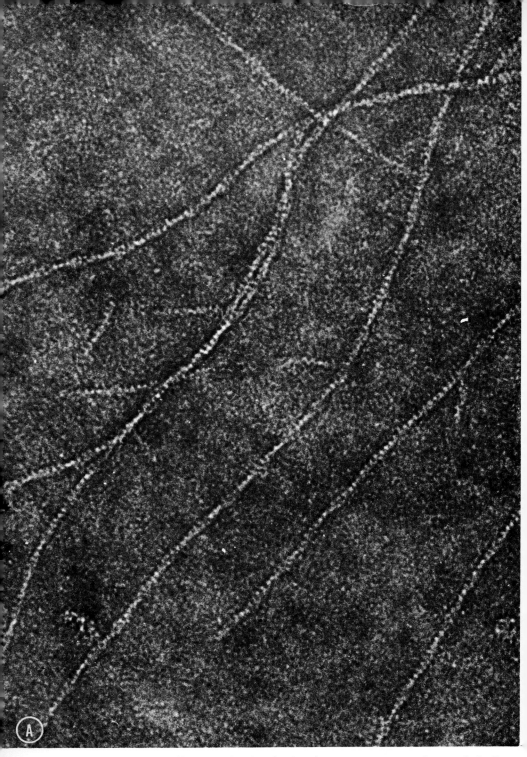

Fig. 8-5. (A) F-actin filaments, showing the G-actin monomers arranged as two helically twisted chains. 450,000×. From Hanson and Lowy (1963).

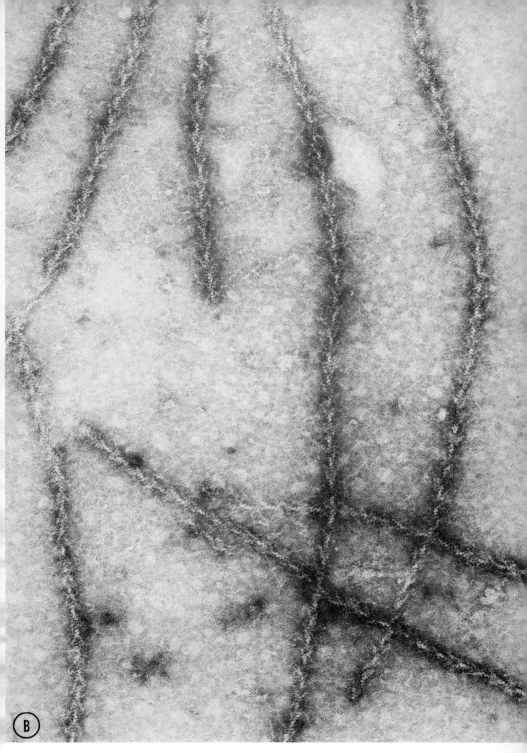

Fig. 8-5. (B) F-actin filaments with the heads of myosin molecules (H-meromyosin) attached. Note arrowlike polarity of the actomyosin complex. 155,000×. From Huxley (1963).

ACTOMYOSIN

When a preparation of pure myosin is mixed with a preparation of actin, the viscosity and flow birefringence of the mixture increases very rapidly, indicating that an actin–myosin complex is forming. The molecular weight of this "actomyosin" complex is very high, in the order of 20×10^6, and complex formation occurs with a definite stoichiometry (according to Szent-Györgyi, about 1 gm of actin for 4–5 gm of myosin); this ratio approaches a 1:1 molar proportion of G-actin monomers to myosin molecules. Huxley (1963) has examined negatively stained actomyosin preparations with the electron microscope and has found that the myosin molecules are bound obliquely and with a directional orientation to F-actin chains; the whole structure has a featherlike appearance with a periodicity of 366 Å (Fig. 8-5B). Huxley interprets this structure to mean that one myosin molecule binds to each G-actin monomer in the chain, forming a double helix of myosin molecules surrounding the F-actin double helix. A similar appearance is presented by mixtures of actin with heavy meromyosin.

It was discovered very early by Needham et al. (1941) and Dainty et al. (1944) that addition of ATP to an actomyosin mixture results in a very sharp drop in viscosity and flow birefringence, indicating that the actin-myosin complex has been disrupted. However, since myosin catalyzes the hydrolysis of ATP, the viscosity of the mixture gradually increases again as ATP is dephosphorylated to ADP, permitting re-formation of actomyosin. Addition of further ATP results in another sharp viscosity drop, again followed by gradual recovery. Such repetitive changes in viscosity in response to ATP are one of the most characteristic and sensitive properties of actomyosin, and are often used to identify actomyosin-like proteins in various cells other than muscle (Fig. 8-6).

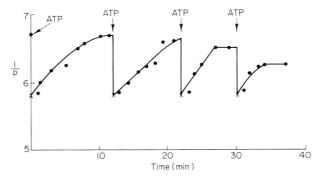

Fig. 8-6. The response of an actomyosin solution to ATP, as measured by fluorescence depolarization. The ATP induces a configurational change, which gradually reverses as myosin catalyzes ATP hydrolysis. From Tsao (1953).

A frequent variation on this experiment is recombination of actin from one source with myosin from another source; for example, Csapo (1960) has demonstrated that actin from striated muscle interacts with myosin from smooth muscle in the manner characteristic of actomyosin, and Ohnishi (1964) has obtained the same effect by recombining appropriate fractions from rabbit muscle and chloroplast "contractile protein."

It has been questioned whether the ATP-induced viscosity change in actomyosin solutions is due to separation of actin and myosin, or to changes in shape by the complex as a whole. However, Weber (1956) demonstrated that ultracentrifugation of actomyosin in the presence of ATP produces two separate sedimentation boundaries, whereas in the absence of ATP only a single boundary is produced. More recently, Huxley (1963) has observed directly with the electron microscope that the featherlike actomyosin complexes disappear on addition of ATP, leaving uncombined F-actin chains. It should be noted that the *separation* of actin and myosin is brought about by the *complexing* of ATP (Nanninga and Mommaerts, 1960) and is reversed by the hydrolysis of ATP; in the first stage, about one mole of ATP is complexed per mole of myosin released from actomyosin. It is believed that these test-tube reactions mimic events which take place *in vivo* during the contraction of muscle.

Tropomyosin

Most or all muscle cells contain a third characteristic protein, tropo-myosin, which lacks ATPase activity and is usually present in smaller amounts than actin or myosin. In vertebrates this protein constitutes about 5–10% of the total protein in both striated and smooth muscle. Tropomyosin is a fibrous molecule about 400 Å long, with a molecular weight of about 54,000; according to X-ray diffraction data, it resembles light meromyosin in being composed of two parallel polypeptide chains in α-helical configuration, but twisted around one another. The most notable property of this compound, as observed by Huxley (1963), is its ability to form quadrangular, crystal-like lattices with intersections spaced at about 200 Å and sides composed of filaments 20–30 Å in diameter. A structure very similar to this occurs in the Z lines of vertebrate skeletal muscle.

A related protein, called paramyosin or tropomyosin A, occurs in certain muscles such as the shell adductors of clams, which are able to maintain a high tension for long periods of time and with little expenditure of energy ("catch muscles"). Both molluscs and annelids possess paramyosin, which in some muscles may constitute 30% of the total protein (sometimes exceeding the amount of actomyosin). Paramyosin typically forms long, ribbonlike filaments about 0.1 μ in diameter inside the muscle fibers. Although neither tropomyosin nor paramyosin seems able to complex with actin in a manner analogous to the myosin–actin complex, Hanson and Lowy (1961) have reported that thick paramyosin filaments in the adductor muscles of the oyster form overlapping arrays with thin filaments, in a manner comparable to the arrangement of actin and myosin filaments in striated muscle. The paramyosin molecule is a rod about 1330 Å long, 20 Å in diameter, and with a molecular weight of 220,000—considerably larger than vertebrate tropomyosin; also unlike vertebrate tropomyosin, it is insoluble in pure water. Nevertheless, Lowey *et al.* (1963) have concluded that paramyosin, like tropomyosin and light meromyosin, consists of two parallel polypeptide chains twisted around each other; paramyosin and tropomyosin also resemble one another in lacking tryptophan or very much proline.

The Immediate Source of Energy in Muscle Contraction

In considering the mechanisms by which a contracting muscle is able to perform work, it is important to note that the unit of energy transfer by a muscle fiber is a complete contraction-relaxation cycle. In this respect a muscle fiber differs from a stretched spring, which may perform work by contracting but operates by expending potential energy stored when the spring was stretched; the stretched spring system cannot spontaneously reset itself, and its contraction is therefore not a cyclic phenomenon. One of the most notable features of muscle contraction, by contrast, is the ability to perform work repetitively. This is especially striking for the flight muscles of certain insects, which produce extremely rapid wing beats and sometimes achieve 1000 or more contraction-relaxation cycles in a second. It has been shown that the frequency of contraction in these muscles is a property inherent in the muscle fiber itself (myogenic rhythmic contraction) and far exceeds the frequency of motor impulses provided to the muscle by the central nervous system. Mammalian skeletal fibers are also capable of spontaneous oscillatory contractions under certain conditions.

Research to discover an energy-yielding reaction coupled to muscle contraction was begun early in the 20th century and led to the pioneer discovery of Fletcher and Hopkins (1907) that lactic acid accumulates in muscle during prolonged activity; later Meyerhof (1921) showed that the amount of lactic acid is proportional to the amount of work done. Subsequent research was directed toward discovering the source of the lactic acid, and led to the elucidation of a reaction series now known to be of universal occurrence in cells, i.e., anaerobic glycolysis (see Chapter 6). In the meantime, creatine phosphate and ATP were discovered in muscle (1927 and 1929, respectively), permitting Lundsgaard (1930) to determine that when lactic acid formation is inhibited, the tension produced by a muscle is proportional to the amount of creatine phosphate hydrolyzed; the lactic acid theory of contraction was therefore replaced by a creatine phosphate theory, supplemented during the 1930's by Meyerhof's generalized concept of high-energy phosphate compounds and the discovery of Warburg and others that the production of lactic acid from glucose is actually coupled with phosphorylation (Chapter 3).

The role of ATP was first inferred from the so-called "Lohmann reaction," i.e., the discovery by Lohmann (1934) that dialyzed muscle extracts do not catalyze hydrolysis of creatine phosphate directly, but do catalyze transphosphorylation to ADP, which is followed by hydrolysis of the ATP:

$$\text{creatine phosphate} + \text{ADP} \rightleftharpoons \text{creatine} + \text{ATP}$$
$$\text{ATP} + \text{H}_2\text{O} \rightleftharpoons \text{ADP} + \text{phosphate}$$

It was not long afterward that Engelhardt and Ljubimova (1939) demonstrated that myosin itself is an ATPase. Then in 1941 the concept of contraction as a specific interaction between ATP and a contractile protein was dramatically supported by Szent-Györgyi, who showed that *artificial* fibers of actomyosin prepared by the method of Weber (1935) contract strikingly *in vitro* on the addition of ATP.

As first reported, this *in vitro* contraction was not oriented in the direction of the fiber's long axis, but occurred proportionately in a transverse direction as well; i.e., unlike muscle fibers the artificial fibers did not become shorter and thicker but simply smaller in all dimensions (suggesting a syneresis effect). It was not until the next decade that Hayashi (1952) developed a technique for making artificial actomyosin fibers which clearly exhibit the most important properties of muscle contraction: i.e., they contract in the long dimension on addition of ATP, they have considerable tensile strength, and in fact they are capable of lifting small weights. The contraction of these artificial actomyosin fibers on addition of ATP is an unforgettable demonstration, clearly relating a biological phenomenon with its physicochemical explanation.

Although these experiments showed that the dephosphorylation of ATP by actomyosin could provide a source of energy for contraction *in vitro,* many careful attempts to correlate ATP expenditure with the work performed by an intact muscle proved to be unsuccessful. A step in this direction was achieved by Szent-Györgyi (1949) when he developed so-called "glycerol models" of muscle, in which whole muscle fibers are extracted with glycerol, removing ATP and most of the soluble proteins but leaving the sarcomeres intact; on addition of ATP, such "dead" muscle fibers show a very striking contraction. Nevertheless, it is only recently that the problem of detecting quantitative dephosphorylation of ATP in intact muscle has been solved. The main difficulty is the extreme rapidity with which ATP is regenerated after a muscle contraction by transphosphorylation from other phosphoryl compounds; it appears, in fact, that rephosphorylation occurs during the contraction phase itself, so that the same ATP molecule may undergo several dephosphorylation-rephosphorylation cycles during a single muscle twitch.

Two alternative mechanisms are involved: the first of these is provided by the enzyme, myokinase, which catalyzes the reaction

$$2 \, ATP \rightleftharpoons ATP + AMP$$

Myokinase probably occurs at the contraction sites themselves and functions to maintain a high ratio of ATP to ADP, thereby ensuring a high free energy of hydrolysis (see Chapter 3). The second rephosphorylation system is provided by the enzyme, creatine phosphoryltransferase, which catalyzes Lohmann's reaction. Cain *et al.* (1962) were able to measure the liberation of creatine and inorganic phosphate during a *single* muscle contraction under conditions when no change in ATP could be observed, and they reported that the amount of creatine phosphate expended is proportional to the external work performed. On the other hand, if creatine phosphoryltransferase was specifically inhibited, creatine phosphate remained the same but ATP diminished during the contraction. In this case the muscle could perform only about three contractions, instead of the 30 contractions obtained if creatine phosphate was available. In these experiments myokinase was uninhibited, and the change in ATP would therefore correspond to the equation

$$n \, ATP \longrightarrow (n - m) \, ADP + m \, AMP + (n + m) \, P_i$$

After correcting for the action of myokinase, Davies *et al.* (1963) observed that 0.64 μmole of ATP per gram of muscle is expended in performing 120 gm-cm of external work.

Although these experiments with *in vitro* and *in vivo* systems have demonstrated fairly conclusively that muscle contraction is directly coupled with ATP hydrolysis, the exact manner of this coupling is still under investigation. As in all coupled reactions, a common intermediate is expected, and it was suggested very early that actomyosin itself may become phosphorylated as a first step in the contraction process. This was in accord with the simplest early concepts of the actomyosin-ATP system, which postulated a reaction of the form

$$\text{actomyosin}_{\text{relaxed}} + \text{ATP} \longrightarrow \text{actomyosin}_{\text{contracted}} + \text{ADP} + \text{P}_i$$

However, the viscosity response of an actomyosin suspension to ATP clearly shows that an immediate configurational change results from the *binding* of ATP, whereas the hydrolysis of ATP is associated with a return to the original state of the suspension. This type of study suggests a cyclic reaction sequence of the form:

$$\text{actomyosin}_{\text{relaxed}} + \text{ATP} \longrightarrow \text{actomyosin-ATP}_{\text{contracted}}$$
$$\text{actomyosin-ATP}_{\text{contracted}} + \text{H}_2\text{O} \xrightarrow{\text{Ca}^{++}} \text{actomyosin}_{\text{relaxed}} + \text{ADP} + \text{P}_i$$

Nanninga and Mommaerts (1960) and others have found that both these reactions are exergonic (i.e., spontaneous). In fact it has long been known that an actomyosin suspension, after addition of ATP, not only changes spontaneously but also recovers spontaneously (Fig. 8-6). Both reactions have been observed to proceed with a 1:1 stoichiometry between ATP and myosin.

From these relationships it might be supposed that muscle contraction *in vivo* would be induced by the presence of ATP and would continue until ATP is entirely expended. However, this supposition does not fit well with the rapid regeneration of ATP that is known to occur during and after contraction. The question has therefore been asked, "What induces the active state in a myofibril *in vivo*, and alternatively, once the active state has been induced what permits the system to relax in the presence of both actomyosin and ATP?"

Marsh (1952) was the first to isolate a factor capable of inducing reversible relaxation in homogenized muscle fibers; in the presence of Marsh's factor, ATP first induced a lengthening and then a contraction of the fibers, the lengthening being associated with diminished ATPase activity (about one-tenth the activity observed in the absence of the factor). The relaxation factor was water soluble, easily extracted, labile, and of high molecular weight (i.e. nondialyzable). Subsequently it was found by Bendall (1953) that calcium ions have an antagonistic effect, tending to counteract the relaxing factor. In 1957, Portzehl found by differential centrifugation that all the relaxing factor activity is associated with fine granules (microsomes), and this was confirmed by Nagai *et al.* (1960), who reported that granular elements 700–3000 Å in diameter are able to inhibit muscle contraction and ATPase activity. Hasselbach and Makinose (1962) then discovered that these granular elements (which were understood to be vesicles of the sarcoplasmic reticulum) have a remarkable capacity for ATP-dependent accumulation of calcium ions; the uptake appears to be an active transport phenomenon in which Ca^{++} is pumped from the medium into the sarcoplasmic reticulum, where it may become concentrated as much as 1400-fold

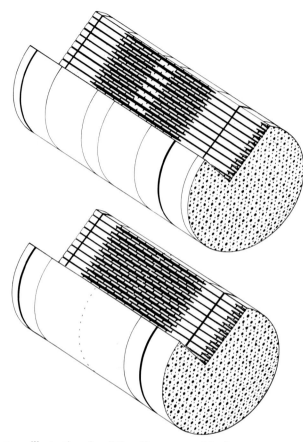

Fig. 8-7. Diagram illustrating the sliding filament model of sarcomere contraction. Thick and thin filaments move past one another, but do not necessarily change in length.

(compare with the massive Ca^{++} uptake by mitochondria described in Chapter 7).

Weber *et al.* (1963) and others have now developed the concept that the relaxed state in muscle is maintained by the absence of free calcium ions, which leads to inhibition of Ca^{++}-dependent ATPase activity by actomyosin. Almost all the calcium in normal, relaxed muscle is thought to be bound up in the vesicles of the sarcoplasmic reticulum; contraction is induced by release of Ca^{++}, which stimulates ATPase activity and is then rapidly removed again by the sarcoplasmic reticulum. Davies (1963) has pointed out that the "latent period" which characteristically intervenes between the stimulation of a muscle and its contraction is approximately the time required for diffusion of Ca^{++}. In muscles that maintain the contracted state for relatively long periods of time, the removal of calcium is thought to be a slow process, whereas in muscles which exhibit 1000 or more contraction-relaxation cycles per second it is extremely rapid. Such a relationship would be generally consistent with the observed development of sarcoplasmic reticulum, which is unusually abundant in rapid muscles and poorly developed in slow ones. Weber *et al.* (1963) have now observed a direct correlation between removal of calcium ion and inhibition of myofibrillar activity, and it has also been shown that ATPase activity and free calcium ions are both very much reduced during relaxation of whole muscles *in vivo.*

The Sliding Filament Model of Muscle Contraction

With the introduction of thin-sectioning techniques for the electron microscope in the early 1950's, it was soon discovered by H. Huxley (1953) that striated myofibrils are constructed of two kinds of filament in overlapping arrays; thick filaments about 110 Å in diameter occupy the A band at the center of the sarcomere, while thin filaments about 50 Å in diameter occupy the I zones at the two ends (Fig. 8-7). Also in the early 1950's, careful observation of changes in the A and I bands of living muscle fibers revealed that during moderate contractions the I bands shorten and finally disappear, whereas no measurable change occurs in the lengths of the A bands. Reasoning from these two primary observations, H. Huxley and Hanson (1954) and A. F. Huxley and Niedergerke (1954) simultaneously proposed that contraction of striated muscle occurs by a sliding together of the A filaments and the I filaments. It was visualized that the filaments themselves remain constant in length, in sharp distinction to previous theories of muscle contraction which postulated an intrinsic shortening of continuous fibrous elements.

Considerable evidence has now been accumulated to confirm that the A and I filaments do, in fact, move past one another when the myofibril shortens or is stretched. For instance, H. Huxley and Hanson (1954) examined thin-sectioned myofibrils with the electron microscope after stretching or contraction, and found that the overlap between thick and thin filaments increases as the muscle shortens (Fig. 8-7). This relationship was confirmed for frog muscle by Carlsen *et al.* (1961), who observed that the length of the overlap zone is linearly correlated with changes in fiber length. Page and H. Huxley (1963) also confirmed that the A and I filaments have the same lengths in both relaxed and contracted frog skeletal muscle (the A filaments measuring 1.6 μ and the I filaments about 1.0 μ from the Z band to their free ends). From these dimensions and the sarcomere length in myofibrils at reference length (2.5 μ) it can be estimated that sliding together of perfectly rigid filaments would be sufficient to account for a contraction to about 65% of resting length (muscle contractions *in situ* are usually less than this).

The chemical composition of the A and I filaments was also inferred very early by Hasselbach (1953) and H. Huxley (1953), who extracted myosin specifically in 0.6 M KCl (with pyrophosphate and Mg^{++}), and determined that this extraction removes most of the mass of the A band, as seen by light microscopy; such treatment also specifically removes the thick 110 Å sarcomere filaments, as seen by electron microscopy. Since the remaining, nonmyosin material (primarily actin and tropomyosin) is concentrated in the I zones, it was also postulated that the thin 50 Å filaments contain actin; subsequently this was confirmed by Hanson and H. Huxley (1955), who showed that specific extraction of actin by potassium iodide removes the thin filaments. More recently Hanson and Lowy (1963) and Huxley (1963) have succeeded in examining isolated thin filaments in the electron microscope after negative staining, and have observed that these filaments are apparently identical with F-actin polymers, i.e., they contain two chains of globular 55 Å subunits wound helically around each other with a cross-over periodicity of 350 Å (Fig. 8-5). In a similar but less detailed manner, Huxley (1963) has also related the structure of isolated thick filaments to aggregates of myosin molecules (Fig. 8-8A).

The existence of visible bridges between the thick myosin filaments and the thin actin filaments was also noted by H. Huxley (1953) in his original electron microscope study. These bridges are now known to be extensions from the thick myosin filaments, measuring about 30–40 Å in diameter and about 180 Å long, and they are positioned on the thick filament at regular intervals along an imaginary spiral line which winds around the filament every 435 Å (Fig. 8-4C). Six bridges project out in the course of each 435 Å turn, contacting each of the surrounding six thin filaments at appropriate angles; consequently, the thick filaments have one bridge every 72 Å (435/6). Owing to the geometry of the hexagonal packing, each thin filament lies equidistant from *three* of the thick filaments, and is therefore expected to be contacted by one bridge from each of the three in the course of one 435 Å period; this means that a thin filament engages one bridge every 145 Å (435/3).

In his studies of isolated thick filaments, H. Huxley (1963) discovered that there is a region about 1500–2000 Å long at the exact center of the filament which is free of bridges (Fig. 8-4); pure myosin molecules also tend to aggregate in a bipolar manner, forming a fiber with the globular heads at the two ends separated by a smooth region about 1500 Å long.

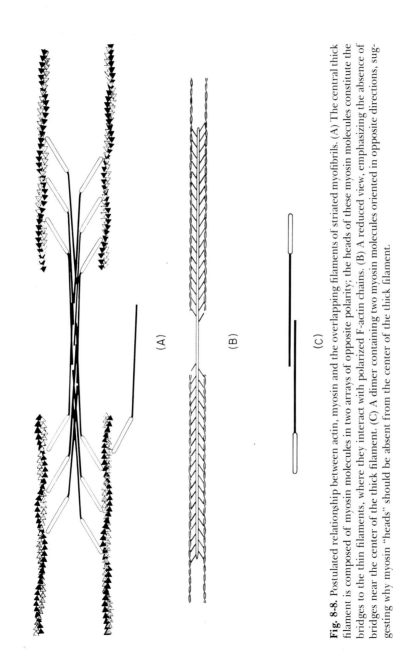

Fig. 8-8. Postulated relationship between actin, myosin and the overlapping filaments of striated myofibrils. (A) The central thick filament is composed of myosin molecules in two arrays of opposite polarity; the heads of these myosin molecules constitute the bridges to the thin filaments, where they interact with polarized F-actin chains. (B) A reduced view, emphasizing the absence of bridges near the center of the thick filament. (C) A dimer containing two myosin molecules oriented in opposite directions, suggesting why myosin "heads" should be absent from the center of the thick filament.

These observations have been interpreted to mean that the thick filaments are bipolar aggregates of myosin molecules, with the bridges "facing" in opposite directions to the left and right of the center (cf. Figs. 8-2 and 8-8). The molecular weight of a thick filament is estimated at about 160×10^6; assuming the filament to be composed entirely of myosin (mol. wt. 47×10^4), one filament would then contain about 300 myosin molecules. The estimated number of bridges per thick filament is also about 200–220, so that these data would suggest that one bridge occurs for each myosin molecule (a correspondence that becomes more exact if some fraction of the thick filaments is non-myosin).

The ultrastructural bridges between thick and thin filaments are therefore regarded as the visible equivalent of chemical linkages between actin and myosin. Since it is specifically the "head" end of the myosin molecule which has all the actin binding activity (i.e., heavy meromyosin), it has been postulated further that the bridges correspond to the globular *heads* of aggregated myosin molecules composing the thick filaments (Fig. 8-8). In fact Huxley (1963) has observed binding of purified myosin heads to F-actin filaments with the electron microscope. Inasmuch as the ATPase activity of myosin is also localized at the head of the molecule, it would follow that this function too is localized in the bridges between the thick and thin filaments.

H. Huxley (1963) also reported an apparent polarity in the thin actin filaments, such that the thin filaments at opposite ends of the sarcomere "point" in opposite directions; this actin bipolarity seems to complement the bipolarity of the myosin filaments at the center (Reedy, 1968). A corollary of this relationship is that the direction of the thin filaments on opposite sides of a Z line (i.e., in two different sarcomeres) must be opposite. At one time it was believed that the thin filaments might be continuous across the Z line, but this newer evidence indicates that the Z line is a true boundary between sarcomeres.

The thin filaments, when seen in thin-sectioned cells or by X-ray diffraction, exhibit a 406 A periodicity, and a similar X-ray periodicity characterizes all types of intact muscle cells (including nonstriated); in striated rabbit psoas muscle, 26 such periods occur in each thin filament from the Z line to its ending in the A band (26×406 Å $= 1.06 \mu$). Strangely enough, however, no 406 A periodicity has been found in *isolated* F-actin threads, and for this and other reasons Huxley (1963) has suggested that thin filaments *in situ* may contain tropomyosin in association with actin. Pure tropomyosin has been observed by Huxley to form quadrangular lattices of form and dimension similar to lattices found in the Z lines by Knappeis and Carlsen (1962). All this evidence suggests that tropomyosin may be a constituent of the Z line and that it may extend out into the thin filaments of the I band, weaving them to the ends of the sarcomere; the combination of actin and tropomyosin might then produce the 406 Å periodicity observed in the thin filaments.

The present detailed state of information concerning the ultra-structure of striated muscle, when considered with previous biochemical data, permits a fairly clear interpretation of the mechanisms involved in muscle contraction. The primary event is cyclic in nature and in-volves a repetitive formation and breakage of actin-to-myosin linkages represented by the bridges between thick and thin filaments. As these linkages are formed and broken, the two sets of filaments are induced to move past one another, leading either to shortening of the sarcomere or to the development of isometric tension (Fig. 8-7). From the viscosity response of actomyosin solutions to ATP, it may be inferred that bridge linkages are formed in the *absence* of ATP and are ruptured in its pres-ence. The cycle of events at each bridge might then be visualized as follows:

1. Formation of a linkage between one myosin head (bridge) and one globular G-actin unit.
2. Rupture of the linkage by one ATP molecule.
3. Hydrolysis of the ATP molecule, catalyzed by myosin ATPase in the presence of Ca^{++}.
4. Formation of a new linkage between the same myosin head (bridge) and the next globular G-actin unit.

The relative movement involved in breaking and re-forming the link-age of any *given* bridge would be the diameter of a single G-actin unit, i.e., 56 Å. However since not all the bridges operate simultaneously, the unit (or increment) of movement between any two filaments could be much less than this. Huxley (1963) has estimated that the difference in register between G-actin units and myosin bridges may be as little as 8 Å, making this the minimum increment of movement.

A number of the general properties of muscle contraction, as deter-mined for striated muscle, can be accounted for in terms of this sliding filament model. For instance, the fact that the myofibril produces less tension at lengths greater than reference length would be a direct re-flection of decreased overlap between thick and thin filaments, accom-panied by a reduction in the number of bridge linkages available. The fall in tension at shorter lengths could be accounted for by the forcing apart of the thick filaments and other progressive distortions. The well-known rigidity of muscle during contraction or in *rigor mortis* would be accounted for by the formation of strong mechanical linkages be-tween the actin and myosin filaments in the absence of ATP. Finally, the existence of an inverse relationship between tension produced and velocity of contraction would also be understandable if each bridge operates at a more or less constant rate (or probability of reaction); in this case, the faster two filaments move relative to one another, the fewer "linkage cycles" can occur and the less energy can be expended per unit of movement. This principle is well illustrated in a "tug-of-war" analogy: as long as the rope is relatively stationary, all the players can exert force on it with both hands simultaneously and tension is maximum (= isometric contraction); however, as soon as one team begins to win, the rope is pulled in rapidly and tension falls as each player removes his hands from the rope to take a new grip.

A particularly attractive feature of the sliding filament model is that, by postulating that ATP is expended only during the *breaking* of linkages, it can account for the "feedback" correlation between amount of energy expended and amount of external work required (or "load"); energy is expended only in proportion to the number of linkages broken and re-formed, while the number of linkages broken and re-formed is determined by the distance and rate at which the filaments slide past one another. In effect, muscle contraction behaves as a one-dimensional chemical reaction, the rate and extent of reaction being expressed directly on a linear scale, i.e., sarcomere length.

Thanks to the precise geometric arrangement and dimensions of the sarcomere filaments, it is also possible to test the sliding filament model by exact quantitative predictions. For example, the mass of thick or thin filaments in a given volume of whole muscle can be calculated, and these masses generally agree with the amounts of myosin or actin which can be extracted. Huxley (1960) has also been able to calculate that the number of bridges contained in a volume of muscle 1 cm square and one-half sarcomere long is approximately 6.5×10^{12}; using this figure, Davies (1963) has estimated that the force produced by each bridge at maximum tension is about 3×10^{-7} dyne, a value which is compatible with the energy available from hydrolysis of one ATP molecule per bridge. The distance through which this force acts can also be estimated from the work produced ($d = W/F$), and is in the order of 50–100 Å. Consequently the energetics of whole muscle is compatible with the idea that each bridge expends one ATP unit as the filaments move through a distance equivalent to one G-actin monomer. For more rapid contractions, empirical data indicate that the number of ATP molecules expended by each bridge becomes much less than one per G-actin unit of contraction; in Davies' experiments, about 7 ATP molecules were hydrolyzed per bridge in a movement of 4700 Å (one per 650 Å). This effect is consistent with the well established decrease in maximum tension which occurs as velocity of contraction increases (Hill equation).

Contraction at the Molecular Level

Szent-Györgyi (1960a) has emphasized that, although the sliding together of overlapping filaments during contraction of striated muscle is well established, it is still necessary to postulate configurational changes at the molecular level which bring about the sliding. These molecular deformations may be regarded as the *primary* mechanism of contraction and can be expected to form a common basis for contractility in smooth muscles, isolated actomyosin fibers, and other systems which do not contain paracrystalline arrays of filaments. Platt (1961) has also developed the concept that contractility, as well as many other "biological" properties of macromolecules, may be partly or entirely a consequence of large molecular size per se. Thus many small molecules contain interatomic bonds which change length or direction under different environmental conditions; it is only in a large fibrous molecule, however, that these tiny bond changes can summate to produce striking changes in overall dimension (i.e., contraction-relaxation). In fact, contraction has been observed in various large molecules other than actomyosin, including both protein and nucleic acid molecules. However, such mechanochemical effects have received little study.

Stated in terms of the sliding filament model, the fundamental question is what molecular changes bring about the *progressive* reattachments of each bridge, i.e., the minimum increment of movement. Two main possibilities have been suggested: (1) that the bridges themselves are flexible and perform a swinging movement akin to the arm movements of a man hauling in a rope; and (2) that the filaments (either the thick or thin ones) perform a wriggling movement, which might be compared to the crawling of an earthworm (the bridges behaving like rigid bristles). There is also a third possibility which has received less attention, i.e., that the filaments spin and progress past one another in the manner of helical gears. These various alternatives will be considered separately.

The hypothesis of cyclical bridge movements has been developed in greatest detail by Davies (1963), who postulates that the axis of each H-meromyosin bridge contains a flexible polypeptide chain and that this chain can exist in either an extended or contracted configuration. This configurational change is compared to the known change from an α to β configuration which has been described for the polypeptide polyglutamic acid; in this example, a chain of 50 glutamic acid monomers would have a length of 180 Å in the β-form (observed at high pH), whereas in the form of an α-helix (observed at low pH) its length would be only 75 Å. The difference of 105 Å would represent the unit of movement produced when the bridge shortens from the β to the α form. Davies further postulates that the linkage between this contractile polypeptide and the moving F-actin chain is established by a calcium ion chelate formed between the bound ATP of myosin and the bound ADP of actin. Initially the contractile myosin chain would be kept extended by repulsion of the negatively charged ATP molecule at its free end, but upon chelate formation (requiring the presence of Ca^{++}) the charge would be neutralized and the bridge would contract; contraction would continue until the ATP was drawn into the myosin ATPase site, when the linkage would be broken by hydrolysis. Subsequent rephosphorylation of the terminal ADP from cytoplasmic ATP would then cause the chain to reextend, and the cycle would be repeated as long as Ca^{++} and ATP remained available.

A somewhat different mechanism of cyclical bridge movements was postulated earlier by A. F. Huxley (1957), who suggested that bridges attached to myosin by elastic connections might be brought to the actin binding sites by Brownian movement (i.e., thermal agitation); the actin filaments would then be moved when the elastic elements "snapped back" from their thermal distortion. The movement would be rendered unidirectional and thermodynamically reasonable by the polarity of an ATPase site capable of breaking the actin-myosin linkage at the expense of ATP energy.

That the thick or thin filaments themselves may undergo some shape change during contraction has been suggested by several lines of research; if indeed the filaments are able to "crawl" past one another, then it becomes unnecessary to postulate armlike contractions by the bridges. High precision measurements of volume changes in isolated myofibrils have revealed that contraction is accompanied by a slight decrease in total volume (0.028 cm³ per gram of muscle), which is best accounted for by net changes in the shapes of the molecules composing the myofibril. Furthermore, Carlsen *et al.* (1961) observed in thin-sectioned frog muscle that, although the extent of overlap between thick and thin filaments increased with contraction (as previously reported), the diameters of the thick filaments also increased from 104 ± 9 to 117 ± 9 Å (after a 50% shortening of the myofibril). Stephens (1965) has also reported that in glycerinated myofibrils from several species of invertebrates, the A bands (= thick filaments) exhibit detectable shortening during isometric contractions (although not when the fiber is allowed to shorten). Shortening of both A and I filaments during isometric contraction has also been observed by Carlsen et al. (1961) in frog skeletal muscle.

It should be noted that striated muscle fibers under nonphysiological conditions are able to achieve much more extreme contractions (e.g., 20% of reference length) than can be provided for by a simple sliding together of rigid filaments (which would permit shortening to about 65% of resting length). In fact such "supercontracted" fibers, when examined by electron microscopy, show severe distortions in both the thick filaments (which crumple up against the Z line) and the thin ones (which meet and crumple up in the middle of the sarcomere). It would seem that shortening of the filaments per se is inadequate to explain such extreme effects.

As noted previously, both the H-meromyosin bridges and the F-actin thin filaments have a helical or screw like organization; in fact, it has been suggested repeatedly (Huxley, 1957; Jarosch, 1964; Reedy, 1968) that the actin filaments may spin in the manner of helical gears as they move past the thick myosin filaments. Another possibility is that the thick filaments, which lie unattached at the center of the sarcomere, may be induced to spin around their long axes by slight changes in their own lengths and pitch, which would "drive" them into the F-actin filaments as a corkscrew is driven into cork. Jarosch (1964) has shown that slight changes in the pitch of a flexible screw are able to produce very significant rotational forces, and in one model system, a 7% change in pitch led to 17.5 rotations of a flexible screw. According to Jarosch, a decrease in helix pitch (which would be expected to accompany a shortening of the thick filaments) would produce a symmetrical contraction movement at the two ends of the A band, whereas an increased pitch would produce a relaxation movement. For a *flexible* screw, these relationships do not depend on whether the "thread" is left- or right-handed. This mechanism may eventually provide a basis for understanding many still-baffling properties of muscle contraction, both in striated and nonstriated systems.

9

PRIMITIVE MECHANISMS OF MOTILITY

> Contractility is a universal property of living cells.
>
> J. HANSON AND J. LOWY *1960*

Although the oriented contraction of muscle cells is one of the most spectacular (and specialized) of cell movements, many other types of specific cell movement have been investigated: these include the beating of cilia and flagella; a wide variety of protoplasmic "streaming" phenomena, including different types of pseudopodal or amoeboid movement; the specific positioning of organelles within cells (e.g., chloroplasts and mitochondria); "saltatory" movements of some organelles; a rapid axial rotation of the nucleus which occurs in some cells; and the various highly ordered movements of chromosomes and cell surface which are involved in cell division. In no instance has the mechanism of movement been as elaborately analyzed at a molecular level as in the contraction of striated muscle; nevertheless, sufficient data are available to show that marked resemblances exist between the more primitive mechanisms of motility and those of muscle contraction.

Certainly the most recurrent theme is the requirement for ATP as a direct energy source. Typically this ATP requirement is correlated with the presence of one or more proteins which exhibit catalytic ATPase activity and which often show actomyosin-like viscosity changes in the presence or absence of ATP. Although it is by no means clear that contractility per se is involved in all mechanisms of cell motility, the possibility that it is has not been excluded; mechanisms involving contractions of only a few percent in length would be entirely sufficient to account for many types of biological movement. Furthermore, Platt (1961) has emphasized that the property of contractility may be a general one for any long, fiber-form macromolecule; thus, if a particular atomic bond is capable of existing in two configurations differing by 1 Ångstrom unit (Å) in length, then any molecule which contains a series of 100 such bonds should be able to exist in two extreme configurations differing by 100 Å in length. It may be recalled that "contractile proteins" have recently been isolated from both mitochondria and chloroplasts (see Chapters 5 and 7), where they are believed to bring about characteristic shape and volume changes in these organelles.

In at least one instance, it has been possible to observe directly the contraction of a structure which is composed primarily of a small number of identical protein molecules. The tail sheath of a T2 bacteriophage virus is essentially a hollow cylinder of protein, which can be detached and purified in bulk. Electron microscopy of negative-stained tail sheaths has been carried out by Brenner *et al.* (1959), who found that the contracted sheath has a length of 350 Å, a diameter of 250 Å, and a central hole 120 Å in diameter (Chapter 15); in the relaxed state, the same sheath has a length of about 800 Å, a diameter of 165 Å, and a cen-

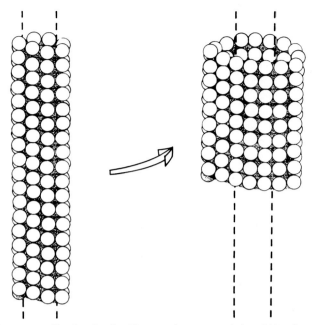

Fig. 9-1. The contractile sheath of a T-even phage, containing 144 spheroid subunits in helical array.

tral hole about 70 Å in diameter. The structure of the sheath, as seen after negative staining, is based on approximately 144 spherical subunits, each about 30–40 Å in diameter and arranged as a helical chain (Fig. 9-1). When solubilized, the sheath protein sediments in the ultracentrifuge as a homogeneous molecule of about 55,000 molecular weight, indicating that all the subunits are identical. Sarkar *et al.* (1964) have also determined that the molecular weight of an entire contracted tail sheath is about 8×10^6 and that the sheath protein contains 144 histidine units per sheath; since the protein is homogeneous, this would indicate that each protein subunit has one histidine residue, confirming that there are 144 such subunits and that the molecular weight of each is about 55,500 (8×10^6 divided by 144).

Wahl and Kozloff (1962) have also found that each tail sheath contains 42 molecules of ATP, plus about 100 molecules of UTP, GTP, and deoxy-ATP, as well as 160 calcium ions; this would correspond closely to one high-energy phosphoryl and one calcium ion per protein subunit. When the virus is exposed to its host, the sheath contracts with an accompanying release of calcium and inorganic phosphate, while the bound ATP is hydrolyzed to ADP. A reverse reaction, involving partial relaxation of the isolated sheaths upon addition of ATP, has been observed by Sarkar *et al.* (1964), who interpret the effect as expansion of a folded polypeptide chain brought about by charge repulsions. Though the precise mechanism of contraction is not yet known, similar 165–250 Å hollow cylinder structures, composed of spheroid protein molecules in helical array, occur widely in the cells of higher organisms (i.e., cytoplasmic microtubules). It is therefore of much significance that, in bacteriophage viruses, this type of structure carries out an active contraction coupled to the hydrolysis of ATP.

Bacterial Flagella

Movement by the beating of one or many whiplike organelles is very widespread among living organisms and occurs in specific types of cell from bacteria to man. However, bacterial flagella are considerably simpler in organization than the flagella of other cells and will be discussed as a class in themselves.

The flagella of bacteria are comparable in length to more complex cilia and flagella, ranging from 3 to 12 μ, but their diameters are much less, in the order of 120–190 Å; individual flagella are much too fine to resolve with the light microscope. On the other hand, many bacteria possess multiple flagella which are composed of individual flagella closely clustered at the poles of the cell and interwoven to form a much larger, cablelike structure; such multiple flagella are light resolvable, especially after staining. When seen by electron microscopy, the individual flagella typically exhibit a long, helical twist, the period of the helix being characteristic for the species (Fig. 9-2).

It is practical to deflagellate mass suspensions of bacteria, isolating the flagella in bulk by differential centrifugation for later chemical analysis; such deflagellated bacteria are viable and can be studied further with respect to regeneration of flagella, which is correlated with the return of motility. Using this type of approach, Weibull (1953) found that bacterial flagella are at least 99% protein and do not contain significant nucleotides or phosphorus (thereby excluding bound ATP). The protein component, which is dissociated into monomers by treatment with heat or acid, was named "flagellin" by Astbury (1955), and the molecular weight was determined as 40,000. Although the amino acid composition of flagellin differs somewhat from species to species, these proteins characteristically lack tryptophan, histidine, proline, and hydroxyproline.

Flagellin monomers have been resolved in electron micrographs of negative-stained whole flagella by Kerridge *et al.* (1962), who reported that they have subspheroid dimensions of 30 Å by 45 Å. Although the exact arrangement of protein monomers in the whole flagellum is difficult to determine with certainty, X-ray diffraction studies of *Proteus vulgaris* by Swanbeck and Forslind (1964) indicate that each flagellum is composed of three spiral filaments about 50 Å in diameter and coiled around each other like the strands of a rope; in addition, the center of the rope is hollow, the hole having a diameter of 10–20 Å. Labaw and Mosley (1955) inferred a very similar structure from electron micrographs of the flagella of *Brucella,* where the triple helix was found to be left-handed, the total diameter of the flagellum being 139 Å and the periodicity of the helix 190 Å. More recently, Abram and Koffler (1964) have found that flagellin monomers in acid solution will aggregate spontaneously to form structures almost indistinguishable from native flagella (Fig. 9-2); this aggregation occurs in phosphate buffer when the pH is raised to 5.4–5.9, and the rate of the reaction increases with the concentration of flagellin.

In deflagellated bacteria, the regeneration of flagella is inhibited by chloramphenicol, which is an inhibitor of protein synthesis; Kerridge (1959) has also found that if such deflagellated bacteria are reared on a medium containing fluorophenyl alanine instead of alanine, the resulting flagella are abnormal in shape and immotile. From these and similar experiments, it seems likely that the ability of a bacterium to form a flagellum is primarily a function of its ability to synthesize the characteristic protein, flagellin. It is known that this ability is absent in some genetic mutants, which consequently produce nonmotile daughter clones. Rates of flagellar synthesis as high as 1 μ per 2–3 minutes have been reported; however, since the length of flagella in a given species is constant, it appears that flagellin synthesis must be subject to some type of "feedback" control, which shuts off synthesis when a given length is achieved.

Although the exact mechanism by which movement is produced in flagellated bacteria is subject to some dispute, the best evidence is that polar flagella rotate in a conical path, causing the bacterium itself to rotate in the opposite direction (due to conservation of angular momentum). Metzner (1920) has measured rotations of 40 revolutions per second in some multiple flagella, producing counterrotation of the cell body at a rate of 12–14 revolutions per second. Since the cell body often has a spiral form, such cells essentially "screw" their way through the medium. Unfortunately, the mechanism which produces rotation of the flagellum has not yet been established, nor is the role of ATP in this movement clearly determined. Jarosch (1964) has pointed out that very slight changes in the periodicity of entwined helical strands can result

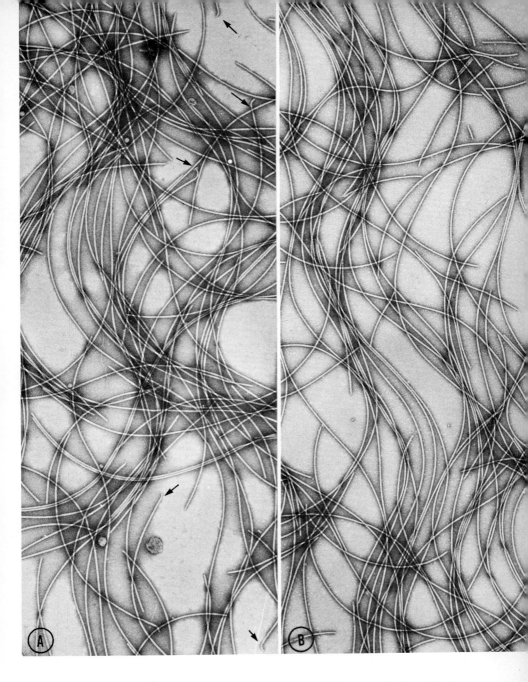

Fig. 9-2. (A) Native isolated flagella from *Bacillus*. Arrows indicate so-called proximal hooks. (B) Reconstituted flagellalike filaments formed in phosphate buffer at pH 5.4, after solubilization of native flagella. 38,800×. From D. Abrams, by permission.

in either rotation or supercoiling of the entire bundle; however no direct evidence is available to indicate that such changes in periodicity actually occur in bacterial flagella.

Cilia and Flagella

Many algal, protozoan, and metazoan cells possess cilia or flagella which, unlike bacterial flagella, are clearly resolvable with the light microscope. In fact, the existence of such organelles was well-established by pioneer microscopists during the late 1700's. These whiplike structures have diameters in the order of 0.2 μ (2000 Å), and some flagella attain lengths as great as 150 μ; in *Paramecium*, a single cell possesses approximately 17,000 cilia, each one about 10 μ long. As in the case of bacterial flagella, the cilia of such cells may be detached and isolated in bulk for chemical analysis. Watson and Hopkins (1962) have reviewed data concerning the composition of *Tetrahymena* cilia, *Chlamydomonas* flagella, and *Polytoma* flagella: the dry weight composition is roughly the same in each case, i.e., approximately 70–84% protein, 13–23% lipid, 1–6% carbohydrate, and 0.2–0.4% adenine and uracil nucleotides. One of the first investigators to detect ATPase activity was Nelson (1954), who found the enzyme relatively concentrated in the flagellar tails of bull sperm. Adenylate kinase activity has also been detected in isolated cilia.

ULTRASTRUCTURE OF CILIA AND FLAGELLA

With respect to the substructure of cilia and flagella, it is remarkable that several of the earlier light microscopists were able to distinguish a central fibril, or in some instances several longitudinal fibrils, within single cilia. After the advent of electron microscopy in 1939, unsectioned ciliated and flagellated cells were among the first biological objects to be examined, and these earliest studies confirmed the presence of longitudinal fibrils having diameters of approximately 300–500 Å. Even before thin-sectioning techniques became available, some workers had arrived at a model of flagellar structure which, in fundamental detail, was surprisingly accurate. Irene Manton (1952), in particular, emphasized the constant presence of 11 fibrils, two of which were centrally located and somewhat smaller or more fragile than the 9 peripheral ones. Thus the basic concept of a "9 + 2" arrangement, which is now known to characterize all functional cilia and flagella, was developed even before it became possible to study cross-sectioned material.

The first significant analysis of thin-sectioned cilia was published by Fawcett and Porter (1954) and served to confirm the general occurrence of the 9 + 2 pattern previously inferred in unsectioned plant sperm.

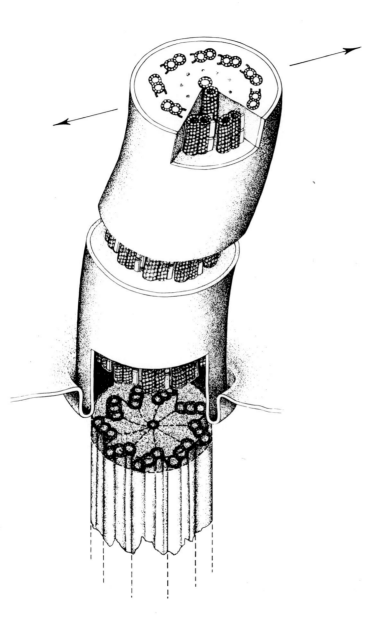

Fig. 9-3. An interpretation of flagellar ultrastructure. Arrows indicate the plane of movement in relation to the two central fibrils. A basal body or centriole is seen just beneath the plasma membrane of the cell, and the latter also forms the outer covering of the flagellum.

These authors also noted that the 9 peripheral fibrils have a double tube substructure, while the central fibrils appear as single tubes (Fig. 9-3). A plane perpendicular to the line joining the two central fibrils divides the cilium into approximately symmetrical right and left halves (bisecting one of the 9 peripheral fibrils); it is now well established that this plane of symmetry coincides with the plane of the ciliary beat, and it is therefore common to find the "sagittal" planes of neighboring cilia oriented closely in parallel (Fig. 9-4). In 1959, Afzelius discovered that the peripheral fibers also possess "arms," which arise from only one side of each fibril and therefore spoil the mirror-image symmetry of the flagellar cross section. Furthermore, since these "arms" all point in one direction (Fig. 9-3), it is theoretically possible for the $9 + 2$ pattern to occur in either a clockwise or counterclockwise configuration; however, only one of these two possible configurations has been found in nature, i.e., the form in which, to an observer looking from the base of the cilium toward its tip, all the arms point in a clockwise direction (Fig. 9-3). The significance of this "clockwise" pattern is not definitely known, but Gibbons (1961) has pointed out that flagellated sperm cells show a tendency to move in counterclockwise circles; it is also known that, in *Paramecium*, the recovery stroke of the cilium exhibits a counterclockwise rotation.

With the realization that asymmetry exists, it became possible to recognize and number each peripheral fibril; in the usual convention, fibril 1 is that fibril which is bisected by the plane of near-symmetry, and the other fibrils are numbered consecutively in the direction that the arms "point."

Both cilia and flagella are enclosed by a semipermeable membrane, approximately 90 Å wide, which is an extension of the surface or plasma membrane of the cell (Fig. 9-3). Within this membrane, the 9 peripheral fibrils are evenly spaced around a circle some 1600 Å in outside diameter. Each peripheral fibril is double, measuring approximately 200–250 Å wide, 350–370 Å long, and is skewed slightly in toward the middle of the cilium. Of the two subfibrils in each doublet, subfibril A is the one which possesses "arms," it sometimes appears slightly larger than the other, and it lies slightly closer to the center of the cilium. Both subfibrils appear to be tubular, possessing a common wall about 45–60 Å wide, and the "arms" of subfibril A measure approximately 150 Å long and 50 Å thick. At the center of the cilium lie the two single fibrils,

Fig. 9-4. Cross-sectioned flagella and centrioles from the flagellate, *Trichonympha*. (A) Free flagella running parallel to the cell surface; (B) flagella cut just above the point of juncture with the plasma membrane; (C) Flagellum cut just above the centriole; (D) The transition plane from flagellum to centriole; (E) The distal region of the centriole; (F) The proximal region of the centriole. 135,000×. From Gibbons and Grimstone (1960).

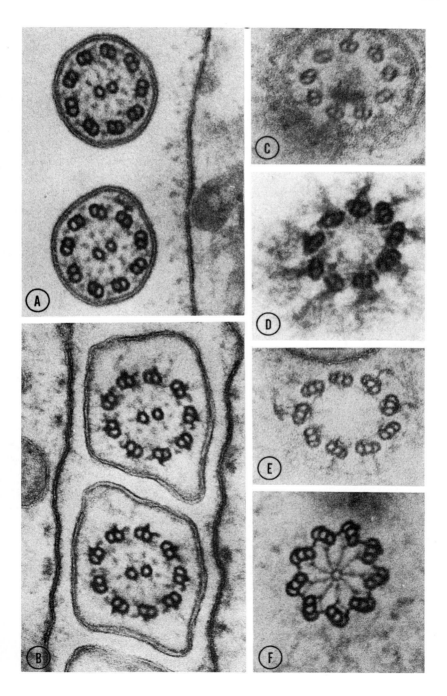

which also appear to be tubular but do not share a common wall; each of these central fibrils is about 240 Å in diameter, with a wall thickness of about 45 Å and a center-to-center spacing of 300–350 Å. In addition to these structures, Gibbons and Grimstone (1960) have found 9 non-tubular fibrils, only 50 Å in diameter, which lie in the matrix between the tubular peripheral and central fibrils of the $9 + 2$ arrangement (Fig. 9-4).

All these components seem to occur universally in functional cilia and flagella. Some additional structures have been reported only in the cilia of certain specialized cells; of these the most notable is a set of arms on subfibril B of fibril 6, which have not been found in protozoa but occur in sea urchin sperm and clam gills; these extra arms point counterclockwise and form a bridge with the usual arms from subfibril A of fibril 5. A sheathlike structure surrounding or connecting the two central fibrils has also been found in certain flagellates by Gibbons and Grimstone (1960). Other structures connecting the peripheral fibrils to one another or to the central fibrils have been reported by different authors, and a "mid-filament" in the vicinity of the two central fibrils has also been seen in some types of cilia. The difficulties involved in preserving finer details make it hard to judge whether some of these structures may eventually prove to be of widespread occurrence.

Important insights concerning the fine structure of the individual fibrils have recently been obtained by high resolution electron microscopy of whole-mount preparations after negative staining (Fig. 9-5B). Using this type of preparation with rat sperm tails, Pease (1963) found that the staining solution directly penetrates the center of each fibril, confirming that the fibrils do in fact have a tubular structure. In addition, Pease was able to resolve beadlike units composing the walls of the fibrils in an oblique or helical arrangement (Fig. 9-3). The periodicity of oblique rows is 88 Å, and the center-to-center spacing of units is about 55–60 Å, indicating an ellipsoid form. Since the units are in longitudinal register, they appear to form 10–12 parallel filaments (or protofibrils) which are tightly bound together to form the wall of each fibril. A very similar picture has been found by André and Thiéry (1963) in negative-stained human sperm and by Grimstone and Klug (1966) in flagellates. The latter authors report that the central fibrils and the peripheral subfibrils have a comparable ultrastructure, and that subfibrils A and B of each doublet can separate from one another as intact tubes. The general appearance and arrangement of subunits observed in the flagellar fibrils is reminiscent of the arrangement of subunits in the contractile tail sheath of T2 bacteriophage (Fig. 9-1). "Arms" have not been observed in negative-stained preparations of flagellar tubules, but certain striking segmental structures observed in the early whole mounts of Manton and Clark (1952) may correspond to these features (Fig. 9-3).

Gibbons (1963, 1967) has recently taken some important first steps toward purifying specific ciliary proteins and toward achieving their spontaneous reaggregation into recognizable ciliary structures. After solubilizing the plasma membranes of isolated *Tetrahymena* cilia, he is able to fractionate the remaining structural protein into EDTA-soluble and EDTA-insoluble components; the latter component, when examined with the electron microscope, contains units of 9 peripheral fibrils still bound together as circlets but lacking the two central fibrils and the asymmetric arms of subfibril A. The EDTA-soluble component, on the other hand, contains about 30% of the structural protein but nearly all the ATPase activity normally associated with the whole cilium. Analysis of the EDTA-soluble component by ultracentrifugation reveals that it contains two ATPase fractions, one sedimenting at 30 S (mol. wt. 5.4×10^6) and the probable subunits of this fraction which sediment at 14 S (mol. wt. 6×10^5). When the 30 S ATPase is mixed with the insoluble peripheral fibrils and Mg^{++} ions, most of the enzymatic activity shifts from the soluble to the insoluble phase, while at the same time "arms" reappear on the "A" subfibrils of the purified fibrils. Gibbons' findings clearly indicate that ATPase activity in cilia is associated with a specific protein (now called dynein), which constitutes the arms of the peripheral fibrils and which can be reversibly dissociated from the rest of the $9 + 2$ configuration. Extensions of this approach are likely to result in further characterization of the proteins composing the peripheral and central fibrils (which obviously differ from one another in EDTA solubility and other features).

Afzelius (1963a) and others have occasionally found cilia or flagella which depart from the $9 + 2$ pattern, constituting freaks or aberrant members of an otherwise typical population of cilia. The observed aberrations include: (1) forms in which the two central fibrils are missing; (2) forms in which more than two central fibrils are present; (3) forms in which peripheral fibrils are missing; and (4) forms in which supernumerary peripheral fibrils are present. In cilia having the $10 + 2$ or $8 + 2$ abnormality, the peripheral fibrils continue to be evenly distributed around a circle; however in $7 + 2$ cilia a gap appears in the circle of fibrils, and in $11 + 2$ cilia the additional fibrils are positioned outside the circle. It has not been possible to determine whether such aberrant cilia are functional, but it is known that a number of specialized sensory structures are derived from cilia and are nonfunctional as far as motility is concerned (for instance, the rods and cones of the vertebrate retina); such nonmotile cilia usually lack the two central fibrils. Very

likely these variations in structure, as well as the normal 9 + 2 pattern
of cilia and flagella, reflect the presence or absence of specific species
of protein together with their specific capabilities for spontaneous
aggregation.

In their lengthwise structure, cilia and flagella sometimes show hair-
like lateral protrusions from the surface membrane, which are believed
to function passively by increasing the resistance of the cilium to the
surrounding medium. Internally however, the fibrils of the 9 + 2 structure usually maintain a constant and parallel relationship throughout
the length of the cilium. At the distal free end, the peripheral fibrils
taper out in an order which Satir has found to depend on the position
of the cilium; the two central fibrils often extend considerably beyond the
tip of the cilium proper. Undoubtedly the most conspicuous structures
visible in longitudinal sections are those concerned with the attachment
of the cilium or flagellum to the cell body, which always include a complex and highly organized basal body or kinetosome.

As early as 1897, Henneguy and Lenhossek suggested that the basal
bodies of cilia might be homologous with the centrioles of the mitotic
spindle. In fact it was observed that in some cells a centriole actively
engaged in mitosis is able simultaneously to act as basal body for a cilium.
After the advent of thin-sectioning techniques in electron microscopy,
this suggested homology between basal bodies and centrioles was strikingly confirmed, and the two terms may now be regarded as designating
essentially identical objects. The basal body is an approximately cylindrical object varying in different species from 1200 to 1500 Å in diameter
and from 3000 to 20,000 Å (2 μ) in length. Its outer wall is made up of
9 tubular fibrils evenly spaced around the circumference of a circle and
somewhat skewed toward the center, essentially like the peripheral
fibrils of the cilium itself. However in the basal body each peripheral
fibril contains three rather than two subfibrils (Fig. 9-4E), and the long
dimension of each fibril in cross section is correspondingly greater
(535 Å as compared with 370 Å for the double fibrils); the transverse
dimension and wall thicknesses are about the same as in the cilium (240–
260 Å and 45 Å, respectively). As in the cilium too, the innermost subfibril in each case is designated subfibril A while the outermost is subfibril C. The spaces between fibrils in the basal body wall are closed by 9
short walls joining subfibrils A and C of adjacent fibrils (Fig. 9-3). Although neither central fibrils nor arms occur in the basal body, a set of
9 curved "spokes" connects the peripheral fibrils with a central "hub"
region, which in many species can be found only near the outer end of
the basal body; morphologically, therefore, the basal body or centriole

shows a top-to-bottom asymmetry (or polarity), as well as a left-right asymmetry caused by skewing of the fibrils. Finally, the basal body is closed at its outer end by a terminal plate about 300 Å thick, which abuts against the base of the cilium proper, giving the basal body the form of an inverted tumbler. In mammals and protozoa a direct continuity exists between the peripheral fibrils of the cilium and subfibrils A and B of the centriole wall. By contrast, the two central fibrils of the cilium end in the vicinity of the terminal plate, where there is a special spherical or crescentic body. Similarly, subfibrils C of the basal body wall end at or before the terminal plate, but on the opposite side.

Various kinds of rootlike, fibrous structure seem to originate from the basal bodies of many cell types. Within a species, these are often very specific in orientation, but they show great diversity between species and are apparently absent in some. Pitelka and Child (1964) distinguish: (1) striated root fibrils, which show a complex 550–700 Å repeat pattern of banding; and (2) tubular fibrils, which are about 200 Å in diameter, unstriated, and sometimes occur in parallel arrays. Striated root fibrils in ciliated epithelium often connect the basal bodies with the cell nucleus or with the Golgi apparatus, and in addition they may be lined by rows of mitochondria; on the other hand, in some ciliate protozoa striated fibrils typically arise at the right anterior margin of each basal body and run anteriorly for about 5–20 μ, overlapping similar root fibrils from adjacent cilia in the same row (or kinety). It is not known whether any of the root fibrils perform a function beyond that of providing mechanical support.

Functional Organization of Cilia and Flagella

It has been emphasized by many authors that the range of movement exhibited by cilia and flagella in various cells is very great. The typical movement of a sperm flagellum, for instance, is an undulatory one in which waves of contraction pass from the base of the flagellum toward the tip. On the other hand, the individual cilia of mammalian epithelium beat in a single plane with a whiplike motion, the cilium bending stiffly from the base during the active stroke and recovering with a limp forward thrust. The cilia of protozoa exhibit a three-dimensional recovery stroke in which the cilium rotates slightly to one side of the action plane, and these cilia (unlike those of mammalian epithelium) are able to change the direction of the active stroke, reversing direction entirely or even rotating uniformly in a conical path. The frequency of beat is also variable from one type of cell to another, the range being about

500–1500 strokes per minute. That all the various ciliary and flagellar movements can be produced by the same basic 9 + 2 structure implies an intriguingly adaptable mechanism of movement.

As long ago as 1868 it was suggested that flagellar movement might be based on some type of contractile process akin to muscle contraction. Soon after the discovery of the 9 + 2 organization, Bradfield (1955) proposed that bending of the cilium or flagellum could be produced by a coordinated contraction of some or all of the 9 peripheral fibrils; at the same time, stiffness or limpness during the active and recovery strokes might be determined by the state of contraction of the two central fibrils. Such a model would be able to account for most known types of ciliary movement, requiring fibril contractions as small as 6% of "rest length."

As might be expected, much of the experimental work aimed at determining the mechanism of ciliary movement has been heavily conditioned by analogies with muscle contraction. Evidence for the involvement of ATP was reported by Mann (1945), who established that loss of motility in ram spermatozoa is correlated with a decrease in ATP content. A corresponding presence of ATPase activity was demonstrated by Nelson (1954) for bull sperm flagella and by Tibbs (1958) for perch sperm flagella and algal flagella. More recently, Gibbons (1967) has demonstrated in *Tetrahymena* cilia that ATPase activity is associated with the asymmetrical arms of subfibril A, and he estimates that this ATPase (dynein) constitutes about 8% of the total ciliary protein. Gibbons has also found that a purified preparation of peripheral fibrils plus dynein is able to respond to added ATP by a configurational change, which is detectable as a reduction in light-scattering ability.

Perhaps the most striking work of this type is based on an extension of the "glycerol model" technique, first introduced by Szent-Györgyi (1949) with striated muscle fibers (Chapter 8) and subsequently applied to sperm and trypanosome flagella by Hoffmann-Berling (1955, 1960). It has now been amply confirmed that isolated, glycerol-extracted flagella and cilia exhibit vigorous, rhythmic movements specifically on exposure to ATP; in fact, even partial fragments of flagella are able to carry on such activity, provided they exceed a minimum threshold length. Furthermore, Satir and Child (1963) have shown that glycerinated cilia of frog epithelium are able to respond to ATP even though they have lost their surface membranes and consist of little more than the 9 + 2 fibrils. These experiments clearly demonstrate that the mechanism of ciliary motion is localized in the fibrils of the ciliary shaft itself, and that the immediate source of energy is almost certainly ATP. Brokaw (1961), in fact, has determined that the frequency of beat in isolated *Polytoma* flagella increases with ATP concentration while the amplitude of beat decreases; under the best conditions, he has obtained swimming by these isolated flagella at a rate of some 20–30 microns per second.

THE ORIGIN OF CILIA AND CENTRIOLE-BASAL BODIES

For several decades it has been recognized that the development of a cilium or flagellum at a cell surface is directly conditioned by the presence of a centriole or basal body. Such a relationship is strongly implicit, for example, in the development of the sperm flagellum at the position of the distal spermatid centriole. In protozoa, if the cilia or flagella are experimentally removed, they regenerate in positions determined by the often complex patterns of the basal bodies. The rate of flagellum regeneration in *Chlamydomonas* has been measured by Lewin (1953) as about 0.2 μ per minute (although the rate of growth is under feedback control and becomes progressively reduced as the flagellum approaches a "zero growth" maximum length). Since no instance has ever been observed in which the 9 + 2 pattern develops in the absence of a centriole, a causal relationship may be regarded as well established; nevertheless, virtually no information is available concerning the mechanisms of induction by the centriole or the factors which determine whether or not a centriole will induce cilium formation at a given stage of the life cycle.

The extremely small size of centrioles has made it difficult to investigate their chemical composition by ordinary cytochemical techniques. Nevertheless an early analysis of this type was carried out by Stich (1954) for the centrosome of *Cyclops*, and led to the conclusion that its constituents include basic albumin, polysaccharides, and RNA. Later Seaman (1960) refined a technique for bulk isolation of the basal bodies or kinetosomes of *Tetrahymena;* his procedure involved dissolution of all cell components except the kinetosomes in digitonin, followed by differential centrifugation at 17,000 g. Kinetosomes sedimented in this manner were found to contain 50% protein, 6% carbohydrate, 5% lipid, 2% RNA, and 3% DNA (dry weight basis). When the isolated kinetosomes were incubated with amino acids and an energy source, net protein synthesis could be detected (with incorporation of glutamic acid-^{14}C); this protein synthesis was inhibited by DNase and RNase. Since no electron microscopy was performed to determine the degree of purity of the kinetosome fraction, Seaman's results have been regarded as preliminary in nature. Recently, however, localization of DNA in the basal bodies of *Tetrahymena* has been confirmed by Randall and Disbrey

(1965), who have estimated from acridine orange staining and thymidine-^{3}H incorporation that each kinetosome contains about 2×10^{-16} gm of DNA. This amount is comparable to the DNA content of a typical mitochondrion, a similarity which may be more than accidental since Ehret and DeHaller (1963) have presented evidence that new kinetosomes in growing *Paramecium* are derived from "vacuolated mitochondria." It is possible that kinetosomes carry out the synthesis of ciliary proteins, and that such synthesis depends on centriolar RNA and DNA components.

Since cilia and flagella in some sense arise from centrioles, the next logical question concerns the manner of origin of the centrioles themselves. During the era of light microscopy, considerable agreement was obtained for the idea that new centrioles arise by "division" of previously existing ones, and in fact these organelles were generally thought to be endowed with a genetic continuity comparable to that of the chromosomes. Unfortunately, analysis at higher resolution with the electron microscope has failed to confirm that centrioles undergo any division process at all, or even that they arise from one another by budding. Of special interest in this regard are careful electron microscope studies by Schuster (1963) and Dingle and Fulton (1966), who have independently investigated the fine structure of *Naegleria*, a protozoan which at different stages of its life cycle exists as either an amoeboid or a flagellated cell. Neither laboratory has been able to detect any centriole in the amoeboid forms, yet these can give rise to flagellated forms with typical centriolar basal bodies in as little as half an hour. The implication is that in these cells the centriole arises *de novo* by assembly of precursor molecules. During the growth of ciliated protozoa as well, division of kinetosomes has not been detected by electron microscopy; rather, new kinetosomes seem to appear very rapidly and more or less fully formed, in a manner that has led Pitelka and Child (1964) to speculate about an "instant kinetosome mix." In *Paramecium*, Ehret and DeHaller (1963) found evidence that new basal bodies arise by condensation from vacuoles inside specialized mitochondria. In embryonic rat tracheal tissue, on the other hand, Dirksen and Crocker (1966) have reported that basal bodies condense in groups of about six, which are positioned radially around a dense spherical "proliferative element."

Although it is clear that centrioles do not arise by the division or budding of previously existing centrioles, a remarkable mother-daughter relationship does occur between old and new centrioles in typical animal cells. As a rule the new centriole first appears as a "procentriole," which resembles the mature centriole in its cross-sectional dimensions and structure but is very much shorter (about 1500 Å); in addition, the procentriole is oriented precisely at right angles to the mature centriole (Fig. 19-4). This one-to-one "induction" process, when viewed at the low resolutions of the light microscope, was primarily responsible for the erroneous concept of centriolar division. It is possible that the induction of one centriole by another represents a mechanism similar to the induction of a cilium by its basal body, and it has been suggested that centrioles may be polarized bodies capable of inducing cilia at one end and other centrioles at the other end. In any case, it is a fairly general rule that a single centriole or one centriole pair (diplosome) can be found in animal cells at every stage of the cell cycle, that reproduction of the centriole under these circumstances is closely integrated with the overall course of cell replication, and that during mitosis "mother" and "daughter" centrioles segregate to opposite poles of the spindle and eventually to different daughter cells. Possibly centriolar DNA may function to regulate this precise form of centriolar reproduction. The peculiar right-angle relationship between new and old centrioles is an extraordinary feature for which no satisfactory explanation is yet available.

Gall (1961) has studied the origin of centrioles in both typical and atypical spermatocytes of the snail *Viviparus*: in typical cells, one new procentriole arises at right angles to one mature centriole in the manner described previously; however, in atypical *Viviparus* spermatocytes a cluster of *several* procentrioles develops simultaneously around each mature centriole, and these eventually form the basal bodies of a multiflagellate sperm. The fact that both modes of reproduction can occur in the same tissue confirms that the mechanics of centriole formation do not depend on a one-to-one relationship with a previously existing centriole. More recently Mizukami and Gall (1966) have found that developing sperm of the water fern *Marsilea* contain 100 or more procentrioles closely packed to form the wall of a spheroid "blepharoplast." These numerous procentrioles develop simultaneously in a manner that rules out either budding from a mature centriole or a geometric reproduction of centrioles by fission.

The nature and function of centrioles is still an intriguing problem for future research. Nevertheless certain major insights have been provided by high resolution electron microscopy, which may be summarized as follows: (1) the structure of the centriole is invariably based on 9 sets of triple tubes arranged as a cylinder; (2) centrioles do not divide and may not have "genetic continuity" in the strict sense; (3) centrioles are almost invariably found in close association with other, more temporary tubular structures, e.g., cilia and flagella, the tubular fibers of the mitotic apparatus, and so-called cytoplasmic microtubules (to be described in the

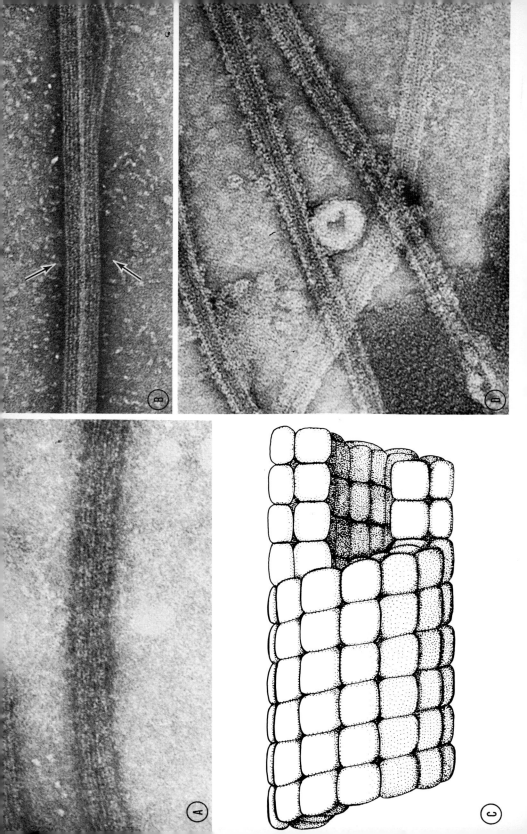

next section). These relationships would suggest that the essential activity of the centriole may be to regulate synthesis and aggregation of protein monomers required for the formation of these tubular structures (Fig. 9-5).

Cytoplasmic Microtubules

After the introduction of glutaraldehyde fixation in 1963, considerable attention was attracted by the discovery of oriented tubular filaments, which occur widely in the cytoplasm of protozoan, plant, and animal cells, and which range around 200 Å in diameter. Because these cytoplasmic microtubules are not well preserved by the standard osmium fixatives, they escaped notice in most earlier studies of thin-sectioned cells. Nevertheless they were detected by Roth (1958, 1959) in various protozoa, particularly ciliates, and as early as 1962 he called attention to the similarity in form and dimensions between microtubules in the cytoplasm and the tubular elements of cilia, flagella, and the mitotic apparatus (Chapter 19). The details of microtubule structure and function are still at an early stage of investigation, but it is already clear that these structures bear a close relationship to cell morphology, cytoplasmic streaming, intracellular transport, and very possibly also to cytoplasmic contractility.

Cross-sectional diameters reported for microtubules range from 150 to 260 Å, with corresponding wall thicknesses of 45–70 Å; consequently, it is not yet clear whether there are actually several types. The lengths are usually so great that it is not possible to trace the full course of any given tubule; however, partial lengths exceeding several microns have been measured. Several authors have also reported configurations of many microtubules lying in closely packed, parallel arrays; the units in such arrays, according to Ledbetter and Porter (1963), are usually separated from one another by a particle-free zone, so that the center-to-center spacing for tubules 230–270 Å in diameter is about 350 Å. Instances of branched microtubules have also been found by Sandborn *et al.* (1964).

In ciliated protozoa, very complex systems of tubular fibers often arise in the vicinity of the basal bodies and run through the cortex

---

Fig. 9-5. (A) Cytoplasmic microtubule from newt RBC. 236,000×. From Gall (1966a). (B) Flagellar microtubule from the flagellate *Trichonympha*. Note the oblique striations at the arrows. 210,000×. From Grimstone and Klug (1966). (C) Interpretation of microtubule substructure, showing globular monomers arranged as protofibrils when viewed longitudinally and as a helical chain when viewed transversely. From Moor (1967). (D) Mitotic spindle microtubules from newt heart culture. 251,000×. From Barnicot (1966).

parallel to the cell surface. The exact pattern varies with the species, but in *Stentor* such tubular elements run posteriorly from each basal body and overlap one another in an anterior-posterior direction like the nontubular (striated) kinetodesmal fibers of *Paramecium*. It has been suggested that the occurrence of tubular fibers in *Stentor* might be correlated with the very marked contractility exhibited by this organism, and the possibility that the microtubules themselves contract is suggested by the absence of any folding or coiling when these fibers are compared in contracted versus relaxed animals. Microtubules are also conspicuous in the contractile tentacles of some suctoria, in the so-called myonemes of the contractile ciliate *Spirostomum,* and in the vicinity of the contractile vacuoles in various protozoans.

The first report of microtubules in the cells of higher plants was published by Ledbetter and Porter (1963), who found tubules 230–270 Å in diameter in two angiosperms and one gymnosperm. These tubules were oriented close under the plasma membrane and in directions corresponding both to the pattern of cytoplasmic flow and to the pattern of cellulose fibers deposited outside the plasma membrane in the cell wall. In their initial report, these authors noted a possible homology between the cytoplasmic microtubules and tubular spindle fibers observed during mitosis in the same species; however, they also noted that the spindle fibers were somewhat smaller, varying from 200 to 230 Å in diameter. More recently Ledbetter and Porter (1964) and Gall (1966a) have been able to show that the 70 Å microtubule wall is composed of subunits, which in cross sections are about 13 in number and have center-to-center spacings of 45 Å (Fig. 9-5). Since this organization is remarkably similar to that found by Pease (1963) and Grimstone and Klug (1966) in the 9 + 2 tubular fibrils of flagella, it has been suggested that some homology may exist between microtubules and flagellar tubules (Fig. 9-5), and that the microtubules may perform "undulatory" movements in the cytoplasm. Nevertheless, the cytoplasmic microtubules appear to be much more transitory structures than cilia and flagella, and they are also notably more difficult to preserve with osmium tetroxide.

A somewhat different concept was developed by Slautterback (1963), who found microtubules conspicuously involved during the genesis of nematocysts in *Hydra*. Early in development, microtubules are found primarily near the centriole complex, but later when the nematocyst capsule begins to form in association with a Golgi vacuole, microtubules become closely arrayed in parallel around the vacuole like "the staves of a barrel" (Fig. 9-6). The expanded Golgi apparatus continues to surround the apical end of the developing nematocyst, in some cases showing apparent connections to individual microtubules. At a still

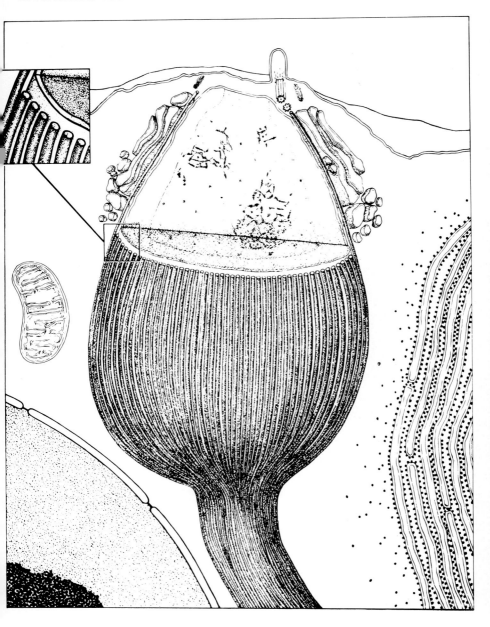

Fig. 9-6. Interpretation of the developing nematocyst in *Hydra*. The nematocyst develops in an enlarged Golgi vacuole, surrounded by numerous microtubules arranged as the staves of a barrel. After Slautterback (1963).

Fig. 9-7. Cytoplasmic fibers interconnect the saltatory granules of honey bee embryonic cells; broken fibers contract into accordionlike configurations (arrows). 101,000×. From DuPraw (1965b).

later stage, when the centriole takes an apical position as basal body of the developing cnidocil (or trigger), the microtubules again radiate from its vicinity. These observations led Slautterback to suggest that the microtubules may be acting as transport ducts (or pipes) carrying water or other small molecules to and from the developing nematocyst. He points out that in order to function in this way, the individual fibers need not be hollow like plumbers' pipes, but might more closely resemble the organization of a packed chromatography column.

Recently DuPraw (1965b) has reported an extensive system of cytoplasmic fibers, varying around 180 Å in diameter, which occurs in honey bee embryonic cells (Fig. 9-7). This fiber system has been studied only in unsectioned cells prepared for the electron microscope by surface spreading on a Langmuir trough and critical-point drying in CO_2; consequently it is not certain that the individual fibers correspond to microtubules as defined in sectioned cells. However the whole-mount fibers do sometimes show the appearance of collapsed tubes. Of particular interest is the fact that the honey bee 180 Å fibers have attachments both to the nuclear envelope and to certain distinctive cytoplasmic granules, which *in vivo* exhibit sudden, independent straight-line movements (i.e., they show saltatory motion). Because of the correspondence between the pattern of granule movements and the pattern of 180 Å fibers, DuPraw has suggested that these fibers (or microtubules) possess contractile properties and act to pull the granules from place to place in the cell.

A possible mechanism for contraction of microtubules is suggested by the structure of the contractile tail sheath in bacteriophages (Fig. 9-1); here the tubular sheath is composed of protein subunits in a helical array, and shortening of the sheath is accompanied by an increase in tubule diameter. That cytoplasmic microtubules are similarly composed of protein monomers in helical arrays, and that the same monomers can assemble as tubules in several alternative configurations with different tubule diameters has been reported by Moor (1967). He found that yeast cells grown anaerobically contain an intranuclear protein crystal composed of 80 Å particles; when the cells are returned to aerobic conditions, this protein crystal gradually reorganizes into an array of microtubules, each of which is 210 Å in diameter and has a wall thickness corresponding to the 80 Å monomers. More or less simultaneously, an intranuclear mitotic spindle is assembled, which consists of about 15–16 microtubules with diameters of 224 Å. Finally, extending into the cytoplasm from the spindle poles there develops a third type of microtubule with an outside diameter of 250 Å. In electron microscope images of yeast cells which have been frozen, fractured, and shadowed (freeze-etch technique), the arrangement of monomers in these tubules is seen to be helical with a pitch of about 10–15 degrees (Fig. 19-3). Consequently Moor has proposed that the principle of construction for all three microtubule types is a helical chain of monomers (Fig. 9-5C), but that the number of monomers per turn of the helix is variable.

There are still insufficient data available to permit a clear assessment of the role or mechanism of action of microtubules. Nevertheless, a good possibility exists that they constitute contractile elements in cilia and flagella, in the mitotic spindle, and in the cytoplasm of highly contractile protozoans and other cells. Since the glycerol model technique of ATP activation has been applied successfully both to isolated spindles (Chapter 19) and to the contractile stalk of the protozoan *Vorticella*

(Hoffman-Berling, 1958), there is at least preliminary evidence that ATP is also involved in these mechanisms. Microtubules may also function as a cellular "microcirculatory system," at least for the transport of small molecules. Conceivably the contractile and transport functions may occur together, as in nerve axons where longitudinally oriented microtubules are often abundant (Fig. 11-1) and where time-lapse films reveal a striking pulsation accompanied by "axoplasmic flow." Microtubules also seem to act as stiff reinforcing elements during the development of surface protuberances or other asymmetric cell shapes, leading to the suggestion that they function as a "cytoskeleton." Although there is often a close association between cytoplasmic microtubules and the centrioles (Fig. 16-3), this relationship is not yet as clear as that between the centrioles and the tubular elements of cilia or the mitotic spindle. Further investigation is required.

Cytoplasmic Streaming, Amoeboid Movement, and Related Phenomena

Some spontaneous movement of organelles and other inclusions occurs universally in cells, and in fact may be regarded as characteristic of the living state. These protoplasmic movements embody a multitude of different forms, many of which seem to be specific to one or another cell type. For instance, streaming in some cells may have a high degree of orientation and in others not; furthermore cytoplasmic flow may result in net locomotion of the cell, in which case it can be considered "amoeboid" movement, or again it may not. Even within the category of amoeboid movement, vast differences occur in the specific form and organization of the cells during locomotion (e.g., see Bovee, 1964). Although there has been a tendency in the past to seek some single mechanism which, by suitable modification, could account for all these various cell activities, it seems clear at present that several types of chemical-mechanical transducer system exist. In fact, as will be shown, there is a clear likelihood that more than one type may occur in the same cell.

Pressure-Hydraulic Streaming

Perhaps the best understood of all cytoplasmic streaming phenomena occurs in the slime mold *Physarum polycephalum*, which has been extensively analyzed by Kamiya and his students. This organism consists of an irregular, branching plasmodium, often attaining 5 cm or more in diameter and possessing hundreds of synchronously dividing nuclei; since no cell partitions exist, the plasmodium has some resemblance to an enormous, multinucleate amoeba. Under the microscope, a single branch or filament of *Physarum* consists of a gel-like tube (plasmagel) containing a central stream of flowing plasm (plasmasol). The most remarkable attributes of *Physarum* concern the cytoplasmic flow, which (1) attains very high velocities, up to 1350 μ per second; and (2) changes direction rhythmically at intervals of about 1 minute. The flow in each branch first accelerates in one direction, then slows, comes to a stop, and begins to accelerate in the opposite direction; accompanying the plasm flow is a visible pulsing of the protoplasmic tubes (and in fact of the whole plasmodium), which is very reminiscent of a beating heart. Since flow volume is often slightly greater in one direction than the other, the plasmodium also shows a slow net locomotion in a corresponding direction.

By developing a so-called "double chamber" technique, Kamiya (1959) was able to make very precise, quantitative measurements of this "shuttle streaming" in *Physarum*, including the volume of flow, strength of the motive force, and the effects of various reagents or physical conditions on these parameters. In Kamiya's technique, the living plasmodium is mounted in such a fashion that its two halves lie in separate, sealed chambers and are connected by a single protoplasmic strand threaded through an opening between the chambers (Fig. 9-8); as plasm flows through the connecting strand, first in one direction and then in the other, the net changes in plasmodium volume can be measured directly by the consequent pressure changes in one chamber or the other. The effective force (or strength) of the streaming mechanism can also be measured by increasing the pressure on one side to just that point at which the plasmodium is no longer strong enough to flow against it.

In the simplest case, the motive force of streaming in *Physarum* is found to fluctuate with the direction of streaming, forming a very regular sine wave with a period of 2–3 minutes and an amplitude of ±3 to 20 cm of water (1 cm of water corresponds to about 980 dynes/cm^2; the maximum motive force observed by Kamiya is about 40 cm of water). If one-half of the plasmodium is bathed in a solution of ATP, the motive force developed on that side becomes considerably greater, while the lag period associated with this effect can be abolished if the ATP is actually injected into the organism (Fig. 9-8). Motive force is quickly abolished by inhibitors of anaerobic glycolysis, but inhibition of oxidative respiration has little effect; consequently Kamiya has inferred that mitochondrial ATP is unavailable to the streaming mechanism and

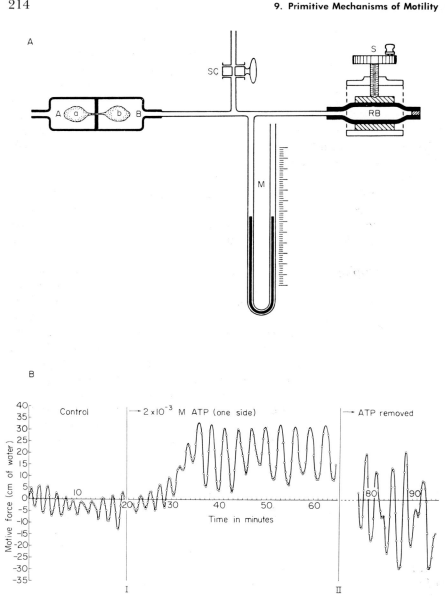

Fig. 9-8. (A) Double chamber apparatus for recording protoplasmic flow in the slime-mold *Physarum*. Flow between chambers A and B leads to pressure changes in the manometer M. (B) Shuttle-streaming in *Physarum*, as recorded with the double chamber apparatus. The flow reverses rhythmically every 1–2 minutes, generating a sinelike curve; addition of ATP at I greatly increases the amplitude of the curve and increases the average flow pressure. From Kamiya (1959).

that the mechanism must be located in the plasm where soluble glyco-lytic enzymes are the primary ATP source (Chapter 6).

Kamiya has also determined the velocity profile at various depths in a single plasm stream, both under natural conditions and when the plasm is forced to flow by a high artificial pressure. The velocity profile of a structureless fluid such as water, when flowing under pressure through a pipe, is parabolic, i.e., water at the center of the pipe flows faster than water at the edge. As determined by Kamiya, *Physarum* plasm also shows a velocity profile similar to that of water flowing under pressure, and this profile is exactly the same whether the flow is produced by the natural motive force or whether it is caused artificially by an external pressure difference. In the case of *Physarum* plasm the parabola is not perfect, i.e., it is somewhat flattened at the apex, indicating that some structural viscosity is present. Nevertheless these results constitute strong evidence that the fluid endoplasm of *Physarum* flows passively under some kind of externally applied pressure. The most obvious and likely cause of this pressure would be a contraction of the gel-like ecto-plasmic tube, which would induce flow in the endoplasm like toothpaste squeezed in a toothpaste tube.

The hypothesis that cytoplasmic streaming, whether in *Physarum* or in *Amoeba,* may be produced by an ectoplasmic contraction similar to muscle contraction, dates from as early as 1849. Impressive support for this concept was provided by Loewy (1952), who extracted a protein from *Physarum* capable of showing a viscosity response to ATP very similar to the characteristic response of muscle actomyosin (i.e., viscosity drops suddenly and then recovers as ATP is hydrolyzed). Subsequently Ts'o *et al.* (1956) confirmed Loewy's findings, purified the protein (named myxomyosin by Loewy) and demonstrated the specificity of its ATPase activity. The same laboratory later determined that the molecular weight of myxomyosin is about 6×10^6, and observed by electron microscopy that it shows a fibrous configuration, about 4000–5000 Å long and 70 Å in diameter. Like actomyosin, the ATPase activity of myxomyosin is stimulated by Ca^{++} and inhibited by Mg^{++}. However, the molecular weight of myxomyosin is considerably less than that of muscle actomyosin preparations (20×10^6), while greatly exceeding the molecular weight of either actin or myosin monomers.

These biochemical data have now been related directly to the contractile mechanism in *Physarum* by thin-section electron microscopy carried out by Wohlfarth-Botterman (1964). This investigator found 70 Å filaments *in situ* in the peripheral ectoplasm of *Physarum* and demonstrated cytochemically that they possess ATPase activity. Of even greater significance, it was found that the filaments often occur as longitudinally oriented bundles or anastomosing fibers which may be 8 μ in diameter and 1/3 mm long; these large fibers are easily visible in thicker sections viewed with the phase contrast microscope, where they are seen to be confined to the peripheral ectoplasm. By isolating single *Physarum* strands and fixing them at moments when maximum force is expected at one end and minimum force at the other, Wohlfarth-Botterman has also been able to show that the frequency of the myxo-myosin fibers increases more or less in proportion to the amount of streaming force being developed. As noted previously, the direction of the motive force alternates rhythmically, and it would therefore appear that the fibers must be transitory structures, which are formed from myxomyosin molecules just before the contraction develops and which disaggregate, at least partially, during the relaxation phase. Although it is not yet known what controls the rhythm of the mechanism, it seems clear that in *Physarum* cytoplasmic streaming depends on hydraulic pressure imposed by active contraction of an actomyosin-like ATPase system.

Shear Forces at an Interface

Some of the most intriguing types of plasmic movement are those which involve endless rotation, either of individual organelles or of the entire endoplasm. For instance, time-lapse films reveal that the cell nuclei in certain tissues spin continuously; the average period of this remarkable nuclear rotation in human nasal mucosa is about 280 seconds (Pomerat, 1953). A much more familiar rotational movement is the phenomenon of cyclosis in plant cells, which involves a circular streaming of the entire endoplasm in its path between the central vacuole and the outside ectoplasmic gel. This phenomenon, in which streaming velocities reach 20–80 μ per second, was first described nearly 200 years ago by Corti (1774). A number of early investigators established that cyclosis is more or less dependent on respiration rate, and slows or stops under anaerobic conditions. Furthermore, since streaming continues even if one or another part of the cell is eliminated with a ligature, the motive force cannot be localized in any one region.

Kamiya and Kuroda (1956) analyzed the velocity profile of streaming endoplasm in the fresh water alga *Nitella* and discovered that velocity is virtually constant at all levels (i.e., not parabolic); on the other hand, a very abrupt velocity gradient exists between the outermost layer of moving endoplasm and the innermost layer of stationary ectoplasmic gel. It appears that the endoplasm does not so much flow, as glide *en masse* over the inner surface of the ectoplasm. Such a velocity profile is incompatible with any type of mechanical pressure-flow system, such as that which occurs in *Physarum,* and it now seems fairly well established that cyclosis is brought about by some type of oriented shearing force applied along the ectoplasm-endoplasm interface. The magnitude of this force has also been measured by Kamiya and Kuroda, using the centrifuge microscope to determine the amount of centrifugal force required to just stop centripetal flow. From these and other data, they could calculate that the motive force for cyclosis is very low, in the order of 1.2–1.8 dynes/cm².

As Jahn and Rinaldi (1959) have pointed out, a streaming mechanism based on lateral shear forces is very reminiscent of the sliding filament model of striated muscle contraction (Chapter 8). In this model actin filaments are believed to undergo a shearing movement past myosin filaments, a movement which may be brought about by a cyclic "pulling" of lateral bridges between the two types of filament. Huxley (1963) has also found evidence that both actin and myosin filaments have a distinct longitudinal polarity (i.e., an anterior and a posterior), and he has noted that if the two can interact only in one possible direction, then single actin filaments might be expected to show oriented translational movement (or swimming) in a solution of myosin and ATP. By such a mechanism, masses of oriented filaments might be expected to produce entire currents or streams, not unlike those observed in cyclosis.

That the source of the shearing force in *Nitella* does not involve the central cell vacuole was also demonstrated by Kamiya and Kuroda (1956), who eliminated the vacuole entirely through centrifugation followed by ligature; rotational streaming continued in cells containing only endoplasm surrounded by ectoplasm, but in this case the velocity profile was modified to resemble a sine curve. As demonstrated by the authors, such a profile exactly mimics the displacement produced in a cylinder filled with ordinary margarine when it undergoes lateral shearing. Further evidence for the existence of an interface shearing force is provided by the constancy in the direction of streaming after the cell contents are displaced through centrifugation; provided that the ectoplasmic gel is not displaced from the cell wall, streaming always resumes in the same direction as before centrifugation. Local damage to the ectoplasmic gel, on the other hand, produces local disruption in the streaming pattern.

The causal role of the ectoplasm has been strongly supported by Kamiya and Kuroda (1957) in a further ingenious experiment with *Nitella.* A cell was placed under negative pressure (or suction) to prevent collapse of the cell wall, after which the lower end was amputated while immersed in salt solution. Under these conditions the cell contents tend to remain in place, except that the part of the endoplasm which is streaming toward the cut end begins to flow out under the influence of the cyclosis motive force. In this way naked droplets of pure endoplasm could be obtained, in which nuclei, chloroplasts, and smaller particles were suspended. Mass streaming in such endoplasm droplets did not occur, in contrast to droplets containing both endoplasm and ectoplasm, which showed a variety of pulsing or streaming movements. Nevertheless, chloroplasts and nuclei suspended in the endoplasm droplets exhibited vigorous axial rotation, which in the case of the chloroplasts proceeded at a rate up to three revolutions per second and continued for 10–50 hours. This was thought to be caused by fine ectoplasmic strands adhering to these organelles. In mixed droplets of ectoplasm and endoplasm, Jarosch has also observed rotating circular fibers which are independent of chloroplasts or nuclei, but which are thought to be the oriented units responsible for the shear force at the ectoplasm-endoplasm interface. More recently, several authors have observed a correlation between the orientations of cytoplasmic microtubules and the direction of cytoplasmic streaming in various cells, including plant cells carrying on cyclosis.

With respect to the energy source for streaming in plants, few biochemical data are available. However, Takata (1958) has reported that the addition of ATP to the seawater environment of *Acetabularia* leads to streaming rates as much as four times the control rate. Furthermore, glycerol models of *Acetabularia* show a certain amount of response to ATP in the proper salt environment. These preliminary findings invite more extensive experiments for the future.

LINEAR TENSION MOVEMENTS

Distinct from the types of mass streaming described in the previous sections is a class of movements characterized by great independence in the rate and direction of motion of individual particles. The pattern of particle movements, in fact, may be highly random, yet may undergo a transition within the same cell to a very organized flow (Fig. 9-9). Often the particles move in single file along long, thin strands of plasm, whose diameters may actually be less than those of the moving organelles. In some instances two chains of particles may move in opposite directions side by side, showing no apparent tendency to mix. In short, the general impression associated with this type of motion is that the individual organelles are being pulled along by stringlike fibers, which are able to exert a linear tension by contraction or otherwise.

The commonest of these movements is a widespread phenomenon known as "saltatory motion," which in its most random patterns resembles Brownian motion (e.g., of ink particles suspended in water). Each organelle moves independently and unpredictably, remaining at rest for a time until it suddenly "jumps" in a linear path at nearly constant velocity for a distance of several microns. However, saltation is easily distinguishable from Brownian motion, since it does not conform with the physical limitations on rate and mean path length that are characteristic of thermal agitation, i.e., the jumps tend to have longer paths and they occur less frequently. It is also sometimes observed that one type of cytoplasmic inclusion may exhibit saltation while simultaneously other organelles in the same cell do not. Often the pattern of movements, though apparently random, actually possesses a distinct trend and results in net accumulation of particles in one or another specific region of the cytoplasm. Parpart (1964) has analyzed saltation in echinochrome granules of *Arbacia* eggs, where the movements before fertilization are random in three dimensions, with velocities of 0.3–0.8 μ per second; within a minute or two after fertilization, the majority

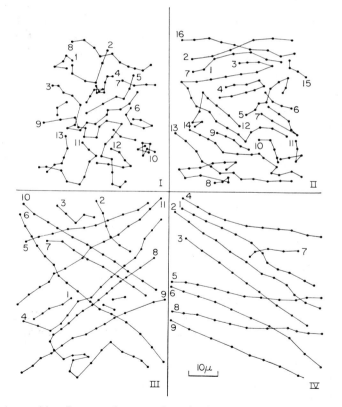

Fig. 9-9. A transition from random to oriented saltatory movement observed in onion cells. I, Immediately after preparation; II, after 40 minutes; III, after 90 minutes; IV, the next day. From Jarosch (1956).

of these granules move up from deeper regions and accumulate markedly just under the cell surface.

Although Parpart concluded from his observations that echinochrome granules are moved by a system of contractile fibers, he was not able to demonstrate these fibers by electron microscopy. More recently, however, DuPraw (1965b) has found an extensive system of cytoplasmic fibers, varying around 180 Å in diameter, which appear to be associated with saltation of certain granules in honey bee embryonic cells. In cells which have been prepared without sectioning, by surface spreading on a Langmuir trough and critical-point drying in CO_2, cytoplasmic granules are often seen to be attached to one another and to the nuclear envelope by cylindrical fibers many microns long (Fig. 9-7). It is not uncommon, furthermore, to find several fibers attached to the same organelle, and in some cases the granule surface exhibits one or several fibrous stumps, which are apparently the broken ends of other attachments. When the same cells are viewed *in vivo* by phase contrast, the conspicuous cytoplasmic granules are seen to exhibit typical saltatory motion. According to the author, the observed motions of these granules can be accounted for on the hypothesis that their fiber attachments are able to develop tension by linear contraction. He suggests that, in effect, the light-resolvable organelles are pulled about by "strings" that are not light-resolvable (but which can be visualized in the electron microscope). The 180 Å cytoplasmic fibers of honey bee embryonic cells are rapidly removed by digestion with trypsin, indicating that they are proteinaceous, and there is some evidence that they correspond to cytoplasmic microtubules.

The occurrence of similar fiber systems in other cells, interconnecting or attaching cytoplasmic organelles to one another, is suggested by a wide variety of data. In *Physarum*, for instance, even though endoplasmic streaming seems to be primarily a passive response to pressure (page 212), individual endoplasmic particles are sometimes observed to move independently in a direction opposite to the main stream. Similarly in *Elodea*, streaming chloroplasts move at rates that are significantly slower than the overall rate of cyclosis. In his experiments with isolated nuclei from *Chaetopterus* and frog eggs, Merriam (1959b) noted the presence of cytoplasmic strands several hundred microns long binding yolk and mitochondria to the nucleus. Numerous observations of cells during and after centrifugation have also shown that specific organelles may resist displacement, or return to their original positions after displacement, as if they were attached by elastic fibers (Conklin, 1951). In experiments of this type, Parpart (1964) concluded that such fibers are, in fact, ruptured by sufficiently high forces, but that when the force is removed they are rapidly reconstituted in a dynamic manner and independently of cytoplasmic streaming. Further evidence for cytoplasmic fibers is provided by many plants cells, where fine cytoplasmic strands traverse the central vacuole, frequently branching or anastomosing; as noted by Mahlberg (1964) and others, organelles moving along these strands do not increase velocity when the strand narrows, as would be expected if the movement depended on fluid streaming under pressure. In fact, individual particles or groups of particles in these strands seem to have independent rates and directions of movement, varying in the range of 2–7 μ per second; they behave very much as though they were being pulled along on separate strings.

Recent studies indicate that, at least in some linear tension systems, cytoplasmic microtubules may be responsible for generating the motive force. These fine, tubular structures are associated with streaming cytoplasm in both plant and animal cells, where their long axes generally coincide with the axis of flow. Perhaps more significantly, various contractile ciliates and other protozoa possess "myonemes" or other presumably contractile structures which, when examined with the electron microscope, are found to consist primarily of microtubules in parallel array. Kitching (1964) has found that the axopods of heliozoans, which are contractile in some species, contain parallel, longitudinal arrays of 68–129 microtubules (each with a diameter of 150–200 Å); in cross sections these microtubules are arranged in a double spiral pattern. Granules in such axopods are sometimes seen to execute linear tension movements at rates of about 0.5 μ per second. Suctorian protozoa also possess contractile tentacles which have been found to contain longitudinally oriented microtubules. These tentacles are used to transport cytoplasm out of captured prey, and Hull (1961) has determined that the rate at which food particles move down the tentacles, though partly a function of temperature, reaches its maximum at about 1 μ per second. When ATP is injected into the body of the suctorian, the rate of transport increases up to 1.5 times the rate in controls. It is not clear whether the microtubules form part of the mechanism by which the entire tentacle contracts, or the mechanism by which food particles stream down the tentacle, or conceivably both. Finally, the anaphase movements of chromosomes may be regarded as a kind of linear tension movement, and this phenomenon is also associated with tubular fibrils composing the mitotic spindle (Chapter 19).

Amoeboid Movement

Amoeboid movement refers essentially to those forms of cytoplasmic streaming which result in net locomotion by the cell, and it implies deformation of the cell surface to form temporary cytoplasmic extensions or pseudopods. Within this broad definition a startling range of variation occurs, including the broad, lobose pseudopodia of *Amoeba proteus*, the extremely long, fine cytoplasmic processes of foraminifera, hornlike pseudopodia with or without a helical twist (the former resembling unicorn horns), fan-shaped, ruffled pseudopodia entirely free of cytoplasmic granules, and many other kinds (see Bovee, 1964). The behavior of organelles during amoeboid locomotion is also highly variable from one cell type to another, though frequently characteristic for a given type. The nucleus, for instance, may typically lead all other cell inclusions, it may travel in the middle of the cell, or it may tag along in a posterior position; similarly, mitochondria and other small inclusions may stream into the main pseudopod in a fountain pattern diverging at the pseudopod tip, or alternatively they may show random saltation, and in some cases they are seen to trail more or less inertly in the most posterior part of the cell. Although various investigators have sought to discover a single "mechanism of amoeboid movement," a cautious appraisal suggests that this phrase really encompasses several different phenomena.

The classic example of amoeboid locomotion is the type exhibited by *Amoeba proteus* and related protozoa; Mast (1926) provided an early but accurate morphological description of these forms during typical unidirectional flow. The anterior end or pseudopod tip is always occupied by a granule-free thickening, the *hyaline cap*, which is continuous with a narrow hyaline ectoplasm entirely surrounding the cell. Internal to this hyaline ectoplasm is a granular ectoplasm, apparently in a state of gel, which contains various inclusions with fixed or "set" positions relative to one another. The innermost core of the amoeba, inside the ectoplasmic tube, is filled with a more fluid, granular endoplasm (called a plasmasol by Mast), which streams actively in the direction of locomotion. Where the streaming endoplasm comes up beneath the hyaline cap at the anterior end of the cell an invisible barrier seems to prevent the endoplasm granules from entering the cap; at this point the stream diverges to right and left producing a "fountain" pattern, and in this anterior fountain zone the fluid endoplasm core becomes transformed more or less abruptly into gel-like granular ectoplasm. Conversely, at the posterior end of the cell there is a region where the ectoplasmic gel continuously leaves the peripheral wall to join the central stream of endoplasm [aptly called the "recruitment zone" by Allen (1961)]. In the fountain zone, some of the streaming endoplasmic particles occasionally seem to "burst through" the invisible barrier separating them from the hyaline cap, and at these times the hyaline cap actually advances in the direction of locomotion, attaining a maximum velocity of about 3–4 μ per second.

In this organism, if the path of any one cytoplasmic particle is recorded for a time it is seen to describe repeated circles around the cell, flowing from posterior to anterior in the central endoplasm, then losing ground from anterior to posterior as part of the peripheral ectoplasmic gel. Provided that the amoeba is attached to the substratum, those particles which are momentarily trapped in the ectoplasmic gel remain stationary relative to an external fixed point, whereas the fluid endoplasm streams forward at a rate somewhat exceeding the net velocity of the entire amoeba (recall that the individual plates of a tractor tread alternately remain stationary on the ground and then move forward at twice the speed of the tractor). Descriptively speaking, this cyclic pattern of amoeboid streaming seems extremely simple, yet extensive efforts to devise a principal mechanism capable of operating the system have encountered frustrating obstacles.

Many investigators have noted the general resemblance of amoeboid streaming to pressure-hydraulic flow as found in *Physarum*. As early as 1849, Ecker suggested that contraction of the ectoplasmic tube in *Amoeba* could cause the endoplasm to flow forward under pressure. Later Mast (1926) proposed that this motive pressure might be induced by nothing else than the observed "setting" of fluid endoplasmic "sol" to gel-like granular ectoplasm. Velocity profiles of the flowing endoplasm, measured in *Chaos chaos* by Allen and Roslansky (1959), revealed an anterior cross section not unlike that of *Physarum*, i.e., a flattened paraboloid indicating viscous structure in the endoplasm but not inconsistent with a pressure flow mechanism. That the posterior end of the moving amoeba might be a special region of maximum contraction was also suggested by Goldacre and Lorch (1950), who reported that ATP injected posteriorly had the effect of speeding locomotion, whereas injection at the anterior end caused a reversal in the direction of locomotion.

More recent evidence has left little doubt that *Amoeba* has the ability to contract, and also that ATP can act as an energy source both for contraction and for normal amoeboid streaming. For instance, striking contractions of the whole animal can be observed if an imposed hydrostatic pressure is suddenly removed; furthermore, Simard-Duquesne and Couillard (1962) have demonstrated marked contractions of glycerol-extracted *Amoeba* on addition of ATP and Mg^{++}. The same authors (1962) succeeded in isolating a myosinlike ATPase from *Amoeba*, similar to the myxomyosin of *Physarum*. In addition, Kamiya (1964) has adapted his double-chamber technique for use with *Amoeba* and *Chaos*, reporting that: (1) the motive force of streaming in these organisms is in the order of 1.5 cm of water; and (2) as in *Physarum*, the addition of ATP (or pyrophosphate) to the external medium results in an increased motive force.

Despite these advances, it is still not clear exactly how contraction is involved in the mechanisms of amoeboid locomotion. In the first place, Mast's concept of contraction as a consequence of the sol-gel transformation has been largely contradicted by the finding that cytoplasm generally *increases* slightly in volume (rather than decreasing) on gelation. Furthermore, the alternative "folding molecule" theory of contraction, proposed originally by Goldacre and Lorch (1950), was largely based on their discovery that the vital stain, neutral red, tends to accumulate at the posterior ends of streaming amoebae. However, it has since been discovered that neutral red and other dyes are taken up in pinocytosis vacuoles by amoebae, and that it is these vacuoles rather than contractile molecules which accumulate in the uropod region. Of even greater significance, Allen (1955) and his co-workers (1960) have found that streaming continues for as long as an hour in *isolated* cytoplasm from *Chaos*, even after the cell membrane has been removed and the normal ectoplasm-endoplasm relationship has broken down; this observation cannot be accounted for by a simple posterior contraction-hydraulic pressure mechanism.

In the isolated *Chaos* cytoplasm, the usual fountain pattern of streaming continues for a time, but then gradually the flowing plasm separates into many independent, U-shaped streams. The bend in each U lies at the position of the original fountain zone, and Allen has determined that: (1) the velocity of the anterior stream is always two to three times faster than that of the posterior one; and (2) both cross-sectional area and viscosity are significantly greater in the posterior stream. Allen has interpreted these and other facts to mean that an active contraction occurs in each stream at the bend of the U, the effect being to draw the anterior stream forward and to force the posterior stream backward. Accordingly, he has proposed an alternative mechanism of amoeboid movement, based not on a posterior ectoplasmic contraction, but on a "fountain-zone contraction" at the anterior end of the intact amoeba.

The essential concept of Allen's fountain-zone theory is that the axial endoplasm is *pulled* forward by the anterior contraction, rather than being pushed forward by a posterior contraction. Since such a mechanism demands considerable tensile strength in the endoplasm, Allen and his students have sought evidence that the endoplasm is not a simple fluid, but rather that significant invisible structure exists there. It will be recalled, for instance, that the velocity profile of the endoplasmic stream is not a perfect parabola, as would be required for a structureless fluid under pressure, but is flattened at the apex, indicating viscous structure. When amoebae are caused to ingest particles of gold or other metals, the paths which these particles take in the endoplasm are also highly irregular, not at all like the "fall" of gold particles through a simple protein solution. As in *Physarum*, occasional endoplasmic inclusions in *Amoeba* are able to move in a direction opposite to that of the main endoplasmic flow. Consequently Allen has concluded that both the ectoplasm and endoplasm have gel-like properties in *Amoeba* (rejecting the plasmagel-plasmasol distinction of Mast), and he believes that sufficient structure exists in the endoplasm to make a fountain zone contraction mechanism feasible.

Various other features of normal amoeboid movement support the idea that fountain zone contraction actually occurs. For instance, Allen has argued that the hyaline cap represents water forced out of the endoplasmic colloid by its contraction (i.e., syneresis); this concept is supported by the fact that the cap has a refractive index very close to that of water (equivalent to approximately a 1% protein solution), and that in the fountain zone immediately beneath the cap, a reciprocal *increase* in dry mass concentration occurs as the fluid endoplasm is transformed to gel-state ectoplasm (Allen and Cowden, 1962). Under certain conditions a visible pulse can be seen in the hyaline cap accompanying the initiation of locomotion in *Amoeba*. In film records of amoeba reversing direction, Allen has clearly recorded that reversal begins at the new (or presumptive) *anterior* end, and is propagated as a visible contraction from anterior to posterior. Finally, by combining polarizing microscopy with film records, he has demonstrated a very impressive longitudinal birefringence in the fountain zone, of a type which provides direct physical evidence for compressive forces originating there during stop-start streaming.

In a sense, the fountain zone contraction theory attempts to describe amoeboid streaming as a kind of massive linear tension movement (see page 218), and it is not surprising that the theory has been extended to systems that are more obviously of the linear tension type. Among amoeboid protozoans, the foraminiferans are remarkable for their complex nets of long, thin cytoplasmic strands (filopodia), many of which are less than a micron in diameter. Movement of cytoplasmic inclusions in these strands exhibits typical linear tension characteristics; i.e., particle velocity does not necessarily increase as the channels narrow, inclusions change velocity suddenly for no obvious reason, and particles may be seen moving past one another in opposite directions even in strands that can barely be resolved with the light microscope. Additional features that have been described for the foraminiferan *Allogromia* are that: (1) the filopodia are in a continual process of splitting or branching longitudinally, as if the main trunk were composed of many separable, bidirectional "wires"; (2) amputated pseudopods continue two-way streaming for a remarkably long time; (3) new filopodia grow out of the cell body as relatively rigid structures, each ending in a droplet-like bulge or knob and capable of waving about like an arm; and (4) a degenerating filopodium loses its rigidity, and often reverts to the form of fluid droplets which gradually move down the cytoplasmic net to the cell body.

The composite nature of filopodia in *Allogromia* has been confirmed by Wohlfarth-Botterman (1961), who found in an electron microscope analysis of thin-sectioned organisms that a single filopod contains scores of parallel substrands, each enclosed in a plasma membrane and containing mitochondria and other inclusions; the smallest of these substrands was only 140 Å in diameter. In this system, not only the behavior of the moving inclusions but also the structure of the pseudopod are incompatible with a pressure-hydraulic mechanism. However, Allen (1964) has suggested that the units of movement in *Allogromia* may actually be U-shaped cytoplasmic strands, and that movement may be produced by a propagated contraction "at the bend" supposedly located at the filopod tip. Such a mechanism would be in conformity with the fountain-zone contraction theory which Allen (1961) proposed for *Amoeba*. However, since he has not yet been able to track individual particles as they move out to the tip, around the bend, and back toward the cell body, there is still no direct evidence that U-shaped units exist in *Allogromia*.

An alternative mechanism, proposed by Jahn and Rinaldi (1959), postulates shearing forces or "crawling molecules" between adjacent cytoplasmic strands moving in opposite directions. The difficulty in this case is that it is not known whether bidirectional flow can occur *within* one of Wohlfarth-Botterman's membrane-enclosed subunits; it seems unlikely in fact that the very smallest strands could manage bidirectional flow, whereas the occurrence of shearing forces between separate membrane-enclosed strands is even more unlikely. These objections would not apply to streaming in *Amoeba*, where it has been suggested that shearing forces may operate at the endoplasm-ectoplasm boundary (as in plant cyclosis). Nevertheless, direct evidence for such a mechanism in *Amoeba* is lacking, and the motive force developed by amoebae in Kamiya's double-chamber experiments was fully a thousand times greater than the shearing forces that are responsible for cyclosis in *Nitella*.

It should be kept in mind that the phenomenon of amoeboid movement is not confined to protozoa, but also occurs widely in specialized cells of higher organisms, where the patterns of pseudopod formation are often difficult to account for by any of the mechanisms discussed so far (i.e., pressure-hydraulic streaming, ectoplasmic-endoplasmic shearing, or fountain-zone contraction). In human blood, for instance, each type of leukocyte (eosinophile, monocyte, etc.) exhibits its own peculiar pattern and rate of amoeboid activity, and the fountain pattern of streaming, as found in *Amoeba proteus,* is generally not a conspicuous feature. Various types of embryo also contain cells which exhibit individual or mass amoeboid movements while performing specific morphogenetic migrations. DuPraw (1965b) has studied amoeboid activity in honey bee embryonic cells, combining the techniques of time-lapse cinematography and electron microscopy. From his time-lapse analysis, he has concluded that two separate mechanisms operate in these cells: (1) a mechanism responsible for translating cytoplasmic inclusions; and (2) a separate mechanism involved in the forming of pseudopods. Although the two types of movement are interrelated, they have also been observed to vary semi-independently. Electron microscopy of the same cells, prepared as whole mounts, indicates that the mechanism responsible for granule movements depends primarily on linear contractions by an extensive system of cytoplasmic fibers (Fig. 9-7). The diameters (180 Å) and overall configuration of these cytoplasmic fibers suggests that they may correspond to cytoplasmic microtubules, as described by other authors in thin-sectioned material.

With respect to pseudopod formation, DuPraw has suggested that net locomotion in these cells may depend on the assembly of new cytoplasmic fibers (or microtubules) in the anterior part of the cell, combined with disassembly of old microtubules in the posterior regions. In this "assembly-disassembly hypothesis," the process of amoeboid locomotion is visualized as analogous to the process of assembly and disassembly that would be necessary to move a locomotive across country, using only two lengths of track. The hyaline cap would correspond to the zone of assembly, and might be envisioned as a "microtubule precursor solution." In this concept, the invisible barrier between hyaline cap and granular endoplasm would represent the effect of leashlike restraints on granules held back by their attachments to the existing cytoplasmic fiber system, whereas the "bursting" of granules through this barrier would correspond to the establishment of new fibers in the advancing pseudopod tip. As pointed out by the author, this concept is compatible with Allen's fountain-zone contraction theory, since the movement of endoplasmic granules is regarded as being brought about by *contraction* of cytoplasmic elements primarily in the fountain zone; at the same time, net locomotion is thought to require *assembly* of new cytoplasmic fibers, primarily in the vicinity of the hyaline cap.

Unfortunately the mechanisms of locomotion that operate in various kinds of amoeboid cell have not yet been satisfactorily clarified at a mac-romolecular level. However, the diversity of data now in hand suggests that more than one mechanism will be found, and in fact that multiple processes may occur within the same cell, either simultaneously or at different stages of the life cycle.

10

THE PLASMA MEMBRANE AND
ITS DERIVATIVES

1. STRUCTURE AND PROPERTIES

> Just as chemistry could not have devel-
> oped without test tubes to hold reacting
> substances, so organisms could not have
> evolved without relatively impermeable
> membranes to surround the cell constit-
> uents.
>
> E. N. Harvey *1943*

Living matter is always characterized by highly ordered arrays of specific macromolecules; by comparison, the inanimate environment is characterized by randomness, or high entropy distributions of unspecific molecules. Between these two distinct phases of matter a boundary or interface is provided by the plasma membrane.

It is now well established that the composition of a cell in terms of unspecific precursor molecules, inorganic ions, and water is largely regulated both passively and actively by the plasma membrane. Beyond this the nature of the macromolecular cell contents, although primarily controlled by specific pathways of biosynthesis, is often influenced by such factors as precursor availability and ionic environment. Information relevant to the mechanisms of plasma membrane function may be found scattered throughout several disciplines, such as neurophysiology, electron microscopy, and biochemistry. Unfortunately, many earlier studies suffered from serious misinterpretations, because important membrane phenomena such as pinocytosis and active transport had not yet been recognized. For these reasons, the literature related to this topic is one of the most complex in cell biology.

The earliest analyses of cell surface properties were intended to determine the passive permeability profile, i.e., what kinds of molecule could diffuse freely into a cell and what kinds could not. It was understood very early that water diffuses rapidly into most cells, and since many other molecules do not, the cell surface behaves as a semipermeable membrane, giving the cell itself the properties of an osmometer. When cells are immersed in solutions of high water concentration (hypotonic solutions), water tends to diffuse into them resulting in swelling and bursting; on the other hand, when they are immersed in low concentrations of water (hypertonic solutions), water tends to diffuse out leading to shrinkage, crenation, or plasmolysis. In isotonic solutions, provided that the external solute molecules cannot penetrate the plasma membrane, the water concentration remains the same on the inside and outside of the cell. Thus, human red blood cells are preserved for long periods in $0.3 M$ sucrose, exhibiting neither crenation nor hemolysis.

On the other hand, in isotonic solutions which contain a solute capable of penetrating the plasma membrane, cell water volume does not remain constant. Red blood cells placed in $0.3 M$ glycerol are osmotically balanced only at time zero; after that glycerol molecules begin to pass through the plasma membrane, tending to accumulate inside the cell (since the glycerol concentration is higher outside). As glycerol accumulates in the cytoplasm the total solute concentration rises, and con-

230

sequently more water molecules are driven into the cell by osmotic pressure. The cell volume gradually increases in proportion to the glycerol and water molecules which have penetrated, until finally hemolysis occurs. In plant and bacterial cells, the presence of a rigid cell wall helps to prevent excessive volume *increases* under normal circumstances; however, the penetration of solutes may be detected in plant cells that have previously *lost* water by plasmolysis in hypertonic solutions. In such cells "deplasmolysis" leads to reestablishment of the normal volume, and the rate of deplasmolysis may be used as a measure of the rate at which a given solute penetrates the plasma membrane.

Composition of the Plasma Membrane

The rate at which red blood cells hemolyze or plant cells deplasmolyze depends on the rate at which the particular solute molecules can penetrate the membrane, and comparative observations of these rates constituted some of the earliest hard data concerning the nature of the plasma membrane. For a given type of membrane and a given solute, the rate of penetration is best expressed as a "permeability constant" defined by the equation

$$k = \frac{\Delta V}{\Delta t} \cdot \frac{1}{A(P_i - P_0)}$$

In this equation $\Delta V/\Delta t$ is the observed change in cell volume per unit time (μ^3 per minute), A is the total area of the cell's surface (μ^2), and $(P_i - P_0)$ is the diffusion gradient or difference in osmotic pressure due to the solute outside and inside the cell (in atmospheres). The permeability constant therefore represents the number of cubic microns of water which penetrate one square micron of membrane in 1 minute with a differential in solute concentration of one atmosphere.

Although the earlier comparative studies contained many inaccuracies due to unrecognized active transport and bioelectric effects, they were correct to a first approximation. The results are summarized by "Overton's rules" (1895), which noted two major trends in penetrability: (1) that lipid-soluble compounds tend to diffuse through natural membranes faster than water-soluble ones (i.e., solutes penetrate approximately in the order of their oil:water partition coefficients); and (2) that small molecules tend to penetrate faster than large ones (Fig. 10-1). Often the larger water-soluble molecules such as sucrose and proteins do not penetrate at all. These findings suggested that the membrane

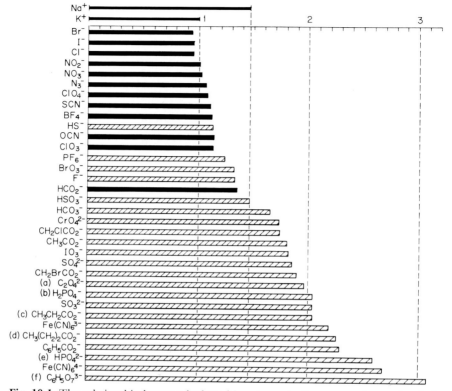

Fig. 10-1. The relationship between hydrated ion size and effect on membrane depolarization in motor neurons. The scale is based on the hydrated potassium ion as unity (above). Black bands designate ions with depolarizing effects, indicating penetration through the membrane. Anions larger than the hydrated sodium ion do not penetrate. From Ito *et al.* (1962).

itself must contain large amounts of lipid, and that penetration is essentially by a "molecular sieve" mechanism, as though the membrane contained holes of molecular dimensions through which solute molecules must pass in order to enter or leave the cell. Both these principles have stood the test of time and are recognized now as representing fundamental features of plasma membrane structure (Collander, 1949).

Other early conclusions and problems, however, have since been invalidated by the discovery of active transport effects. For instance, many cells behave as if they are impermeable to salts or charged ions like Na^+ and Cl^-; it is well known that red blood cells maintain their volumes in isotonic NaCl as well as in isotonic sucrose. On the other hand, the presence of Na^+ or K^+ ions often alters the permeability constants measured for other solutes—potassium generally decreasing membrane permeability, and sodium increasing it. After the introduction of radioactive tracer techniques in the 1940's, it was discovered that a slow but constant flux of potassium, sodium, and chloride ions takes place across all typical plasma membranes; nevertheless ion penetration does not necessarily result in accumulation and swelling, because most cells contain mechanisms which permit them to pump ions out again, thereby maintaining a fairly constant osmotic pressure and water volume. Tosteson and Hoffman (1960) have shown that when this osmoregulatory mechanism is blocked by an inhibitor, sheep erythrocytes do swell in isotonic salt solutions.

Earlier studies also indicated surprising variability in the permeability constants obtained for the same solute measured for different cell types or for the same cells under different metabolic conditions. This variability was thought to reflect major differences in the composition and structure of the different membranes. Thus the permeability constants for glycerol, as measured for the red blood cells of different mammalian species, differ by a factor of 240 times. Nevertheless, more recent evidence shows that in some species glycerol is actually taken up by an active metabolic process, so that the observed variations do not necessarily imply any major structural variation. In fact, at present it is reasonable to suppose that the broad chemical and structural properties of the plasma membrane are similar in all cells.

The early attempts to define membrane permeability constants were followed shortly by efforts to isolate the plasma membrane in bulk for chemical analysis. Mammalian red blood cells were a convenient material in this type of study as well, since after hemolysis the empty membranes could be separated as "ghosts." Using such ghosts, Gorter and Grendel (1925) performed the classic experiment of extracting the membrane lipid, spreading this lipid as a monomolecular layer on water, and comparing the total area of the monolayer with the estimated total area of membrane before extraction. Such calculations for a number of species showed that each red blood cell ghost typically contains about enough lipid to cover the entire surface two molecules thick. From their analysis, Gorter and Grendel proposed that the plasma membrane is in fact composed of lipid molecules arranged in two concentric layers, with hydrocarbon ends (CH_3) innermost and polar ends ($C{=}O$) outermost; this concept, too, remains one of the most useful generalizations in membrane theory.

Many detailed chemical analyses have since made it clear that high amounts of lipid, particularly of phospholipid, are characteristic of biological membranes, including not only the plasma membrane but

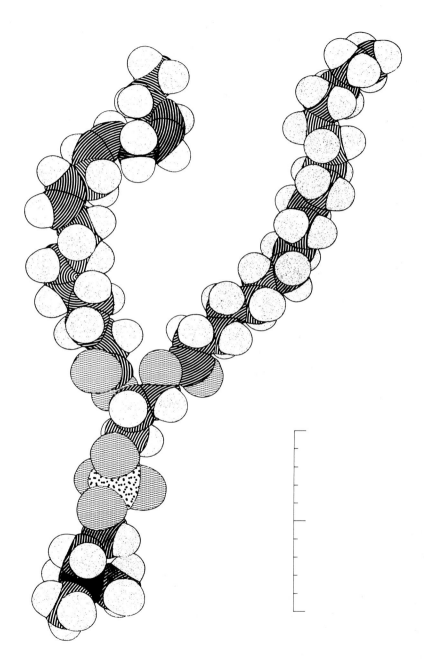

also intracellular membranes such as those of mitochondria, chloroplasts, endoplasmic reticulum, and the Golgi apparatus. Except for cholesterol, all the membrane lipids are formed by ester linkages joining relatively simple precursor molecules in different combinations; these precursors include: (1) α-glycerophosphate (an intermediate in anaerobic glycolysis); (2) saturated or unsaturated long-chain fatty acids; (3) ethanolamine; (4) choline (trimethylethanolamine); (5) serine (an amino acid); (6) sphingosine (a long-chain, 18-carbon compound); and (7) galactose or glucose. The "building-block" structure of a phospholipid is illustrated in Fig. 10-2, which shows phosphatidylcholine (lecithin) containing one saturated and one unsaturated fatty acid bound in ester linkages with the two hydroxyl groups of α-glycerophosphate; in addition, a choline molecule is bound in ester linkage to the phosphate group.

The different types of membrane lipid vary in their proportions to one another, but they invariably include *glycerophosphatides* (phosphatidylserine, phosphatidylethanolamine, phosphatidylcholine = lecithin), *sphingolipids* (sphingosine phosphatide = sphingomyelin, and sphingosine galactoside = cerebroside), and *cholesterol*. Although sphingosine galactoside and cholesterol do not contain phosphate, they are polar molecules like the phospholipids, and like them they are capable of orienting perpendicularly at a lipid-water interface. In the glycerophosphatides other than lecithin (known as cephalins), choline is replaced by ethanolamine or serine. The structure of sphingosine phosphatide differs in being based on choline and sphingosine units bound by ester linkages with phosphoric acid, while a fatty acid molecule forms an ester with the sphingosine. Finally, sphingosine galactoside is compounded from sphingosine, a fatty acid, and galactose. It is believed that choline and sphingolipids are absent in bacteria.

DeGier and Van Deenen (1961) have compared the lipid composition of red blood cell ghosts in six species of mammal. They found relatively little variation in total lipid (22–31%), percentage of cholesterol (21–31% of total lipid), or percentage of phospholipid (53–61% of total

---

Fig. 10-2. A lecithin (phosphatidylcholine) molecule, with the polar phosphate chain to the left and the neutral fatty acid chains to the right. Linoleic acid is shown in the β position (above) and stearic acid in the α position. Scale indicates 10 Ångstrom units. Structural formula is:

lipids). However, marked differences occurred in the percentages of the different phospholipids: phosphatidylcholine varied from 1% in sheep to 56% in rats; phosphatidylethanolamine and phosphatidylserine varied from 32–36% in sheep, ox, and pig to 18% in rats; and sphingosine phosphatide together with other lipophosphatides varied from 63% in sheep to 26–29% in rabbits and rats. The composition of nerve myelin, which is derived from Schwann cell plasma membranes, has also been determined by Brante (1949), who found a ratio of about 8 cholesterol:4 sphingosine galactoside:2 phosphatidylserine:2 plasmalogen:2 sphingosine phosphatide:1 phosphatidylcholine. Parpart and Ballentine (1952) have emphasized that some of the membrane lipids are more firmly bound than others, cholesterol being easily extractable whereas phosphatidylcholine is more firmly bound (cephalins vary in ease of extraction).

In addition to lipids, significant amounts of protein are also present in natural membranes; for instance, the dry weight ratio of protein to lipid in red blood cell ghosts is about 1.6 to 1.8. Taking into account the relatively high molecular weight of protein, it can be calculated that this ratio corresponds to about one protein molecule for every 70 lipid molecules. Encouraging progress has begun recently in characterizing the specific proteins associated with plasma membranes. Paradoxically, much of this progress is an outgrowth of investigations with isolated mitochondria and chloroplasts, both of which possess phosphorylation mechanisms closely bound to internal membrane systems. It has been found that both chloroplast and mitochondrial membranes contain ATPase activity, together with an actomyosin-like contractile protein and a characteristic structural protein; the latter is water insoluble at neutral pH and forms complexes with phospholipids (see Chapters 5 and 7). Similar techniques have now been extended to red blood cell plasma membranes, from which a structural protein has been extracted by Richardson et al. (1963). Ohnishi (1962b) has also isolated two contractile proteins from the red blood cell membrane, one of which resembles actin (erythroactin) and the other myosin (erythromyosin); each of these proteins is able to cross-react with actin or myosin from rabbit muscle, giving the characteristic viscosity increase upon mixing and viscosity decrease upon addition of ATP. Erythromyosin also shows the characteristic Ca^{++}-activated ATPase properties of muscle myosin. Localization of an intense ATPase in the plasma membrane of HeLa tumor cells has been observed more directly by Epstein and Holt (1963), using a combined cytochemical-electron microscope technique. In fact, there is now a considerable body of evidence which implicates membrane ATPase activity in the processes of active transport (Chapter 11).

Structure of the Plasma Membrane

Danielli and Davson (1935) were the first to propose that the plasma membrane is organized like a "sandwich," with a bimolecular layer of lipid at the center (as suggested by Gorter and Grendel), but with protein films adsorbed on the inside and outside surfaces. Danielli carried out a number of investigations to support this concept, showing that protein molecules tend to accumulate at an oil-water interface, where they become trapped as a very thin layer of unfolded polypeptide chains (the hydrocarbon side chains tending to associate with the oil layer and the polar side chains with the water layer). Evidence for this type of structure in natural membranes was obtained by Schmitt (1936) in an early analysis of birefringence with the polarizing microscope; from the polarized light responses of red blood cell ghosts, he was able to conclude that the lipid molecules are probably oriented perpendicularly to the cell surface, while the protein molecules are oriented tangentially.

The earliest attempts to estimate the thickness of the plasma membrane were also remarkably in accord with such a model. Since the length of a fully extended phospholipid molecule is about 35 Å, the overall thickness of a protein-lipid sandwich should be in the order of 100 Å. Waugh and Schmitt (1940) made direct optical comparisons between red blood cell ghosts and thin layers of barium stearate, reporting that membrane thickness varies with pH from 125 to 225 Å. Electrical impedance measurements by Cole and Curtis (1936) also indicated a lipid layer about 50 Å thick; they found that membrane capacitance is remarkably uniform from one type of cell to another, with a value of about 1 μfarad/cm². Of special interest were the pioneer X-ray diffraction studies carried out at this time on nerve axon myelin by Schmitt and his co-workers (Schmitt and Bear, 1939; Schmitt and Palmer, 1940), which led to a remarkably early realization that the organization of the myelin sheath is similar to that of the plasma membrane. Periodicities of 63.5 Å and 160 Å were found in dried motor nerve roots, whereas a periodicity of 63 Å occurred in preparations of various purified phospholipids and dried lipid extracts of spinal cord. From these data, Davson and Danielli (1943) concluded that: (1) the 63.5 Å periods represent bimolecular lipid layers; (2) each 160 Å myelin unit represents two bimolecular lipid sheets with associated proteins; and (3) protein contributes about 25 Å to the 160 Å myelin period.

With the advent of thin-sectioning techniques for electron microscopy, a new phase began in plasma membrane studies. Largely through the investigations of J. D. Robertson (1959, 1964), it has been recognized that a highly similar fine structure occurs universally at the surfaces of plant, animal, and protozoan cells. In cross section and after fixation in osmium tetroxide, this fine structure appears as two parallel dark (osmiophilic) lines separated by a light (osmiophobic) space (Fig. 10-3A). Although the exact dimensions of these three layers vary somewhat with the fixative and other conditions, typical values are about 20 Å for each of the dark layers, 35 Å for the light layer, and a total thickness of 75–100 Å. It was Robertson's (1959) insight that these *three* lines together constitute *one* membrane, which he called a "unit membrane." Since preparations of pure cephalin, fixed in osmium tetroxide and thin-sectioned, show alternating dark and light layers at a 40 Å periodicity, Robertson has concluded that the dark layers represent the polar ends of phospholipid molecules together with associated protein molecules. Consequently the observed dimensions and pattern of Robertson's "unit membrane" correspond well with those expected for a bimolecular lipid-protein sandwich of the type postulated by Danielli.

Robertson's earliest insights were based on an electron microscope analysis of the nerve axon myelin sheath. Previously Ben Geren (1954) had shown by thin-section electron microscopy that the myelin sheath of a peripheral neuron develops from a Schwann cell plasma membrane "wrapped" around the axon into a structure of multiple spiral layers (something like a roll of wrapping paper; Fig. 10-4). The developing axon becomes associated with a series of Schwann cells, each of which engulfs a different segment of the axon; in this manner each segment becomes entirely surrounded by the plasma membrane of a Schwann cell, which meets itself and fuses into a double-membraned "mesaxon" (Fig. 10-4). As development proceeds the Schwann cell flows around and around the axon, a process which results in winding of the mesaxon spirally around the axon to form an ever-thickening sheath (Fig. 10-4). In this process, of course, the total amount of mesaxon becomes greatly increased, so that in effect plasma membrane is synthesized and "spun out" by the Schwann cell. Ben Geren's work therefore confirmed and extended the relationship between the myelin sheath and the cell membrane which had been inferred by Schmitt and Palmer (1940) from their X-ray diffraction analysis.

Robertson (1959) was able to carry this investigation to a much finer level of resolution, analyzing the sheath in terms of a triple-layered or "unit membrane" at the surface of the Schwann cell. If the mature myelin sheath is cross-sectioned after osmium fixation, it is seen to contain a series of conspicuous dark, concentric layers or circles with a periodicity of 120 Å (Fig. 10-5); in addition to these, another series of less distinct intraperiod lines occurs, one of which divides the space between each pair of major lines (Fig. 10-5). Robertson showed that if

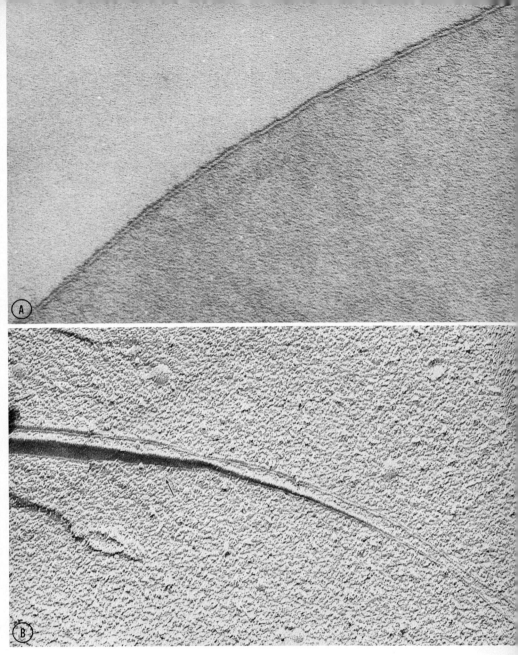

Fig. 10-3. (A) Thin-section of a human RBC, showing triple structure of the "unit" plasma membrane. 237,000×. From Robertson (1964). (B) Two unit membranes prepared by freeze-etching. Each membrane shows a triple structure, and one membrane has split, probably along the mid-plane of the lipid bilayer (arrow). 105,000×. From Branton (1966).

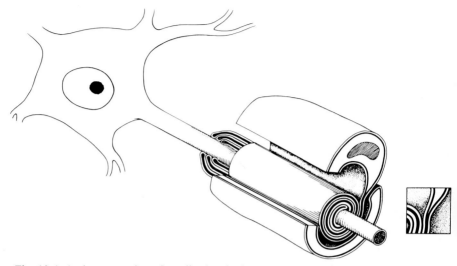

Fig. 10-4. An interpretation of myelin sheath ultrastructure. A Schwann cell has wrapped itself repeatedly around the axon of a neuron, generating multiple layers of plasma membrane. The major lines correspond to two fused inner layers of the Schwann cell unit membrane, while the intraperiod (lighter) lines correspond to two fused outer layers (inset).

these major and intraperiod lines are traced down the spiral to their origins the major lines correspond to two fused *inner* layers of the Schwann cell plasma membrane, while the intraperiod lines represent two fused *outer* layers of this membrane. The topology of the spiral winding process is such that, not only do the outer surfaces of the Schwann cell membrane meet in the mesaxon, but the inner osmiophilic layers meet and fuse as well (Fig. 10-4, inset). The very fact that the triple-layered plasma membrane can be "wrapped" in this manner provides convincing evidence that it represents a structurally cohesive organelle.

Since the intraperiod lines are not as well preserved by osmium tetroxide as the major lines, there is evidently some chemical difference between the outer and inner osmiophilic layers of the plasma membrane. Nevertheless, potassium permanganate fixation preserves both layers equally, so that the myelin sheath then appears to contain nothing but major lines, at a periodicity of only 60 Å. Further evidence for a dif-

Fig. 10-5. (A) Thin section of myelin sheath, showing alternating major and intraperiod layers. 275,000×. From Robertson (1964). (B) Myelin sheath after freeze-fracturing, showing smooth plasma membrane faces. 105,000×. From Branton (1967).

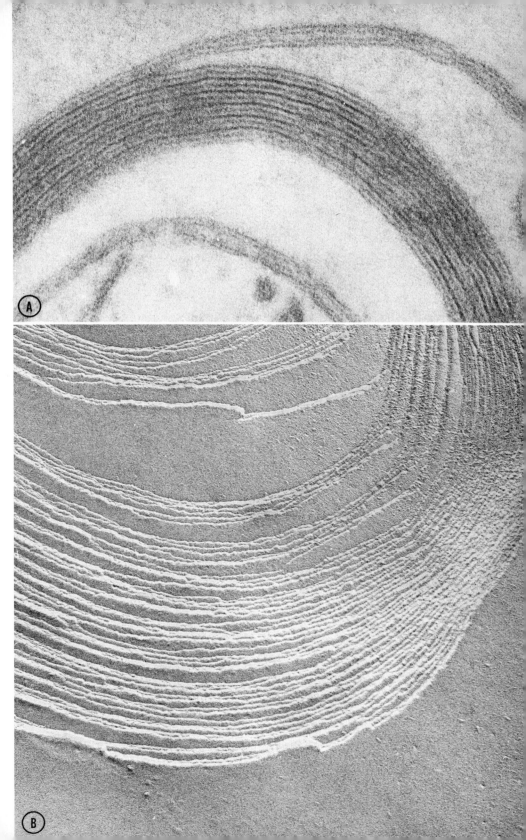

ference between inner and outer layers has been found after soaking the myelin sheath in hypotonic solutions (e.g., distilled water); the water apparently penetrates the myelin along the outer but not the inner surfaces of the unit membrane, thereby splitting the intraperiod lines into their two fused components but leaving the major lines intact. This observation demonstrates that the outer surface is hydrophilic, and suggests that it is more hydrophilic than the inner surface. Accordingly, Robertson has emphasized that the lipid-protein sandwich structure is in some way asymmetrical (as if the sandwich were made of rye bread on one side and white on the other). A similar asymmetry has been observed by Sjöstrand as slight but consistent differences in the thicknesses of the inner and outer osmiophilic layers at various cell surfaces. Possibly this asymmetry is related to a general principle that the outer surfaces of plant, animal, and bacterial cells commonly secrete some form of polysaccharide coat, e.g., cellulose in plant cells, chitin in arthropods, chondroitin sulfate in cartilage cells, mucus in epithelial cells, etc.

In the past, various questions have been raised as to whether the observed permeability and other physical properties of plasma membranes would be accounted for if they contained unbroken lipid bilayers; for instance, how readily would water penetrate such a structure? Until recently this question could not be investigated, since no one had succeeded in obtaining isolated lipid bilayers for analysis. However important steps in this direction have been achieved by Mueller *et al.* (1962) and Thompson (1964), who employed an apparatus consisting of two compartments filled with NaCl solution and separated by a vertical partition containing a round hole. When a solution of lipids is applied to the hole at 36°C, a thin lipid film is formed in direct contact with the aqueous medium on both sides; optical measurements indicate that the thickness of this film is 61 ± 10 Å, a value too high for a monomolecular layer but about right for a double lipid layer. Thompson has worked with purified lipids and finds that the film forms only if: (1) both a phospholipid and a neutral lipid are present; and (2) the phospholipid has zero net charge and contains unsaturated but not overly oxidized fatty acids. In practice, his films have been formed from a mixture of lecithin and *n*-tetradecane, sometimes supplemented by an admixture of cholesterol. The properties of such bimolecular lipid films are not only unusual, they also mimic many of the properties of natural plasma membranes, including high refractive index (1.66), high electrical resistance (0.2 to 4×10^6 ohm cm²), low surface tension (1 dyne/cm), and phase changes in response to temperature. Most surprising of all, these lipid membranes have a fairly high permeability coefficient for water, amounting to about 0.16 μ/min/atm (as determined in a tracer study using tritium-labeled water molecules). The films may also be deformed by pressure without breaking and, very significantly, they are in a fluid or liquid state.

Although these results with continuous lipid films are promising, various authors in the past have found it necessary to postulate a mosaic type of membrane in order to account for specific permeability effects. For instance, one of the earliest principles expressed in Overton's rules is that smaller molecules tend to penetrate the plasma membrane more rapidly than larger ones; this "sieve effect" seems to require the existence of restricted areas or small pores in the membrane, whose permeability properties differ from those of the membrane-at-large. In fact, an elaborate "lipid gate" model based on water-filled pores in the membrane was originally proposed by Parpart and Ballentine (1952). More recently the discovery that charged ions leak through the cell surface, and the development of techniques for measuring the exact rates of leakage with radioactive isotopes, has served to renew interest in the existence and dimensions of membrane pores. Thus it is possible to estimate the theoretical diameters and density of such pores if the true diffusion rates can be determined for various small molecules or ions of known atomic radii; it is also expected that particles larger than the maximum pore diameter will not be able to cross the membrane by diffusion (although they may still enter the cell by pinocytosis or active transport). Villegas and Barnda (1961) and Villegas et al. (1962) used six nonelectrolyte solutes, plus tritium-labeled water, to calculate pore size for the plasma membrane of squid giant axons; they came to the conclusion that the observed diffusion rates could be accounted for if the membrane contains cylindrical pores 4.25 Å in radius (8.5 A diameter) and if the frequency of such pores is $1.3 \times 10^{10}/cm^2$. A similar analysis, based on diffusion of hydrated ions through the membrane of frog sartorius muscle, led Mullins (1961) to conclude that this membrane also contains ion-permeable pores of about 4 Å radius (8.0 Å diameter). Ito et al. (1962) have also found evidence that resting mammalian neurons do not pass ions larger than 2.9 Å nonhydrated diameter (=8.34 Å hydrated diameter; see Fig. 10-1). The pore radii found by all these workers are surprisingly similar, and are somewhat larger than the radii of water molecules (1.36 Å) or hydrated K^+ (4.0 Å), Na^+ (3.7 Å), or Cl^- (3.9 Å) ions.

Further insights concerning the organization of the plasma membrane have been obtained from the fine structure of regions where two adjacent tissue cells contact one another. In most tissues the separate plasma membranes of the two cells approach each other closely but remain separated by a light (osmiophobic) gap approximately 100–200 Å wide; whether water or some other material occupies this gap has not as yet been determined. In certain rare instances, however, no gap occurs and the two outer layers of the separate unit membranes become fused or closely appressed; the result is an apparently five-layered structure (three osmiophilic and two osmiophobic layers). Robertson (1963) has found this type of structure forming disks about 0.3–0.5 μ in diameter in the synapse contacts between certain types of neuron in the goldfish medulla (Mauthner cells); in this instance the total thickness of the 5-layered regions is about 130 Å. More excitingly, high resolution micrographs of such cross-sectioned synaptic disks reveal a striated or beaded substructure with a periodicity of 85 Å; in tangential sections the same membranes exhibit a kind of irregular lattice, which is composed of pentagonal or hexagonal units, each having a central dense granule 25 Å in diameter. Although Robertson considers it likely that this hexagonal lattice is partly or entirely an artifact, it is also possible that the "cobblestones" are molecular or multimolecular units of the plasma membrane, at least as it is constituted in these goldfish synaptic disks. The general appearance is remarkably similar to that of chloroplast and mitochondrial membranes as recently described by Weier *et al.* (1965) and Sjöstrand (1963; see Figs. 5-3 and 7-2).

These discoveries, together with the fact that globular proteins such as ATPases occur in the plasma membrane, have led some authors to suggest that natural membranes may not be based on lipid bilayers after all, but on a skeleton of protein monomers self-assembled into a two-dimensional sheetlike aggregate. However, it is more likely that there is a spectrum of membrane types, ranging from a pure protein aggregate in bacteriophage head membranes (Chapter 15) to a classic lipid bilayer in the myelin sheath. At intermediate points in the spectrum there are protein polymer membranes with interspersed lipid (as in mitochondria) or lipid bilayers with embedded globular enzymes (as in the plasma membrane and possibly chloroplasts). Transitions from one to another of these structural types can probably occur at different places and different times in the same membrane.

Recently Branton (1966) has brought forward an entirely new and unexpected type of evidence to confirm the reality of lipid bilayers in plasma, nuclear, vacuolar, and Golgi membranes. He has been able to use the electron microscope to study unfixed, unsectioned cells which were frozen rapidly in liquid nitrogen, then fractured and shadowed with platinum-carbon. In such preparations the fracture planes tend to follow the various cell membranes, and Branton has observed that in fact the splintering frequently splits each unit membrane into two half-membranes (Fig. 10-3B). These split inner membrane faces have a much lower sublimation rate than the nearby aqueous cytoplasm, providing evidence that the newly exposed faces are largely lipid. In addition, Deamer and Branton (1967) have provided evidence that the hydrophobic lipid-lipid bonds along the central plane of a lipid bilayer would be the membrane's weakest point under conditions of liquid nitrogen freezing ($-196°C$). Branton (1967) has strongly supported his interpretation with freeze-etch micrographs of the myelin sheath (Fig. 10-5B), which reveal an organization in accord with the unit membrane concept of Robertson. However, Branton and Park (1967) emphasize that some biological membranes, such as those of chloroplasts, are seen to be highly particulate after freeze-etching (Fig. 5-4).

As originally formulated (1959), Robertson's "unit membrane" concept proposed a basic morphological similarity in *all* the membranes of the cell, including not only the plasma membrane, but also the two mitochondrial membranes, the two nuclear membranes, the membranes of the endoplasmic reticulum, of the Golgi apparatus, of the chloroplast, and of various smaller cytoplasmic vesicles. The fixation and embedding methods of that time seemed to reveal a three-layered structure in all these membranes, and led Robertson to propose the remarkable hypothesis that all the cell's membranes might be derived from one another, and might also remain to some extent continuous with one another. In its most elaborate form this hypothesis viewed all the cell's organelles as one intricate but continuous "three-phase" system, consisting of a topographically complex membrane phase, an equally complex cytoplasmic phase inside the membrane, and a tortuous external phase on the opposite side of the membrane. In this scheme, the space between the two nuclear membranes might be continuous with the exterior environment by way of connections with the endoplasmic reticulum channels, and in a sense would therefore be outside the cell. The hypothesis also postulated an elaborate, double invagination process by which mitochondria could arise from the plasma membrane by budding.

Although structural continuities between different cell membranes, such as the nuclear envelope and endoplasmic reticulum, sometimes do occur and probably have functional significance, newer discoveries have made the three-phase concept untenable. As noted by Sjöstrand (1963), different biological membranes lying side by side in the same sections do exhibit differences in ultrastructure after preparation by more sophisticated techniques; Branton's more recent freeze-etch preparations have also provided strong evidence for structural variations among membranes. In terms of membrane synthesis, Luck's (1963) elegant isotopic choline experiments indicate that new mitochondrial membranes are synthesized in association with existing mitochondria and do not derive precursor material from nonmitochondrial membranes (Chapter 7).

The plasma membrane sometimes exhibits visible differentiations involving fairly large areas of the cell surface. For instance, Robertson (1964) cites a number of instances in which this membrane shows consistently different thicknesses (in the range of 75–100 Å) on different sides of the same cell and in the same section. Epstein and Holt (1963) have also found that ATPase activity in the HeLa cell membrane is confined to specific areas (microvilli) and cannot be detected in other areas. Still another differentiation of the plasma membrane is the desmosome, which occurs in areas of contact between adjacent tissue cells. Desmosomes seem to be formed by local deposits of some dense (osmiophilic) material between and around the two separate unit membranes; sometimes the gap between the membranes is considerably greater than the usual 200 Å but is filled with the dense deposit, while similar dense material extends into the cytoplasm on both sides for a distance of 150 to several hundred Ångstrom units. In epithelial cells the desmosomes seem to act as "attachment plaques," holding the cells together.

The site and mechanism of plasma membrane synthesis is a problem which is still largely unresolved. New membrane is formed during cell division, and, at least in plant cells, the developing telophase mid-plate seems to arise from coalescence of small, preexisting cytoplasmic vesicles. However during pinocytosis in *Amoeba*, formation of new membrane apparently occurs in association with the existing membrane and without "promembrane" vesicles. Some cells, upon fragmentation, have the ability to form a "precipitation membrane" almost instantly, which in electron micrographs exhibits the typical appearance of a "unit membrane." This type of observation suggests that the plasma membrane may arise more or less spontaneously from precursor molecules by means of surface forces operating at the interface between cytoplasm and external medium. The fact that artificial bimolecular lipid membranes are in a fluid state also suggests that the plasma membrane may be capable of molding and extending itself on the cell surface in the manner of a liquid or semiliquid.

Pinocytosis, Phagocytosis, and Related Phenomena

One of the most striking and dynamic properties of the plasma membrane is its ability to capture external materials by pinching them off into membrane-lined packets or vacuoles; these vacuoles may then be transferred rapidly to the deeper parts of the cytoplasm, where they undergo fusion, fragmentation or other appropriate kinds of processing. Through this elegant mechanism the passage of specific materials from outside to inside the cell is achieved in an efficient, controlled manner and without involving any break in the structural continuity of the surface membrane (Fig. 10-6).

Such surface vacuolization, or endocytosis, has been observed in many kinds of cell including neurons, muscle fibers, intestinal epithelium, kidney tubule cells, liver cells, gall bladder epithelium, adipose tissue, osteoclasts, fibroblasts, insect oocytes, pollen mother cells of tomato and pumpkins, and of course, leukocytes and amoeboid protozoa. Although it could not be detected in certain other cell types, there is nevertheless a good possibility that all cells can exhibit endocytosis under the right environmental conditions. The most detailed studies of the phenomenon have been carried out with amoeboid protozoans and

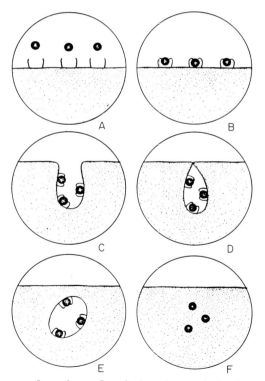

Fig. 10-6. The concept of membrane flow during pinocytosis. In (A) and (B), particles of solute attach to the plasma membrane surface, which then flows inward to pinch off a vacuole in (E). From Bennett (1956).

leukocytes, whose ability to "engulf" food particles was well known to 19th century cytologists and was named "phagocytosis" by Metchnikoff (1883). The closely related process of "pinocytosis," in which the cell drinks or ingests particle-free globules of the external medium, was first noted by Edwards (1925) in *Amoeba* and named by Lewis (1931) after he observed it in tissue amoebocytes (or macrophages). In secretory tissues such as the pituitary and pancreatic glands, a reverse process occurs in which membrane-lined vacuoles fuse with the plasma membrane and release their secretory contents to the cell exterior; presumably the term "exocytosis" would be appropriate for this process, although it has also been called emeiocytosis (cell vomiting).

Endocytosis in response to a pure solution (i.e., pinocytosis) or to a suspension of colloidal particles is the most convenient form for a careful quantitative investigation. Impressive variability has been found from one cell type to another with respect to the rate of pinocytosis, the specific solutes which induce it, and the form of surface activity that results in vacuolization. In *Amoeba*, Mast and Doyle (1934) found that proteins or dilute seawater induce pinocytosis. The process begins with cessation of streaming or locomotion, detachment from the substratum, wrinkling of the cell surface, and paralysis of contractile vacuole activity; next, short hyaline pseudopodia form at various points on the surface, giving the amoeba a "rosette" appearance; finally, at the tip of each hyaline pseudopod, a narrow, actively undulating channel is formed, from the innermost end of which small vacuoles begin to be separated into the cytoplasm. Undulations of the plasma membrane are also observed during pinocytosis in metazoan tissue cells, but channels as such are not usually formed. Instead, spherical or ovoid vacuoles appear immediately beneath the undulating surface, and often accumulate rapidly to give a "foamy" appearance to the cytoplasm. Mitochondria are conspicuously oriented near these active surfaces, and can sometimes be seen to exhibit remarkable saltatory or linear tension movements in a direction perpendicular to the plasma membrane. In both *Amoeba* and tissue cells, the size of individual vacuoles varies widely, partly due to rapid coalescence of small vacuoles into larger ones and to a reverse process, in which smaller vacuoles are seen to bud off from large ones. Pinocytosis vacuoles sometimes occur whose diameters are well below the limits of resolution of the light microscope (reaching a limiting diameter of about 300 Å), and there is evidence that "micropinocytosis" occurs exclusively in some cells, where it is impossible to detect with the light microscope and difficult to observe even with the electron microscope.

An extensive quantitative analysis of pinocytosis in *Amoeba proteus* has been carried out by Chapman-Andresen (1963), who developed techniques for making statistical counts of the number of pinocytosis channels in samples of amoebae under different conditions, and also for following the uptake of isotopically labeled solutes from the medium. In her earlier studies during the 1950's, Chapman-Andresen established standard conditions for inducing pinocytosis based on 0.125 M NaCl as the inducer presented in 0.01 M phosphate buffer at pH 6.5 and 21.5°C. When amoebae are transferred to this standard medium, they begin to form channels within a few minutes, reaching a maximum number in about 15 minutes and tapering off to zero after 30 minutes; subsequently the complete pinocytosis cycle cannot be induced again until after the end of a "digestive" phase of 3 to 4 hours, when streaming locomotion is resumed.

According to Chapman-Andresen, the average number of pinocytosis channels varies predictably with temperature, pH, and the nutrient condition of the amoebae. The total volume of vacuoles formed in a standard cycle can be estimated by three methods: (1) from the number and surface area of the channels formed; (2) by staining the surface irreversibly with Alcian blue, which marks the vacuoles for measurement from the time they are formed until they are extruded (or defecated) about 48 hours later; and (3) from quantitative measurement of isotopically labeled solutes taken up by the amoebae. These various methods indicate that the total volume of fluid taken up in a single pinocytosis cycle is 1–10% of the total volume of the amoeba, and that the area of new membrane which must be synthesized is about 3×10^4 μ^2, corresponding to about 6% of the total surface area of a streaming amoeba. In experiments during which the pinocytosis cycle is interrupted and then resumed, or during which amoebae are permitted to alternate between pinocytosis and phagocytosis, they behave as if there is an absolute limit in the amount of endocytosis that they can carry out in a given time; this limit is believed to correspond to the limit in precursor material available for the synthesis of new plasma membrane.

Of considerable interest are the types and behavior of inducing solutes, which fall into three general classes: (1) proteins, (2) basic dyes, and (3) charged ions. Among the proteins, bovine serum albumin and RNase have been found to induce, whereas pepsin lacks activity. By testing the change in inducibility at different pH's, Chapman-Andresen has found that activity is closely related to the isoelectric point of the protein, such that induction occurs primarily on the acid side of the isoelectric point when the protein molecules carry a net positive charge. Since pepsin has a very low isoelectric point (about pH 1), it is always negatively charged in the range of physiological pH's and therefore lacks inducing ability. A very similar principle holds true for the vital stains, i.e., inducing activity is exhibited primarily by the basic stains, such as thionin, toluidine blue, methylene blue, basic fuchsin, methyl violet and neutral red, which carry a net positive charge at physiological pH's. In the third group of inducers are found a number of salts, including the chlorides, sulfates, and nitrates of sodium, potassium, magnesium, lithium, and ammonium. In addition, a similar inducing activity is shown by certain amino acids, such as glutamic acid, aspartic acid, arginine, lysine, cystine, and glutathione. All the inducing amino acids are acid or basic in character, whereas the neutral amino acids lack inducing activity. It appears, therefore, that all the solutes which induce pino-cytosis in *Amoeba* are charged particles, and most of them carry positive charges. Amoebae do not respond to carbohydrates such as glucose or to nucleic acids, although these may be taken up during pinocytosis in the presence of an active inducer.

The concept that selective transport across the plasma membrane might occur by a specific *binding* of particles to the outer surface, fol-lowed by an inward membrane flow and vesiculation, was first proposed on theoretical grounds by Bennett (1956; Fig. 10-6). Subsequently it has been clearly demonstrated that pinocytosis in amoeboid protozoans begins with a binding and concentrating of the inducer molecules on the outside of the plasma membrane. This was first shown by Brandt (1958) in experiments with the giant amoeba *Chaos chaos*, in which he used as inducer rabbit γ-globulin labeled with the fluorescent dye fluo-rescein; when the amoebae were fixed, sectioned, and examined under the ultraviolet microscope, fluorescent γ-globulin was clearly seen to be concentrated on the plasma membrane and on the membranes of the pinocytosis vacuoles. At about the same time, Schumaker (1958) mea-sured the amount of ^{131}I-labeled RNase or cytochrome *c* taken up by *Amoeba proteus* during pinocytosis, and found that these amounts were far greater than could be accounted for if the protein was taken up in solution. He determined that under certain conditions an amoeba could take up in 5 minutes an amount of protein corresponding to 5% of its own dry weight and approximately 50 times its own volume of the pro-tein-containing medium. More recently, Chapman-Andresen and Holter (1964) have demonstrated the specificity of this membrane binding by exposing amoebae simultaneously to ^{131}I-labeled serum albumin (an inducer) and ^{14}C-labeled glucose (a noninducer); at the end of the pinocytosis cycle the amoebae were found to have taken up about 14 times more protein than would be expected if the serum albumin had been ingested as a solution with the glucose. These experiments clearly show that endocytosis is a form of membrane activity which leads to a selective uptake of materials from solution, and which is able to account for the rapid transport of large, water-soluble molecules across a lipid-rich plasma membrane.

In *Amoeba* and *Chaos*, the solute-binding reaction is closely associated with a mucous layer which is known to coat the outside surface of the unit plasma membrane. Lewis and other classical light microscopists were able to detect the presence of a "slime coat" in these amoebae, and electron microscopy by Brandt and Pappas (1960) confirmed that the outside of the plasma membrane exhibits a furlike fringe of fibers up to 2000 Å long. Bairati and Lehmann (1953) had concluded earlier that acid mucopolysaccharides occur at the surface of *Amoeba proteus*, and their results are further supported by the fact that the surface stains deeply with Alcian blue and with the periodic acid-Schiff test (the former a mucous stain and the latter a test for polysaccharides). Since acid mucopolysaccharides are expected to carry a strong negative charge (and a negative charge has also been measured directly at the surface of *Amoeba*), the binding of positively charged inducer molecules very probably takes place by electrostatic attraction and formation of salt linkages with the mucous coat. It is also possible that the consequent reduction of net charge at the surface may play a role in inducing membrane flow and pinocytosis.

The fate of material ingested in pinocytosis vacuoles has also been followed by Chapman-Andresen and Holter (1955), using ^{14}C-labeled glucose. It was found that although the plasma membrane itself is highly impermeable to glucose, the membranes of the pinocytosis vacuoles apparently undergo a rapid change which permits glucose to diffuse through the vacuole interface into the cytoplasm, where it is metabolized to ^{14}CO$_2$. Visible changes in the ultrastructure of the vacuole membranes have also been described by Roth (1960): i.e., vacuoles which have just been formed still possess the mucous fringe which is characteristic of the plasma membrane, but this fringe begins to disappear in deeper vacuoles. Another important process which proceeds rapidly in endocytosis vacuoles is a progressive concentrating of the contents by removal of water. This process was clearly demonstrated by Holter and Marshall (1954), who observed that when amoebae are centrifuged at intervals following a pinocytosis cycle, the vacuoles behave as though they become progressively much denser.

Time-lapse films by A. C. Taylor and others have clearly established that mammalian liver, kidney, and other tissues are able to carry out pinocytosis in tissue cultures. In these cells too a rapid decrease in the size of pinocytosis vacuoles can be observed, presumably reflecting the removal of water; Gropp (1963) has noted that erythrocyte ghosts trapped in endocytosis vacuoles behave as though the vacuole fluid becomes progressively more hypertonic. Coalescence of small vacuoles to form larger ones is also a conspicuous and frequent event in time-lapse films, resembling the coalescence of soap bubbles in a foam. In some film records, the membrane of the pinocytosis vacuole itself can be seen to undergo a further, pinocytosis-like process, in which smaller vacuoles are budded off and distributed to different parts of the cytoplasm. The vacuoles may also persist in some cells as a kind of nutrient storage mechanism. Telfer (1963) has found evidence that yolk spheres in the eggs of the cecropia moth represent membrane-enclosed vacuoles taken up from the maternal blood by endocytosis in the oocyte stage.

In the intact animal as well, electron micrographs have revealed that microendocytosis often occurs at a level undetectable with the light microscope. For instance, the cells of vertebrate intestinal epithelium possess extremely fine, fingerlike processes or microvilli, which extend into the intestinal lumen from the free surface of each cell; at the bases of the microvilli, goblet-shaped depressions and spherical vacuoles provide morphological evidence that an endocytosis process is occurring. The so-called "brush border" of epithelial cells lining the kidney tubules presents a very similar appearance. In both these instances, the morphological evidence is supported by the fact that these cells are known to carry out an active and selective transport of solutes across the plasma membrane. Furthermore, endocytosis by mammalian tissue cells *in vivo* has been demonstrated experimentally by injecting live rats or mice with colloidal gold or ferritin molecules, which can be found later in cell vacuoles by electron microscopy. Hampton (1958) reported that colloidal mercuric sulfide appears in vacuoles near the cell surfaces in rat liver as little as 30 seconds after injection. In mouse kidney tubule cells, Miller (1960) found that injected hemoglobin passes into tubular invaginations at the base of the brush border, where it is pinched off into vacuoles and transported to the deeper regions of the cytoplasm for digestion. Neurons too have been observed to take up ferritin molecules by pinocytosis (Novikoff *et al.*, 1964).

That endocytosis is a process which requires the expenditure of metabolic energy seems likely from the active and often violent undulations exhibited by the plasma membrane in time-lapse films. It is interesting to speculate that actomyosin-like contractile proteins possessing ATPase activity, such as those found recently in erythrocyte plasma membranes, may play an active role in endocytosis. Gropp (1963) has observed that the rate of activity in tissue culture cells is increased by addition of ATP to the medium, and in *Amoeba* ATP acts as an inducer of pinocytosis. Other evidence indicates that endocytosis is inhibited or stopped by respiratory and other metabolic poisons. If, as seems likely, endocytosis is an energy-dependent mechanism for the selective transport of materials across the plasma membrane, and if it is of wide or universal occurrence in cells, then this process can account for at least some of the "active transport" phenomena detected at the level of tissue physiology. This is an important point, which will bear on later discussions in the next chapter.

Lysosomes

During the early 1950's, isolation of mitochondria by tissue homogenization and differential centrifugation sometimes led to anomalous behavior by the enzymes uricase and acid phosphatase. Since these hydrolytic enzymes were sometimes found in the mitochondrial fraction and sometimes not, a question arose whether all mitochondria were enzymatically the same, or whether there might be different kinds of mitochondria within the same tissue. In 1952 this problem was given special attention by DeDuve et al., who discovered that appropriate centrifugation of rat liver homogenates could separate the acid phosphatase from the respiratory enzymes, indicating the existence of a special "acid phosphatase-containing" particle (somewhat slower to sediment than the mitochondria). Various reagents or the fractionation procedure itself could lead to sharp increases in acid phosphatase activity, as though the enzyme were being released from an inactive or masked condition (called structure-linked latency). At about the same time, Walker (1952) discovered similar behavior by the enzyme β-glucuronidase, and subsequently several other hydrolytic enzymes of acid pH optimum were added to the list. The unmasking of activity for all these enzymes was often observed to occur synchronously in response to certain treatments, such as hypotonicity, as if all were contained in one kind of membrane-enclosed particle. Consequently, DeDuve et al. (1955) introduced the term "lysosome" to designate what at that time was a largely hypothetical organelle, detected biochemically in rat liver homogenates by the anomalous behavior of certain enzymes which catalyze the acid digestion of phosphoproteins, mucopolysaccharides, DNA, RNA, and carbohydrates.

From the sedimentation characteristics of lysosomes, it could be estimated that their dimensions were quite variable, but in the order of 0.13–0.8 μ in diameter. Perfectly pure lysosome fractions could not be obtained, but Novikoff et al. (1956) examined lysosome-rich preparations by electron microscopy and found characteristic, ovoid "dense bodies" about 0.25–0.5 μ in diameter. Similar dense bodies were detected in thin-sectioned liver parenchyma cells, particularly near the plasma membrane lining the bile canaliculi. Characteristically these dense bodies are enclosed by a single "unit membrane," they often contain very dense, ferritin-like particles about 60–70 Å in diameter, and as shown in tissue sections by Novikoff *et al.* (1964), they are sites of acid phosphatase activity. These general cytological and cytochemical properties (particularly acid phosphatase activity) are still the best-established criteria for recognizing lysosomes in electron microscope preparations.

Simultaneously with the first studies of lysosome fine structure, a conceptual difficulty was encountered and clearly expressed by Bennett (1956). In the first place, the hydrolytic nature of the lysosome enzymes makes it necessary to regard lysosome particles as part of the mechanism for intracellular digestion. In many cells, however, another part of the digestive mechanism is the endocytosis vacuole, a structure which also appears as a membrane-enclosed particle containing dense inclusions and exhibiting acid hydrolase activity. The problem is whether lysosomes are the *same* as endocytosis vacuoles or whether, as originally conceived by DeDuve *et al.* (1955), lysosomes are preformed packages of hydrolytic enzymes, synthesized and held in reserve by the cell to be released into the endocytosis vacuoles. At present good evidence exists that both types of lysosome occur, and it is therefore useful to distinguish the preformed but passive organelle as a "primary lysosome," whereas endocytosis vacuoles containing acid phosphatase activity may be designated "secondary lysosomes" (DeDuve, 1964). In practice it is often difficult to recognize the primary and secondary types; although lysosomes have been isolated and recognized in many animal tissues by biochemical fractionation procedures, in most instances it has not been determined which type of lysosome is actually under investigation.

Biochemically, lysosomes are characterized by the presence of the acid hydrolytic enzymes listed in Table 10-1. In addition, a second type of lysosome, or "uricase particle," is also recognized which contains the enzymes uricase, catalase, and D-amino acid oxidase. The activity of the lysosome enzymes in centrifuge fractions is released by a number of different agents which might be expected to disrupt the integrity of a protein-phospholipid membrane. These include digestion with lecithinase or protease, hypotonicity, mechanical shock, and treatment with carbon tetrachloride. It has also been found that vitamin A tends to increase permeability, whereas vitamin E seems to protect the lysosome membrane. Shibko *et al.* (1965) have also succeeded in isolating and studying kidney lysosome "ghosts," i.e., the empty membranes that remain after release of enzymes from supposedly primary lysosomes.

Table 10-1
LYSOSOME ENZYMES

Enzyme	Substrate	Product
Acid ribonuclease	RNA	Ribonucleotides
Acid deoxyribonuclease	DNA	Oligodeoxyribonucleotides
Acid phosphatase	Phosphate mono-esters	Orthophosphate and product
Phosphoprotein phosphatase	Phosphoprotein	Orthophosphate and protein
Cathepsin	Polypeptides	N-Terminal dipeptides
Collagenase	Collagen	Proline, amino acids
α-Glucosidase	α-D-Glucosides	Alcohol and D-glucose
β-N-Acetylglucosamine hydrolase	Chitobiose	Two 2 acetylamine-2-deoxy-D-glucose
β-Glucuronidase	β-D-Glucuronides	Alcohol and D-glucuronic acid
β-Galactosidase	β-D-Galactosides	Alcohol and D-galactose
α-Mannosidase	α-D-Mannosides	Alcohol and D-mannose
Aryl sulfatase	Phenol sulfate	Phenol and H_2SO_4

The best-established instance of cytologically recognizable primary lysosomes, in the original sense of DeDuve, has been found by Cohn and Hirsch in the white blood cells of rabbits. By light microscopy, rabbit polymorphonuclear leukocytes are seen to contain very conspicuous cytoplasmic granules that stain pink with Wright's stain (acidophilic granules). Techniques for isolating these granules were developed by Cohn and Hirsch (1960), who showed that the purified particles contain acid phosphatase, RNase, DNase, β-glucuronidase, nucleotidase, cathepsin, and, in addition, alkaline phosphatase, lysozyme, lipase, and peroxidase. When endocytosis was induced in the leukocytes, Hirsch and Cohn (1960) observed that the number of visible cytoplasmic granules decreased in proportion to the amount of material ingested; furthermore, the proportion of hydrolytic enzymes found in the granule fraction also decreased, while the enzyme content of the soluble supernatant increased. More recently Hirsch (1962) has been able to record by microcinematography the actual fusion of a primary lysosome particle with an endocytosis vacuole. Similar results have been obtained with other types of rabbit leukocyte, including mononuclear phagocytes and eosinophiles.

These analyses of lysosome properties and behavior, when considered in relation to known mechanisms of pinocytosis, provide a fairly clear picture of the intracellular digestive mechanisms operating in animal cells (Fig. 10-7). Materials of molecular or colloidal size enter the cell

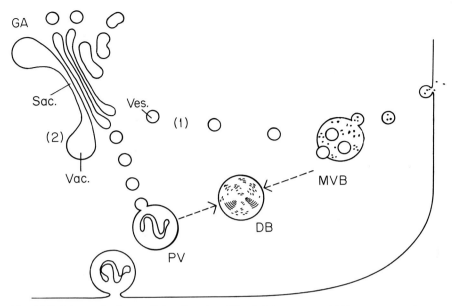

Fig. 10-7. Scheme for intracellular digestion. The Golgi apparatus (GA) generates primary lysosomes, which contain hydrolytic enzymes and are capable of fusing with pinocytosis vacuoles (PV). Dense bodies (DB) and multivesicular bodies (MVB) are intermediate stages in the digestive process. Undigestible residues are released to the environment (right). From Novikoff *et al.* (1964).

by adsorption to the plasma membrane, followed by membrane flow and formation of endocytosis vacuoles. These vacuoles then move into the deeper parts of the cytoplasm, losing water as they go, and eventually fuse with one or more primary lysosomes. The contents of the vacuole are then catalytically hydrolyzed by the lysosome enzymes, after which the undigestible residues become highly concentrated as "residual bodies" and may be egested from the cell. The evidence for such a mechanism in leukocytes is very convincing, and a highly similar digestive process seems to occur in kidney epithelium. For example, Straus (1963) has carried out an elegant series of experiments in which horse radish peroxidase was injected into live rats and later detected in endocytosis vacuoles of the kidney epithelium and liver. In Straus's technique, vesicles containing peroxidase were stained blue, vesicles containing acid phosphatase were stained red, and vesicles containing both had a purple color. Fifteen minutes after injection of the peroxidase, activity could be observed in blue endocytosis vacuoles just under the brush border of the kidney cells; at the same time red lysosomes were present at the apical ends of the cells. After 30 minutes, purple vacuoles could be detected in which the extracellular peroxidase had mixed with intracellular phosphatase. Eventually the blue peroxidase reaction disappeared, suggesting that the enzyme had been inactivated by proteases.

The abundance of lysosomes isolated in cell homogenates varies considerably from tissue to tissue, being highest in liver and spleen and relatively low in muscle. Cytologically, a wide variety of cell particles are suspected of being lysosomes, usually because they show a positive cytochemical test for acid phosphatase and are enclosed in a single "unit membrane." Primary lysosomes, where they have been clearly identified, appear to be particles with rather homogeneous contents and lacking ferritin granules (Fig. 16-3). On the other hand the original "dense bodies" described by Novikoff *et al.* (1956) probably represent late stages in the digestive process, the ferritin granules being digestive residues of cytochrome molecules. Other types of particle, such as "multivesicular bodies" and "residual bodies," probably are earlier and later stages in the mechanism of intracellular digestion (Fig. 10-7).

Although there is no reason to doubt that the primary lysosome-endocytosis combination operates in many cells, present evidence suggests that variations in this scheme are common. For instance, the multivesicular bodies of neurons may represent independent "depots," which receive the contents of both endocytosis vacuoles and lysosomes. Furthermore, some cells (for example, plant cells) seem not to contain lysosomes as such, while others may lack primary lysosomes; in the latter type of cell, hydrolytic enzymes could be secreted directly into the endocytosis vacuoles. A corresponding variability is indicated for the origin of lysosome particles. Novikoff *et al.* (1964) have found that in secretory cells and neurons, acid phosphatase activity is present in the Golgi apparatus, and they suggest that primary lysosomes in these cells are formed from specialized Golgi vacuoles; at the same time, their evidence indicates that the Golgi apparatus is not involved in formation of "dense bodies" in the liver cells of starved rats, where the lysosomes make their appearance close to the endoplasmic reticulum.

11

THE PLASMA MEMBRANE AND
ITS DERIVATIVES

2. ENERGETICS

Biopotentials have been thought to arise from uneven distributions of ions on the two sides of a membrane impermeable to one or a few of the ion species present (Gibbs-Donnan potential). This explanation at present is not only unsatisfactory but also unnecessary.

B. ANDERSEN AND H. H. USSING *1960*

The earliest evidence that living cells have the capacity to regulate their internal ionic concentrations dates from the time of Liebig (1847), who noted that muscle tissues contain a much higher concentration of potassium and a much lower concentration of sodium than the blood in which they are bathed. Investigations of this and similar phenomena during the late 19th and early 20th centuries generally attempted to explain this effect by purely passive membrane properties. Much attention was devoted to the passive permeability profiles of cell membranes, to their probable structure, and to the behavior of ions in model systems composed of two solutions separated by a natural or artificial membrane. In such model systems, the ion concentrations often attain an equilibrium state which is much higher on one side of the membrane than on the other, yet does not require energy expenditure by the membrane itself. The possibility that natural membranes might actively mobilize energy to transport specific molecules either into the cell or outward into the surrounding medium was not given serious thought until the 1930's and 1940's.

In 1933, Wilbrandt and Laszt found that the uptake of glucose and galactose into intestinal cells is greatly inhibited by iodoacetate, which poisons the cells' source of energy from anaerobic glycolysis; shortly thereafter, Huf (1936) demonstrated that a frog skin stretched between two salt compartments could transport inorganic ions "uphill" against the physical gradient. These findings were reviewed and augmented by Krogh (1946) and his collaborators, who were the first to emphasize the widespread occurrence and general importance of active transport mechanisms. Subsequently, many different kinds of cell have been shown to expend energy in this way, and indeed active transport is very possibly a universal property of both the plasma membrane and the various intracellular membranes (mitochondria, endoplasmic reticulum, nuclear envelope, etc.). Just as muscle fibrils constitute a kind of chemical-mechanical energy transducer, so the membranes of the cell operate as transducers of chemical energy for the specific accumulation or transport of water, ions, and other molecules. Associated with this type of energy transduction is the important class of bioelectric phenomena, which includes most notably the propagated nerve impulse.

The Steady-State Condition of the Plasma Membrane

Based on the investigations summarized in the preceding chapter, the following concept of a typical cell-environment relationship emerges: *inside* the cell there are concentrated a large variety of organic molecules,

259

of medium to large size, many of which are arranged in ordered structural arrays and all of which are prevented from leaving the cell by the impermeability of the plasma membrane; *outside* the cell, the environment consists primarily of water and inorganic ions, which are found in a wide range of concentrations and which, unlike the internal molecules, *are* able to pass through the plasma membrane; as a result of this permeability, the macromolecules inside the cell are bathed in a medium of water and ions whose composition to some extent reflects that of the external medium. Superimposed on the whole system are various mechanisms of membrane activity, such as endocytosis, by which specific external molecules are actively accumulated by the cell and specific internal molecules are disgorged. The analysis of such intricate systems in terms of strictly physical and chemical forces, sometimes operating together and sometimes in opposition, has generated an extensive, highly complex literature, unfortunately combined with a slow rate of net progress in understanding.

Perhaps the most important principle governing the distribution of *charged* particles across the membrane is that these particles must respond not only to their *chemical* concentration gradients, but also to any *electrical* gradient in the system. Consequently, whether a particular kind of ion will move to the inside or outside of the cell, and what its distribution will be at equilibrium, are determined by the combined electrochemical potential for that type of ion. The electrical gradient itself may be partly or entirely the result of asymmetries in the overall ion distribution, i.e., a greater concentration of negative ions on one side of the membrane and of positive ions on the other. Such asymmetries in ion distribution may be brought about, in turn, by differences in the membrane's active or passive permeability to molecules of different sizes or other properties.

One of the earliest theoretical analyses for such systems was that of Donnan (1911), who developed a model to predict the equilibrium state for a solution of negative and positive ions when one species of negative ion is unable to penetrate the membrane (and is therefore confined to one side, representing the inside of the cell). Under these conditions, the cations and anions which do penetrate reach an equilibrium in which the positive diffusible ions are more concentrated inside than outside, whereas the negative diffusible ions are more concentrated outside than inside. This relationship is most easily visualized in terms of a hypothetical living cell, which in the Donnan model is postulated to contain a permanent internal negative charge produced by nondiffusible anions. If such a cell is immersed in a solution of KCl, the positively charged potassium ions will be driven to the inside by both the concentration gradient and the electrical gradient, whereas the negatively charged chloride ions will be driven to the outside by the electrical gradient but to the inside by the concentration gradient. Consequently, at equilibrium there will be a lower concentration of chloride and a higher concentration of potassium inside the cell than outside. As shown by Donnan, these equilibrium concentrations have an exact quantitative relationship such that the chloride and potassium asymmetries must be exactly reciprocal:

$$\frac{[K^+_{in}]}{[K^+_{out}]} = \frac{[Cl^-_{out}]}{[Cl^-_{in}]}$$

As it happens, many or most cells do contain a higher concentration of potassium and a lower concentration of chloride than the external fluids in which they are immersed, and these concentration differences often are approximately reciprocal. Furthermore an "internal negative" charge has been demonstrated for a wide range of resting cells; as early as 1907, Tschachotin measured an internal-negative cell voltage of 0.1 V (100 mV). Later Osterhout (1931) observed that an electrode inserted into the giant algal cells *Nitella* and *Valonia* became about 80–200 mV negative to another electrode at the outside cell surface. Hodgkin and Huxley (1939) succeeded in inserting a fine electrode into the cytoplasm of squid giant neurons (the axons of which attain diameters of 500 μ) and found that the axon cytoplasm is about 50 mV negative to the outside medium. Since these pioneer studies, resting membrane potentials have been found to exist in many if not all cells, their magnitudes being very generally in the order of 50–100 mV with the inside negative to the outside. To earlier investigators, therefore, it appeared that this electrical gradient could account for observed ion asymmetries, and that living cells satisfied all the essential conditions for a Donnan equilibrium. An important advantage of this concept was that it invoked only physical forces and did not imply any expenditure of energy by the membrane itself.

Precise quantitative tests of the relationship between the resting membrane potential and the concentration asymmetry for any given ion were made possible by the Nernst equation (1908). If E is the electrical gradient in volts and $\ln C_1/C_2$ is the natural logarithm of the concentration gradient, then

$$E = \frac{RT}{znF} \ln \frac{C_1}{C_2}$$

(where R is the universal gas constant, F is the Faraday constant, z is the valency of the ion, n is the number of moles, and T is the absolute temperature). For univalent ions at 20°C the Nernst equation can be simplified to the form

$$E = 58 \log \frac{C_1}{C_2}$$

where E is given in millivolts. As applied to a Donnan equilibrium based on KCl, the equation has the form

$$E = 58 \log \frac{[K^+_{in}]}{[K^+_{out}]} = 58 \log \frac{[Cl^-_{out}]}{[Cl^-_{in}]}$$

It is important to note that these equations can be read in either direction, i.e., a given increase in membrane voltage will lead to an increased asymmetry in the ion distribution, or alternatively the ion asymmetry itself can produce a membrane potential. Only an experimental investigation can show which is a cause and which an effect.

The earliest attempts to determine quantitative relationships between the resting potential in a specific type of cell and the ion asymmetry across its membrane seemed to confirm the existence of a Donnan equilibrium. For example, Boyle and Conway (1941) found a resting potential of about 99 mV in frog sartorius muscle, where the relationship between potassium and chloride concentrations was

$$\frac{[K^+_{in}]}{[K^+_{out}]} = \frac{[Cl^-_{out}]}{[Cl^-_{in}]} = \text{about } 50$$

and

$$E = 58 \log 50 = 99 \text{ mV}$$

However, subsequent and more precise measurements with a variety of cells have revealed marked discrepancies, either from the relationships expressed in the Nernst equation or from the requirements of the Donnan equilibrium itself. For example, Hodgkin (1951) noted in a review paper that the Donnan equilibrium clearly does not hold for mammalian red blood cells, where intracellular $[K^+] \cdot [Cl^-]$ exceeds extracellular $[K^+] \cdot [Cl^-]$ by as much as 15 times (and the Donnan equilibrium calls for equality). Even in neurons, where the fit is much closer, recent precise measurements have now established that the intracellular concentration of potassium ions is somewhat higher than can be accounted for by the electrochemical gradient alone. Furthermore, in both plant and animal cells that are metabolically blocked by anoxia or by specific poisons, potassium ions begin to leak out and the membrane resting potential falls precipitously. For instance, in the alga *Halicystis* Blinks (1940) found that the resting potential in a low oxygen atmosphere falls from 80 mV to 10 mV or less. Ling and Gerard (1949) made similar observations for muscle cells, where resting potential falls to zero during anoxia combined with poisoning of glycolysis. These effects would not be observed if a true physical equilibrium existed; they indicate that the state of the "resting" plasma membrane is not really an equilibrium, but as suggested by Krogh (1946), a "steady state" involving constant energy expenditure by the cell.

It has now been reasonably well established that the voltage gradient across the resting cell membrane is brought about by the asymmetrical distribution of potassium ions, rather than the reverse. This conclusion was first suggested by experiments of Curtis and Cole (1942), who measured changes in membrane potential when squid axons were immersed in different concentrations of potassium salts; a change of 10 times in potassium asymmetry was accompanied by a change in resting potential of about 50 mV (close to the 58 mV which would be predicted by the Nernst equation). In *Nitella* and other cells it was also found that the resting potential could be reversibly abolished by immersing the cells in a medium of high potassium concentration. Since other positive univalent ions such as sodium did not have this effect, these experiments suggested that it was primarily potassium which produced the resting membrane potential. An elegant confirmation of this conclusion has recently been achieved by Baker *et al.* (1962), who squeezed the cytoplasm from squid giant axons and reinflated the axon membranes with salt solutions of known composition. Electron microscopy confirmed that 95% of the axoplasm had been removed, whereas the axon plasma membrane and myelin sheath were still intact. This technique therefore permitted the authors to regulate the ionic composition of the medium on *both* sides of the cell membrane while simultaneously monitoring the value of the membrane potential. They found that, in general, the resting potential continued at about -50 mV so long as the interior of the axon was provided with an isotonic (high) potassium ion concentration while the external medium contained isotonic sodium but no potassium. If the same medium was present on both sides of the membrane the resting potential fell to zero. Even more dramatically, if the internal K^+ and external Na^+ solutions were reversed, the membrane potential also reversed and the inside of the axon became 50 mV *positive* to the outside. In these experiments manipulation of the negative ions had little effect on the membrane potential. Consequently Baker concluded that the potassium ion gradient from inside to outside the membrane is the immediate source of the resting potential. The mechanisms responsible for maintaining this potassium ion gradient in living cells will be discussed in the next section.

Active Transport

Perhaps the most notable way in which cells depart from the Donnan equilibrium is in the low intracellular content of both water molecules and sodium ions. Since the interior of a living cell is characterized by high concentrations of nondiffusible macromolecules, many carrying ionic charges, purely physical forces should tend to force diffusible salts into the system. This penetration of ions according to the Donnan equilibrium should be accompanied by penetration of water or osmotic swelling. Tosteson (1964) has calculated that mammalian red blood cells at Donnan equilibrium should have an excess osmotic pressure of 5800 mm of water, whereas in fact the excess is almost negligible (about 2.3 mm). Since these cells are permeable to both water and ions, it is clear that they are carrying on some active process which defeats the Donnan equilibrium and provides control over both internal osmotic pressure and total water volume.

That cells and tissues typically contain much less sodium than the external medium has been known since the time of Liebig (1847). Whereas the asymmetrical distributions of potassium and chloride are in the direction of a Donnan equilibrium, the distribution of sodium is exactly opposite to the prevailing electrochemical gradient; this discrepancy in neurons amounts to about 130 mV, as calculated by the Nernst equation. Observations of this type led earlier investigators to suspect that the plasma membrane might be completely impermeable to sodium, but the introduction of isotopic tracer methods demonstrated unequivocally that a constant flux of sodium ions does occur in both directions across the membrane. The inescapable conclusion, as pointed out by Dean (1941), was that some type of "ion pump" mechanism must be widespread in cells, which provides a means for the cell to extrude sodium ions selectively and thereby to maintain a low internal osmotic pressure. It has since been amply confirmed that there is a fundamental linkage between osmotic balance, volume control, and sodium ion extrusion in many cells, and the ion pump concept has also been extended to other ions (notably potassium, hydrogen, and chloride).

In the absence of ion pump mechanisms a Donnan equilibrium would necessarily establish itself, but only at the cost of uncontrolled water influx and disruption of the cell's internal macromolecular organization. The steady-state distribution of ions is therefore a summation of two distinct processes: (1) simple electrochemical diffusion forces, which tend to establish a Donnan equilibrium; and (2) energy-dependent ion transport processes, which tend to reduce the water volume of the cell. This means that certain types of ion, such as sodium, are constantly being pumped across the membrane in one direction while leaking back again in the other direction. The actual concentration difference across the membrane, as well as the membrane potential, therefore depends both on the rate of pumping and the rate of leaking. Changes in either process can and do lead to changes in the membrane potential, and in fact such changes play a fundamental part in the propagation of nerve impulses.

The most fascinating examples of active transport are those in which an ion or other solute is concentrated by a factor of tens or hundreds in direct opposition to both the electrical and chemical gradients. In these phenomena, expenditure of metabolic energy by the cell achieves essentially a decrease in the total entropy of the system. This is most easily visualized by considering the reverse case: if a single crystal of copper sulfate is placed in a beaker of water, the blue color of the crystal immediately and spontaneously begins to diffuse throughout the beaker until it uniformly fills up the space available to it. This diffusion represents a change from the relatively restricted and improbable state of the molecules when they are concentrated in the crystal (i.e., low entropy state) to the less restricted, more numerous and therefore more probable states available during random movement through the solution (high entropy state). Although theoretically there is always a small possibility that all the molecules will at some moment spontaneously reaggregate in one part of the beaker to re-form the original crystal, the unlikelihood of their doing so is a measure of the great increase in entropy associated with diffusion. Yet it is precisely this improbable "entropy reversal" which biological systems achieve by active transport. For example, the retrieval of calcium and phosphate ions from solution, as carried out by isolated mitochondria, results in a 1000-fold concentration increase and crystallization of unidentified calcium and phosphate salts inside the mitochondrion (Chapter 7).

Phenomena of this type have been demonstrated and analyzed in a wide variety of biological systems. In some cases, such as isolated frog skin, vertebrate stomach, intestine, or kidney, transport is measured across an entire layer of cells (i.e., the solute is taken up by the cells on one side and pumped out on the other side). In other systems, such as mammalian red blood cells or yeast and bacterial suspensions, transport is measured across a single membrane, between the inside and outside of individual cells. Still a third type of system involves active transport phenomena in intracellular organelles that have been isolated in bulk by cell fractionation techniques. As just noted, cell-free suspensions of mitochondria are able to carry out a massive uptake of calcium, magnesium, and phosphate ions, and preparations of isolated sarcoplasmic reticulum also concentrate Ca^{++} as much as 1400-fold—a process which appears to be responsible for relaxation of striated muscle fibers *in vivo* (Chapter 8). Active accumulation of phosphate is also known to occur in isolated chloroplasts, and active accumulation of sodium in isolated nuclei. The possibility exists that mechanisms for carrying out active transport occur generally in all biological membranes.

In analyzing these diverse systems, very similar types of experimental design have been used since the inception of active transport investigations. First and foremost, a requirement for metabolic energy is an important criterion of active transport; this requirement is usually demonstrated by blocking metabolism with respiratory inhibitors, anoxia, 2,4-dinitrophenol (which uncouples oxidative phosphorylation), glycolytic poisons, or low temperature. A complementary type of experiment attempts to exclude purely physical forces from accounting for the distribution of molecules, and requires the investigator to determine the true electrochemical gradient across the membrane. For ions this can be achieved elegantly by counteracting the ion flow with an imposed external electric potential. Another familiar experimental approach is to test the specificity of the uptake mechanism, presenting the cells with similar chemical analogs and comparing those that are accepted against those rejected. Finally the two inhibitors, ouabain and strophanthidin, are regarded as specific inhibitors of active transport and are often used in a diagnostic fashion. In the discussion to follow, active transport of small molecules (water and ions) will be analyzed separately from active transport of larger molecules (sugars, amino acids, proteins), although the two classes have many characteristics in common.

Transport of Small Molecules

The earliest clear demonstrations of active ion transport were achieved with isolated frog skins, which were stretched between two compartments containing experimental salt solutions. Using such a system, Huf (1936) showed that chloride ions and water are transported from the outside surface of the skin to the inside, where they become more concentrated. Later Ussing and Zerahn (1951) noted that the inside of the skin is about 100 mV positive to the outside and suspected that the movements of chloride and water might be passive ones accompanying an active movement of sodium. They succeeded in confirming this by a classic experiment in which the two sides of the skin were short-circuited, so that the electric charge as well as the ion concentrations were identical on both sides; under this condition of zero electrochemical gradient, only sodium continued to be transferred from outside to inside the skin. In this system the flow of sodium ions is accompanied by an electric current of about 100 mV, which in Ussing and Zerahn's experiments could be quantitatively accounted for by the movement of the charged ions (as measured with ^{24}Na); when sodium flow was inhibited with CO_2, the current also fell off to zero. The authors were therefore able to conclude that in frog skin the active transport of sodium is the cause of the resting potential, rather than the reverse.

With respect to the uptake of potassium ions, a dependence on metabolic energy was first clearly established by Harris (1941), using human red blood cells. He observed that potassium leaked out of erythrocytes while they were stored in the refrigerator, but if they were reincubated some of this potassium was taken up again. The uptake was shown to increase on the addition of glucose; under these conditions, as potassium increased inside the cells, sodium decreased. Subsequently Harris and Maizels (1951) found that extrusion of sodium by red blood cells is inhibited in a medium of low potassium content, and they therefore suggested that the same carrier mechanism might transport potassium in and sodium out. A similar interdependence of sodium extrusion and potassium uptake was observed at about the same time in giant squid axons by Hodgkin and Keynes (1955). However the concept of a sodium-potassium exchange pump was not definitely accepted until the detailed quantitative analysis of Glynn (1957), who showed that below a certain threshold concentration of potassium, sodium efflux in red blood cells declines in parallel with potassium uptake until both processes disappear together. At present it is accepted that sodium-potassium exchange pumps of this type occur in many kinds of cell, including neurons, yeast, and others; the exchange is sometimes on a 1:1 molar basis, but ratios of 3 Na:2 K or higher have been found; some cases are also known in which sodium extrusion and potassium uptake are apparently separate processes. In red blood cells, the number of exchange sites required to account for observed rates of K^+ transport is fairly low, in the order of 1000–10,000 per cell.

Sodium-potassium exchange in most cell types is inhibited by any factor which impairs respiration, although in a few instances the process seems to depend primarily on energy from glycolysis. This duality suggests that it may be ATP which is the direct energy source for the pump. More direct evidence for this conclusion was provided by Gardos (1954), who discovered that even red blood cell *ghosts* are able to accumulate potassium ions if they are provided with ATP. More recently this finding has been extended by Hoffman (1960), who showed that ghosts are also able to extrude sodium if they are provided with ATP, but that ITP (a similar high energy phosphoryl compound) cannot substitute. Similar results were obtained for the giant squid axon by Caldwell *et al.* (1960), who found that when an axon is poisoned with cyanide (a respiratory inhibitor) sodium extrusion declines, whereas injection of ATP or arginine phosphate reactivates the ion pump.

An important step in the direction of isolating the transport mechanism was achieved by Post *et al.* (1960), who discovered that red blood cell membranes contain a characteristic ATPase requiring *both* sodium and potassium ions for activation. This ATPase could be purified about 31-fold from the fragmented membranes, and it was found to share many of the characteristics associated with the sodium-potassium pump: for instance, both systems are inhibited by ouabain, both require sodium and potassium together, both accept ammonium ions instead of potassium, and the concentrations of reagents necessary for a half-maximal effect are quantitatively the same in both cases. More recently Glynn (1962) and Whittam (1964) have been able to show that the membrane ATPase is also spatially asymmetrical, i.e., its activity in intact ghosts seems to be stimulated by extracellular (but not intracellular) potassium and intracellular (but not extracellular) sodium. Ohnishi and Kawamura (1963) have suggested that the myosinlike ATPase which they have isolated from erythrocyte membranes may also be involved in the ion transport mechanism.

A theoretical model that can account for ion transport in terms of asymmetrical ATPase molecules in the plasma membrane has been proposed by Mitchell (1961). In this scheme the ATPase catalyzes hydrolysis of ATP molecules on its intracellular side, using hydroxyl ions from inside the cell but hydrogen ions from outside. The result of such asymmetrical enzyme activity would be a progressive separation of charges, rendering the inside of the membrane more acid and the outside more alkaline. The membrane might then behave in effect like an ATP-driven battery, whose energy could be transferred to the transport of other ions by suitable coupling reactions. In fact it has been shown that in a low-sodium environment, the exchange of sodium and potassium in yeast cells is replaced by exchange of hydrogen ions and potassium.

Membrane ATPases which are inhibited by ouabain and which specifically *require* both Na^+ and K^+ are very widely distributed. It seems likely, therefore, that the transport mechanism itself is somewhat more specific than would be the case in Mitchell's model. On the whole, the most generally satisfactory models of specific active transport are those which postulate a special "carrier molecule" in the membrane, whose linkage or separation from the substrate (i.e., the transported solute) is coupled to metabolism. An actual physical model of this type was constructed and studied very early by Osterhout (1933); the "membrane" of the model was a nonaqueous mixture of 70% guaiacol and 30% p-cresol, which separated an external KOH solution from an internal carbonic acid solution. Osterhout found that in such a model potassium was "carried" across the membrane in the form of organic salts such as potassium guaiacolate, which were formed at the outer surface, diffused across the membrane, and decomposed at the inner surface (to form $KHCO_3$). In this manner potassium ions were concentrated as much as 10-fold inside the "cell," the driving force being the OH^- gradient from outside to inside (compare with Mitchell's model).

Similar membrane carrier models have been proposed in which the driving force for transport would be provided by ATP hydrolysis. For instance, K^+ might combine with a protein carrier at the outer surface of the membrane, where protein-K^+ molecules would attain a high concentration and tend to diffuse toward the inner surface. At the inner surface a Na^+-dependent phosphokinase would phosphorylate the protein at the expense of ATP, leading to release of K^+ inside the cell and formation of a phosphoprotein–Na^+ complex in high concentration. The phosphoprotein–Na^+ complex would then tend to diffuse to the outer surface, where a K^+-dependent phosphorylase would dephosphorylate the carrier, releasing Na^+ to the external medium. In effect, the carrier molecule would shuttle back and forth across the membrane, transporting K^+ on the inward trip and Na^+ on the outward trip. Movement of the carrier–passenger complex would always be in the direction of a diffusion gradient, this gradient being determined by the state of phosphorylation of the carrier. Moreover, the reciprocal action of a phosphokinase with a phosphatase would account for the observed ATPase activity.

A somewhat simplified version of this model would postulate that the ATP-ATPase enzyme–substrate complex might itself be the carrier. In this scheme, a single ATPase molecule could occupy the entire breadth of the membrane; the complexing of ATP with ATPase on the inside would bind internal Na^+ and lead to a stereorotation of the molecule. After rotation, Na^+ would be on the outside of the membrane, where it would be released on hydrolysis of the ATP. Rerotation of the unbound ATPase could then be postulated to transfer K^+ *into* the cell. Alternative theories based on similar behavior by other enzyme–substrate complexes, such as cholinesterase, have also been suggested. In summary, it may be said that many different versions of the "membrane carrier" model are energetically feasible, and could in fact account for the observed transport phenomena; however, it remains to be determined which if any of these models actually corresponds to a transport mechanism operating in living cells.

The general picture which has emerged from studies of active ion transport in various systems is that sodium extrusion represents a primitive mechanism for the control of cell water and total volume, particularly in high sodium environments such as seawater (or blood). The sodium pump in turn results in voltage gradients across the "resting" membrane and influences the distribution of other ions between the cell and its environment. In various specialized cells such as plant cells, where the presence of a firm cellulose wall makes volume control less critical, the primitive sodium pump has been variously modified or supplemented with other ion pumps. Finally, the membrane voltage itself has undergone refinements which adapt it to transmit information about the state of the environment, and this refinement has reached its maximum development in the neurons of higher animals (to be discussed).

Transport of Large Molecules

Even before it was demonstrated that cells actively control their internal ion concentrations, an energy-dependent uptake of simple sugars and similar nutrients had been recognized. As early as 1925, Ege et al. noted that the rate at which glucose achieves equilibrium across the red blood cell membrane is much more sensitive to temperature than would be expected of a simple diffusion process. Not long after, Wilbrandt and Laszt (1933) showed that the ability of intestinal cells to take up glucose and galactose is inhibited if glycolysis is blocked with iodoacetate.

It is now well known that both intestine and kidney cells actively concentrate monosaccharides, amino acids, and certain dyes. An elegant experimental system has been developed for vertebrate intestine, in which a length of intestine is turned inside out, immersed in nutrient solution, and then tied shut at the ends; initially the nutrient concentration is the same inside and outside the intestine, but as active transport proceeds the interior becomes progressively more concentrated. According to Wilson (1964), such an intestine can concentrate sugars as much as 100-fold.

Unfortunately, the nature of the nutrient transport mechanisms in intestine and kidney cells is somewhat confused by the fact that both types of cell carry on pinocytosis at their brush borders (Chapter 10). For all practical purposes endocytosis possesses the same diagnostic properties as "true" active transport, including the ability to concentrate specific molecules from solution, the requirement for metabolic energy, and a high selectivity. Consequently it seems likely that various instances of active transport which have been studied at the tissue level actually represent endocytosis at the cell level. This possibility is supported by recent autoradiographs of intestinal cells taking up labeled sugars and amino acids, which show that the solute molecules are highly concentrated at the brush border. The ability of chick kidney cells to concentrate the dye, phenol red, has also been studied as a typical example of active transport; nevertheless, the accumulation of such dyes in amoebae is now known to occur by membrane binding and endocytosis. Since intestinal cells transport so many different nutrient molecules, it seems unlikely each could have its own unique coupling reaction with the pathways of metabolic energy. On the other hand, most of the available data would be accounted for by a specific binding of molecules at the brush border and subsequent endocytosis. Extensive investigation of sugar transport in vertebrate intestine and kidney cells has shown that uptake requires a specific atomic configuration of the D-pyranose ring and in addition a hydroxyl group on carbon 2.

Sugar transport by human red blood cells is an example of "facilitated diffusion," in which certain specific monosaccharides are able to reach a diffusion equilibrium across the membrane, but usually cannot exceed it; other monosaccharides, by contrast, cannot pass the membrane at all. Since the rate of facilitated diffusion is very sensitive to temperature and shows a "saturation effect" at high sugar concentrations, the system behaves as though a limited number of specific "sugar carrier" molecules are operating in the membrane.

Transport systems for sugars and amino acids have also been studied extensively in bacteria, for example in *E. coli*, where their existence was first inferred during analyses of enzyme induction in both wild-type and mutant cells. Some mutants are unable to form the enzyme β-galactosidase, yet they concentrate its sugar substrate lactose by a factor of several hundred times. By contrast other mutants have been found which contain β-galactosidase, but which cannot grow when lactose is the only carbon source; chemical analysis shows that these mutant cells are unable to take up lactose from the medium. The transport factor, which is present in the one case and absent in the other, exhibits high stereospecificity and its formation is blocked by inhibitors of protein synthesis; in addition it is controlled by a specific genetic locus (y) situated near the gene for β-galactosidase (*lac*). These enzyme-like characteristics led Cohen and Monod (1957) to name the transport agent *β-galactoside permease*.

Recently Kennedy *et al.* (1966) have succeeded in isolating and partially purifying a lipoprotein (M protein) which has all the functional characteristics expected of β-galactoside permease. Their M-protein is localized in the membrane fraction of *E. coli,* it is absent in y^- mutants and uninduced cells, and it has a high affinity for thiodigalactosides. Since an average *E. coli* contains only about 9000 molecules of M-protein, the key to isolating this compound depended on marking it with a ^{14}C-labeled inhibitor (*N*-ethylmaleimide). Kennedy has also proposed a model in which his permease operates as a "membrane carrier" similar to that described previously for the sodium-potassium exchange pump, i.e., the protein combines with lactose at the outer membrane surface, and the protein–lactose complex then diffuses across the membrane to the inside of the cell in accord with its own concentration gradient. On the inside the substrate is released from the carrier, possibly by the action of β-galactosidase, and the free protein then follows its concentration gradient back to the outside. An interesting feature of Kennedy's model is that it requires no energy merely to carry lactose into the cell, but in order to *accumulate* lactose against a gradient the same system is coupled with a source of metabolic energy. According to Kepes (1964) a stoichiometry exists under certain circumstances, in which approximately three molecules of thiomethylgalactoside are taken up per atom of oxygen consumed by the cell. Since in bacteria the respiratory enzymes, like the permeases, are localized in the plasma membrane, this indicates a fairly close coupling of sugar transport with oxidative phosphorylation and is reminiscent of the stoichiometric uptake of calcium ions by mitochondria (Chapter 7).

Action Potentials

In order to understand the nature of an action potential, it is useful to visualize two electrodes placed at different points on the surface of a large cell, such as a neuron, a muscle fiber, or a giant algal cell; these electrodes are connected with one another through a voltage measuring device, such as a voltmeter or an oscilloscope. While the cell is in the "resting state" no current flows between the electrodes, indicating that the outside potential of the membrane is everywhere the same. However if the cell is now stimulated in the vicinity of one electrode, a sudden voltage difference appears and the electrode nearest the point of stimulation becomes negative to the farther one; after a brief flow of current this voltage difference rapidly falls again to zero, but then it suddenly reappears in a reverse pulse, i.e., the electrode farthest from the point of stimulation now becomes negative to the nearer one. Finally the second voltage difference disappears too, and no further response occurs. An oscilloscope tracing of these voltage fluctuations has the appearance of a sharp "spike" followed by an inverted spike of the same amplitude. In effect, the stimulus has set off a wave or impulse of negative potential which travels across the membrane at a relatively slow velocity, reaching first one electrode and then the other; the result is a diphasic curve of the type described. The fact that the amplitude of the spike does not diminish with the distance traveled is an important property of these bioelectric phenomena, indicating that the spike is energetically renewed as it passes each given point on the membrane.

Such a propagated voltage change in response to a stimulus is known as an "action potential," and the occurrence of such potentials in living organisms has been known ever since the discovery of electricity in the late 1700's. At that time Galvani (1791) himself accumulated evidence for electric currents in nerves. His contemporary, Volta, developed a great interest in the electric organs of certain fish, which are now known to contain modified muscle fibers from which tiny action potentials are coupled in series to produce charges of many volts. The voltaic cell, an early type of battery, was actually patterned by Volta on the structure of these electric organs.

However, sophisticated research with action potentials depended on the application of the sensitive cathode ray oscilloscope for this work, an approach which was pioneered by Gasser and Erlanger (1922). Since then it has been shown that "all or none" spike potentials occur in many kinds of cell besides neurons and electric organs; these include plant cells, eggs at the moment of fertilization, and muscle fibers as they are stimulated to contract. Somewhat different action potentials also accompany rhythmic cytoplasmic flow in slime molds, and ciliary movement in protozoa, where the changes in potential can be related to the timing and direction of ciliary beat. The magnitude of the spike potential, its duration, and the velocity of propagation vary considerably from one type of cell to another; however, in giant squid axons the action potential is about 90 mV, its duration is about 1 msec, and its rate of propagation is about 1 meter per second. By comparison, the rate of propagation in the plant cell, *Nitella*, is only about 1 cm per second, and in a large vertebrate neuron it is 100 meters or more per second.

Hodgkin and Huxley (1939) were the first to measure an action potential from *inside* a neuron. If the potential of the external electrode is taken as zero, then the resting membrane of the squid giant axon shows a typical internal-negative charge of -50 mV; when stimulation occurs the inside potential rapidly disappears, rising to zero and continuing up until the inside of the membrane is actually positive to the outside by 40 mV (50 + 40 equaling the spike potential of 90 mV). The action potential therefore involves a disappearance of the normal resting potential (i.e., depolarization of the membrane) plus a certain amount of reversal in the usual voltage gradient (i.e., the overshoot). When measured from the *outside*, the action potential represents the difference between the external positive 50 mV charge of the resting membrane, and the external-negative 40 mV charge which appears at the point where the membrane is excited.

Just as early experiments showed that changes in external potassium ion concentration lead specifically to changes in the resting potential, so it was found that changes in the external *sodium* ion concentration lead specifically to changes in the action potential. In general, a decrease in external sodium is accompanied by a decrease in the spike potential. On the basis of this and other data, Hodgkin (1951) proposed that the reversal of the membrane charge is due to a sudden penetration of sodium ions to the interior of the cell; the fundamental mechanism of the action potential was therefore related to a physical change in the plasma membrane, resulting in an altered permeability to sodium. Soon afterward this hypothesis was strongly supported by Keynes (1951), who used isotopic ^{24}Na and ^{42}K to measure the ion flux across the squid axon membrane at rest and during stimulation. He found that the sodium flux increases from 18 to 22 times during stimulation, and that the potassium flux also increases, but to a lesser extent (about 9 times in the outward direction). Keynes therefore established that the nerve impulse is accompanied by a sudden influx of sodium and efflux of potassium, which would be expected to abolish or even to reverse the normal resting potential across the membrane. For both types of ion, the net movement is in the direction of the electrochemical potential, which has been built up beforehand by the sodium–potassium exchange pump (i.e., high external sodium, high internal potassium). It should not be supposed that the normal sodium and potassium asymmetries are abolished during depolarization of the plasma membrane; the actual number of ions which flow through the membrane during a single brief (1 msec) period of increased permeability is extremely small, and the change is almost undetectable except by its effect on the membrane potential.

Recently Baker *et al.* (1962), in an elegant experiment, have conclusively demonstrated that the asymmetries in sodium and potassium distributions across the axon membrane do in fact provide the immediate source of energy for the propagated action potential (or nerve impulse). Up to 95% of the cytoplasm was squeezed out of a squid giant axon, after which the axon membrane was reinflated with a perfusion medium of known salt composition; in this way the ionic composition on both sides of the membrane could be altered at will. Baker found that, so long as the inside of the membrane contained potassium salts (e.g., potassium isethionate or potassium sulfate) and the outside was bathed in isotonic Na^+, these "model" axons could respond with action potentials of 90–130 mV for as long as 5 hours; during this period as many as 3×10^5 impulses could be conducted. Although the reconstituted axons remained excitable for hours in the absence of any metabolic source of energy, it is clear that maintainance of excitability *in vivo* must depend on continued sodium extrusion and potassium uptake, which are coupled to metabolism through the ion exchange pump.

The precise sequence of events during excitation in squid giant axons has been worked out in greater detail by Hodgkin and Huxley (1952), who introduced a special "voltage clamp" technique. In this method an artificial voltage is imposed on the membrane, the magnitude of which is kept constant by electronic feedback control; small electric currents caused by changes in ion flow across the membrane can then be recorded and measured relative to the constant imposed voltage. Hodgkin and Huxley found that during the spike potential, *two* currents appear successively in the course of 3–4 msec: first a sudden inward current lasting about 1 or 2 msec, and then a more gradual outward current. Since the inward current could be reduced or eliminated by reducing the concentration of sodium ions in the external medium, it was concluded that the first sudden response is due to an inward penetration of sodium; conversely, the second outward current was found to vary with the external concentration of potassium ions, showing that it is due to an outward diffusion of potassium. Essentially the same sequence of events has since been shown to occur at the nodes of Ranvier in vertebrate neurons.

From these studies, Hodgkin *et al.* (1952) proposed that the spike potential is the result of the following series of changes: first, a sudden and specific increase in the membrane's permeability to sodium; second, an inflow of positively charged sodium ions driven by the high electrochemical gradient (about 110 mV; this inflow causes the inside of the axon to become positive to the outside and is detectable as the ascending part of the spike potential); third, a return of the membrane to a condition of low sodium permeability, very likely accompanied by a specific increase in potassium permeability; and fourth, an outflow of positively charged potassium ions, which is primarily driven by the positive charge brought into the axon with the sodium ions and which results in descent of the spike potential to the usual resting potential. In this conception, the action potential involves two successive ion "pulses": first a pulse of sodium ions inward and then an equal and opposite pulse of potassium ions outward; the result is a zero net change in the membrane potential at the end of the spike. Using muscle, Keynes (1954) has measured the actual net gain in sodium during a single impulse as 6.6×10^{-12} mole/cm^2 and the net loss of potassium as 4.7×10^{-12} mole/cm^2 (a very small difference which does not exceed the experimental error expected for the technique).

It should be noted that the *sequential* changes in permeability, first to sodium and then to potassium, are responsible for causing the large positive overshoot, i.e., *reversal* in membrane charge during the spike; by contrast some specialized membranes, such as those of the synapse, respond with a simultaneous increase in permeability to all ions, which leads to gradual depolarization tending toward a maximum membrane potential of zero. Presumably the sodium and potassium ions displaced during the spike discharge are later pumped back through the membrane by the ion exchange pump, but this process is not necessary before immediate additional impulses can be produced. A very large store of potential energy is provided in advance by the continuing active transport of potassium in and sodium out of the cell, and this stored energy is sufficient to support many spike potentials. It is as though two storage batteries were facing each other across the resting membrane, a potassium battery on the inside and a sodium battery on the outside; each of these batteries is continuously being "charged" by the sodium-potassium pump. During the action potential a brief contact is made in the sodium circuit, which results in a current pulse from the sodium battery in one direction, followed by a second brief contact in the potassium circuit with a resultant current pulse from the potassium battery in the opposite direction. Because of the stored energy available, these action potential "pulses" can be produced repetitively at a very high rate, reaching frequencies of 50 per second in vertebrate neurons under physiological conditions, and 1000 or more per second under experimental conditions.

Unfortunately, the exact nature of the selective changes in the plasma membrane which result in the action potential are not well understood. Some theorists conceive of the plasma membrane as alternating, switch-like, between two or more possible physical states, one of which is more stable than the others. The key to solving this problem may lie in recent techniques, pioneered by Mueller *et al.* (1962) and Thompson (1964), for creating artificial membranes based on bimolecular lipid layers (Chapter 10). In the work of Mueller *et al.* (1962), the artificial lipid membrane could be made to adsorb unspecified proteins derived from egg white. Very remarkably, such an artificial lipid-protein membrane was able to respond to a direct current "stimulus," at a threshold value of 15–50 mV, by a sudden, reversible 5-fold change in membrane resistance. In fact, the response curve exhibited by this artificial membrane was generally similar in form to response curves measured with intact cells.

Regarding the velocity of propagation of an action potential, this parameter is known to vary more or less independently of the duration or magnitude of the spike voltage itself; thus even though most action potentials have values in the vicinity of 100 mV, the *rates* of conduction vary from less than 1 cm per second to about 120 meters per second. However, all such velocities are very slow when compared with the velocity of an electric current through an electrolyte solution. This fact, plus the fact that the potential does not diminish with distance, suggests an analogy with a gunpowder fuse; the release of energy at any one point on the fuse triggers a similar reaction at the next point, yet the actual source of energy is provided by equivalent local reactions at each site. In such a system, the velocity of conduction is expected to be proportional to the distance across which one local response can trigger the next.

For an action potential, this "triggering distance" is determined primarily by the character of small electric currents which radiate out laterally from the site of the spike. If a tiny, subthreshold voltage is applied at one point on the membrane, a lateral redistribution of ions occurs above and below the membrane, which can be detected by electrodes located in neighboring regions. Unlike the spike voltage this lateral voltage diminishes rapidly with distance, and the percentage diminution at any given distance is a property of both the membrane and the electrolytes above and below it (which carry the current). In the case of a spike potential, it can be shown that the lateral currents are often strong enough to set off another spike at a distance of one to several millimeters. Furthermore, it is clear that the farther these lateral electric currents reach out from the spike potential, the more rapidly can distant parts of the membrane be excited and the greater will be the velocity of conduction.

In principle, the "distance of excitation" is expected to be greater the less ion leakage occurs across the membrane (since ion leakage has the effect of short-circuiting the local currents). In fact, it appears that in myelinated nerve fibers the myelin sheath has the effect of reducing this charge leakage, thereby raising the effective electrical resistance of the axon membrane and increasing the rate of impulse conduction. Leakage is also proportionately less as the surface-volume ratio declines, leading to higher conduction velocities in axons of larger diameter.

The Functional Organization of Neurons

For many decades the prevailing concept of the neuron was as a kind of inert impulse conductor or organic telephone wire; in recent years, however, neurons have been increasingly recognized as among the most dynamic and metabolically active of all animal tissues. They are often enormously large cells, which carry out intracellular transport over distances of a meter or more by cytoplasmic streaming and striking axonic undulations; the requirements for synthesis and metabolic energy just in maintaining such cells are very great. Beyond this, neurons frequently assume the functions of *bona fide* secretory glands; for instance, in insects control of pupation from the caterpillar to the butterfly stage depends on the hormonal output of certain secretory neurons in the brain. In vertebrates too, the regeneration of amputated limbs as well as many morphogenetic processes in the embryo depend on specific but as yet unclarified neuronal influences. The dynamic qualities of the individual neuron are particularly apparent when an axon is severed: the cell rapidly reextends a new, thin cytoplasmic process, which advances by means of an amoeboid hyaline tip at the rate of 3–4 mm per day, carries on active pinocytosis, and shows great specificity in finding and recognizing its proper insertion. After contact is established the total mass of the axon continues to increase in a synthetic process which is supported by striking morphological changes in the vicinity of the nucleus and which continues until the axon diameter approaches its original size.

Neurons must therefore be regarded as impressively endowed cells, even above and beyond their obvious specializations for impulse conduction. With respect to excitatory properties too, recent analyses have tended to stress the great individuality of each neuron, particularly in responses occurring at points of cell-to-cell contact (i.e., synapses, which often number several thousand for a single fiber). It is true that the mechanisms of long-distance conduction along the axon, based on an all-or-none spike potential, have been relatively well elucidated. Nevertheless, it appears that information transmitted along the axon in spike frequencies goes through a complex coding or decoding process at cell junctions, which involves graded threshold responses, facilitation and summation of simultaneous inhibitory and excitatory stimuli. These mechanisms, which lie at the heart of animal behavior (including human memory, consciousness, and intelligence), depend on the characteristics of individual neurons and are still only poorly understood.

The concept that the nervous system is composed of independent cells, rather than of a syncytium-like network of fibers, was first proposed and supported by the classical researches of His (1886), Cajal (1888), and Waldeyer (1891). It is now understood that each neuron consists of a single nucleus in an enlarged cytoplasmic region called the perikaryon (or cell body), from which emanate both a large single axon and numerous smaller, branching dendrites. The axon diameter in different neurons of the same individual is highly variable, from less than 1 μ to 30 μ or more in vertebrates (squid giant axons attain 500 μ). At the tip, which may be a meter or more from the perikaryon, the axon typically branches into numerous smaller fibrils, each of which ends in a button- or bulblike enlargement perhaps 0.3–7 μ in diameter, where the neuron makes contact with another cell. In addition, distributed over the surfaces of the perikaryon, dendrites, and proximal part of the axon are numerous axon terminals or synapses where impulses are received from other neurons. The entire structure is therefore polarized for the receiving of impulses in the vicinity of the perikaryon and the transmitting of impulses in the direction of the axon terminals. Hydén (1960) has estimated that the number of incoming synapses may be from 2,000 to 10,000 for a large motor neuron, and the total volume of the cell may approach a million cubic microns. Active cytoplasmic streaming in the axon was first discovered by Weiss and Hiscoe (1948), and Pomerat (1957) subsequently recorded axoplasmic flow in striking time-lapse films which show that the axon wall carries on undulatory or peristaltic movements.

The fine structure of the neuron is largely that which would be expected for a cell which is active in synthesis and which carries on intracellular transport by streaming. The nucleus is well developed, with a single prominent nucleolus. In the vicinity of the nucleus, as well as in the dendrites and proximal axon, are accumulations of endoplasmic reticulum with attached ribosomes; these RNA-containing regions are sufficiently abundant to have been detected by classical light microscopists, who recognized their nucleoprotein nature as early as 1895 and called them the "Nissl substance." The Golgi apparatus is usually well developed—in fact Golgi (1898) first discovered this organelle in the cerebellum of the owl and cat. Numerous 100–200 Å, longitudinally oriented neurofibrils and neurotubules occur in the axon cytoplasm, extending on into the axon terminals (Fig. 11-1). It is probable that the tubules correspond to cytoplasmic microtubules, which have been found recently in many other types of cell and are typically associated with both

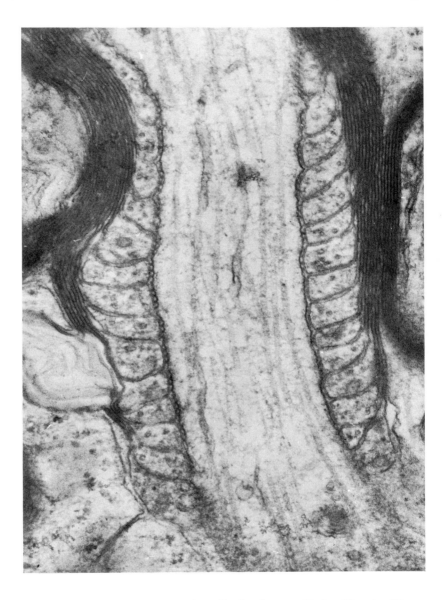

Fig. 11-1. Thin-section of an axon and myelin sheath near a Node of Ranvier. The axon contains both microtubules and neurofilaments in longitudinal orientations. 60,000×. From H. J. Ralston, by permission.

streaming and the transport of small molecules. The presence of abundant, longitudinally oriented fibrils in the axoplasm was also known to the earlier light microscopists, and shown to confer a low birefringence on the axon when viewed with polarized light. Maxfield (1953) purified a protein from extruded squid axoplasm, which at physiological pH occurred in the form of filaments having a molecular weight of 10^8. This protein accounted for 10% of the total axon protein, and at high pH it dissociated into globular subunits of about 70,000 molecular weight. However the relationship between tubules and fibrils, and between both these elements and the protein isolated by Maxfield, remains to be clarified.

Mitochondria are distributed throughout the neuron, including perikaryon, dendrites, axoplasm, and axon terminals. Some special features of the oxidative metabolism, which are not yet fully understood, concern the unique occurrence of γ-aminobutyric acid (GABA), found in vertebrate and crustacean central nervous systems. Oxidative metabolism of this compound is mediated through the enzyme GABA transaminase, which DeRobertis (1964) has found to be localized in the neuronal mitochondria. Since the central nervous system contains very little carbohydrate reserve, various investigators have speculated that the amino acid glutamic acid might be a primary energy substrate in neurons. It is now known that GABA is formed by decarboxylation of L-glutamic acid, a reaction mediated by the enzyme glutamic decarboxylase (also found only in the central nervous system). In effect, GABA metabolism constitutes an alternative pathway, or shunt, which has been estimated to account for up to 40% of the oxidative metabolism in the nervous system. Although the function of this shunt is not settled, GABA may act as an inhibitory agent in some synapses.

In neurons which are specialized to function as secretory cells, both gross and fine structure are essentially similar to those of typical neurons except that synthetic organelles like endoplasmic reticulum and the Golgi apparatus are especially well developed. These neurosecretory cells are recognizable primarily by the presence of membrane-enclosed secretion granules, 1000–3000 Å in diameter, which are often abundant at all levels in the axon. This type of cell occurs in the hypothalamus-hypophysis part of the pituitary gland in vertebrates, where the neurosecretory product consists of two polypeptides, oxytocin and vasopressin. The medulla of the adrenal gland is also regarded as modified neural tissue, secreting epinephrine and norepinephrine. Since vacuoles containing norepinephrine are very electron dense, they appear dark in the electron microscope; the course of secretion in adrenergic neurons can therefore be followed in thin sections. In this manner Sano and Knoop (1959) were able to establish that norepinephrine-containing secretory granules are formed from Golgi vacuoles in the perikaryon, are transported down the axon, and are released at the axon terminal. The axons of neurosecretory cells do not end in synapses with other neurons, but contact the endothelial lining of blood capillaries; in effect the axons function as a type of secretory duct. Such axons nevertheless are known to retain the capacity to propagate spike potentials, and it is an interesting question whether spike transmission plays any part in the release of the hormonal secretion. As DeRobertis (1964) has aptly noted, neurosecretory cells bridge the gap between the two great coordinating systems of higher animals, i.e., the endocrine and nervous systems.

At the sites of cell-to-cell contact, such as a myoneural junction (between a neuron and a muscle fiber) or a synapse (between two neurons), propagation of the neural impulse becomes extremely complex. In a few special cases it has been found that transmission proceeds relatively simply, by direct electrical conduction of the spike potential; electron microscopy of the synapse in these instances reveals that the plasma membranes of the two cells actually touch, forming an intimate physical contact. However in most instances a gap of about 200 Å separates the plasma membrane on the first cell's axon terminal (presynaptic membrane) from the plasma membrane of the second cell's dendrite or perikaryon (postsynaptic membrane). The impulse is carried across this gap by a special chemical transmitter, which is released (or secreted) from the presynaptic axon tip. The postsynaptic membrane is evidently specialized to respond to this transmitter in one of several possible ways, but invariably by a *graded* response; that is, this membrane is apparently unable to fire a local all-or-none spike (and thereby differs from the typical plasma membrane).

It was in relation to the myoneural junction that the existence of a chemical transmitter was first demonstrated. A single motor neuron usually innervates from a dozen to several thousand muscle fibers, the entire complex forming a "motor unit"; however, there is normally a one-to-one contact between an individual muscle fiber and a single branchlet from the axon, the site of this contact being marked by a "motor end plate" several microns in diameter. In this motor end plate the naked tip of the axon emerges from the myelin sheath and embeds itself in a grooved trough formed on the plasma membrane of the muscle fiber. Dale (1914) suggested that it might be acetylcholine which serves to transmit excitation from nerve to muscle at the motor end plate. Supporting evidence for this concept was obtained by Loewi (1921), who demonstrated experimentally that the release of acetylcholine from the vagus nerve slows or inhibits the beating of the vertebrate heart. During the 1930's Dale and his co-workers also succeeded in showing that the excitation of skeletal muscle by motor neurons is mediated by acetylcholine.

Thus the concept developed that acetylcholine is released at the axon terminal in response to a spike potential, that this compound then initiates an excitatory spike potential in the plasma membrane of the muscle fiber (inducing contraction), and that it is almost immediately (within 10 msec) hydrolyzed to choline and acetate by the action of the enzyme acetylcholinesterase. A more complete confirmation of this hypothesis was provided by Koelle and Friedenwald (1949), who showed by histochemical techniques that cholinesterase is specifically concentrated at the motor end plate; since degeneration of the axon terminal does not lead to immediate loss of cholinesterase activity, the enzyme is apparently synthesized on the postsynaptic (muscle fiber) side of the junction. On the other hand, resynthesis of acetylcholine from choline and acetyl-CoA is mediated by a different enzyme, cholineacetylase, which presumably is formed on the presynaptic (neuronal) side of the junction.

An important step forward in understanding the mechanism of chemical transmission was achieved by Fatt and Katz (1952), who while measuring membrane potentials in the vicinity of the end plate discovered the occurrence of very tiny "spikes" about 0.5 mV in magnitude, which seemed to be arising from the end plate in an entirely random sequence. These miniature end plate potentials were below the threshold necessary to excite the muscle fiber, they disappeared if the axon terminals were killed, and variations in their amplitude followed a random (normal) distribution. By contrast, the arrival of a nerve impulse at the end plate resulted in a sudden depolarization about 100 times greater than one miniature potential. From these observations it was inferred that the miniature potentials represent a random release of acetylcholine in "quantum" packets; these packets were conceived to be present in the axon terminal near the presynaptic membrane, waiting to be released in groups of about 100 under the stimulus of a nerve impulse.

Soon afterward, when techniques for making electron microscope thin sections were introduced, DeRobertis and Bennett (1954) reported a fine structural component corresponding to these acetylcholine packets. These are small vesicles 200–650 Å in diameter enclosed in 50 Å "unit membranes," which are found in abundance on the presynaptic, but not the postsynaptic, side of synapses and myoneural junctions. In some micrographs, individual synaptic vesicles can be seen to have fused with the presynaptic membrane in such a way as to release their contents into the space between the two cells. The number of synaptic vesicles in a single frog myoneural junction has been estimated at about 3×10^6, and DeRobertis (1964) has also shown that their number is increased by moderate impulse frequencies but decreased by excessive impulse frequencies. The hypothesis that the synaptic vesicles contain acetylcholine was confirmed by DeRobertis *et al.* (1963), who succeeded in isolating these organelles in bulk by fractionation and differential centrifugation of rat brains; in the synaptic vesicle fraction, both acetylcholine and its enzyme of synthesis, cholineacetylase, were found to be highly concentrated; on the other hand, the hydrolytic enzyme acetylcholinesterase seems to be associated with the synaptic membranes rather than with the vesicles. From general physiological data it has been estimated that about 900 acetylcholine molecules are contained in an average synaptic vesicle. Although both the origin of the vesicles and the mechanism by which a spike potential induces their release are still unknown, it seems clear that they represent the visible manifestation of functional polarity in the synapse; that is, nerve impulses pass the synapse in only one direction because the chemical transmitter, contained in the synaptic vesicles, is available for release only on the presynaptic side and can initiate a response only on the postsynaptic side. Essentially the same acetylcholine-cholinesterase mechanism is now known to occur in many different (cholinergic) neurons, including all motor neurons, all the preganglionic neurons of the autonomic nervous system, and the postganglionic neurons of the parasympathetic system.

In the postganglionic neurons of the sympathetic system the chemical transmitter is not acetylcholine, but norepinephrine, a nonmethylated precursor of epinephrine (adrenaline); the existence of adrenergic (rather than cholinergic) neurons was first demonstrated by Von Euler (1946). Inactivation of the norepinephrine in the synapse has been found to occur by methylation to form normetanephrine, a reaction which is catalyzed by the enzyme O-methyl transferase. Recently DeRobertis (1964) has found that norepinephrine too is concentrated in isolated synaptic vesicles, and it appears that a similar mechanism for the release of chemical transmitter occurs in both adrenergic and cholinergic synapses. The cells forming the medulla of the adrenal gland, which secretes both epinephrine and norepinephrine, are considered to be modified sympathetic postganglionic neurons; in this system a close relationship between impulse transmission (at short range) and secretion (at long range) is very evident. Vertebrate sensory neurons contain neither acetylcholine nor norepinephrine, so that still other chemical transmitters are believed to exist.

According to the present understanding of neural organization then, any given neuron is characterized by the type of chemical transmitter released at its own axon terminals (i.e., cholinergic, adrenergic, etc.). The *response* to this transmitter, however, is primarily a function of the *post*synaptic receptor membranes. For instance, in vertebrate heart muscle fibers some postsynaptic membranes respond to acetylcholine with an inhibition effect, whereas the same transmitter induces excitation in vertebrate skeletal muscle fibers. These special response characteristics of postsynaptic membranes first received attention when Grundfest (1957) showed that the membranes are unusual in being insensitive to direct electrical stimulation. Furthermore, if an action potential is initiated artificially at a remote part of a muscle fiber, it is propagated in the usual way across the surface of the fiber but is not propagated when it reaches the end plate plasma membrane. The responses of such postsynaptic membranes tend to be graded and specific, rather than of the usual "all or none" spike potential variety.

At least two distinct categories of postsynaptic membrane have now been recognized in vertebrate heart fibers: in the excitatory membranes the response is a gradual depolarization, brought about by an increase in permeability to all ions simultaneously. Such membranes fail to exhibit the sodium "overshoot" caused by *sequential* permeability changes during the typical spike potential. Depolarization proceeds until a threshold is reached, when the postsynaptic membrane induces firing of a spike potential in the neighboring plasma membrane. Commonly this threshold is at about -45 mV, representing a change of only 15–20 mV in a positive direction from the resting potential. By contrast, the response of inhibitory postsynaptic membranes leads to a more *negative* resting potential, which Eccles has shown is due to a selective outflow of potassium ions from inside the neuron (following an electrochemical gradient of about 20 mV from inside to outside). In neurons or muscle fibers which possess both excitatory and inhibitory synapses, the opposing tendencies toward depolarization and repolarization of the membrane are summated, so that the triggering of a spike depends on the total spatial and temporal flux of excitatory and inhibitory impulses.

At the level of multineuron systems, these special properties of the synaptic membranes lead to formidable complexities in interpreting even a comparatively simple system, such as a reflex arc. In the reflex arc, a specific environmental stimulus induces a graded generator potential in an appropriate sense organ; this generator potential is then immediately "coded" for axon transmission in the form of all-or-none spikes. In the simplest cases it is possible to discern a mathematical relationship between the magnitude of generator potential and frequency of spikes, but this relationship is nonlinear at best and is subject to such effects as upper and lower threshold limits, fatigue, etc. When the sensory spike potentials reach a motor neuron synapse, their frequency is again "decoded" by chemical transmission into a graded and specific generator potential in the postsynaptic membrane. This generator potential may have either an inhibitory or an excitatory effect. Assuming that it has an excitatory effect, the original impulse may undergo marked amplification (since a depolarization of 15 mV can initiate a spike potential of 90 mV), facilitation (in which later impulses have greater effects than earlier ones), or antifacilitation (in which later impulses have lesser effects); furthermore if the motor neuron has previously received inhibitory stimuli, the sensory impulse may never achieve the threshold necessary for further transmission. Assuming that a spike frequency is initiated in the postsynaptic motor neuron, this frequency may differ measurably from the original frequency in the sensory neuron. Finally when the impulses reach the myoneural junctions, they are once again retranslated into graded generator potentials in the muscle fibers. As explained previously, each motor neuron sends axon branches to hundreds or thousands of muscle fibers, and it has been found that the percentage of fibers that contract in this "motor unit" is a general function of the frequency of arriving motor impulses (varying, for instance, from 5/sec to 35/sec). However, the exact quantitative relationship involves the same processes of facilitation, amplification, threshold, and inhibition, which presumably occur at each of the hundreds of motor end plates contacted by the given axon.

In view of these complexities, it should not be surprising that large variations occur from one organism to another in exact stimulus-response relationships. An extreme example is found in the high-frequency flight muscles of insects: some species show a one-to-one relationship between action potentials and fiber contractions, which may continue up to frequencies of 16 per second or more. In species which show wing beat frequencies of 100 per second or higher, however, the one-to-one relationship is not found; instead the high frequency of contraction becomes a function of the contractile actomyosin fibrils themselves, and is maintained by action potentials of relatively low frequency (in the order of 3 per second). An analogous situation seems to occur in the smooth muscle fibers of vertebrates, where motor end plates are lacking and excitation is apparently induced simply by diffusion of norepinephrine from an adrenergic axon to neighboring muscle cells.

It is clear that the elucidation of animal behavior in terms of neuron function is still at a very early stage. The great histological complexity of the central nervous system, which was apparent to classical light microscopists, is now known to be based on and compounded by impressive functional complexities at the molecular level.

12

PHYSICAL CHEMISTRY OF PROTEINS, NUCLEIC ACIDS, AND NUCLEOPROTEINS

Living matter, while not eluding the laws of physics as established up to date, is likely to involve other laws of physics hitherto unknown, which, however, once they have been revealed, will form just as integral a part of this science as the former.

E. SCHRÖDINGER *1945*

Of the major biological macromolecules, the proteins were the first to receive systematic investigation because of their ability to influence the rates of chemical reactions *in vitro;* thus the enzyme diastase was first isolated by Payen and Persoz in 1830 (see Payen and Persoz, 1833), ptyalin was isolated in 1831, and the term "protein" was introduced by Mulder in 1839. It was another thirty-five years before nucleic acid was first described by Miescher (1874). The physical structure of both protein and nucleic acid molecules remained obscure for many decades, but after 1950 the development of powerful new chemical and physical techniques introduced a period of very rapid progress. In this period, the primary role has undoubtedly been played by high resolution X-ray diffraction analysis; nevertheless, the electron microscope has also provided a unique and important tool, which is able to link the morphologies of single molecules (easily visible after shadowing or negative staining) with the organization of cell organelles at the level of ultrastructure. This encounter between biochemical and cytological concepts and methods of investigation is still in progress, and provides a major theme for current research in cell biology.

Physical Structure of Proteins

PRIMARY STRUCTURE

It was understood very early that the products of protein hydrolysis (e.g., as catalyzed by digestive proteases) consist primarily of amino acids; in fact, the simplest of the amino acids, glycine, was isolated in 1820. However, the manner in which the different amino acids are linked together to form protein was not discovered until 1902, when Emil Fischer and Hofmeister independently discovered the peptide bond. This chemical link consists of a covalent bond between the α-carboxyl group of one amino acid and the α-amino group of another; during formation of the bond a molecule of water is removed as a by-product (dehydration synthesis):

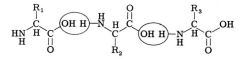

In this way a very large number of different amino acids may be linked in tandem as a "polypeptide chain," or polymer strand, which always has one amino end and one carboxyl end. In the diagram, the groups designated "R" are characteristic for each particular amino acid and protrude as side groups from the main polypeptide chain.

288

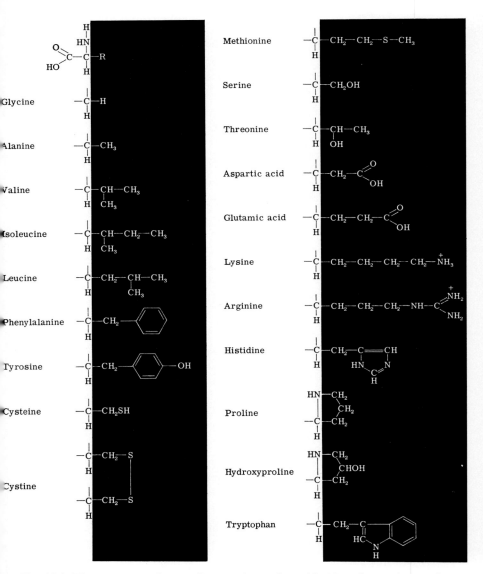

Fig. 12-1. The structures of naturally occurring amino acids. Note that cystine consists of two linked cysteine units. Asp and Glu have acidic side chains, while Lys, Arg, and His have basic ones.

The dimensional geometry of amino acids and peptide bonds was first investigated systematically by Albrecht and Corey (1939), who began a detailed X-ray analysis of glycine and later of small peptides. These early investigations were summarized by Corey and Donohue (1950), who reported that the C—C bond has a length of 1.53 Å, C=O a length of 1.23 Å, and C—N a length of 1.32 Å. Because of resonance, the amide group at each peptide bond occupies a plane;

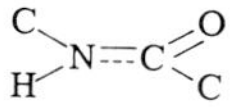

$$\underset{H}{\overset{C}{\diagdown}} N = C \underset{C}{\overset{O}{\diagup}}$$

However in a polypeptide, rotation of successive amide planes can occur freely around the α-carbon atoms. In a fully extended polypeptide, the distance between peptide linkages is about 3.6 Å, while the periodicity of side chains is approximately 7.27 Å (Fig. 12-2).

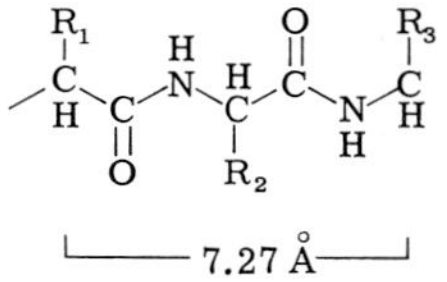

|—— 7.27 Å ——|

Considerable progress has now been made in interpreting the properties of polypeptide chains and proteins based on the properties of the various amino acids which compose them. Only about 20 different amino acids occur naturally in proteins and these units differ from one another by possessing acid, basic, or nonpolar side groups; at neutral pH, proteins which contain a high proportion of basic or acid amino acids behave as bases or acids themselves. When the net charge of a protein molecule is measured at different pH's, a characteristic isoelectric point (pH) can be found at which the charge is zero; this isoelectric point is largely a function of the amino acids composing the protein, being in the alkaline or acid range for basic or acid proteins, respectively. A protein molecule at a pH below its isoelectric point carries a positive charge and behaves as a weak base, whereas above the isoelectric point it has a negative charge and behaves as a weak acid.

The various common amino acids are illustrated in Figure 12-1.

Fig. 12-2. A molecule of polyglycine, the simplest possible polypeptide chain. Carboxyl end is uppermost, amino end below. Scale indicates 10 Angstrom units. Structural formula follows the sequence:

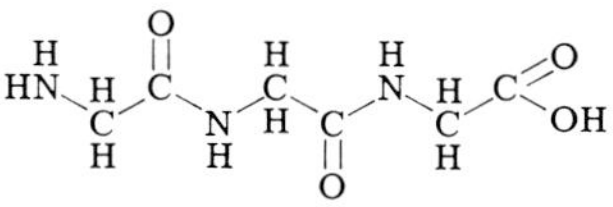

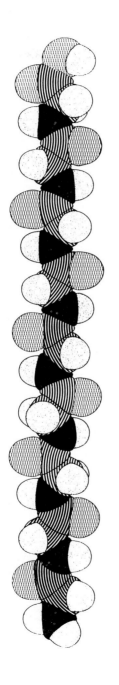

Glutamic acid and aspartic acid both contain a second carboxyl group which gives them an acidic character, and both also occur as amide derivatives (glutamine and asparagine). The basic amino acids are arginine, lysine, and histidine (in order of decreasing basicity). It is noteworthy that the size of the side chains varies greatly from the simplest amino acid (glycine, which lacks any side chain) to the more complex, heterocyclic forms such as tryptophan (Fig. 12-1). It will be shown that the structure of some protein molecules imposes geometric restrictions such that only certain amino acids can fit at particular points in the polypeptide chain. The only sulfur-containing amino acids are methionine and cyst*e*ine, two molecules of the latter being able to form a covalent disulfide bridge to constitute one molecule of cystine. Proline and hydroxyproline are also notable since the α-amino group is part of a five-member ring, which imposes special restrictions on peptide bonds involving this amino nitrogen.

During the early 1950's, chemical techniques were developed for determining the exact sequence of amino acids in a polypeptide chain. The first naturally occurring polypeptides to be analyzed were the pituitary hormones, oxytocin (mol. wt. 1007) and vasopressin, each of which contains a sequence of eight amino acids (DuVigneaud *et al.*, 1953). Almost simultaneously, Sanger and Thompson (1953) completed the amino acid sequence for cattle insulin (mol. wt. 5780), which contains two polypeptide chains of 30 and 21 amino acids, respectively; the chains are held together by two disulfide bonds linking four apposed cysteine residues. Complete amino acid sequences have also been reported since 1960 for ribonuclease (124 residues), tobacco mosaic virus protein (158 residues), cytochrome *c* (104 residues), human hemoglobin (α chain = 141 residues, β-chain = 146 residues), myoglobin (153 residues), chymotrypsinogen (246 residues), and others.

For many of these proteins, comparative studies of similarities and differences in amino acid sequence between different strains or species have also been published. Such studies have made it clear that the functional properties of a protein depend not only on which amino acids are present, but also on their positions in the chain (i.e., the amino acid sequence). Depending on the protein, some residues seem to be space fillers and can be substituted by other amino acids without changing the properties of the protein; other residues, however, provide essential functional groups whose relative positions remain constant across a

---

Fig. 12-3. A mixed polypeptide chain, showing characteristic side chains when compared with Fig. 12-2. From amino end at bottom, the sequence is: glycine-lysine-glutamic acid-histidine-leucine-glycine-arginine-glycine-glycine. For structural formulas, see Fig. 12-1.

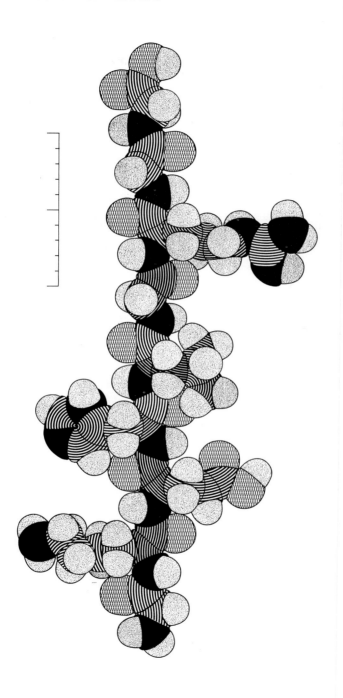

broad spectrum of evolution. In some instances, alterations in a single amino acid side chain result in marked changes in the functional properties of the molecules; an excellent example is provided by the pituitary hormones–oxytocin, which induces contraction by the uterine muscles, and vasopressin, which induces contraction by the smooth muscles of the arterial walls. These hormones differ in two amino acids, but seem to be related through "vasotocin," a frog hormone from which each differs by only one amino acid.

Vasotocin	Cys-Tyr-Ileu-GluNH$_2$-AspNH$_2$-Cys-Pro-Arg-Gly-NH$_2$
Vasopressin	Cys-Tyr-*Phe*-GluNH$_2$-AspNH$_2$-Cys-Pro-Arg-Gly-NH$_2$
Oxytocin	Cys-Tyr-Ileu-GluNH$_2$-AspNH$_2$-Cys-Pro-*Leu*-Gly-NH$_2$

Amino acid sequences such as these constitute the primary (or covalent) structure of a protein. The influence of covalent structure on the higher orders of structure and function will be the subject of later paragraphs.

SECONDARY STRUCTURE

During the 1930's and 1940's, X-ray diffraction analysis of protein fibers (such as silk and hair) made it clear that polypeptide chains are not usually fully extended in the native state. Various types of secondary folding or coiling were proposed, but a satisfactory model depended on the precise measurements of bond lengths and angles which were worked out by Corey and his colleagues. Using these data Pauling *et al.* (1951) were able to show that a single polypeptide chain can coil up into at least two helical configurations, each of which is stabilized by intramolecular hydrogen bonding between the nitrogen and oxygen molecules of neighboring amino acid residues. The more stable of these two configurations is termed the α-helix, and it is characterized by having 3.69 amino acid residues per turn with a rise per residue of 1.5 Å; the pitch of the helix is therefore 5.4 Å (3.69 × 1.5). An alternative configuration, known as the γ-helix, possesses 5.13 amino acid residues per turn, with a rise of 0.99 Å per residue.

Soon after publication of Pauling's theoretical models, confirming evidence for the reality of the α-helix was found in the form of a previously unnoticed meridional X-ray diffraction ring at 1.5 Å (corresponding to the peptide bond periodicity). Evidence also accumulated that the naturally occurring form of the α-helix is a right-handed coil (although a left-handed α-helix is theoretically possible). Finally, the existence of a right-handed α-helix in the myoglobin molecule was dramatically confirmed by Kendrew *et al.* (1960) in a three-dimensional X-ray diffraction analysis calculated at 2 Å resolution; the 1.5 Å spacing of side chains, although less than the distance of resolution, could be visualized because each side chain advances about 100 degrees around a helical axis (Fig. 12-4). It was also possible to observe the 5.4 Å periodicity along the backbone, corresponding to the pitch of the helix.

Although the α-helix has become the best known of the secondary polypeptide configurations, it is now well established that this type of structure is rare in some proteins; RNase for instance is estimated to contain only 15% α-helix. In globular proteins, the absence of α-helix implies a relatively irregular (although reproducible) pattern of folding; however in fibrous proteins a variety of other highly ordered configurations are known to occur. Chief among these are the "pleated sheet" or β configurations, in which hydrogen bonding occurs between different adjacent polypeptide strands (rather than within the same strand). In commercial silk, for instance, 44% of the amino acid residues are glycine, and these high-glycine polypeptide chains lie in parallel with all the amino ends pointed in one direction and all the carboxyl ends pointed in the opposite direction. Fibroin, on the other hand, contains polypeptides arranged in antiparallel, i.e., with amino ends of adjacent strands pointing in opposite directions. In fibroin, each strand has alternating glycine and alanine side chains, and these strands collectively form sheets, so arranged that all the methyl side chains of the alanine residues protrude from one side. Still another type of order is found in collagen, where each polypeptide chain has a left-handed coil and three such chains twist around one another in a right-handed direction to form a single molecule. This structure will be considered later in more detail.

Highly ordered polypeptide configurations, such as the α-helix, have a relatively low configurational entropy, and at higher temperatures they tend to transform to more random (high entropy) arrangements. During this transition from α-helix to "random coil," the overall length of the polypeptide chain increases as intramolecular hydrogen bonds are broken. This helix–coil transition can be induced in some polypeptides by repulsion of charged side chains; for instance, Doty and co-workers have studied configurational changes in artificial polypeptides, such as poly-L-glutamic acid and poly-L-lysine, which occur as α-helices at isoelectric pH but in charged forms (negatively or positively charged at higher or lower pH respectively) open out as random coils. Davies (1963) has speculated that the reverse transition, from random coil to α-helix, may play a role in molecular mechanisms of contraction (Chapter 8).

TERTIARY AND QUATERNARY STRUCTURE

Three-dimensional X-ray diffraction analysis of globular proteins, such as myoglobin and hemoglobin, has shown that a long polypeptide chain,

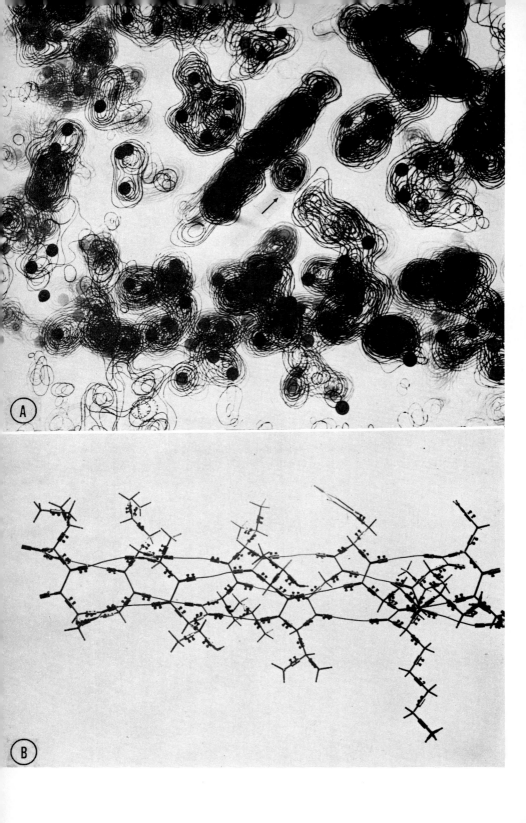

predominantly in the form of an α-helix, can bend back on itself or fold up in a specific pattern to constitute a higher order of tertiary structure. The existence of such tertiary structure was recognized quite early from studies of enzyme "active sites," which lose activity after unfolding of the peptide backbone by various denaturing agents. Nevertheless, it was not possible to describe the exact pattern of folding for any protein until the 2 Å X-ray description of sperm whale myoglobin achieved by Kendrew *et al.* (1960) and the 5.5 Å analysis of horse oxyhemoglobin by Perutz *et al.* (1960). Subsequently a 5.5 Å analysis of reduced human hemoglobin has been achieved by Muirhead and Perutz (1963), and 2 Å structures have been obtained for lysozyme by Blake *et al.* (1965), for α-chymotrypsin by Matthews *et al.* (1967), for carboxypeptidase A by Lipscomb and his collaborators (Reeke *et al.*, 1967), and for ribonuclease by Kartha *et al.* (1967). Major principles of protein structure which have emerged from these crystallographic studies are summarized in a recent review by Stryer (1968).

Hemoglobin and myoglobin are both oxygen-carrying molecules (occurring in blood and muscle, respectively), which show close similarities in amino acid sequence, in pattern of tertiary folding, and in possessing one heme prosthetic group per polypeptide chain. They differ, however, at the level of quaternary structure, i.e., in the association of independent polypeptide chains to form dimers, tetramers, etc. Whereas each myoglobin molecule consists of a single polypeptide chain with a molecular weight of 17,000, each hemoglobin molecule contains four such chains and has a molecular weight of about 65,000; correspondingly, a hemoglobin molecule possesses four heme groups, one for each chain. Because these proteins are very completely known both with respect to amino acid sequence and three-dimensional folding, and because the biosynthesis of hemoglobin has been extensively studied in cell-free systems to be discussed in Chapter 14, their structures will be described here in considerable detail (Fig. 12-4).

Myoglobin

The single polypeptide chain of myoglobin contains 151 amino acids of 17 kinds, 77% of which occur in α-helical segments (118 residues). If the chain were entirely in the form of one straight α-helix, it would be

Fig. 12-4. (A) Part of the sperm-whale myoglobin molecule, resolved at 1.4 Å by X-ray diffraction. The center of the picture is occupied by a flat heme group, viewed from the side, with a spheroid water molecule attached on its lower face at the ligand site for oxygen (arrow). The opposite face of the heme shows a bond with a histidine side chain. At upper right an α-helical segment is seen end-on as a doughnutlike profile. Along the bottom of the picture another α-helical segment is seen in lateral view. (B) Stick model of the α-helical segment at the bottom of (A). From Phillips (1963) by permission of J. C. Kendrew.

about 230 Å long; however, in the native molecule it is tightly and asymmetrically folded as a triangular prism about 45 by 35 by 25 Å in size (Fig. 12-4). The molecule actually contains eight separate segments of α-helix varying in length from 7 to 24 residues and joined at seven corners by nonhelical segments. Since the chain contains only four proline residues, it is considered significant that each of these occurs near a different corner, occupying the last turn of a helical region; the unique shape of proline makes it impossible for this amino acid to fit into the middle of an α-helix, and it appears that in myoglobin proline functions to disrupt the helix, thereby helping to determine the pattern of folding. The α-helical segments themselves are fairly rigid structures which resist bending.

Another interesting feature of the folding pattern is that almost all the polar side chains are on the surface of the molecule (contributing to its water solubility), whereas almost all the nonpolar residues are in the interior (permitting close packing and little internal water); this is a well-nigh universal rule for the globular proteins which have now been analyzed at 2 Å resolution. Although the pattern of folding is complex and asymmetrical, it is highly reproducible from one molecule to another in the crystalline state. The folding seems to be largely stabilized by van der Waals forces between nonpolar side chains, rather than by covalent or electrostatic bonds.

The oxygen carrying properties of myoglobin are due to its iron-containing heme group, which is disk-shaped and lies in a pocket on the surface of the molecule (Fig. 12-4). The heme is not covalently bonded to the polypeptide chain, but is held in place primarily by some 90 van der Waal's contacts. Most of the side chains in the heme pocket are nonpolar, but two histidine residues have a special relationship to the heme; one of these is actually linked to the iron atom, while the other is in a nearby position where it is able to link with a heme-bound oxygen molecule. Despite these preliminary discoveries, it has not yet been possible to interpret the reversible oxygen binding properties of myoglobin in terms of its amino acid structure.

Recently Kendrew has extended his X-ray analysis to a resolution of 1.4 Å, which permits him to recognize individual amino acid side chains by their characteristic shapes (Fig. 12-4). The sequence of amino acids in myoglobin has therefore been determined independently both by chemical analysis and by X-ray diffraction techniques. The correspondence in the findings provides an elegant confirmation for both methods.

Hemoglobin

The hemoglobin molecule is spheroid in shape, with a molecular weight of 64,500 and dimensions of 64 by 55 by 50 Å. It contains four polypeptide chains occupying different quadrants of the molecule, and these always consist of two identical pairs; consequently hemoglobin is technically a dimer. Four distinctly different hemoglobin chains are known to exist, designated α, β, γ, and δ, but not more than two of these can occur in any one molecule. In the commonest hemoglobin A, two α chains are combined with two β chains, while in hemoglobin A_2 (about 2.5% of the hemoglobin in normal adult blood), two α chains are combined with two δ chains. Human embryos also possess a special hemoglobin which consists of two α chains and two γ chains. For the most part the amino acid sequences for all these chains are known (Ingram, 1963), and it is understood that the β, γ, and δ chains have a high degree of similarity; however, each is under the control of a separate gene.

The three-dimensional structure of horse oxyhemoglobin was first analyzed at an X-ray resolution of 5.5 Å by Perutz et al. (1960), more or less simultaneously with Kendrew's 2 Å analysis of myoglobin in the same laboratory. The most startling discovery was that the pattern of tertiary folding in each hemoglobin polypeptide chain is almost identical to the "myoglobin fold" described by Kendrew. Likewise the positions of the four heme groups are similar, since each lies in a pocket on the surface of its own folded polypeptide, and the iron atom in each is linked to a histidine residue. This similarity in tertiary folding is all the more surprising since major differences in amino acid content and sequence are now known to exist between the hemoglobin chains and myoglobin. Konigsberg et al. (1961) worked out the complete sequence of the human α chain and showed that it contains only 141 amino acids (Fig. 12-5); the β, γ, and δ chains, on the other hand, all contain 146 residues (compared to 151 in myoglobin). Watson and Kendrew (1961) compared the amino acid sequences in human α and β chains with the sequence in sperm whale myoglobin, and concluded that of 91 possible identities between the β chain and myoglobin, only 25 actually occur. It is therefore clear that many amino acid substitutions (and some deletions) have occurred without disrupting either the tertiary folding or the general oxygen-binding properties of the molecule.

On the other hand, a number of constant features were detected by Watson and Kendrew; for example the proline residues in the hemoglobin chains, as in myoglobin, occur next to nonhelical "corners." Furthermore, at two points where α-helical segments pass close to one another and where only glycine residues (lacking side chains) would be expected to fit, glycine is actually found to occur in all three polypeptides. Possibly of greater significance is the finding that two histidine residues have a constant relationship to the heme groups in both myoglobin and hemoglobin—one histidine linked to the iron atom and the other in position to link with oxygen (Fig. 12-4). A genetic variant of the

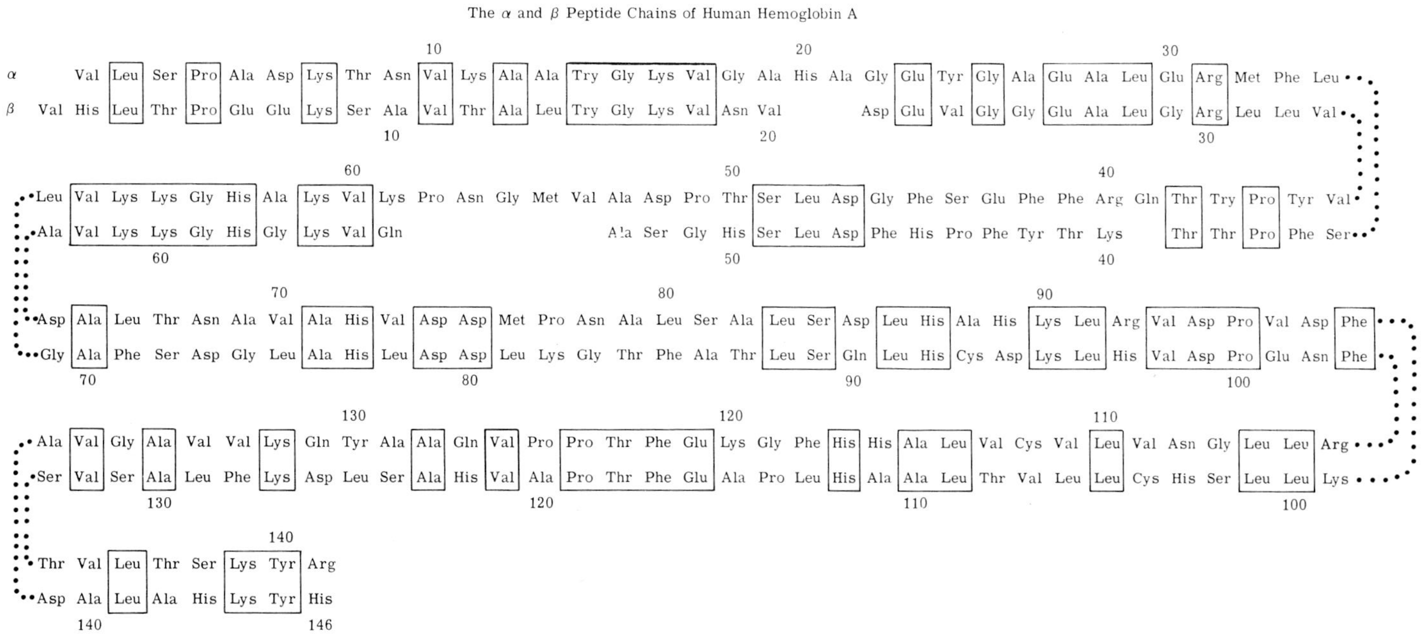

The α and β Peptide Chains of Human Hemoglobin A

α Val | Leu Ser Pro | Ala Asp | Lys | Thr Asn Val | Lys | Ala Ala | Try Gly Lys | Val Gly Ala His Ala Gly | Glu Tyr | Gly Ala Glu Ala Leu Glu | Arg Met Phe Leu
β Val His | Leu | Thr Pro Glu Glu | Lys | Ser Ala Val | Thr | Ala Leu | Try Gly Lys | Val Asn Val | Asp | Glu Val Gly Gly Glu Ala Leu | Gly Arg Leu Leu Val Val
      10   20   30

α Ser Phe Pro Thr Thr | Lys | Thr Tyr Phe Pro His Phe | Asp Leu Ser | His Gly Ser Ala Gln | Val | Lys
β Tyr Pro Try Thr Gln Arg | Phe Phe Glu Ser Phe | Gly Asp Leu Ser Thr Pro Asp Ala | Val | His | Val
      40   50

α Leu | Val Lys | Lys Gly His | Ala | His Ala Gly | Lys | Val | Ala Asp | Ala Leu Thr Asn Ala Val Ala His | Val Asp Asp Met | Pro Asn Ala | Leu Ser Ala | Leu Ser Asp Leu | His Ala His | Lys Leu Arg | Val Asp Pro Val | Asn Phe | Lys Leu Leu | Ser His Cys | Val | Leu Val Asn
β Ala | Val Lys | Lys Gly His | Gly | Lys Lys Val | Leu Gly Ala | Phe Ser Asp Gly Leu Ala His Leu | Asp Asn Leu Lys Gly Thr | Phe Ala Thr | Leu Ser Glu | Leu His Cys Asp | Lys Leu His | Val Asp Pro Glu Asn | Phe Arg | Leu Leu Gly Asn | Val Leu Val Cys Val
      60   70   80   90   100

α Leu Ala Ala His | Leu | Pro Ala Glu Phe | Thr Pro Ala Val His Ala
β Leu Ala His His | Phe | Gly Lys Glu Phe | Thr Pro Pro Val Gln Ala Ala
      110   120

α Ala | Val Val | Lys | Gln Tyr Ala | Val | Ala | Gly Phe | Lys | Gln Val Ala His His | Ala | Ser Leu Asp Lys
β Ser | Val Ser | Ala | Leu Phe Lys | Val | His | Asp Pro | Lys | Glu Asn Phe Arg Leu Leu
      130   140

α Thr Val | Leu | Thr Ser | Lys | Tyr | Arg
β Asp Ala | Leu | Ala His | Lys | Tyr | His
      140   146

Fig. 12-5. Amino acid sequences of α and β chains in human hemoglobin A, arranged to show the maximum homology of residues. From Ingram (1963).

α-hemoglobin chain is known in which this second histidine (residue 58) is replaced by tyrosine, and results in a loss of oxygen binding activity by the heme group. A relationship between histidine and oxygen-binding has also been detected in cytochrome c, another heme protein. Margoliash *et al.* (1961) have shown that the heme in this molecule is covalently bound to the polypeptide chain by sulfhydryl bonds with two cysteine residues (residues 14 and 17, near the amino end); when the amino acid sequence in this region of cytochrome c is compared for several species, it is found that the two cysteines are always present, and in addition a histidine always occurs adjacent to one of the cysteines. By contrast, the two "space-filling" amino acids (residues 15 and 16) are found to vary somewhat from one species to another.

The α and β chains of hemoglobin resemble one another somewhat more closely than either resembles myoglobin; for example, Ingram (1963) has compared the amino acid sequences in the two chains, finding 61 residues which match (44% similarity). Both chains also contain a so-called "basic center," which includes lysine and histidine residues and is present unchanged in hemoglobins from the cow, horse, sheep, rabbit, and goat; the function of this basic center is not yet clear. Just as the α and β chains resemble one another more than either resembles myoglobin, the β, γ, and δ chains are more similar to one another than to the α chain; Schroeder *et al.* (1962) determined the amino acid sequence of the (fetal) γ chain and reported that it corresponds to the adult β chain in 104 residues (71% similarity). Also according to Ingram and Stretton (1962), the β and δ chains differ in only 7 or 8 residues; it is of interest that the latter two chains are controlled by genes which, though separate, are closely linked genetically.

Mutant hemoglobin chains have been extensively analyzed with respect to amino acid sequence, and in most cases they differ from the norm only by a single amino acid substitution. For example, the glutamic acid residue at position 7 of the normal β chain is replaced by glycine in hemoglobin G, a substitution which evidently has no serious effect on the functional properties of the hemoglobin (but is detectable by electrophoresis due to the altered isoelectric point). In hemoglobin S on the other hand, another glutamic acid at position 6 of the same chain is replaced by valine, and this substitution results in greatly altered solubility properties that cause the disease symptoms known as "sickle-cell anemia." It is not yet understood why the one substitution produces so drastic and deleterious a change while the other, very similar substitution has almost no detectable effect; nevertheless, this example dramatically illustrates the importance of the amino acid sequence for the properties of the protein molecule as a whole. It seems clear that the various normal or mutant hemoglobin chains, together with myoglobin, represent a spectrum of variation in amino acid substitutions. Whereas simple Mendelian alleles differ by single substitutions, other chains may differ by seven or eight (β and δ), or even a majority of residues (myoglobin and hemoglobin β). Similar examples of such evolutionary divergence at the level of amino acid substitutions have been described in tobacco mosaic virus protein, in cytochrome c, and to a lesser extent in several other polypeptides.

It appears that the quaternary structure of hemoglobin develops more or less spontaneously, since the association of α and β hemoglobin dimers in human beings follows a probability distribution. For instance an individual who is doubly heterozygous for two hemoglobin mutations, one affecting the α chain and the other the β chain, produces four kinds of hemoglobin chain and four types of hemoglobin in about equal amounts. The mutant α chains can also combine with nonmutant γ chains in the fetal hemoglobin. Other abnormal hemoglobins are known in which four β chains or four γ chains are combined to form tetramers. This type of "self-assembly" is in accord with the concept that the primary or covalent structure of a polypeptide chain largely determines its higher orders of structure, including tertiary folding. Thus a polypeptide of given amino acid sequence is expected to assume spontaneously its most stable configuration for a given temperature, pH, or other set of physical conditions. In fact, spontaneous folding of a specific protein has been demonstrated during studies of the single polypeptide, ribonuclease. If it is true that most or all proteins have the capacity to assemble themselves into functionally active units under physiological conditions, then the primary problems of inheritance can be referred directly to the determination of amino acid sequences (Chapter 14).

Enzymes

The ability of proteins to alter the rates of chemical reactions in solution was recognized in the 1830's, and led to a long series of attempts to define or predict the course of enzymatically catalyzed reactions. The key to the problem was not discovered until 1902, when A. Brown proposed that enzyme kinetics are based on the formation of an enzyme–substrate complex, which dissociates at a finite rate to release the reaction product. Henri (1903) then developed the first equations for enzyme kinetics based on such an enzyme–substrate complex; his equations were later extended and improved by Michaelis and Menton (1913), who were able to take into account the pH variable defined by Sorenson in 1909. Generally speaking, the rate of an enzymatic reaction is described by the Michaelis-Menton equation:

$$v = \frac{V[S]}{K_m + [S]}$$

in which v is the reaction rate at the substrate concentration $[S]$, V is the maximum reaction rate for the particular enzyme at a saturating substrate concentration, and K_m is a constant which reflects the affinity of the enzyme for its substrate. When the substrate concentration, $[S]$, is very high, the equation reduces to $v = V$, i.e., reaction rate becomes independent of substrate concentration (since the enzyme molecules are entirely saturated with substrate). On the other hand when $[S]$ is very small, the equation reduces to

$$v = \frac{V}{K_m} [S] = k[S]$$

and reaction rate is directly proportional to substrate concentration. It can also be calculated that when $v = 1/2 V$ (half-maximal velocity), then $K_m = [S]$; this relationship provides one means of determining the value of K_m for a particular enzyme and substrate (i.e., their affinity). However, a more popular method is that introduced by Lineweaver and Burk (1934), who pointed out that when $1/v$ is plotted against $1/[S]$ the points fall on a straight line (rather than on a hyperbola, as when v is plotted against $[S]$); this line has a slope of K_m/V, it intersects the horizontal axis at $-1/K_m$, and it intersects the vertical axis at $1/V$. The Lineweaver-Burk plot is therefore a very convenient way to measure and compare the rate constants for different enzymes on a single graph (Fig. 12-6).

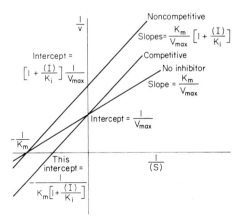

Fig. 12-6. A Lineweaver-Burk plot of reaction rate for an enzymatically catalyzed reaction. The three lines compare rates for the reaction alone, and in the presence of competitive or noncompetitive inhibitors. From Patton (1965).

Although these kinetic relationships revealed that an enzyme–substrate complex must form in the course of an enzyme reaction, Chance (1943) was the first to measure an ES complex directly. He achieved this photometrically, using the enzyme peroxidase and taking advantage of the fact that the peroxidase–peroxide complex possesses a characteristic absorption spectrum. Subsequently many systems have been developed for studying the kinetics and energetics of enzyme–substrate binding. In some cases substrate analogs have been found which bind to the enzyme but do not otherwise react; in other cases, an ES complex can be made to accumulate by omitting one of the reactants (e.g., oxygen in the luciferin–luciferase reactions). By such techniques it has been repeatedly demonstrated that each enzyme molecule possesses one or more "active sites," which show a high degree of stereospecificity in binding substrate molecules and which constitute the immediate catalysts of the reaction. Often the active site is a relatively restricted part of the protein molecule; in the protease papain (mol. wt. 20,700), for example, an appreciable fraction of the 180 amino acid residues can be lost without any reduction in enzymatic activity. The much longer polypeptide yeast enolase (mol. wt. 64,000) can also sacrifice 150 amino acids from either end of the chain without loss of activity (Nylander and Malmstrom, 1959). In some cases it has been shown that the mode of enzyme–substrate binding is by means of a covalent bond; thus the binding of substrate molecules to aldolase occurs by formation of a Schiff base between the substrate and a lysine residue.

Recently the steric relationship between an enzyme and its specific substrate has been observed directly by Blake *et al.* (1965) in an elegant X-ray diffraction analysis of egg-white lysozyme. This enzyme is a single polypeptide chain of 129 residues, folded into a globular configuration and cross-linked internally by 4 disulfide bonds. Its substrate is a particular polysaccharide found in bacterial cell walls, which is composed of alternating residues of *N*-acetylglucosamine (NAG) and *N*-acetyl-muramic acid (NAM). X-ray diffraction at 2 Å resolution reveals that the substrate chain fits very precisely into a groove on the surface of the enzyme molecule; furthermore, binding of the substrate results in a slight change of the enzyme's configuration in the active site, together with a significant distortion in one sugar ring of the substrate. These alterations can be related to the mechanism by which hydrolysis of the polysaccharide chain is catalyzed. X-ray visualization of the binding between an enzyme and its substrate has also been achieved for carboxypeptidase A, in which an atom of zinc occurs at the active site and participates in peptide hydrolysis. Reeke *et al.* (1967) have found that binding of glycyl-L-tyrosine in the active site induces a 14 Å movement by one of the enzyme's tyrosine residues; the phenolic hydroxyl group on this tyrosine seems to function by donating a proton to the amide nitrogen at the peptide bond as it undergoes hydrolysis.

According to Dixon and Webb (1964), approximately 842 enzymes had been described as of mid-1962, of which nearly 200 had been crystallized. These enzymes are classified into six categories according to the conventions adopted in 1961 by the International Union of Biochemistry. The number of known enzymes belonging to each category was as follows:

1. Oxidoreductases	216	
2. Transferases	224	
3. Hydrolases	206	
4. Lyases	105	(these enzymes remove a group from a substrate, leaving a double bond)
5. Isomerases	46	
6. Ligases	45	(these enzymes couple ATP hydrolysis with a bonding together of two substrates)
	842	

Although the hallmark of an enzyme is its substrate specificity, some recent investigations have shown that a relatively slight alteration sometimes permits the same protein to catalyze widely different reactions. For instance, Harting-Park *et al.* (1961) found that phosphoglyceraldehyde dehydrogenase, a familiar enzyme of anaerobic glycolysis (Chapter 6), can also act as an esterase, a phosphatase, or a transferase; removal of bound NAD from the enzyme molecule suppresses dehydrogenase activity and favors esterase activity, whereas blocking of the enzyme's sulfhydryl group induces phosphatase activity. The ability of a small unspecific molecule to alter the substrate specificity or reaction rate of a much larger enzyme molecule is termed an allosteric interaction; such allosteric modifications are currently receiving a great deal of study because they represent one mechanism by which a cell can control its internal synthetic activities. Colman and Frieden (1966) have shown that the respiratory enzyme glutamate dehydrogenase is markedly influenced by the binding of GTP or ADP to the enzyme, which occurs at a site different from the substrate binding site; addition of GTP inhibits activity whereas ADP increases it.

Enzymes sometimes exhibit puzzling, tissue-specific variations in pH optima, isoelectric point, or other intrinsic properties; in some cases, two or more enzymes of similar substrate specificity but slightly different physical or chemical properties can also occur together in the same cells.

Markert has termed these multimolecular forms "isozymes," and has shown that five isozymes of lactic dehydrogenase are generated at the level of quaternary structure by different combinations between two monomer chains to form tetrameric enzyme molecules. If the two monomers are designated A and B, the series can be represented as A_4B_0, A_3B_1, A_2B_2, A_1B_3, and A_0B_4; in a given tissue, the relative proportions of each isozyme seem to be controlled by the relative rates of synthesis for A and B. This implies that the assembly of tetramers from monomers takes place spontaneously and results in random combinations of A and B, in a manner similar to the assembly of hemoglobin molecules from α, β, or γ chains.

Ribonuclease

Among the smallest known enzyme molecules are cytochrome c and pancreatic ribonuclease (mol. wt. 13,683), for both of which complete amino acid sequences are known. In the case of cytochrome c, covalent bonding of the active heme group to two cysteine residues has been described in a previous paragraph. In RNase also, several "active site" amino acids have been identified chemically, and their three-dimensional configuration has now been clarified by Kartha *et al.* (1967) using X-ray crystallography.

The amino acid sequence of RNase, first reported by Hirs *et al.* (1960) and later revised by Smyth *et al.* (1963), includes 124 residues in a single polypeptide containing 15% or less α-helix. The chain is specifically folded and is internally cross-linked at four points by cystine disulfide bonds; the intricacy of this folding is suggested by the fact that residues 26 and 84, 40 and 95, 58 and 110, 65 and 72 are covalently linked in pairs. When these disulfide links are broken by reduction to sulfhydryl groups, enzymatic activity is lost; however it appears that partial reduction, possibly affecting three of the four bonds, does not impair activity. Anfinsen *et al.* (1961) have also shown that complete inactivation of RNase by reduction with mercaptoethanol in urea is strikingly reversible, i.e., the polypeptide can spontaneously reoxidize and return from a random coil configuration with 8 cysteine residues to a specifically folded and active enzyme with 4 cystine cross-links. This provides direct evidence that the secondary and tertiary folding of the chain is primarily a function of the amino acid sequence.

It was discovered fairly early that the last three amino acids at the C-terminal end of the chain (residues 122–124) are not required for enzyme activity; later Anfinsen (1956) found that removal of a tetrapeptide from this end *does* inactivate the molecule, indicating that residue 121 (aspartic acid) is essential. Crestfield (1963) also showed that a histidine at position 119 is required, as well as a second histidine at position 12; treatment with iodoacetate transforms one or the other of these two histidines into a monocarboxymethyl derivative, inactivating the enzyme. The fact that it is not possible to alkylate both histidines in the same molecule showed that these two residues, located at opposite ends of the polypeptide chain, are actually brought into close spatial relationship by the pattern of tertiary folding (estimated to be within 5 Å of one another). That both ends of the polypeptide chain contribute to the active site was shown earlier by Richards (1958), who reversibly separated the molecule into two units, one containing residues 1–20 and the other residues 21–124; separately, neither polypeptide showed enzymatic activity, but when they were recombined full activity was restored. In addition to the "active" amino acids near the ends of the chain, it is now known that a lysine residue at position 41 is also part of the active site.

The tertiary folding configuration of the RNase chain has now been elucidated in Harker's laboratory at 2 Å resolution (Kartha *et al.*, 1967). The molecule is approximately kidney-shaped, measuring 38 by 28 by 22 Å, and the active site is a deep depression in the middle of one side. It has been possible to visualize a phosphate group attached in the active site, and to confirm that the residues closest to the substrate are histidines 12 and 119. The chain assumes an α-helical configuration only at short intermittent regions involving about 15% of the residues. Although the chain is less tightly folded than in the myoglobin molecule, a core composed primarily of hydrophobic amino acid side chains is conspicuously present.

It is therefore clearly established that residues located at both ends and near the middle of the RNase polypeptide chain are brought together by three-dimensional folding to constitute the enzyme's active site. The cooperation between histidine, lysine and aspartic acid residues is especially significant, since one or another of these charged side chains has been shown to be essential in nearly all the active proteins so far investigated. Other features of the ribonuclease molecule, such as intrachain disulfide bonds, are clearly not of universal occurrence and suggest that each functional protein may be built on a somewhat different pattern.

STRUCTURAL PROTEINS

Proteins in general are often categorized as either globular or fibrous, the globular proteins containing highly folded polypeptide chains (e.g., most enzymes), and the fibrous ones possessing more or less extended chains (e.g., keratin and other insoluble or structural proteins). This distinction is not an absolute one, as illustrated by the myosin molecule, which appears to have a "globular" head possessing ATPase activity connected to a "fibrous" tail that confers low solubility in deionized water (Chapter 8). The dual structure of myosin is nicely correlated with its dual role as an energy-transducing structural element.

However, as a rule fibrous protein molecules tend to contain much higher percentages of α-helix than globular ones, and correspondingly there is a tendency for proline contents to be low. These generalizations are true for the muscle proteins (tropomyosin, paramyosin, and light meromyosin, the tail of the myosin molecule), which contain more than 90% α-helix. Each of these molecules is composed of two α-helices lying next to one another and slightly twisted to form a coiled coil; the result in paramyosin is a rod about 1330 Å long and 20 Å in diameter (mol. wt. 220,000). By comparison, globular actin contains less than 30% α-helix.

Collagen

The above rules clearly do not apply to the widespread fibrous protein, collagen, in which proline and hydroxyproline constitute 22% of the amino acid residues; in fact, the organization of collagen represents a unique type of ordered protein structure which differs strikingly from all those considered previously. Though the polypeptide configuration is unusual, collagen itself is one of the most abundant proteins in all nature, forming a major part of cartilage, bone, skin, and connective tissues in both vertebrates and invertebrates; it has been determined that over 20% of the total body protein of a mouse is collagen. In addition to its abundance and unique structure, collagen is noteworthy because its structure has been worked out at both the molecular and cytological levels, providing a fairly complete molecular explanation for one type of visible biological order.

In the vertebrates, collagen is synthesized by a particular kind of cell, the fibroblast, which deposits the protein in the form of visible extracellular fibers 2–200 μ in diameter. These fibers in turn are composed of bundles of fibrils, each of which measures 600–1300 Å in diameter and shows, by electron microscopy, a characteristic banding periodicity of 640–700 Å (depending on degree of hydration; Fig. 12-7). After staining with phosphotungstic acid or uranium, a number of finer bands as short as 15 Å can be seen within each 640 Å period. Though the relative intensities vary with different stains, this band pattern is highly reproducible, and in fact there is good evidence that the stained bands

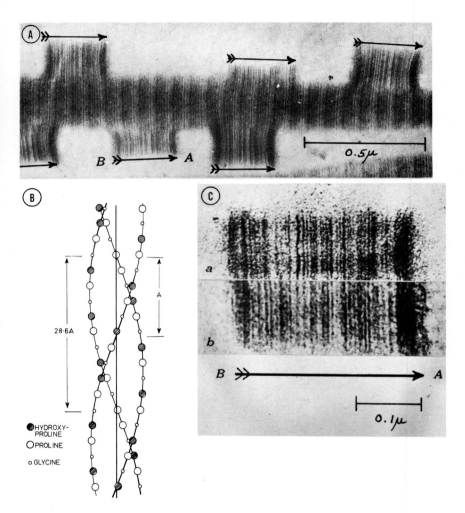

Fig. 12-7. (A) Collagen segments artificially reaggregated on a native collagen fiber. The short reaggregated segments are approximately as long as one tropocollagen molecule (2820 Å), and consist of many such molecules arrayed in parallel, 63,000×. From Hodge and Schmitt (1960). (B) Model of a tropocollagen molecule, showing three polypeptide chains helically wound around one another; every third residue is glycine, which lacks a side chain and fits into regions of close interchain contact. From A. Rich, by permission. (C) A single collagen period, stained to show regions rich in aspartic and glutamic acid (above) and in arginine (below); the positions of acidic and basic residues correspond closely, but differ in intensity. 170,000×. From Hodge and Schmitt (1960).

correspond to short regions of the collagen polypeptide chain which are rich in acidic or basic side chains (Fig. 12-7); the interband regions, on the other hand, probably represent sequences of neutral amino acids. Collagen fibrils can be dissolved in weak acetic acid or 1 M NaCl, and if the solution is then diluted with 5% NaCl, the molecules spontaneously reaggregate as fibrils showing the same banding patterns and periodicity as native collagen.

An important key to the structure of collagen fibrils was discovered by Highberger *et al.* (1951). They found that, under special conditions of reaggregation, dissolved collagen reconstitutes a new kind of fibril having a periodicity of about 2800 Å, approximately four times the usual periodicity; in one of these "long periods," about 50 minor bands can be distinguished (Fig. 12-7). This and other facts led Gross *et al.* (1954) to propose that the basic unit of collagen structure is a molecule some 2800 Å long (the tropocollagen particle). They postulated that in "long-period fibers" these molecules are arrayed in exact register, so that the period corresponds to the true length of the collagen particle; in native collagen, on the other hand, the tropocollagen particles are out of register by one-fourth of a length, giving rise to the 700 Å period. Subsequently Hall and Doty (1958) succeeded in visualizing tropocollagen molecules by electron microscopy, confirming that they have an average length of 2820 Å and a diameter of 14–15 Å (mol. wt. 360,000). Furthermore, Hodge and Schmitt (1960) were able to confirm the staggered packing arrangement in the native fibrils by using native (short period) collagen to induce reaggregation of long-period segments (Fig. 12-7); the long-period bands correspond to short-period bands in exactly the manner predicted by Gross's hypothesis.

Simultaneously with these electron microscope analyses, the substructure of the collagen molecule itself was analyzed by X-ray diffraction techniques. Initially it was known that collagen has a unique amino acid content in that: (1) it has an extremely high proline content (22%); (2) it is the only protein known to contain hydroxyproline and hydroxylysine; and (3) almost exactly one-third of the amino acid residues in collagens from a wide variety of species are glycine. Cowan and Mc-Gavin (1955) investigated the effect of the high proline content by analyzing the structure of synthetic poly-L-proline, concluding that proline tends to form a left-handed helix with three residues per turn and a 3.12 Å rise per residue. Shortly afterward Ramachandran and Kartha (1955) arrived at the correct plan of the collagen molecule, which consists of three side-by-side polypeptide chains, each in the form of a left-handed, somewhat modified "proline helix"; these three left-handed helices are then further twisted around one another to form a major, right-handed helix (Fig. 12-7). The three chains are held together by hydrogen bonds and are very close to one another, their axes being 4.5 Å apart and 2.6 Å from the common central axis. One consequence of this close packing is that every third amino acid residue must be glycine, since this amino acid lacks a side chain and is the only one that can fit; the 33% glycine actually found in collagen is thereby accounted for. Analysis of collagen amino acid sequences also confirms that there is always at least one glycine per tripeptide. In the latest collagen model proposed by Ramachandran *et al.* (1962), two interchain hydrogen bonds occur for every three residues, providing the molecule with a high degree of rigidity. Each left-handed minor helix has 3.28 residues per turn, a radius of 1 Å, and a rise per residue of 2.95 Å; the major right-handed helix, on the other hand, makes one turn for every 36 residues (in each chain), it has a radius of 2.5 Å, and it repeats at a pitch of about 108 Å.

It has been shown by Piez *et al.* (1961) that two of the three polypeptide chains in tropocollagen are very similar in amino acid composition (α_1), while the third (α_2) differs by having less proline, hydroxyproline, and alanine, but more valine, leucine, and isoleucine. More recently Bornstein and Piez (1965) have demonstrated that the positions of methionine residues in the two α_1 chains are different, indicating that no two of the three collagen chains are exactly alike. Denaturation of the tropocollagen molecule leads to separation of four chromatographic fractions, two of which represent single polypeptides (α_1 and α_2), while the other two components are double-chain complexes (α_1-α_1, and α_1-α_2). In the ultracentrifuge all the single chains form one peak with molecular weight about 120,000, while the duplex molecules form a second peak with about twice the molecular weight. Further degradation of the chains can be brought about by hydrazine, which separates fragments of 25,000–30,000 mol. wt. It has been hypothesized that 4 subunits of 30,000 mol. wt. might be linked in tandem to make up one chain of 120,000 mol. wt., three of these chains constituting the tropocollagen molecule of 360,000 mol. wt. Current research is aimed at unraveling the exact relationship between amino acid sequences in the three collagen chains and the highly specific, three-dimensional configuration of the molecule. It is believed, for instance, that the characteristic inextensibility of collagen is due to steric hindrance by proline and hydroxyproline residues; there is also reason to think that hydroxyproline OH groups, which point away from the tropocollagen axis, are involved in the specific aggregation or "self-assembly" of collagen fibers; this is evidenced by the thermal stability of different collagens, which is correlated with their hydroxyproline content.

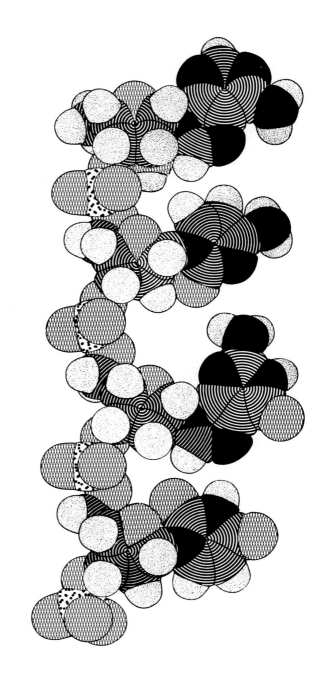

Physical Structure of Nucleic Acids

Following Miescher's (1874) first purification of nucleic acid from salmon sperm, a number of investigators carried out chemical analyses of nucleic acids from yeast and thymus gland. Consistent differences were found, and during the early 1900's it came to be generally accepted that yeast nucleic acid is characteristic of plants whereas thymus nucleic acid is characteristic of animals. Not until 1924 did Feulgen and Rossenbeck develop a specific histochemical test (Feulgen reagent) which permitted them to demonstrate that "thymus nucleic acid" (DNA) actually occurs in the nuclei of plant as well as animal cells. At about the same time "yeast nucleic acid" (RNA) was also found in animal cells, and the concept developed that two types of nucleic acid occur side by side in all cells.

After chemical or enzymatic degradation, both types of nucleic acid exhibit residues of pentose sugar, phosphoric acid, 6-keto and 6-amino purine bases (guanine and adenine), and the 6-amino pyrimidine base cytosine (Fig. 12-8). However, an important difference, discovered by Ascoli about 1900, was that RNA also contains the 6-keto pyrimidine base, uracil, whereas DNA lacks uracil but contains thymine (5-methyl-uracil; Fig. 12-10). Still another difference was demonstrated by Levene and London in 1929, when they found that the pentose sugar of thymus nucleic acid is 2'-deoxyribose; earlier (about 1910) Levene had shown that the pentose of yeast nucleic acid is ribose (Fig. 12-8). Consequently during the 1930's and 1940's, the designations deoxyribose nucleic acid (DNA) and ribose nucleic acid (RNA) gradually replaced the older terms, thymonucleic acid and yeast nucleic acid.

Early measurements of nucleic acid molecular weights established that these compounds form very large molecules (then thought to be in the order of 500,000 to one million mol. wt.), and that the molecules are typically shaped like long rods or fibers. Furthermore, it was already

Fig. 12-8. RNA polynucleotide chain, showing 3'-5' diester linkages, and the base sequence A-C-G-U (from top). Scale indicates 10 Angstrom units. Structure is:

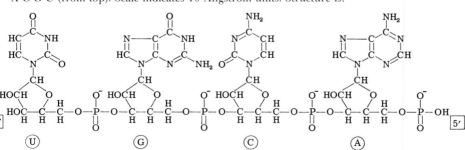

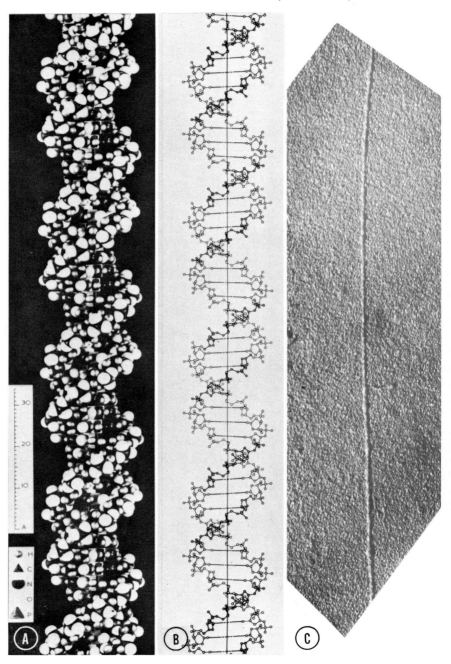

suspected that the unit of structure is the nucleotide, in which one phosphoric acid residue and one purine or pyrimidine base are covalently linked to different carbons of a single ribose or deoxyribose unit (Fig. 3-1). Nucleoside triphosphates such as ATP were known to be 5'-phosphate esters, but the hydrolysis products of RNA were found to include 3'-phosphate esters; consequently by 1949 the primary structure of nucleic acid was already visualized as a long-chain polymer in which four types of nucleotide are held in a polynucleotide chain by 3'-5' diester linkages (Fig. 12-8).

DNA

One of the universal characteristics of DNA but not RNA is that the molar ratios, adenine:thymine, guanine:cytosine, and total purine:total pyrimidine are all approximately equal to 1 in a wide range of organisms (Chargaff, 1950). By contrast, the ratio of A + T:G + C is highly variable, ranging from 0.45 to 2.7 in different bacteria (Sinsheimer, 1962). A stacked arrangement of these bases in the DNA molecule was inferred very early by Signer et al. (1938), who deduced from DNA optical anisotropy that "the purine and pyrimidine rings lie in planes perpendicular to the long axis of the molecule." This was confirmed by Astbury's (1947) preliminary X-ray diffraction studies, which showed that the bases are spaced at 3.4 Å "like a pile of pennies." Aside from these facts, relatively little was known about the molecular structure of DNA until 1953.

In that year Watson and Crick (1953) arrived at their now-classic, double-helix model of DNA. This was worked out in partial collaboration with another group of investigators headed by M. H. F. Wilkins, who were analyzing the structure of DNA by refined X-ray diffraction techniques (Fig. 12-9). In the Watson-Crick model, two 3'-5' diester polynucleotide chains lie next to one another "pointed" in opposite directions (i.e., the free 5' ends of the two chains are at opposite ends of the molecule). The two polynucleotide strands are held together by hydrogen bonds between pairs of bases, one base extending from each chain in a plane perpendicular to the chain axis (Fig. 12-10). In addition, the two polynucleotide strands are twisted around one another to

Fig. 12-9. (A) A long segment of DNA helix, including more than four turns and 40 base pairs; note the major and minor grooves on the surface of the molecule. From Wilkins (1963b). (B) Diagram of the B configuration of DNA, corresponding to (A). From Wilkins (1963b). (C) Electron micrograph of a single DNA helix isolated from phage lambda and heavily coated with platinum. 81,180×. Micrograph by DuPraw.

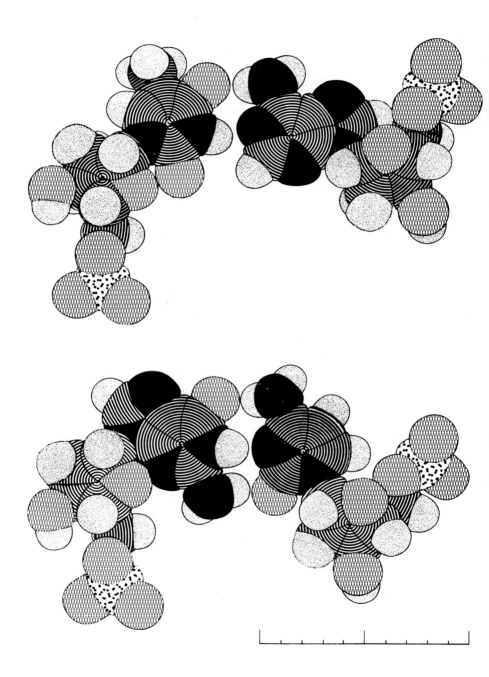

form a right-handed helix which completes one turn every 34 Å; since the bases are spaced 3.4 Å apart, this means that there are about 10 base pairs per turn (34/3.4). In effect, the base pairs form a stack, and the two pentose-phosphate chains coil around the outside of this stack with the phosphorus atoms spaced every 7.1 Å (Fig. 12-9).

The diameter of the Watson-Crick molecule (ca. 20 Å) is primarily a function of the base pair dimensions. One of the important insights represented by the model is the fact that only two kinds of base pair can yield a molecule of regular diameter; these are the pairs adenine-thymine and guanine-cytosine, each of which combines one "long" purine base, hydrogen-bonded to one "short" pyrimidine base (Fig. 12-10). This restriction on base pairing immediately accounts for the one-to-one ratio of total purine to total pyrimidine in DNA, as well as for the equivalence of adenine with thymine and guanine with cytosine. Although A-T and G-C base pairs can follow one another in any sequence along the length of the molecule, the presence of adenine in one chain dictates that thymine must have an opposite position in the other chain. The two polynucleotide chains are thus complementary to one another, each representing a template of the other; because they are complementary rather than identical they can have widely different base compositions, e.g., a high ratio of C to G in one chain implies a low ratio of C to G in the other.

The X-ray diffraction data of Wilkins *et al.* (1953), published simultaneously with Watson and Crick's model, served to confirm a fundamentally helical structure for DNA (Fig. 12-9). Subsequent work, to be described, has demonstrated that the two polynucleotide chains are independent entities which can be separated by heat or alkali denaturation (which breaks the hydrogen bonds); the separate chains can also be recombined by annealing. The exact pitch at which the two chains wind around one another, as well as the number of base pairs per turn and

---

Fig. 12-10. 5'-Deoxyribonucleotide molecules oriented to show hydrogen bonding between base pairs as it occurs in a DNA helix. Two hydrogen bonds link thymine (upper left) with adenine (upper right), while three hydrogen bonds link guanine (lower left) with cytosine (lower right). Scale indicates 10 Angstrom units. Base structures are:

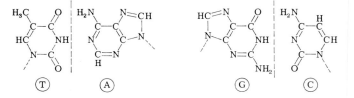

the angle of one base pair relative to the next, all seem to be subject to some variation. For example, Bode and MacHattie (1968) have found that the twist of a DNA helix in solution changes slightly with the salt concentration of the medium. Printz and Von Hippel (1965) have also investigated the dynamics of DNA molecules in solution by measuring the exchange of DNA hydrogens with ^{3}H-labeled water. Their study shows that the protons involved in hydrogen bonding of base pairs in DNA exchange with a half-time of 300 seconds, suggesting that the double helix frequently "breathes" or partially unwinds at local sites. In the crystalline state, as studied by X-ray diffraction techniques, DNA can assume one of three major configurations (Wilkins, 1963a). The most common is the B configuration, similar to that proposed by Watson and Crick, which Langridge *et al.* (1960) characterized as having a pitch of 33.6 Å (instead of 34 Å), and in which the radius of the phosphorus atoms from the axis is 9.05 Å (instead of 10 Å). The A configuration exhibits a helix pitch of only 28 Å, has 11 base pairs per turn, and the bases, instead of occupying planes perpendicular to the long axis, are tilted by about 20 degrees. Another C configuration, with only 9-1/3 base pairs per turn, has been described in dried DNA. An important feature of all these two-stranded helical molecules is the presence of two spiral grooves on the molecule surface, one larger than the other; in the B configuration, the two polynucleotide chains are alternately 18.8 Å and 14.8 Å apart, while the actual width of the grooves is about 14 Å and 6 Å, respectively (Fig. 12-9).

Recent studies of molecular weight in native DNA have clearly established that the early measurements of one million or less were much too low. Since the B configuration of DNA has a fairly constant mass per unit length, molecular weight can be estimated directly from the total length of the molecule as determined by electron microscopy or autoradiography. A double-stranded Watson-Crick molecule (sodium salt) should have a molecular weight of 196 per Ångstrom unit of length, or 1.96×10^6 per micron (roughly two million per micron). In the bacteriophage λ, MacHattie and Thomas (1964) found continuous DNA chains 17.2 μ long, corresponding to a measured molecular weight of 33 million; the DNA of T2 bacteriophage is also a single molecule some 50 μ long (mol. wt. 130×10^6). Even more strikingly, in the bacterium *E. coli* Cairns (1963b) has obtained autoradiographic evidence for continuous DNA chains in the order of 1100 μ long (over a millimeter; mol. wt. 2.8×10^9). In higher organisms too, Solari (1965) has used the electron microscope to photograph single DNA molecules 50–93 μ long from sea urchin sperm; in autoradiographic studies, Cairns (1963c) reported molecules 1000 μ long from human (HeLa) cells, and Huberman and Riggs (1966) have detected strands 1800 μ long in Chinese hamster cells. It seems clear, therefore, that the lower early values for DNA molecular weight were the result of fragmentation brought about by the violent isolation procedures that were commonly used.

Aside from accounting for X-ray data and other physical properties of DNA, the Watson-Crick model has provided a way to visualize biological replication at a molecular level. As pointed out by Watson and Crick (1953), each of the two DNA polynucleotide chains contains full information specifying the base sequences in the other; consequently, if the two chains should separate, each might form a template for synthesis of a new complementary chain, and the result would be two double-stranded daughter molecules identical to the one parent molecule (Fig. 13-1). Although there is now clear evidence that such a process of DNA replication occurs, two serious difficulties in the scheme have not yet been resolved. In the first place, since the two polynucleotide chains are wound in a double helix around one another, they presumably cannot separate without unwinding; however, there are about 30,000 turns in a DNA molecule 100 μ long ($100 \times 10^4/34$), and it is conceptually difficult to imagine so tedious an unwinding and rewinding each time replication occurs. The second difficulty is that in the intact molecule, the two complementary DNA chains have opposite directions so that one chain ends in a 3' hydroxyl group where the other chain ends in a 5' phosphate ester; from the point of view of enzymatics, replication of the two chains involves two separate reactions, whereas at present only one such reaction is known (which specifically replicates from the 3' end). Although the mechanism is unknown, autoradiographic studies of Cairns (1963a) established that *in vivo* the two chains replicate simultaneously and in parallel. The enzymatics of DNA synthesis *in vivo* and *in vitro* will be discussed in more detail in Chapters 13, 15, and 17.

With respect to the unwinding problem, an important simplification was introduced by Levinthal and Crane (1956), who showed that unwinding and rewinding can occur simultaneously without the necessity for long free strands that whip around one another. They visualized replication at a fork (as postulated by Watson and Crick), the two daughter strands forming a Y with the parent strand (Fig. 13-1). If then all three strands are imagined as rotating, each around its own axis, the result is that the parent arm unwinds as the two daughter arms rewind. For a Watson-Crick molecule containing 6000 turns (20 μ), Levinthal and Crane calculated that the energy required for this unwinding-rewinding process would be only 1.2×10^{-22} cal per revolution, whereas the energy required to form 20 phosphate bonds during the same revolution would be over 1000 times greater (3.3×10^{-19} cal). It is important to note that in each polynucleotide chain, adjacent bases are able to swivel freely relative to one another, since the pentose-phosphate backbone contains 5 rotating bonds per nucleotide.

Further insights concerning DNA unwinding come from analysis of the melting or denaturation process. Doty *et al.* (1960) obtained DNA from *E. coli* in which one chain of each molecule contained isotopic ^{15}N, while the other chain contained only ^{14}N; heating such DNA resulted in the separation of one heavy chain and one light chain, which could be distinguished in the ultracentrifuge. When such denatured DNA strands are cooled rapidly they do not recombine, but Doty showed that slow cooling does permit renaturation, when the complementary strands complex and rewind in pairs to form intact DNA helices. Melting of DNA therefore involves a reversible unwinding more or less comparable to that which must occur during replication; an important difference is that melting and renaturation seem to proceed by a migration or "unscrewing" of the two polynucleotide chains past one another in a lateral direction. Analysis of the melting process shows that the longer the DNA helix, the slower the rate of denaturation, i.e., rate is proportional to $1/L^2$. Longuet-Higgins and Zimm (1960) have proposed a theoretical formula to estimate the unwinding time during replication as:

$$t = 4.6 \times 10^{-18} \, (\text{M.W.})^{5/2}$$

For a DNA molecule of 10^7 molecular weight (5 μ), the unwinding time would be calculated as 1.4 seconds.

Denaturation of DNA can be followed spectrophotometrically by changes in the optical density at 260 mμ (in the ultraviolet); absorption at this wavelength is primarily a function of the purine and pyrimidine bases, but the percentage of light absorbed is less when the bases are hydrogen bonded into pairs than when they are free (a phenomenon known as hypochromicity). Thus if the 260 mμ optical density of a DNA solution is plotted at various temperatures, it is found that a very sudden increase in absorption occurs in the vicinity of 90°C as the paired polynucleotide chains separate. Since thymine-adenine pairs are held together by two hydrogen bonds but cytosine-guanine pairs are linked by three (Fig. 12-10), it might be anticipated that G-C pairs would be thermodynamically more stable than A-T pairs; the exact temperature of melting would therefore increase with the proportion of G-C to A-T in the molecule. Doty (1962) observed just this effect, and extrapolated his measurements to obtain a value of 70°C for the melting of a pure A-T molecule and 110°C for a pure G-C molecule. From these data, the actual ratio of A-T to G-C in an unknown DNA can be estimated very closely from the observed temperature of melting (T_m).

Although A-T and G-C are the most common base pairs, various other pairings are known to occur either naturally or under experimental conditions; the relative stability of these unusual combinations can be compared directly from their melting curves. For example in the T-even bacteriophages guanine is paired with 5-hydroxymethylcytosine instead of cytosine, and in mammals and plants a small fraction of cytosine is replaced by 5-methylcytosine (6% in mammals, 30% in plants). Some or all of the hydroxymethylcytosine of phages is also linked to glucose, forming α- or β-glucosylhydroxymethylcytosine; Kornberg has shown that the glucose residues are added after the DNA double helix has been completed. In the bacterium *E. coli*, 6-methylaminopurine replaces a small fraction of the adenine. Also under experimental conditions, 5-bromouracil (or 5-chloro- and 5-iodouracil) can substitute for thymine both *in vivo* and *in vitro*.

An important and physically distinctive type of DNA is represented by double helices that form closed circles; these occur in viruses such as ϕX174, phage λ, and polyoma, as well as in the bacterium *E. coli* (Fig. 15-3B), in animal mitochondria (Fig. 7-6), and probably in nucleoli (Chapter 17). Such DNA circles may be completely covalent, in which case both polynucleotide chains are closed circles and an interwound pair is topologically inseparable; alternatively, a circular helix may contain single-strand breaks in one or both chains, so that circularity is maintained only by hydrogen bonding between the two strands. For a completely covalent circle, any factor which increases the amount of twist in the helix (e.g. the salt concentration) tends to throw the molecule into a super-coiled configuration (Bode and MacHattie, 1968). On the other hand, a single-strand break acts as a swivel point and makes it possible for the circle to assume an open configuration.

RNA

Until the early 1950's, RNA was characterized in much greater detail than DNA. In crude RNA preparations, a 1:1 ratio of A:T and G:C was not observed, and consequently after Watson and Crick proposed their helical model for DNA it was generally assumed that RNA molecules occur as unpaired, single strands rather than in the paired configuration of DNA. X-ray diffraction analysis of RNA also yielded much more complex patterns than for DNA, as might be expected for flexible single strands. It was even proposed by Watson and Crick (1953) that the presence of ribose in a polynucleotide chain might interfere with formation of a double helical configuration. It is understood now, however, that RNA does form double helices both between and within strands, and that the earlier difficulties in analysis were due to the occurrence of several distinct types of RNA, each with radically different molecular weights and other properties.

In 1956, Ochoa isolated an enzyme, polynucleotide phosphorylase, which made it possible to synthesize artificial, single-stranded RNA's of predetermined base composition. Chains containing all adenine (poly A) could be made, as well as poly U, poly C, and mixed AUCG polymers (with random base sequences). For unknown reasons poly G could not be made, but the analog polyinosine has been used instead; here the base hypoxanthine differs from guanine only by the absence of an amino group. Almost immediately Warner (1956) discovered that mixtures of artificial poly A and poly U exhibit a stoichiometric 1:1 complexing; further study of the complex by X-ray diffraction analysis revealed that these complementary RNA strands spontaneously form double helices almost indistinguishable from the B configuration of DNA. Complementary pairing of poly C and Poly I strands has also been observed, as well as formation of poly A-poly A complexes (at low pH) and other unusual pairings. From the melting temperatures of such artificial complexes, it has been possible to confirm that the most stable ones are the G-C and A-T pairs of native nucleic acids. Natural double-stranded RNA's have now been found in certain viruses and during the replication of single-stranded viral RNA's.

The discovery that RNA can form double helices suggested the possibility of DNA-RNA "hybrid" molecules. Artificial hybrids, in which a single deoxyribonucleotide strand is base-paired with a complementary ribosepolynucleotide strand, were synthesized by Rich (1960) and others; these DNA-RNA hybrids are resistant to digestion by both DNase and RNase. According to Spiegelman *et al.* (1961), a natural double-stranded DNA-RNA hybrid appears during proliferation of T2 bacteriophage. A slightly different type of "mixed" nucleic acid has also been formed experimentally by Berg *et al.* (1963); in this case, ribose nucleotides alternate with deoxyribose nucleotides in the same polynucleotide chain.

That *single*-stranded RNA's also exhibit hypochromicity and other properties of double helical molecules was discovered more or less unexpectedly by Doty *et al.* (1959). Although the hypochromicity is less marked than in double-stranded DNA, it is definite enough to establish that intrastrand base-to-base hydrogen bonds exist in single poly-nucleotides. Previously it had been thought that base pairing could occur only between complementary sequences of nucleotides; however, even in artificial single-stranded RNA's of random base sequence (e.g., the AUCG polymer) hypochromicity measurements indicate that about 62% of the chain is hydrogen-bonded with itself. Fresco *et al.* (1960) have shown that this high degree of base pairing is achieved by "looping out" of odd nucleotide sequences which cannot find appropriate mates. Apparently the single RNA strand folds back on itself at many places and explores various possible configurations by lateral migration until the maximum number of H-bonds have been established; at this point the configuration of the single polynucleotide chain possesses maximum thermodynamic stability for its particular base sequence. The final RNA configuration is thought to be highly asymmetrical, something like the secondary and tertiary structure of a globular polypeptide chain (e.g., myoglobin). Just as a polypeptide may orient into several longer or shorter segments of α-helix, so a polynucleotide may orient into several longer or shorter segments of base-paired double helix.

In recent years it has become possible to characterize different types of RNA and to isolate more or less pure fractions. One of these, an RNA of low molecular weight (ca. 25,000) known as "soluble RNA" or "trans-fer RNA," shows a base composition in which the ratios of A:U and G:C approximate 1, as in native DNA (Miura, 1967). Although the mole-cule consists of a single chain with some 70 nucleotide residues, hypo-chromicity and hydrogen exchange studies indicate that about 82% of the chain is in double helix form. Another unusual feature of sRNA is its content of rare substituted bases, such as 5-ribosyl-uracil, which comprise about 6 of approximately 14 unpaired nucleotides in each molecule (Englander and Englander, 1965). Another RNA fraction from yeast ribosomes has been crystallized by Spencer *et al.* (1962; Spencer and Poole, 1965) for X-ray diffraction analysis. This RNA was found to consist of DNA-like double helices about 100 Å long and with 3-1/2 helix turns per molecule; however, the shape resembles the "A" configuration of DNA, with a helix pitch of 28–30 Å and tilted bases, rather than the more common "B" configuration. Where the chain doubles back on itself at one end, there apparently must be at least three unpaired nucleotide units to permit the 180 degree turn.

Both RNA and DNA can exist either as rodlike double-stranded helices, or as single strands with partial base pairing and complex ter-tiary folding. Still another nucleic acid configuration has been found, which consists of a triple-stranded helix. In such molecules it appears that the large groove which is normally present on the surface of a nucleic acid double helix is occupied by still a third polynucleotide chain. The existence of triple-stranded complexes was first inferred by Rich and Davies (1956) during studies of pairing between artificial poly A and poly U RNA strands. In the presence of $MgCl_2$, the expected $1:1$ stoichiometry was shifted to a $1:2$ ratio, with one strand of poly A complexed to two strands of poly U. Subsequent analysis by Felsenfeld and Rich (1957) confirmed the formation of a three-chain molecule and showed that the adenine-uracil duplex can react in this way only with poly U, but not with poly C, poly A, or poly I. Zubay (1958) proposed a specific helical model of three-stranded RNA in which all strands are hydrogen-bonded and the number of nucleotides per turn is 10 (as in double-stranded DNA). On the basis of these specific RNA triple helices, it has been speculated that the transfer of information from DNA to RNA may occur by formation of a complex involving two DNA strands (i.e., a Watson-Crick double helix), plus one newly synthesized RNA strand. In fact, natural DNA-RNA complexes of this type have been reported in *Neurospora* by Schulman and D. Bonner (1962), and in pea seedlings by J. Bonner *et al.* (1961). Specific three-stranded DNA complexes have also been studied recently by Inman (1964).

Physical Structure of Nucleoprotein

Both DNA and specific types of RNA usually occur in cells as chemical complexes with proteins, i.e., as nucleoprotein particles or fibers. Indeed, it was as a nucleoprotein complex (nuclein) that nucleic acid was first discovered by Miescher (1871) in pus cell nuclei; only later was he able to isolate pure nucleic acid from the DNA-protamine complex of salmon sperm (1874). Although Miescher understood that basic protamine is held in a saltlike linkage with nucleic acid, he did not recognize protamine as a protein. This relationship was first established by the work of Kossel (1884), and it was also Kossel who first defined the histones as a class of basic proteins occurring in avian erythrocyte nuclei. In addition to these basic proteins, it has become clear since the 1940's that nonbasic proteins also form important complexes with nucleic acids. The basic proteins themselves include widely different types of compound, which are expected to form very different types of nucleoprotein complex. Marked differences exist between the ribonucleoprotein (RNP) complexes and the deoxyribonucleoprotein complexes, both with respect to protein composition, three-dimensional configuration and cell function. RNP particles (or ribosomes) will be discussed in Chapter 14 as part of the mechanism of protein synthesis.

Although the DNA-protein complexes are much better characterized, there has been surprisingly little progress in purifying and analyzing specific DNA-linked proteins or in defining exact molecular relationships within the complex. Since most of the earlier studies dealt with reconstituted, extracted or precipitated DNA-protein, analyses of the native complexes have been comparatively few. Nevertheless, X-ray diffraction analysis of both native and reconstituted DNA-protein has served to establish two major points: (1) the B configuration (or Watson-Crick structure) of DNA persists after formation of various protein complexes; and (2) except for the regularity of the DNA molecule itself, there is relatively little repetitive orderliness, or crystallinity, in most DNA-protein arrays. As noted previously, native DNA occurs in the form of extremely long, 20 Å fibers of high molecular weight; it is expected that the much smaller protein molecules fit themselves to the long DNA helices, and in fact a variety of physical techniques have now served to establish that DNA nucleoprotein is notably fibrous in structure both *in vivo* and *in vitro*.

The analysis of nucleoproteins from cell nuclei was systematized by Mirsky and Pollister (1942, 1946), who showed that 1 M NaCl dissolves and extracts essentially all the DNA and a large part of the protein from a wide variety of animal, plant, and bacterial nuclei; redilution with 6 volumes of distilled water (yielding 0.14 M NaCl) results in a strikingly fibrous precipitate in which both histone and nonhistone proteins are complexed to DNA in a fairly constant nitrogen/phosphate ratio. Since both pure DNA and the isolated proteins are soluble in 0.14 M NaCl, the insolubility of the DNA-protein complex is considered a characteristic property. Specific separation of the (basic) histone proteins can be achieved by dissolving them with HCl, after which a relatively large amount of nonhistone protein remains complexed to the DNA. In a modern variation of this technique employed by Steele and Busch (1963), isolated nuclei are extracted successively in (1) 0.14 M NaCl (giving a soluble or nuclear sap fraction); (2) 0.10 M Tris buffer (giving a ribonucleoprotein fraction); (3) 2 M NaCl (giving a chromatin or DNA-protein fraction); and (4) 0.05 N NaOH (giving an acidic protein and RNA fraction). For liver nuclei, the percent dry weight composition for each fraction is given in Table 17-1. The 1–2 M NaCl-soluble, "chromatin" fraction is actually quite complex, as indicated by the early work of Mirsky and his collaborators; in fact, DNA accounts for only about 30% of this fraction, while the remainder includes histones, non-histone proteins, and RNA.

TOBACCO MOSAIC VIRUS

Strange though it may seem, the only nucleoprotein complex for which the spatial arrangement of both nucleic acid and protein is known in precise detail is the tobacco mosaic virus (TMV). Although the nucleic acid in this case is a single-stranded RNA, the relationship of protein and RNA is suggestive of possible relations between protein and DNA in the 230 Å chromatin fibers described from somatic nuclei by Ris (1956), DuPraw (1965a), and others. Whether or not this proves true, the exact detail elaborated for TMV serves as a standard by which to measure the state of knowledge concerning nonviral nucleoprotein.

The TMV particle itself is cylindrical, about 180 Å in diameter, 3000 Å long, and with a molecular weight of 39×10^6. Its nucleic acid is a continuous strand approximately 33,000 Å long with a molecular weight of 2.1×10^6 (corresponding to about 6400 nucleotides); both ends of the RNA strand terminate with unphosphorylated adenosine groups. The protein component consists of many identical monomers, each of which is a single polypeptide chain and has a molecular weight of only 17,500. From the molecular weight of the total protein (37×10^6) and each protein monomer (17.5×10^3), it is simple to calculate that one virus particle contains some 2130 identical protein molecules. This is one protein monomer per three RNA nucleotides (6400/2130), and in fact X-ray diffraction data confirm that there are exactly three nucleotides associated with each polypeptide chain (Fig. 12-11).

Since the RNA strand is 11 times longer than the intact virus particle, it is evident that some type of secondary structure must exist. X-ray diffraction analysis shows that the virus RNA is in the form of a coil with a diameter of 80 Å, a pitch of 23 Å, and 49 nucleotides per turn. The protein monomers form a coat encasing this polynucleotide coil, and are themselves helically stacked with a pitch of 23 Å, but with only 16-1/3 monomers per turn (49/3). Each protein monomer is approximately 70 Å long, 23 Å thick, and 21 Å wide, tapering somewhat toward the center of the TMV cylinder; since the protein molecules in opposite walls do not meet at the center, each virus particle contains a hollow channel ca. 34 Å in diameter, which is ordinarily filled with water (Finch, 1964). It has been shown that, in the absence of a protein coat, the isolated RNA strands assume a complex pattern of tertiary folding in which 71% of the nucleotides form intrachain base pairs and helical segments (page 323); consequently it is clear that the protein moiety of this nucleoprotein complex determines the precise secondary structure of the nucleic acid, stabilizing and cross-linking the 11:1 coil. This conclusion is confirmed by the fact that the monomers, in the absence

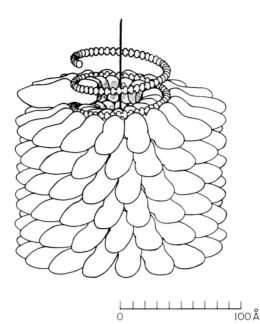

Fig. 12-11. Schematic illustration showing the organization of a tobacco mosaic virus (TMV). There is one protein monomer for every three bases in the RNA chain. The RNA is packed as a helix with an 11:1 ratio of extended to coiled length, and is held in this configuration by the associated protein units. From Klug and Caspar (1960).

of nucleic acid, are able to reaggregate spontaneously to form rod-shaped particles.

Tsugita *et al.* (1960) have worked out the complete amino acid sequence of the TMV monomer, which consists of a single polypeptide chain with 158 amino acids (about 30% of which lie in α-helical configurations). Beyond the fact that each monomer is roughly ellipsoid, the pattern of tertiary folding is poorly known. A threonine residue, which forms the C-terminal amino acid, evidently lies near the surface of the virus (since it is accessible to enzyme digestion); on the other hand, the N-terminal group is formed by acetyl serine, which is thought to be folded into the interior. Although there is one cysteine residue in each monomer, aggregation does not depend on disulfide bonding, but seems to be a function of the N-terminal part of the chain; a short polypeptide can be separated from this end by appropriate digestion, and shows a remarkable tendency to aggregate. Eight proline residues occur in the TMV monomer, most of which are well spaced out in the chain and suggest a high degree of folding. Probably the most intriguing property of TMV protein is its acidic character, since it contains a preponderance of dicarboxylic over dibasic amino acids and has an isoelectric point at pH 3.5. According to the usual theory of nucleoprotein complexes, such a negatively charged polypeptide (−3) would not be expected to complex readily with three negatively charged nucleotide units; nevertheless, X-ray diffraction studies show that the RNA chain is surrounded by protein, passing through a notch in each protein monomer. Evidently the pattern of polypeptide folding determines the ability of this globular acidic protein to form complexes with nucleic acid, possibly by concentrating some of the molecule's eleven basic arginine residues at the notch position (Fig. 12-11).

NUCLEOPROTAMINE

In higher organisms, the best-understood nucleoprotein is the saltlike complex between basic protamine and DNA, which was first discovered in salmon sperm by Miescher (1874). DNA-protamine has been found only in developing and mature spermatozoa, where it is usually the only nucleoprotein present; however, the common belief that all sperm nuclei contain nucleoprotamine is in error. Miescher himself was aware that in the sperm of other fish, such as the carp, DNA is complexed with a histonelike protein, and more recently it has been found that mammalian sperm contain a unique nucleoprotein based on neither histone nor protamine. The occurrence of protamines in different species is still a puzzle, since these compounds have been found not only in salmon, herring, and trout sperm, but also in rooster sperm and in sperm of the snail *Helix*; yet Vendrely *et al.* (1960) have confirmed that this type of protein is not a major constituent in carp sperm, and the same is true of sperm from plants, sea urchins, and mammals.

Protamines vary somewhat depending on the species of origin, but they have in common an extremely high content of arginine, which often comprises two-thirds of all the amino acid residues, and a very low molecular weight (in the order of 4000); due to the high arginine content, the isoelectric point is about pH 10–11. In crude extracts of protamine from salmon sperm, only seven kinds of amino acid are present (Arg, Leu, Val, Ala, Gly, Pro, Ser). Callanan *et al.* (1957) found that arginine comprises 68% of the residues in salmon protamine, being the only polar amino acid present; furthermore, proline is the major nonpolar amino acid, characteristically forming the N-terminal residue with one N-terminus per 4000 molecular weight. Using ultracentrifugation, Callanan confirmed that the molecular weight is uniform near 4000; however, since alanine and leucine were present in amounts much less than one residue per 4000 gm of protamine, it was necessary to conclude that the physically uniform molecules include species differing in amino acid content. On the basis of Callanan's results it can be estimated that an average molecule of salmon protamine consists of 19 arginine residues and about 8 or 9 nonbasic amino acid residues. Such a 28-residue polypeptide would have a fully extended length of about 100 Å.

Pollister and Mirsky (1946) were able to prepare DNA-protamine extracts from trout sperm by the same M NaCl extraction they developed for somatic nucleohistones; on redilution to 0.14 M NaCl, a similar, strikingly fibrous nucleoprotein precipitate formed. However, unlike extracts from somatic nuclei, the sperm nucleoprotamine contained no RNA and no protein other than protamine; almost the entire protein component could be separated from DNA by simple dialysis. Pollister and Mirsky's data showed that in sperm, the virtually pure DNA-protamine complex accounts for 91% of the dry weight of the nucleus and 81.6% of the entire sperm cell! The fact that the complex is dissociated by NaCl provides good evidence that the protein and nucleic acid components are held together by saltlike electrostatic bonds between negatively charged phosphate residues and positively charged arginine residues. The proportionality between these two groups was investigated by Felix et al. (1956), who reported that the ratio of arginine to phosphate both in whole sperm nuclei and in reprecipitated DNA-protamine fibers is 0.92–0.95 for four different species of fish. Phosphate groups that are not complexed with protamine would be expected to complex with smaller cations, such as Na^+ or K^+; in fact, Feughelman et al. (1955) reported that whole sperm heads and reprecipitated nucleoprotamine show a ratio of Na^+ and K^+ to phosphate of about 0.1 (compared to 1.0 for deproteinated DNA). These relationships show that essentially all the arginine residues of protamine are linked to phosphate groups of DNA, but that 5–10% of the DNA phosphates are neutralized by Na^+ and K^+ ions rather than protamine.

Of the various nucleoproteins, DNA-protamine is unusual in that it tends to form crystalline arrays that are even more regular than those of pure DNA. The X-ray diffraction patterns obtained from crystalline nucleoprotamine and from intact sperm heads are identical, and both patterns differ only slightly from the diffraction pattern characteristic of pure DNA in its B configuration. According to Feughelman et al. (1955), the repeat unit of sperm heads is based on single DNA molecules packed in parallel hexagonal arrays, with a center-to-center spacing of 28.7 Å. These authors tested various models for pairing of poly-L-arginine with DNA phosphates and found that the only scheme that provides for close 1:1 pairing is one in which the polyarginine is fully extended and is wrapped helically around the DNA molecule in its shallow groove (Fig. 12-12). Under these conditions the repeat distances of the polypeptide side chains and polynucleotide phosphates are identical (about 7.1–7.2 Å), while the lateral extension of the arginine side chains matches closely with the diameter of the small groove (ca. 8 Å). In this model, a single polyarginine molecule would bond alternately with both of the DNA polynucleotide chains, thereby further stabilizing the double helix (Fig. 12-12). Approximately 75 Å of polypeptide would be required to extend around one complete turn of the DNA helix, and this 75 Å would have to contain 20 arginine side chains to complex with 20 DNA phosphate groups; this relationship, in fact, is nearly fulfilled by single salmon protamine molecules (see above).

That protamine actually has an extended, nonhelical configuration in the DNA-protamine complex has been confirmed by Bradbury *et al.* (1962), who found that the exchange between hydrogen and deuterium in the complex is very rapid (in contrast to an α-helix). The main difficulty, therefore, is to account for the nonbasic amino acid residues of protamine, which spoil the perfect periodic structure of polyarginine. Feughelman *et al.* (1955) suggested that neutral parts of the polypeptide chain could "loop out" from the DNA groove, provided that such residues occur in pairs. Such a scheme is supported by preliminary studies of amino acid sequences in protamines from herring sperm; thus Felix *et al.* (1956) found that the sequence, Arg·Arg·Arg·Arg, is of frequent occurrence, accounting for 35% of the total nitrogen in herring protamine, while neutral residues tend to occur together in pairs. Their data are consistent with a fundamental protamine amino acid sequence in which four arginines alternate regularly with two neutral residues:

N-terminal   Pro·Ala $(\text{Arg}_4\text{X}_2)_n$ Arg·Arg   *C-terminal*

For salmon protamines, the number of (Arg_4X_2) groups would be in the order of four. Although the biological significance of the neutral residues is not entirely understood, the high proline content probably prevents the polyarginine segments from coiling up into an α-helix.

The process by which nucleoprotamine-containing sperm nuclei develop from histone-containing spermatocyte nuclei has been studied cytochemically by Alfert (1956). He found that a progressive replacement of histone by protamine occurs after the completion of the two meiotic divisions, i.e., in the late spermatid. A similar protamine-histone replacement had previously been demonstrated *in vitro* by Mirsky and Ris (1951), who found a direct correlation between protamine added and histone released from a reprecipitated nucleoprotein preparation.

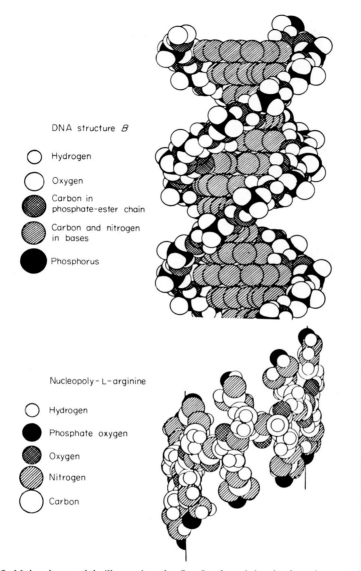

DNA structure *B*

○ Hydrogen

○ Oxygen

● Carbon in phosphate-ester chain

◑ Carbon and nitrogen in bases

● Phosphorus

Nucleopoly - L - arginine

○ Hydrogen

● Phosphate oxygen

◕ Oxygen

◪ Nitrogen

○ Carbon

Fig. 12-12. Molecular models illustrating the fit of polyarginine in the minor groove on the surface of a DNA helix. The DNA configuration B is shown above, and in the lower model the basic arginine side chains are shown ionically bonded to phosphoric acid residues in the two polynucleotide chains. From Feughelman *et al.* (1955).

It appears that large quantities of protamine are synthesized by the spermatid, and that because protamine has a higher affinity for DNA than histone, it forces the latter out of the nucleohistone complex; the result is a progressive crystallization of nucleoprotamine in the developing sperm nucleus. As noted previously, the sperm of many species do not go through such a protamine-replacement cycle; the two types of spermatogenesis are very evident in the data of Vendrely *et al.* (1960), who compared the basic amino acid content of erythrocytes and sperm for three species of fish (trout, carp, and pike). Their data, given in Table 18-3, indicate that protamine replaces histones in trout sperm but not in carp sperm.

NUCLEOHISTONES

In contrast to the state of information about nucleoprotamine, present understanding of DNA-histone complexes is at a relatively primitive stage. One reason for this is that the basic histones exhibit much greater heterogeneity within the same nucleus than protamines, whereas experimental procedures for isolating homogeneous fractions have had only limited success. Another problem is that extraction of DNA-histone is always accompanied by extraction of DNA-bound acidic proteins, suggesting that multimolecular structural complexes may exist in the native nucleoprotein (Chapter 17). The histones resemble protamines in their very basic isoelectric points (pH 10–11) and in containing abundant arginine; however, these molecules are three or four times larger than salmon protamine (histone mol. wt. = 10,000–18,000), and arginine residues never constitute more than about 13% of the total (compared to 68% in protamine). In addition, histones contain variable amounts of the other charged side chains, including basic ones (lysine and histidine) and acidic ones (glutamic acid and aspartic acid). In mixed histones only about one residue in four represents a basic amino acid. Bradbury *et al.* (1962) and Bradbury and Crane-Robinson (1964) have also shown that, unlike protamines, histones contain significant amounts of α-helix, which they estimated by hydrogen-deuterium exchange to be about 58%.

Earlier investigators understood that the term histone is at best a general one and includes a variety of compounds; the most important diagnostic features established by Mirsky and his collaborators (1942, 1946) were: (1) coextraction with DNA from isolated nuclei in 1 M NaCl; (2) coprecipitation with DNA in 0.14 M NaCl; (3) extractability with HCl; (4) absence of tryptophan; (5) solubility in 0.34 M HgSO$_4$-1.88 M H$_2$SO$_4$ solution at 60°C; and (6) precipitation at the isoelectric point near pH 10.6. Later Daly and Mirsky (1954) discovered a unique class of "lysine-rich" histones which do not precipitate at their isoelectric point (and which consequently had been discarded with the supernatant in earlier studies). By 1960, Johns et al. were able to distinguish three major histone classes by means of column chromatography—the very lysine rich (F1, or histone I), the slightly lysine rich (F2, or histone II), and the arginine rich (F3, or histones III and IV). Subsequently Johns and Butler (1962) divided the slightly lysine-rich histones into two major subfractions on the basis of end-group analysis—subfraction 2a possessing an N-terminal acetylalanine, and subfraction 2b with an N-terminal proline. The primary distinguishing features among these four types of histone are summarized in Table 12-1.

Of these histone fractions, the very lysine-rich and arginine-rich have been shown by electrophoresis and chromatography to be relatively heterogeneous, each containing perhaps four or five different compounds; on the other hand, Busch (1965) has obtained the N-proline and N-acetylalanine proteins as fairly homogeneous preparations, and he points out that these two (possibly three) compounds constitute about 50–60% of the total thymus histones. Although these are the most abundant fractions, at least 16 components have been recognized in thymus nucleohistone by Neelin and Neelin (1960), using starch gel electrophoresis.

Table 12-1

DISTINGUISHING AMINO
ACID CONTENT AND OTHER
PROPERTIES OF THE MAJOR HISTONE CLASSES

		Slightly lysine rich		
	Very lysine rich	2a	2b	Arginine rich
% Moles				
Alanine	23.5	10.5	10.5	12.5
Arginine	2.5	11.5	7.5	13.0
Lysine	26.3	10.5	14.5	9.0
Proline	7.9	3.0	4.5	4.5
Most frequent				
N-terminal residue	Acetyl, various	Acetyl-alanine	Proline	Alanine
C-terminal residue	Lysine	—	Lysine	Alanine, Glycine
Min. mol. wt.	10,000	9000–12,500	22,000	10,000 +
Tendency to aggregate	None	—	—	Very great
Percent of total thymus histone	20%	35%	25%	20%

The degree of similarity among the various histone fractions in different tissues and species has been intensively studied, beginning with the early investigations of Daly *et al.* (1951). For vertebrate nuclei the similarities have generally been remarkable. Crampton *et al.* (1957) obtained nearly identical chromatograms from trypsin digests of histones representing calf thymus, calf liver, calf kidney, and guinea pig testis. About the same time Vendrely *et al.* (1958) reported very similar amino acid compositions for erythrocyte histones from carp, trout, pike, duck and frog. Electrophoretic techniques of high resolving power have tended to confirm the high similarity among vertebrate histones, while revealing some minor differences. Using these methods, Lindsay (1964) could detect 14 histones in adult chicken liver, but found only slight differences among other tissues or embryonic stages. Neelin (1964), however, detected a major histone fraction in chicken erythrocytes which does not occur in liver or spleen, and which is unusual in containing 20% lysine together with 10% arginine. Species differences among rat, mouse, guinea pig, and rabbit have also been found by Neidle and Waelsch (1964), but they could not find significant differences in brain, liver, or kidney histones of the same species.

The histones of plants have been studied to a lesser extent, but they seem to resemble vertebrate histones in major outline (Bonner *et al.*, 1968). However, some differences have been reported; for instance, Iwai (1964) compared chromatograms of histones from calf thymus with those from rice embryos, finding one thymus peak (slightly lysine rich) absent from rice and one rice peak (unusually arginine rich) absent from thymus. In the green unicell *Chlorella* examined by the same author, most of the histone was of the lysine-rich type. Butler (1964) and others have also found a preponderance of lysine-rich histones in wheat germ.

With respect to bacterial histones, there is still an unresolved controversy. Although it has been established that bacterial DNA-protein complexes do occur, it is not certain whether all or only part of the DNA is complexed, whether the protein is of a histone type, or how much variation there is among species. Zubay and Watson (1959) isolated DNA from *E. coli* as an extract containing 50% protein, but they concluded that the protein is not a histone. Butler (1964) also failed to find a basic protein in "nuclear fractions" from *Bacillus megaterium*. On the other hand, Cruft and Leaver (1961) have detected histone-like basic proteins in *Staphylococcus* and *Micrococcus*, and Mirsky and Pollister (1946) identified histone as 50% of the nucleoprotein isolated from *Pneumococcus*. Although it is a common belief that bacterial DNA does not occur as a nucleoprotein complex, this concept may need to be revised when more complete information is available.

Like the protamines, the histones are bound to DNA primarily by ionic bonds between positively charged basic side chains and negatively charged phosphate groups (Akinrimisi *et al.*, 1965). The ratio of total basic residues in histone (Lys + Arg + His) to total phosphates in DNA has been determined as approximately 0.9 by Davison and Butler (1956), Crampton *et al.* (1957), and others. This approximate equality in basic amino acids and phosphate groups is accompanied by an approximate equality in total mass of histone and DNA extracted from a wide variety of tissues. For example, Mirsky and Ris (1948) found 45% nucleic acid and 55% histone in reprecipitated thymus nucleohistone, and Bonner *et al.* (1968) have reported nearly a 1:1 ratio of DNA to histone in a wide range of plant and animal chromatins (Table 12-2). Experiments by Huang *et al.* (1964), using nucleohistone reconstituted from different histone fractions, have shown that the histone/DNA mass ratio is essentially constant (1.32–1.45) for all major histone classes. In intact somatic nuclei, Barnard (1960) was also able to confirm by cytochemical techniques that the number of bound arginine side chains is directly related to the amount of DNA. However it appears that in native nucleohistone, as in nucleoprotamine, some of the DNA phosphate groups are neutralized by sodium rather than by protein.

Even though the ratio of total basic groups to total phosphate is very similar in both nucleoprotamines and nucleohistones, perfect ionic pairing is much more difficult to visualize in DNA-histone, where the protein component has a preponderance of nonbasic residues and a high content of α-helix. The very lysine-rich fraction seems to have a greater resemblance to protamines than do the other groups; this fraction contains nearly one basic amino acid for every three residues, whereas the ratio in the other histones is closer to one in five; furthermore, the very lysine-rich group is notable for its relatively high proline content (Table 12-1), which resembles that of protamine and suggests an extended polypeptide configuration. Other distinctive properties of the very lysine-rich histones are that they do not form aggregates (whereas the arginine-rich fraction has a strong tendency to aggregate at neutral or alkaline pH), and they are less firmly bound to DNA both in native preparations (Daly and Mirsky, 1954) and in reconstituted DNA complexes (Akinrimisi *et al.*, 1965). X-ray diffraction studies of artificial complexes between DNA and lysine-rich histone have also revealed patterns similar to those of nucleoprotamine, but different from those of native nucleohistone (Wilkins, 1956). From these and other properties, Wilkins (1960) has concluded that the lysine-rich histones occur primarily in extended β configurations, and that the α-helix content observed in mixed histone preparations is primarily in non-lysine-rich fractions.

According to Zubay and others an α-helix, though not flexible enough to wind around the DNA double helix, would fit nicely into the larger of the two spiral grooves on the DNA molecule. Consequently various schemes have been proposed whereby flexible nonhelical segments might alternate regularly with helical ones, and at the same time the basic side chains might be regularly spaced out among the nonbasic ones (e.g., at every fourth residue). However, preliminary studies of amino acid sequences in histones do not support a regular periodicity of basic residues. Busch (1965) and his collaborators have initiated a full-scale analysis of the N-proline histone (F2b) from calf thymus nuclei, since it can be obtained in higher purity than any other histone (about 80–95%). His preliminary findings indicate that this polypeptide contains 176 amino acids, but yields 29 different kinds of peptide fragment after digestion with trypsin (which breaks the chain preferentially at arginine and lysine sites). One of these peptides contains 9 nonbasic amino acids in sequence; other peptides are highly variable in size, ruling out the possibility that arginine and lysine residues are distributed with a regular periodicity along the chain. Similar conclusions have been reached by Phillips (1964) for the arginine-rich fraction; it is of interest, however, that in the very lysine-rich fraction he finds at least 50% of all the lysine residues in lysine-lysine sequences.

A satisfactory nucleohistone model must account for the following general properties:

1. Over half of the histone probably has an α-helical configuration.

2. Basic residues are in the minority but are approximately equal to DNA phosphate groups.

3. Histone amino acid sequences do not show great regularity with respect to the distribution of basic residues.

4. Different types of histone vary in their tendency to aggregate and in the closeness of their binding to DNA.

5. Native nucleohistone gives an X-ray diffraction pattern which is very different from that of nucleoprotamine; in particular, the DNA filaments do not show a regular parallel, or crystalline, orientation.

6. The units of chromatin structure in somatic nuclei, as seen by electron microscopy, are 200–300 Å fibers consisting of single DNA molecules packed inside proteinaceous sheaths (Chapter 17).

PHYSICAL STATE OF DNA-PROTEIN IN LIVING NUCLEI

A much-debated issue has been whether the units of DNA structure in living plant and animal nuclei are single Watson-Crick molecules with proteins attached, or whether several DNA molecules are linked in parallel by protein. Zubay and Doty (1959) were the first to investigate this question in material that had not been previously dissociated into separate DNA and protein molecules by extraction in M NaCl. They prepared calf thymus DNA-protein in distilled water, and found that the never-dissociated units are fiberlike, containing about equal weights of DNA and protein, with a fragment molecular weight of 18.5×10^6; since the DNA alone, after dissociation, had a molecular weight of 8×10^6, their data demonstrated that the units of structure in thymus nuclei are single DNA molecules with associated proteins. This conclusion was questioned by Luzzati and Nicolaieff (1963), who determined by X-ray diffraction that DNA-protein gels contain DNA rods which are cross-linked by histones to form multimolecular units. However, Bonner (1965) has largely confirmed Zubay and Doty's work in his extensive studies with pea chromatin; according to Bonner, native chromatin forms soluble preparations and consists of separate Watson-Crick molecules, whereas reconstituted nucleoprotein forms gels and consists of DNA extensively cross-linked by histones.

That DNA-protein complexes in intact interphase nuclei are based on single Watson-Crick molecules has recently been demonstrated with the electron microscope by DuPraw (1965a); unsectioned nuclei from honey bee embryonic cells are seen to contain long, irregularly twisted fibers varying around 230 Å in diameter, some of which are firmly attached to the nuclear envelope at the edges of the annuli (Fig. 17-3). In nuclei which have been torn open, the broken fibers leave their ends still attached to the nuclear envelope, confirming that the 230 Å fibers represent the original *in vivo* state of the DNA-protein. The organization of individual fibers was examined by digesting the preparations with weak trypsin, or with trypsin followed by DNase. DuPraw found that after protease digestion each fiber contains a single, trypsin-resistant filament having the dimensions of a Watson-Crick double helix (see Figs. 12-9C and 17-5); additional digestion with DNase entirely removes these filaments, but leaves the nuclear envelopes intact. Consequently this evidence shows that each 230 Å fiber consists of a single DNA molecule packed into a proteinaceous sheath.

Since a DNA molecule is only 20 Å in diameter, whereas diameters of 200–300 Å have been reported by several investigators studying native chromatin fibers (Ris, 1956; DuPraw, 1965a; Rae, 1966; Gall, 1966c), it is of some importance to determine how the DNA helix is arranged in the larger fiber. Significant insights about this question have been obtained recently by DuPraw and G. F. Bahr (1968), who have extended the analysis of trypsin-dissected chromatin fibers by a quantitative technique of electron microscopy introduced by Bahr and Zeitler (1965). In this method the exact dry mass per unit length of fiber can be determined by its electron scattering ability, which is compared with the electron scattering of a standard object such as a small polystyrene sphere; electron scattering, in turn, is measured by the density of silver grains exposed in a photographic plate as determined by a scanning densitometer. This technique has shown that the mass of undigested 230 Å chromatin fibers from human cells is about 6×10^{-20} gm/Å (DuPraw and Bahr, 1968). Various authors have supposed that one, two, or four DNA molecules lie relatively extended in each 230 Å chromatin fiber (Gall, 1963; Ris and Chandler, 1963; Ris, 1966a,b), but these simpler models are now ruled out by the quantitative determination of fiber mass; for example, a single DNA helix has a mass of only 3.26×10^{-22} gm/Å, and consequently one fully extended DNA helix would account for only 0.54% of the dry mass in a 230 Å fiber. Even four helices would barely exceed 2%. By contrast, it is well established that DNA makes up about 30% of the dry mass in interphase chromatin (Table 12-2), and 15–20% in isolated metaphase chromosomes (Chapter 18); these percentages require a packing ratio of about 56:1 for the total extended length of DNA helix in a unit length of 230 Å fiber.

As noted above, chromatin fibers partially digested with weak trypsin solution spring out to give a beads-on-a-string structure (Fig. 17-5); in such preparations, the very narrowest filaments have the diameters of single DNA molecules, and they cannot be seen except after coating with platinum. However two other classes of fiber in the same preparations can be seen without platinum coating, and these are suitable for quantitative comparisons: (1) apparently undigested fibers 200–300 Å in diameter; and (2) partially unraveled fiber regions with diameters of 35 to 60 Å. Figure 12-13 illustrates a typical density tracing comparing the cross-sectional mass distribution of these two fiber classes in specimens lying side by side. The tracing reveals that the mass distribution in the narrower fiber regions (type A) is strikingly different from that in intact chromatin fibers (type B), giving a sharp symmetrical peak rather than the flattened asymmetrical peak typical of undigested fibers; this means that the substructure of the two fiber regions is distinctly different.

Table 12-2
PERCENT COMPOSITION
OF CHROMATIN FRACTION

Component	Liver[a]	Pea embryo[b]
DNA (%)	31	31
RNA (%)	5	17.5
Histone (%)	36	33
Nonhistone (acid) protein (%)	28	18

[a] Data from Steele and Busch (1963).
[b] Data from Huang and Bonner (1962).

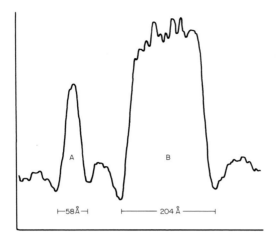

Fig. 12-13. The cross-sectional mass distribution in thick and thin chromatin fibers such as those illustrated in Fig. 17-5B, which have been digested for 5 minutes in 0.001% trypsin solution. Type A fibers have a more symmetrical substructure and a higher density than type B fibers. Other observations indicate that a type B fiber is built up by supercoiling of a single type A fibril, together with addition of protein. From DuPraw and Bahr (1968).

Although the sharp peak of the type A fibril might represent a single extended DNA molecule coated with protein, the type B regions must have a more complex structure. Moreover, because the two types of structure alternate along the same fiber, the tracing implies that the type B regions are built up from a single type A fibril, probably by a process of supercoiling. It can be calculated from the areas under the two peaks in Fig. 12-13 that the mass of a type B fiber is at least 6–7 times as great as the mass of its type A subfibril (comparing equivalent lengths), whereas the density is somewhat higher in the smaller type A fibrils.

X-ray diffraction data eliminate the possibility that larger chromatin fibers are built up by parallel hexagonal packing of extended DNA helices, since the patterns from native nucleohistones fail to reveal the highly crystalline, hexagonal packing found in nucleoprotamine; although the classic helical configuration of DNA is still detectable in nucleohistone, the orientations of DNA filaments are much less regular than in nucleoprotamine. These observations led Zubay (1964) and others to suggest that histones may induce or stabilize a supercoiling of the long DNA molecules; in fact, Zubay and Doty (1959) observed that their native thymus nucleoprotein contained molecular weights of DNA equivalent to helices 4 μ long, yet exhibited maximum dimensions less than one-tenth as great. Zubay and Wilkins (1964) have also pointed out that native nucleohistone exhibits characteristic diffraction rings at

27 Å, 35 Å, and 55 Å, which do not appear in DNA alone, histone alone, or in reconstituted nucleohistone after the histone has been denatured. The 35 Å spacing was interpreted by Wilkins *et al.* (1959) as an unknown periodicity along the *length* of the DNA-histone fiber, which may represent the spacing of supercoils in a type A subfibril as it winds into a 230 Å (type B) chromatin fiber; a similar very sharp 38 Å spacing appears in diffraction patterns from intact calf thymus nuclei.

The best working model for *in vivo* organization of chromatin is that each type B chromatin fiber (200–300 Å) consists of a single, supercoiled type A filament of DNA-protein (35–60 Å). In the type A filament the packing ratio of helix length to fiber length is between 1 and 10, and the composition is about 50:50 DNA to protein. Thus a molecule of very lysine-rich histone with a molecular weight of 10,000 would contain about 30 basic amino acid residues, and could establish ionic pairing with one and a half helix turns of DNA (i.e., 30 phosphate groups); the total length of this helix would be 51 Å (1.5 × 34 Å), and therefore its molecular weight would also be 10,000 (51 × 196). On the other hand, the composition of the supercoiled type B fibers is only 15–30% DNA, while the packing ratios of helix length to fiber length are 56:1 or higher. This means that the DNA-linked proteins probably include at least two major categories: (1) those which are wrapped around the DNA helix in the manner of polyarginine to generate the primary, type A filaments (Fig. 12-12); and (2) those which are not wrapped around the helix but still form part of the type B fibers, possibly by occupying space inside the DNA supercoil. These two protein classes may correspond approximately to the subdivision of histones noted in the previous section, i.e., very lysine-rich histones which occur primarily in β-configurations capable of occupying the small groove on the DNA helix, and arginine-rich histones containing significant percentages of α-helix (which would resist bending and in which the periodicity of amino acid side chains does not correspond well with the periodicity of DNA phosphates). For an arginine-rich histone it can be estimated that a molecule of 18,000 molecular weight would contain about 40 basic residues, enough to form phosphate pairings along 68 Å of DNA molecule with a molecular weight of 13,000 (two helix turns). If the arginine-rich molecule were in globular form it would be about the same size as myoglobin, with an average diameter of 38–40 Å, whereas in the form of a straight α-helix it would be a thin rod about 230 Å long, and in β-configuration it would be over 550 Å long. Consequently, in order to occupy 68 Å of DNA, this type of histone should be intermediate between the globular (38 Å) and helical (230 Å) forms, possibly including basic β-configurations at the polypeptide ends for cross-linking the DNA supercoils.

Direct evidence that the different histone classes form complexes of somewhat different structure with DNA has been obtained by Huang *et al.* (1964), who showed that reconstituted nucleohistones of various types differ in their melting temperatures (T_m). In DNA alone and in nucleoprotamine, the complementary DNA chains separate at 70°C, whereas in DNA complexed with very lysine-rich histones, they do not separate until 81°. The value for whole thymus nucleohistone is intermediate (76°) and for arginine-rich histones is only 71–72.5°C. These variations in T_m reflect markedly different effects by the separate histone types in cross-linking and stabilizing the two interwound DNA chains.

The possibility exists that in native chromatin nonhistone proteins, together with widely different types of histone molecule, are complexed with DNA filaments to form specific functional arrays of great complexity. If this is so, nucleohistones reconstituted from single histone fractions or from dissociated histone mixtures might have only superficial resemblance to the organization of native nucleohistones in functional nuclei. Support for this concept can be found in the work of Crampton (1957), who compared the partial dissociation of native and reconstituted nucleohistones under identical conditions; he found that the sequence in which different histone fractions dissociate is not the same for native and reconstituted fibers. Bonner (1965) has also pursued the same line of inquiry, showing that reprecipitated pea nucleohistone is electrophoretically homogeneous, as if the different histone classes bind to the DNA at random; by contrast, native chromatin shows many electrophoretically distinct nucleohistone species. Bonner has also shown that pea nucleohistones can be reconstituted in much more native form if the salt concentration is lowered very slowly; apparently this gives the various histone species enough time to seek out their most stable positions. A native multimolecular histone complex has recently been isolated by Huang and Bonner (1965), in which the histones are associated with a minor but unique RNA having an average chain length of only 38 nucleotides (mol. wt. about 12,700); since the composition of the whole complex is 8% RNA, 92% histone, it must link together 6–10 histone monomers of molecular weight 10–20,000.

Nonhistone Nucleoproteins

In 1946, Mirsky and Pollister called attention to the fact that reprecipitated nuclear extracts from calf thymus, calf liver, chicken erythrocytes, *Pneumococcus*, and a variety of other cells always contain a significant percentage of DNA-linked protein that is not histone. This nonhistone fraction was characterized by its higher tryptophan content (absent from histones) and in calf thymus accounted for 27% of the DNA-associated proteins. Other characteristics of the nonhistone fraction were insolubility in $HgSO_4$ and the fact that it was extractable from the reprecipitated fibers by alkaline solutions but not by HCl.

During ensuing years a confusing terminology evolved, which was not used consistently even by the same authors; the nonhistone, DNA-linked proteins were referred to variously as "tryptophan protein," "tryptophan-containing histone," "residual protein," "chromosomin," and "acid protein." In an unfortunate terminology introduced by Mirsky and Ris (1948), the nuclear fraction insoluble in 0.14 M NaCl was referred to as "isolated chromosomes," and the subfraction insoluble in 1 M NaCl was called "residual chromosomes" (consisting largely of "residual protein"). These authors recognized that nonhistone protein was present in the "nucleohistone" fraction as well as in the "residual" fraction; nevertheless, the concept developed that most nonhistone nuclear proteins are linked with RNA rather than DNA, and that they form a kind of backbone fiber for the metaphase chromosome. Pollister (1952) called this concept into question at an early date, and electron microscope analysis of chromosome structure has clearly established that there is no residual protein backbone in metaphase chromosomes (Chapter 18). Consequently, in the most fruitful modern concept, it is recognized that the typical interphase nucleus contains abundant nonhistone protein, some of which is linked to DNA (1 M NaCl soluble) and some of which is not (1 M NaCl insoluble; see Busch *et al.*, 1963).

As first reported by Mirsky and Ris (1951), the ratio of nonhistone protein to DNA varies widely in the nuclei of different tissues, contrasting with the fairly constant ratio of histone to DNA. In carp erythrocytes, for instance, nonhistone proteins have only one-tenth as great a mass as the DNA fraction, whereas in calf liver their mass is 1–1.5 times greater than that of DNA. Calf thymus nuclei, which have been the most thoroughly studied with respect to histones, are a generally poorer source for nonhistone proteins than liver cells; Mirsky and Pollister (1946) found that 27% of the DNA-linked protein in thymus is nonhistone, but the comparable figure for liver, as measured by Busch *et al.* (1963), is 43% (i.e., almost equal to histone). The DNA-linked acid proteins in liver nuclei are only about 70% of the total acid proteins; taking both the DNA-linked and nonlinked fractions into account, Busch *et al.* (1963) have estimated that 21% of the total dry weight of the liver nucleus is due to acid proteins, whereas about 20% is due to histones.

In general, the acid or nonhistone protein fraction is highly insoluble in aqueous solutions, and that part which is linked to DNA is not easily dissociated by concentrated NaCl. These properties have made physical and chemical analysis difficult, so that the nonhistone proteins are even more poorly known than the histones. Preliminary estimates of molecular weight range from 300,000 to one million. Some measurements of amino acid composition by Busch *et al.* (1963) show that arginine residues make up only 5–7% and lysine 6–8% of the total, whereas the content of glutamic acid is 12–15% and of aspartic acid is 9–10%. Since these proteins are highly acidic, they can form ionic complexes with basic histones as well as complexes of an unknown character with DNA. These facts have led DuPraw (1965a) to suggest that they may constitute another structural component of the proteinaceous sheath in which each DNA molecule is packed in intact interphase nuclei (Fig. 17-5).

At least one type of specific, nonhistone nucleoprotein complex has been demonstrated in the nuclei of animals, plants, and bacteria. This is the complex which forms between DNA and the enzymes of nucleic acid synthesis, DNA polymerase and RNA polymerase (Chapter 13). With respect to RNA polymerase, Huang and Bonner (1962) found that DNA extracted from pea embryos retains a firmly bound protein component, amounting to only 4% of the purified DNA preparation, yet showing concentrated RNA polymerase activity. In mammalian cells also, RNA polymerase preparations are particulate or of low solubility, and the enzyme is closely bound to DNA. Although DNA polymerase is a relatively more soluble enzyme (mol. wt. about 109,000), Billen (1962) has shown that in extracts of the bacterium E. coli it centrifuges down with the DNA-containing pellet and is released from the pellet by DNase digestion. According to Keir et al. (1962) DNA polymerase in rat liver nuclei is an acid-insoluble protein which precipitates at pH 4.8; a calf thymus polymerase purified by Bollum (1960) also precipitates at pH 5.4. Although the properties of the polymerases are still poorly known, they almost certainly account for part of the DNA-linked acid proteins. The mechanisms of binding between acid proteins and DNA, or between polymerases and DNA, are still essentially unknown.

A number of other, more poorly defined complexes between DNA and nonhistone proteins are known to occur either naturally or under experimental conditions. For instance cytochrome c, a mitochondrial respiratory enzyme, is a very basic heme protein which contains 20% lysine residues, has an isoelectric point at pH 10.5, and forms artificial DNA–cytochrome c complexes. A natural DNA-linked respiratory enzyme has also been found in yeast by Montague and Morton (1960). This enzyme is known as cytochrome b_2, but it is also a lactic dehydrogenase, and contains one heme group and one flavin group per molecule. In the purified compound there are 15 DNA nucleotides per heme group, with a proportion of 6 A:5 T:2 G:2 C; this suggests that the DNA, though small (mol. wt. about 10,000), is double-stranded. Since the DNA component is not necessary for enzymatic activity, its significance is not known; it is necessary, however, for crystallization of the protein. Artificial DNA-myosin fibers have also been studied by Hayashi et al. (1962), who found that low pH induces some contraction. Evidence for other, naturally occurring complexes between DNA and nonhistone proteins will be discussed in Chapter 17.

13

CELL-FREE SYNTHESIS OF NUCLEIC ACIDS

Nature makes so gradual a transition from the inanimate to the animate kingdom that the boundary lines which separate them are indistinct and doubtful.

ARISTOTLE—Parts of Animals, Book IV

The publication of Watson and Crick's (1953) complementary strand model of the DNA molecule provided a concept with which to visualize biological replication at a molecular level; however, this model did not clarify many aspects of replication (e.g., the enzymatics of the process), and it left the relationship of RNA to DNA somewhat uncertain. Previous cytochemical research by Caspersson (1950) and Brachet (1950) had established the importance of RNA in growing tissues as a concomitant of protein synthesis. In terms of the Watson-Crick model, it seemed likely that DNA must somehow serve as a template for RNA synthesis, and that newly formed RNA must then support protein synthesis by some still unknown mechanism. These broad features of macromolecular synthesis have now been confirmed, and their detailed biochemical mechanisms elucidated, largely through the successful development of systems for cell-free nucleic acid and protein synthesis.

The first *in vitro* polynucleotide synthesis was achieved with RNA by Grunberg-Manago *et al.* (1955) in Ochoa's laboratory. These investigators isolated an enzyme, polynucleotide phosphorylase, from the bacterium *Azotobacter* and showed that this enzyme could catalyze synthesis of high molecular weight RNA polymers (mol. wt. 70,000 or about 30 residues) from 5' ribonucleoside diphosphates. However in this first system the sequence of bases incorporated was not governed by a DNA template; in fact, this particular enzyme seems to incorporate nucleoside diphosphate precursors in random order. If all four nucleotides are present, an AUCG chain is synthesized in which the base composition depends on the percentage of each nucleotide in the reaction mixture. On the other hand, if only one nucleotide is present a homopolymer chain is synthesized, e.g., poly A, poly U, poly C, or poly I. This polymerization reaction requires Mg^{++}, it releases 1 mole of orthophosphate per nucleotide incorporated, and the reaction is readily reversible, indicating a low ΔF° and a free equilibrium between the polymer and single nucleotides. Although polynucleotide phosphorylase seems not to be directly involved in cellular mechanisms of information transfer, the synthetic polymers made with this system have been of great importance in the experimental analysis of nucleic acid structure and function (Chapters 12 and 14).

DNA Replication

In 1956, Kornberg *et al.* reported a low incorporation (50 counts out of a million) of ^{14}C-labeled thymidine into DNA, mediated by a combination of two crude enzyme fractions from the bacterium *E. coli*. Although the mechanism of incorporation was not known, Kornberg reasoned that polynucleotide synthesis might proceed by the general reaction:

$$\text{nucleoside-P—P—P} + \text{X} \rightleftharpoons \text{nucleoside-P—X} + \text{PP}$$

This type of reaction was known to occur during the synthesis of dinucleotide coenzymes, such as NAD and FAD, from ATP and other precursors (Chapter 3). In accord with this hypothesis, Kornberg (1957) soon demonstrated that the synthesis of DNA *in vitro* requires all four deoxynucleoside triphosphates (dATP, dTTP, dGTP, dCTP), Mg^{++}, and in addition, a small amount of "primer" DNA. If all these are provided, only a single enzyme fraction is necessary and the reaction can proceed until the product exceeds the primer by some 20 times.

Lehman *et al.* (1958) were able to purify the enzyme some 2000-fold and named it "polymerase"; it is now designated by the more specific term DNA polymerase (or alternatively, DNA nucleotidyl transferase). The molecular weight of the bacterial DNA polymerase has been determined from ultracentrifugal and electrophoretic analysis as 109,000 (Goulian *et al.*, 1968). Since a kilogram of *E. coli* yields less than 10 mg of purified DNA polymerase, the amount of enzyme per cell is relatively small. Catalytic activity by DNA polymerase is enhanced if the primer DNA contains 3′ hydroxyl groups, but inhibited by 3′ phosphoryl groups; consequently it appears that the enzyme catalyzes the reaction:

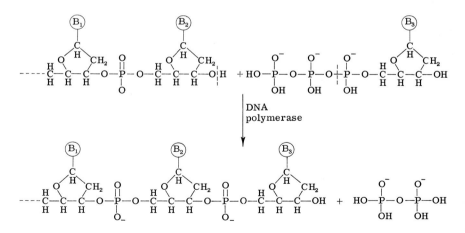

The fact that DNA polymerase requires DNA in order to make more DNA naturally suggested that the enzyme is catalyzing replication of the primer molecule in the manner postulated by Watson and Crick (1953). However, it has been necessary to establish this by very careful experiments, since less specific types of autocatalysis are well known; for instance, Commoner (1962) has pointed out that ATP is required to make more ATP during anaerobic glycolysis (Chapter 6). That the base composition of DNA produced in the DNA polymerase reaction corresponds closely to the base composition of the primer has been shown by Lehman *et al.* (1958), using primer DNA's of widely different base composition, e.g., from *Mycobacterium* (AT:GC = 0.49), calf thymus (AT:GC = 1.25), or bacteriophage T2 (AT:GC = 1.92). The product DNA is also both double-stranded and of high molecular weight (6×10^6). Further evidence for replication has been obtained with a technique introduced by Josse *et al.* (1961) for measuring "nearest neighbor" nucleotide frequencies. In this method, DNA is synthesized from a reaction mixture in which *one* of the four nucleotides is labeled with ^{32}P at the 5' phosphate group; the resulting polynucleotide chain is then enzymatically degraded by rupture of the 5' bonds, yielding 3' nucleotide residues. In effect, the ^{32}P is passed from the labeled nucleotide to its nearest neighbor nucleotide, so that subsequent quantitative measurement of the ^{32}P distribution among four possible nucleotide fractions indicates the relative frequency of dinucleotide sequences in the product DNA. This procedure may be repeated four times, each time with a different labeled nucleotide; the relative frequencies for all 16 possible types of dinucleotide are then known. From such experiments, it has been found that product DNA's do closely match primer DNA's in the relative frequencies of dinucleotide sequences, as well as in overall base ratios. Most recently Goulian *et al.* (1967) have demonstrated that DNA synthesized *in vitro* from a circular phage ϕX174 template is biologically active, as judged by its infectivity for *E. coli* cells; this demonstrates that the product DNA matches the primer in exact base sequence as well. Despite these impressive similarities between product and primer DNA's, it appears that DNA polymerase *in vitro* does catalyze the synthesis of some abnormal DNA's, which become most noticeable after the first round of replication (to be discussed).

Although originally the DNA polymerase reaction seemed to have an absolute requirement for primer DNA, Schachman *et al.* (1960) later discovered that a special type of polynucleotide synthesis can occur in the absence of primer and after a lag period of several hours. In the unprimed reaction, a large double-stranded product DNA is formed which contains only adenine and thymine, the two types of nucleotide alternating precisely along each chain:

$$
\begin{array}{c}
\text{T—A—T—A—T—A} \\
\vdots \quad \vdots \quad \vdots \quad \vdots \quad \vdots \quad \vdots \\
\text{A—T—A—T—A—T}
\end{array} = \text{dAT}
$$

There is strong evidence that the reaction is possible because during the lag period a small number of short copolymer molecules form spontaneously, after which they are able to act as primers for further synthesis according to the usual polymerase kinetics (but at about $20\times$ the rate for native primer). More recently Kornberg *et al.* (1964) have used small A—T oligonucleotides to investigate the relationship between the size of the primer DNA molecule and its priming ability. They found that the oligonucleotides $(AT)_5$ through $(AT)_7$ all have the ability to prime rapid synthesis of high molecular weight dAT copolymers; on the other hand, $(AT)_4$ lacks immediate priming activity but shortens the lag period before spontaneous dAT synthesis, and $(AT)_2$ and $(AT)_3$ have no measurable effect. Since relatively short oligonucleotides can prime synthesis of much longer polynucleotides, Kornberg and his collaborators have concluded that "slippage" between the primer strand, the product strand, and the polymerase molecule must occur.

An important insight regarding the mechanism of DNA polymerase activity was achieved by Wake and Baldwin (1962), who used the dAT copolymer as primer DNA but replaced deoxythymidine-TP in the precursor mixture with deoxy-5-bromouracil-TP. After prolonged synthesis this results in an artificial, high molecular weight product DNA in which adenine alternates with 5-bromouracil in the base sequence of each strand (—A—$\overline{BU}$—A—$\overline{BU}$— = $dA\overline{BU}$). The question of greatest interest concerns the fate of the —A—T—A—T— primer, for which there are three major possibilities: (1) the primer might be conserved as a double-stranded dAT, in which case replication could be imagined as occurring without unwinding of the primer double helix; (2) the primer might be "semiconserved" in the form of intact single dAT strands, each hydrogen-bonded to a complementary $dA\overline{BU}$ strand; in this case, replication would involve unwinding of the primer in the manner originally postulated by Watson and Crick (1953), with formation of a parent-daughter hybrid molecule; or (3) the primer nucleotides might be dispersed among the nucleotides of product DNA, indicating that DNA polymerase induces a type of synthesis in which the covalent bonds of the primer DNA are disrupted. Wake and Baldwin could distinguish these possibilities because pure dAT and $dA\overline{BU}$ polynucleotides have somewhat different densities and melting points; not only can the parent molecules be distinguished by ultracentrifugation or T_m

Fig. 13-1. Interpretation of a replicating DNA helix. The two complementary strands separate (A), and each one acts as template for the synthesis of a new complementary strand (B). Precursor molecules are 5'-nucleotide triphosphates. The cloudlike form at the replication fork represents a molecule of DNA polymerase, the enzyme which catalyzes the replication. In (C) replication has been completed.

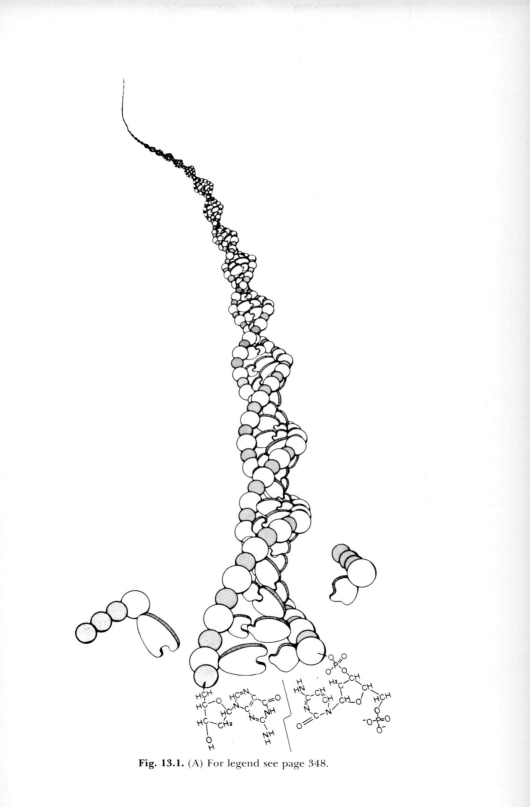

Fig. 13.1. (A) For legend see page 348.

Fig. 13.1. (B) For legend see page 348.

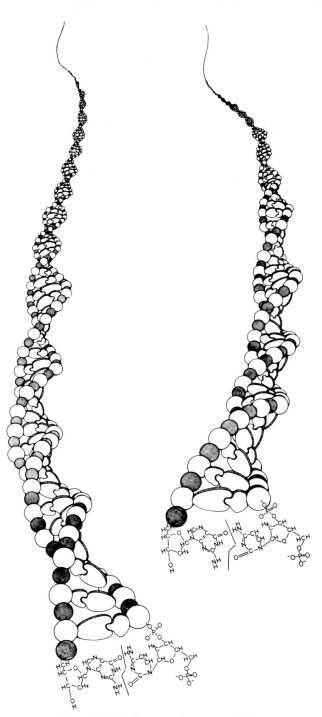

Fig. 13.1. (C) For legend see page 348.

measurements, but the properties of hybrid double-helices containing one strand of each are intermediate between those of the pure forms. Taking advantage of these properties, Wake and Baldwin followed the course of the reaction by which dA$\overline{BU}$ is synthesized from a dAT primer; they found that early in the reaction, hybrid molecules appear which contain AT: A$\overline{BU}$ base pairs, and these hybrids continue to be present throughout the synthesis. Later in the reaction, product DNA molecules appear which are pure dA$\overline{BU}$, i.e., free of any primer nucleotides. These results rule out a dispersive mechanism of cell-free DNA synthesis, and they strongly support the semiconservative, template mechanism first proposed by Watson and Crick (Fig. 13-1). Evidence for semiconservative DNA replication *in vivo* will be discussed in Chapters 15 and 17.

Still another line of evidence confirms that the individual polynucleotide strands act as templates during the DNA polymerase reaction. This is the fact that single-stranded DNA, obtained either by melting native DNA or from the single-stranded DNA virus ϕX174, is able to prime DNA synthesis with an efficiency equaling or exceeding that of native (double-stranded) DNA. When single-stranded DNA is used as primer, the early stages of the reaction lead to a restoration of the double-stranded condition, and the base ratio of the product DNA is the complement of the primer base ratio (i.e., product A does not equal product T, but does equal primer T); however, in the later stages of synthesis more double-stranded molecules are formed, at which time the ratios of A:T and G:C in the product approach 1. At this stage, the ratio of AT/GC is that expected if *both* complementary strands of the double helix are acting as templates. Richardson *et al.* (1964) have studied the fate of *partially* single-stranded DNA in the presence of DNA polymerase and precursor nucleotides; in their experiments the primer was a double-stranded DNA molecule partly degraded by enzymatic digestion of terminal nucleotides from one strand at either end. Using the electron microscope, they were able to compare the appearance of these partially single-stranded molecules before and after synthesis, and concluded that DNA polymerase begins by repairing the single-stranded regions, reconstituting the native DNA; after this repair phase, the unbranched primer molecules give rise to a product DNA which contains a high percentage of aggregated or "branched" molecules.

In addition to DNA polymerase from *E. coli*, enzymes of the same type have now been demonstrated in *Bacillus subtilis* (Okazaki and Kornberg, 1964), phage T2-infected bacteria (Aposhian and Kornberg, 1962), rat liver (Bollum and Potter, 1957), calf thymus gland (Bollum, 1960), and sea urchin embryos (Mazia and Hinegardner, 1963). As a rule these DNA polymerases are found in the soluble fraction of the cell homogenates; however if special precautions are taken during fractionation, they are found concentrated in the DNA-containing parts of the cell, such as the nuclei of regenerating rat liver or the sedimentable DNA fraction of *Bacillus megaterium* (Chambon, DuPraw, and Kornberg, 1968). In all cases, DNA synthesis requires Mg^{++}, four deoxynucleoside triphosphates and a primer DNA. However, the polymerases from phage T2 and from calf thymus gland are unusual because they *require* single-stranded primer DNA's, being almost completely inactive with double-stranded primers. Bollum and Houts (1963) have investigated the mechanism of synthesis with calf thymus DNA polymerase, using a tritium-labeled single-stranded primer and ^{32}P-labeled precursor nucleotides; they found that early in synthesis a "hybrid" DNA molecule is formed which contains one ^{3}H-labeled strand and one ^{32}P-labeled strand; during heat denaturation the two strands separate, but each remains intact. From these experiments it appears that calf thymus polymerase catalyzes a semiconservative replication similar to that catalyzed by *E. coli* polymerase.

The polymerase systems for cell-free DNA synthesis have served to confirm the theory of Watson and Crick that polydeoxynucleotide strands are able to act as templates for the synthesis of complementary strands, and have shown that the main precursors in this synthesis are 5'-nucleoside triphosphates. However, it is not yet clear how these *in vitro* systems are related to the normal processes of synthesis *in vivo*. As noted above, some of the polymerases are almost inactive with native, double-stranded primers; furthermore, although the enzyme from *E. coli* seems to produce "good" native DNA from single-stranded or partially single-stranded polynucleotide chains, it produces abnormal DNA molecules during extended synthesis. For example, Inman *et al.* (1965) have shown by electron microscopy that about 66% of the product DNA molecules are branched, with as many as 12 free ends, and the total lengths of these branched molecules also tend to be less than the length of the unbranched primer. Furthermore, denaturation (or melting) of product DNA is a more readily reversible process than denaturation of primer DNA. It seems likely that these difficulties stem from the specificity of purified DNA polymerases for the 3'-ends of primer polynucleotide chains.

It must be emphasized that the replication of a double-stranded DNA molecule involves a much more complex series of events than the synthesis of a simple complementary strand on a single-stranded template. As confirmed by Kornberg's (1961) analysis of nearest-neighbor frequencies, the polarity of the two complementary chains in native DNA is opposite, so that one strand ends in a 3' hydroxyl group at a point where the other ends in a 5' phosphoryl. If both these chains are to be replicated in the same direction simultaneously, then two separate reactions are required. That replication *in vivo* does proceed in both chains simultaneously and in the same direction has been reported by Cairns (1963a) in an autoradiographic analysis with *E. coli;* his data also indicate that there is a mechanism for unwinding the two parent strands while simultaneously rewinding parent and daughter strands in a semiconservative pattern [as first proposed on theoretical grounds by Levinthal and Crane (1956)]. In *E. coli* the unwinding-rewinding mechanism proceeds sequentially at a rate of 20–30 μ per minute along a double-stranded DNA molecule some 1100 μ long. As yet, the equivalent of this *in vivo* process has not been achieved with an *in vitro* system. Since known polymerases incorporate 5'-phosphorylated precursors, and are inhibited by substitutions at the 3'-hydroxyl ends of polynucleotide chains, they behave as if they are specific for only one of the two oppositely-polarized DNA chains. Consequently, as pointed out by Mitra and Kornberg (1966), the unwinding of a double-helical template during *in vitro* replication of the 3'-strand must leave the unreplicated 5'-strand dangling in a branched configuration. Under artificial conditions permitting template slippage and other anomalies, such 5'-branches may eventually participate in synthesis to generate the anomalous branched product DNA reported by Inman. The problem is somewhat complicated by the fact that some of the micrographs which have been published to illustrate "branched" molecules probably represent lateral aggregates of multiple DNA helices.

Because the full mechanism of DNA replication is not known either *in vivo* or *in vitro*, a number of highly speculative proposals have been made. Some authors have questioned whether hydrogen-bonding between bases is a sufficiently precise steric mechanism to specify nucleotide incorporation during synthesis. They emphasize that DNA may not be a "self-replicating" molecule in the strict sense, if information from the DNA polymerase molecule is required for its construction. As noted by Commoner (1962), the enzyme alone catalyzes synthesis of the dAT copolymer in the absence of any primer DNA at all, and more recently it has been found that a poly dG-poly dC molecule is also synthesized without primer if adenine and thymine nucleotides are not present; in the latter molecule, the two types of base do not alternate within the same chain, but pure poly dG chains are hydrogen bonded to pure poly dC chains. Alterations of DNA polymerase specificity have also been demonstrated experimentally by Berg *et al.* (1963), who found that if Mn^{++} is substituted for Mg^{++} the *E. coli* polymerase will accept some ribose nucleotides (e.g., rATP instead of dATP) and incorporates them side-by-side into a mixed, deoxyribose-ribose polynucleotide chain. Interestingly enough, the enzyme will not accept ribose uracil as a substitute for deoxyribose thymidine, although presumably either could base-pair with adenine. Evidently the specificity of this enzyme for a DNA primer is also subject to modification, since Lee Huang and Cavalieri (1963) obtained synthesis using an artificial, double-stranded RNA primer (the complex between poly A and poly U); in this case, the product was a poly-deoxyA—poly-deoxyT dyad. On the other hand, Okazaki and Kornberg (1964) have emphasized that base pairing with the primer DNA has a major influence on the *rates* of DNA synthesis, as compared for different templates and polymerases. For instance, the reaction rate with a dAT primer is twenty times higher than with a native primer, and the relative slowing of reaction rate after substitution of different base analogs in the reaction mixture is similar for polymerases from *E. coli, B. subtilis,* and phage T2.

It seems likely that steric specificity in DNA replication is a function of the spatial relationship between an intact template DNA chain, a growing 3' primer end, and the active site of the enzyme DNA polymerase. That bacterial DNA polymerase has a single active site which can bind any of the four deoxynucleoside 5'-triphosphates has recently been shown by Paul Englund in Kornberg's laboratory. Inasmuch as known polymerases seem to be specific for the 3'-ends of DNA chains, synthesis of the anti-parallel 5'-strand might proceed simultaneously in one of the following ways: (1) it could be synthesized discontinuously in short segments about 1000 to 2000 nucleotides long (ca. 0.5 μ); within each segment the direction of synthesis would be the usual one (5' to 3'), but the segments themselves would come up for synthesis in a 3' to 5' sequence; (2) the usual interaction of a 3'-OH (on a polynucleotide chain) with a 5'-triphosphate (on a precursor nucleotide) might reverse polarity to become a reaction between the 3'-OH of the precursor and a 5'-triphosphate on the growing end of the polynucleotide (Bishop *et al.*, 1967); (3) the 5'-strand might be synthesized by a still undiscovered 5'-polymerase. The first of these three mechanisms, originally suggested by Okazaki, has been supported by his discovery that newly synthesized DNA seems to appear as short, single-stranded fragments that sediment in the range 7 to 11 S (Sugimoto *et al.*, 1968).

Since major uncertainties about the mechanism of replication still exist, the exact structure of the enzyme-DNA complex during replication must also remain uncertain. Kornberg's group has shown that a given DNA polymerase molecule binds to a double helix only at one of the helix ends or at a single-strand break ("nick"). An interesting suggestion has been made by Jehle (1965) that the replication site of one daughter strand might lie immediately *behind* the replication site of the other (Fig. 13-2A). Finally, there is evidence that bacterial DNA polymerase may be membrane-bound during synthesis *in vivo*. The higher degrees of free-

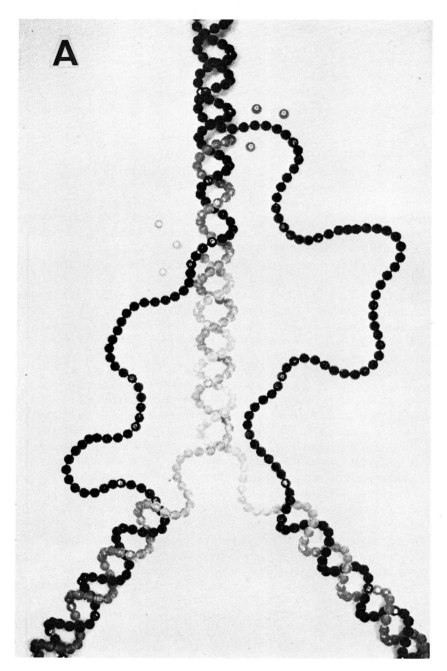

Fig. 13-2. (A) A model for DNA replication in which one chain of the helix is replicated slightly ahead of the other. The dark beads represent parental strands, while the light beads designate newly synthesized daughter strands. From Jehle (1965).

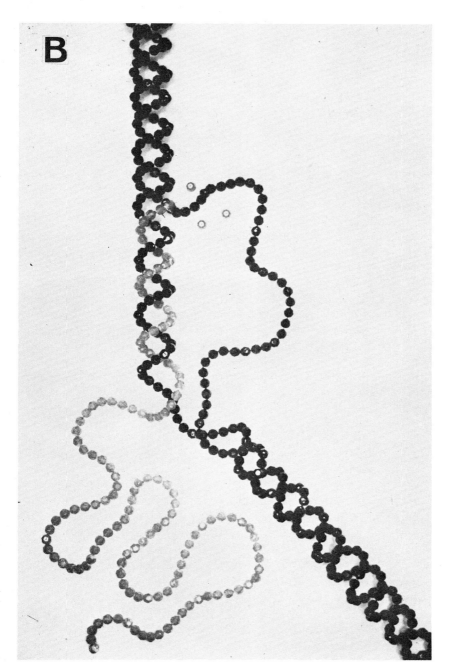

Fig. 13-2. (B) A model illustrating transcription of an RNA chain from a DNA helix. The original helix (dark beads) unwinds only locally, then rewinds in a fully conserved form. From Jehle (1965).

dom which prevail in a cell-free system, as compared with the tightly structured conditions inside a living cell, may account for some of the difficulties encountered with *in vitro* DNA replication.

DNA-Directed RNA Synthesis (Transcription)

During the 1950's a great deal of speculation was directed toward possible mechanisms by which a specific DNA base sequence might direct the synthesis of a specific base sequence in RNA. The discovery by Rich and Davies (1956) that nucleic acid homopolymers are able to form triple helices swung the direction of thought toward a model in which the DNA double helix might serve as a template without unwinding, the RNA being synthesized as a third strand occupying the major groove on the DNA surface. Later the formation of artificial "hybrid" DNA-RNA double helices by Rich (1960) supported an alternative possibility, i.e. that the DNA template might unwind (as in DNA replication) to permit base pairing of ribose nucleotide precursors with each of the two deoxyribose polynucleotide strands. The effort to distinguish between these alternative "3-stranded" and "2-stranded" models governed much of the experimental work in this field.

Despite the early widespread conviction that DNA must direct RNA synthesis, little chemical evidence was found during the 1950's to support such a hypothesis. The base composition of crude RNA extracts generally shows little complementarity to DNA preparations from the same cells. Furthermore, the first cell-free systems capable of carrying on RNA synthesis turned out not to require a DNA template; these included the early polynucleotide phosphorylase system of Grunberg-Manago and Ochoa (1955), as well as several later systems which incorporated only cytosine and adenine nucleotides in terminal positions (Chapter 14). The earliest detection of a minor RNA component with properties related to a specific DNA is generally credited to Volkin and Astrachan (1957), who studied RNA synthesized immediately after infection of *E. coli* with phage T2 DNA; however, their *in vivo* experiments were of a very preliminary sort.

As it happened, the long-sought-for DNA-dependent RNA synthesis was finally discovered by three laboratories in 1960, one working with animal, one with plant, and one with bacterial cells. In each instance, the requirements for the reaction included all four ribose nucleoside triphosphates (rATP, rUTP, rGTP, and rCTP), Mn^{++} (or Mg^{++}), and a primer DNA. Because these requirements are very similar to those of Kornberg's DNA polymerase, these DNA-dependent RNA synthetases are usually designated "RNA polymerases." Weiss (1960) was the first to report an RNA polymerase, which he found as an "aggregate enzyme" in the nuclei of rat liver, calf thymus, and ascites tumor cells. This mammalian enzyme is closely associated with the nuclear fraction soluble in 1 M NaCl, i.e., with the nucleohistone or chromatin extract; because it resists purification by conventional biochemical techniques, it has not been widely studied. A very comparable RNA polymerase was also isolated from plant tissue by Huang *et al.* (1960), who have continued to analyze the system in greater detail. When first isolated from pea seedlings, this enzyme contained 80 mg of protein with 8 mg of DNA and 1.6 mg of RNA; in fact, since the active fraction included over 90% of the total seedling DNA, the plant RNA polymerase virtually corresponded to a "chromatin fraction." Subsequently, Huang and Bonner (1962) found that the RNA polymerase could be separated from most of the DNA by centrifugation in a cesium chloride gradient, after which the bulk of the enzyme is soluble; nevertheless, the DNA fraction still contains about 4% tightly bound protein exhibiting a 1000-fold enriched RNA polymerase activity, and the soluble enzyme still contains some DNA. In the intact RNA polymerase system, newly synthesized RNA continues to be held in a DNA-protein complex which, according to Bonner *et al.* (1961), has a ratio of 1 RNA:2 DNA. Since the RNA is released from this complex by temperatures as low as 60°, it apparently is not hydrogen-bonded to the DNA but is held in the complex by some protein component. It appears therefore that in both higher plants and animals, the enzymes of specific RNA synthesis are components of a DNA-nucleoprotein complex. This fact supports the concept that RNA polymerase forms part of the proteinaceous sheath in which each DNA molecule is packed in interphase nuclei (DuPraw, 1965a) (Fig. 17-5).

By contrast, bacterial RNA polymerase (mol. wt. 320,000) is a readily soluble enzyme, which is amenable to a fairly high degree of purification; for this reason, beginning with the first description of the enzyme from *E. coli* by Hurwitz *et al.* (1960), it has been the favored material for analysis of DNA-dependent RNA synthesis. Using DNA primers from different sources, Furth *et al.* (1961) showed that the base ratio of RNA synthesized by *E. coli* RNA polymerase is complementary to the base ratio of the primer DNA (as in the DNA polymerase reaction); furthermore, Hurwitz *et al.* (1962) demonstrated that the nearest-neighbor nucleotide frequencies are similar for both primer and product. Comparison of the priming efficiencies of single- and double-stranded template DNA's has shown that *E. coli* RNA polymerase reacts best with native double-stranded DNA (in contrast to DNA polymerase from the same cells). Hurwitz *et al.* (1963) have also shown that DNA from *Diplococcus* or *B. subtilis* does not lose its genetic (transforming) activity even after serving as primer for prolonged RNA synthesis. These facts indicate that the *E. coli* RNA polymerase reaction differs from the DNA polymerase reaction, in that the two polynucleotide chains of a double-stranded primer DNA are not separated semiconservatively among the newly synthesized RNA molecules. In other words, the synthesis of RNA from a Watson-Crick DNA template is a fully conservative process in which the template survives as a double-stranded molecule.

The fact that the product of the RNA polymerase reaction (RNA) differs in density and other properties from the primer (DNA) made possible a very precise demonstration of base *sequence* complementarity between the template and its product. The fundamental method is a modification of a technique introduced by Marmur, Doty, and their colleagues, in which double-stranded DNA is melted and then slowly cooled in the presence of complementary RNA; this "annealing" process leads to formation of artificial DNA-RNA hybrid helices, but only if the RNA base sequences are exactly complementary to those of the DNA. Hall and Spiegelman (1961) adapted this technique to show that RNA synthesized *in vivo* after infection of *E. coli* with phage T2 is complementary to the purified phage DNA. In their experiments the new RNA was marked with ^{32}P and the DNA with ^{3}H, so that after co-melting and ultracentrifugation of the purified nucleic acids, the presence of ^{32}P in the ^{3}H DNA peak revealed specific hybrid formation. Other RNA fractions did not form such hybrids, showing that the effect requires a high degree of complementarity between the particular RNA and DNA. The same technique has since been used by Geiduschek *et al.* (1961) to demonstrate that RNA formed *in vitro* by *Micrococcus* RNA polymerase has high complementarity for the primer DNA; thus, when product and primer are melted together, hybrid molecules of intermediate DNA-RNA density are formed.

As pointed out by Geiduschek, there are at least two different ways in which a double-stranded DNA template could be conserved during RNA synthesis. In one mechanism the RNA strand would be synthesized in the major groove on the surface of the DNA molecule, essentially forming a triple helix, and no unwinding of the two DNA strands would be necessary. Both Zubay (1962) and Stent (1958) outlined triple helical models which could dictate nucleotide sequences in an RNA strand by one of several possible hydrogen-bonding schemes. In the other possible mechanism, the DNA double helix would unwind, but unwinding would be local, the two DNA chains winding up again immediately and sequentially as each part of the DNA fulfills its template function. Determination of RNA base sequences would be essentially by Watson-Crick pairing with (temporarily) single deoxypolynucleotide strands (Fig. 13-2B).

Earlier evidence that double-stranded primers are conserved during transcription was directly confirmed by Chamberlin *et al.* (1963), who used the dAT copolymer (from an unprimed DNA polymerase reaction) to prime synthesis of an rAU copolymer RNA. The dAT and rAU molecules are both double-stranded helices, but they can be distinguished by different melting temperatures and densities in the ultracentrifuge. Although a hybrid helix containing one strand of each type would also be distinguishable, such hydrids could not be detected during the reaction. By contrast, Chamberlin and Berg (1964) did find DNA-RNA hybrids during the RNA polymerase reaction when single-stranded (ϕX174) DNA was used as primer. In the latter experiments, when all the available single-strand primer had been complexed in DNA-RNA hybrid helices, additional synthesis proceeded by displacement of the older RNA strands; these separated from the hybrid molecules as new RNA strands were synthesized. Such a process is more or less analogous to the semiconservative synthesis of DNA strands by DNA polymerase, and suggests that even with double-stranded primers the actual template during transcription is probably a short segment of "unwound" single strand. This would correspond to the second mechanism described above.

The earliest experiments with RNA polymerase *in vitro* indicated that both strands of the template DNA were copied. For example, the base composition of product RNA was the same as the base composition of double-stranded DNA used as primer (A = U, G = C), which could not be so unless both DNA chains influenced the product RNA. However, later evidence established that RNA polymerase *in vivo* transcribes only one strand of the Watson-Crick double helix (Fig. 13-2). Thus Hayashi *et al.* (1963) discovered that living cells infected with phage ϕX174 contain RNA which is complementary to only one of the two replicative strands (as determined by DNA-RNA hybrid formation after heating). Similar findings with *in vivo* systems from several other laboratories (Chapter 15) made it seem likely that the transcription of two DNA strands *in vitro* must be due to artifacts inherent in the cell free technique. If the DNA double helix is visualized as a freely suspended rod, its two ends are sterically identical and the two polynucleotide chains cannot be distinguished in any way except by base sequence; on the other hand, if one end of the molecule is attached or otherwise marked, then the two chains are distinguishable by their opposite polarities. It appears that under the usual *in vitro* conditions RNA polymerase cannot distinguish one end of the template DNA from the other, and consequently transcribes from either end.

Nevertheless, after the discovery that fully native ϕX174 DNA is a closed circle, Hayashi *et al.* (1964) found that during synthesis from primer molecules which are intact double-stranded circles, only the one "mature" strand of the DNA is transcribed *in vitro;* by contrast, if the circles are broken (which occurs easily during the usual preparative methods), then both strands of the rod-shaped DNA are transcribed. From these and other experiments, it seems clear that RNA polymerase transcribes base sequences from DNA to RNA using either single- or double-stranded DNA templates, but with a double-stranded primer, the reaction is notably different from that of the DNA polymerase system in that: (1) the primer DNA is conserved, and (2) only one of the two complementary polynucleotide chains acts as template. Under experimental conditions, on the other hand, RNA polymerase can function with an entirely single-stranded template, and the pattern of synthesis is essentially semiconservative like that of DNA polymerase. Hayashi (1965) has recently detected complexes between double-stranded primer DNA and RNA during transcription; he found that although the total amount of RNA in the complexes increases as synthesis proceeds, only a small 3–3.5 S fraction is resistant to RNase digestion. This indicates that only a short segment at the head of each RNA chain is in the form of a DNA-RNA hybrid (Fig. 13-2B).

In the absence of a primer DNA, RNA polymerase from *Micrococcus* catalyzes synthesis of an adenine-uracil double-stranded polymer somewhat comparable to the adenine-thymine polymer formed by primerless DNA polymerase; the product differs in the RNA polymerase reaction because each molecule contains one poly A and one poly U chain (rather than alternating A-U-A-U sequences). Another interesting type of synthesis is catalyzed when a primer is present but only rATP is available as a precursor nucleotide. In this case the enzyme synthesizes poly A chains in the manner of polynucleotide phosphorylase, but it differs from the latter in requiring a single-stranded DNA primer (which can be of almost any origin), and by failing to show a comparable reaction with any of the other three nucleoside triphosphates (i.e., it cannot make poly U or poly C under the same conditions).

Another important modification in RNA polymerase activity was discovered by Nakamoto and Weiss (1962), who found that the enzymes from *Micrococcus* and *E. coli* are able to catalyze complementary RNA synthesis using an *RNA* primer. Although the priming efficiency is less than with a native DNA primer, definite RNA-directed reactions occur with single-stranded poly C, poly A, or virus RNA as templates. In bacteria, this RNA-dependent activity cannot be separated from the DNA-dependent activity, so that it seems likely both are catalyzed by the same enzyme. Weiss and Fox (1964) have shown, however, that the two types of reaction differ in their response to low molecular weight poly-

Fig. 13-3. Molecules of RNA polymerase attached to template DNA molecules. 140,000×. From Slayter and Hall (1966).

amines, such as spermidine:

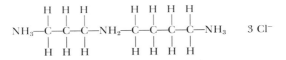

Whereas such polyamines enhance DNA-dependent RNA synthesis by 35–50%, they have little effect on synthesis with single-stranded RNA (or DNA) primers. Presumably the effect is due to complexing between the polyamines and phosphate groups in either the DNA template or the RNA product, but the details of the phenomenon are not yet clear.

The molecular weight and substructure of RNA polymerase have been the subject of conflicting reports. Maitra and Hurwitz (1967) have recently reported a single sedimentation peak of 11 S for the *E. coli* enzyme, which corresponds to a molecular weight of 320,000. From this datum they can estimate that there are approximately 1200 molecules of RNA polymerase in an average bacterium. A somewhat higher molecular weight was calculated for the same enzyme by Fuchs *et al.* (1964), who did the first electron microscopy with the enzyme, and by Richardson (1966). Although Fuchs' negatively stained preparations seemed to indicate a hexameric structure, this was not seen by Slayter and Hall (1966) in positively stained material. The technique used by the latter authors permitted them to see the enzyme bound to a long DNA template (Fig. 13-3), and it was found that the molecules attach at an average distance from one another of 1700–2200 Å. This indicates that long regions of the DNA helix are not available to the enzyme for its initial binding, and suggests that special initiator sites exist.

RNA-Directed RNA Synthesis

After infection of *E. coli* cells with a DNA-containing bacteriophage (T2), the cells synthesize a new DNA polymerase which is characteristic of the phage particles and which serves to catalyze replication of the phage's DNA (Aposhian and Kornberg, 1962). This discovery suggested that those phages and other viruses which contain RNA rather than DNA might induce synthesis of specific RNA-dependent RNA polymerases for their own replication. Such virus-specific enzymes have now been isolated and by appropriate experiments distinguished from the *E. coli* (DNA-dependent) RNA polymerase, which can also synthesize complementary RNA from single-stranded RNA primers under experimental conditions.

Haruna *et al.* (1963) were the first to isolate a virus-specific RNA-dependent RNA polymerase from *E. coli* cells infected with the RNA phage, MSϕ2; they proposed that the enzyme should be called a "replicase" to distinguish it from (DNA-dependent) DNA polymerase and (DNA-dependent) RNA polymerase. This replicase shows a remarkable specificity for the phage RNA as primer, and although it has some activity with other viral RNA's it is completely inactive with either *E. coli* ribosomal or transfer RNA fractions, or with DNA. The enzyme continues to synthesize *in vitro* for some hours, yielding up to 65 times as much product as primer. Later Haruna and Spiegelman (1965) isolated still another replicase from cells infected with the RNA phage, $Q\beta$; although both the MS-2 and $Q\beta$ enzymes require all four riboside triphosphates and Mg^{++}, each is specific for its own RNA primer:

Enzyme	Label incorporated with:	
	MS-2 RNA	$Q\beta$ RNA
MS-2	4742	0
$Q\beta$	36	2871

Both these enzymes have been considerably purified, and they are distinguishable from *E. coli* RNA polymerase not only by their primer selectivity, but also by their inability to use a DNA template and by their insensitivity to actinomycin D. The mechanism of the primer selectivity is not known, but it is likely to involve the secondary and tertiary structure of the single-stranded viral RNA's.

Several laboratories have isolated double-stranded "replicative forms" of RNA from cells infected with single-stranded RNA viruses. It appears that one of the first stages in the replication of such viral RNA is synthesis of a complementary strand to form a double-stranded RNA template. Weissmann (1965) has shown for the MS-2 phage that although some of the RNA product is double-stranded, most consists of single RNA chains of the parental type. These results are consistent with a mechanism of synthesis involving two steps: (1) Synthesis of an RNA chain complementary to the parental RNA, resulting in a double-stranded primer molecule; (2) synthesis of additional single parental strands by transcription from the one (newly synthesized) complementary strand in the primer RNA. This step would be very analogous to the action of (DNA-dependent) RNA polymerase, since only one strand of a double-stranded template would be transcribed, producing the complement of a complement.

Recently Spiegelman's group has confirmed the synthesis of complementary Qβ (−) strands during replication of parental Qβ (+) strands; however they have discovered, in addition, that minus strands alone are efficient templates for synthesis of parental strands, so that the significance of double helical and other complex intermediates has become obscure. Both the parental and minus strands seem to be synthesized primarily in the 5′ to 3′ direction characteristic of DNA-dependent polymerases. The enzyme itself (replicase) has been characterized as containing two subunits, a heavy one (m.w. 130,000) which is coded by the viral RNA and a light one (m.w. 80,000) which occurs naturally in uninfected bacteria. Although the basis for the unique template specificity of the replicases has not yet been solved, enzyme binding has been shown to survive in modified Qβ RNA molecules which have lost up to 83% of their original length.

Inhibition of Cell-Free Nucleic Acid Synthesis by Histones and Other Compounds

In a paper antedating the recognition of DNA as the hereditary material, Stedman and Stedman (1943) deduced from the apparent amounts of histone in growing and nongrowing tissues that these proteins inhibit the processes leading to chromosome replication and mitosis. Although their data would now be regarded as uncertain, the concept of histones as genetic regulators has survived, and with the development of cell-free systems for DNA and RNA synthesis, several laboratories have investigated the effect of adding histones to the reaction mixtures. There is widespread agreement that the addition of histone does in fact inhibit synthesis of both DNA and RNA *in vitro*, but it is not yet clear whether this represents a specific regulatory capability or a relatively unspecific interference with the template activity of the primer DNA by formation of (insoluble) nucleohistone complexes.

The first investigation of histone inhibition employing a soluble enzyme system was that of Huang and Bonner (1962), who worked with the soluble form of pea seedling RNA polymerase. They found that transcription from primer DNA to product RNA is markedly inhibited by the presence of mixed pea histones; furthermore the magnitude of the effect depends on the ratio of added histone to primer DNA, inhibition being complete at ratios of 1 or greater. This relation indicates that the inhibition is effected through the primer DNA rather than through the RNA polymerase, a conclusion which is also supported by the recovery of synthetic activity when a pure DNA template is added to the inhibited system. More recently, Huang *et al.* (1964) have compared the effectiveness of different calf thymus histone fractions for inhibiting synthesis by RNA polymerases from pea seedlings and from *E. coli;* in their experiments, a fairly constant histone/DNA ratio of 1.32–1.45 was maintained and precautions were taken to ensure that the primer DNA-histone was present as a soluble nucleoprotein complex. They found that the very lysine-rich histones are potent inhibitors of *in vitro* RNA synthesis, but that the arginine-rich histones inhibit only weakly. The same relationships were found for both the plant and bacterial enzymes, and regardless whether the DNA and histone were added separately or as a reconstituted nucleohistone. Surprisingly, nucleoprotamine showed almost as high a primer activity as DNA alone. Nevertheless the authors noted that the degree of inhibition is directly related to the influence of the various histones and protamine in increasing the melting temperatures of the DNA-protein complexes, i.e., their effectiveness in stabilizing the DNA double helix (Chapter 12).

Evidence that histone inhibition can be relatively specific in its effects has been reported by Hurwitz *et al.* (1963), based on *in vitro* experiments with *E. coli* RNA polymerase. They found that the synthesis of RNA in this system is inhibited by various agents which bind to the template DNA, including histones, actinomycin D, and base analogs; however, when the inhibition is only partial, these agents have the effect of switching synthesis to somewhat different types of RNA. For example, the addition of actinomycin D to the reaction mixture results in a product RNA which has fewer C and G "nearest-neighbor nucleotides" than the control RNA, presumably because actinomycin binds to DNA at G-C sites and prevents them from being transcribed. Somewhat more complex alterations in nearest-neighbor frequencies result from the addition of thymus histones at low concentrations. That the histones of living nuclei are actually linked to DNA at specific sites or in specific combinations has been supported by experiments of Bonner (1965) and Crampton (1957), which revealed differences in physical properties between "native" and artificially reconstituted nucleohistone (Chapter 12). It has also been reported by Barr and Butler (1963) and by Bonner *et al.* (1968) that native chromatin from calf thymus or pea embryo nuclei has greatly reduced template activity as a primer for RNA synthesis *in vitro* (Table 17-2); after removal of histones, however, the priming activity approaches that of pure DNA. All these investigations support the idea that histones may impose specific controls on genetic transcription in living cells, by preventing all but a few specific DNA loci from participating in the RNA polymerase reaction.

A number of authors working with cell-free systems have noted that the mechanism of histone inhibition may be simply a nonspecific precipitation of the primer DNA by formation of insoluble nucleohistone complexes. For instance, Barr and Butler (1963) noted that their calf thymus nucleohistone preparations were gelatinous suspensions, while the control DNA was in true solution. Other investigators, particularly Bonner and his collaborators, have taken special precautions to work only with nucleohistone primers that could be obtained in soluble form. Surprisingly enough, both approaches have yielded very similar conclusions, i.e., that the very lysine-rich fraction inhibits DNA-dependent RNA synthesis more or less completely, while the other fractions have less extreme effects. Barr and Butler also observed marked inhibition by artificial polylysine, and they pointed out that the amount of very lysine-rich histone in a calf thymus nucleus is sufficient by itself to inhibit RNA synthesis completely; the fact that RNA synthesis is not inhibited completely *in vivo* implies that the complexes between different histones and DNA must have some specific organization.

Allfrey *et al.* (1964) have recently detected a class of enzymes in calf thymus nuclei which specifically acetylate histones; this discovery led them to investigate the inhibitory effects of acetylated compared to nonacetylated histones during RNA synthesis by the "aggregate" calf thymus RNA polymerase. They found that in this system arginine-rich histones inhibit synthesis by 60–75%, but that the inhibition is reduced or even eliminated after acetylation. Among the various acetyl-histone fractions, the very lysine-rich retain the most inhibiting capability, while the arginine-rich no longer inhibit at all. Similar effects were observed with RNA polymerase from *E. coli* and *Azotobacter*. The authors showed that the loss of inhibition was not due to loss of ability to form histone-DNA complexes, and they speculated that acetylation of histones may play an important regulatory role *in vivo*.

Investigations discussed so far have concerned DNA-dependent RNA synthesis, but it is also well established that histones inhibit DNA-dependent DNA synthesis as well. Generally speaking, the DNA polymerase systems are somewhat less sensitive to a given histone concentration than the RNA polymerase systems. For example, Gurley *et al.* (1964) found that the *in vitro* DNA polymerase reaction from regenerating rat liver is inhibited only 15% by mixed histones at a histone/DNA ratio of 1.5 or less. The very lysine-rich histones are again the most efficient inhibitors, followed in descending order by the slightly lysine-rich and the arginine-rich; in each case, synthesis is almost completely stopped when the histone is present in a sufficiently high concentration. Similar results were reported by Billen and Hnilica (1964) for *E. coli* DNA polymerase after addition of calf thymus histone fractions. They also found that polylysine is four times as efficient an inhibitor as any of the histone fractions, and they consider that all the inhibitory effects in their system are due to precipitation of the DNA primer.

Inhibition of these template-dependent reactions is not surprising if the inhibitor is known to form chemical complexes with the template. This is the case for histones and also for certain other inhibitors such as actinomycin D and proflavin. Actinomycin D is known to act by binding to DNA, presumably at guanine sites; as in histone inhibition, DNA-dependent RNA synthesis is more sensitive to actinomycin than DNA-dependent DNA synthesis, suggesting that the template-enzyme relationship is different in the two reactions. Actinomycin does not inhibit RNA-dependent RNA polymerases at all, providing one means to detect the presence of these enzymes experimentally. A curious effect which remains to be explained is the fact that polyamines, such as spermidine, actually enhance DNA-dependent RNA synthesis, although they probably form saltlike bonds with DNA phosphates in the same manner as polylysine and the very lysine-rich histones. The lack of inhibition by protamine and by acetylated histones is also a puzzle of similar nature.

14

CELL-FREE SYNTHESIS OF PROTEINS

. . . our hard-won factlet poses at once a whole series of new questions; it is but the trunk of a problem tree.

J. BONNER *1965*

Unlike the cell-free synthesis of nucleic acids, the synthesis of proteins *in vitro* depends on the presence of complex, multimolecular structures, i.e., ribosomes. Historically, therefore, systems for cell-free protein synthesis developed from a cytochemical rather than from a purely biochemical direction; in fact, the same experiments in cell fractionation that produced the mitochondrial cell-free systems for oxidative phosphorylation (Chapter 7) led also to the ribosomal systems for protein synthesis.

This line of investigation was pioneered by Claude (1941), who homogenized liver cells and separated them by differential centrifugation into three fractions: one containing free nuclei and cell fragments, one containing microscopically visible granules (mainly mitochondria), and one containing invisible granules of high RNA content (estimated to be about 600–2000 Å in diameter). The submicroscopic fraction, or microsomes, could not be fully characterized until electron microscopic techniques became sufficiently refined in the 1950's; then Palade and Siekevitz (1956) established that the microsomes correspond to elements of the "rough" endoplasmic reticulum as seen in thin-sectioned liver cells. It was shown that the term "microsome" includes two distinct components: (1) the membrane fraction, or endoplasmic reticulum proper (which is soluble in deoxycholate); and (2) the ribosomes (DOC-insoluble), which are osmiophilic granules 150–250 Å in diameter attached to the membranes on their cytoplasmic surfaces (Fig. 16-1). Since most of the RNA of the microsome fraction is associated with the DOC-insoluble granules, they are often referred to as ribonucleoprotein (or RNP) particles.

It was shown by Hultin (1950) that the *in vivo* incorporation of isotopically labeled amino acids leads to labeling of cell elements later found in the microsome fraction. This pioneer discovery led directly to a definitive demonstration by Siekevitz (1952) that the rat liver microsome fraction is capable of incorporating labeled alanine into proteins *in vitro*. Siekevitz's rat liver system, which was the first cell-free system for protein synthesis, also required a soluble factor from the mitochondrial fraction. A second system, derived from mouse pancreas by Allfrey *et al.* (1953), depended on the addition of whole mitochondria to the microsomes, and this system was inhibited by pretreatment with RNase. Further clarification of the reaction was contributed by Littlefield *et al.* (1955), who compared the synthetic activity of the ribosomes versus the ER membranes during microsomal synthesis; they found that, both *in vivo* and *in vitro,* it is the ribosomes which show the highest activity during the early phases of synthesis, exceeding the membrane fraction by some 22-fold. Nevertheless Siekevitz and Palade (1958)

371

later showed that ribosomes attached to the membranes are more active in protein synthesis than unattached ribosomes (i.e., the post-microsomal fraction).

Beginning in 1954, the requirements for protein synthesis in the rat liver system were systematically analyzed by Zamecnik, Hoagland, and their collaborators. They soon discovered that the requirement for mito-chondria and aerobic conditions could be eliminated by providing the system with ATP, together with a biochemical triphosphate-regenerat-ing mechanism. It was also discovered that a soluble protein fraction (supernatant) was required, which was characterized by its ability to catalyze an amino acid dependent exchange between labeled pyrophos-phate ($P^{32}P$) and ATP. From this property Hoagland (1955) inferred that the soluble fraction must contain enzymes capable of carrying out an ATP activation (or adenylation) of free amino acids:

$$\text{Enzyme}_1 + \text{AA}_1 + \text{ATP} \rightleftharpoons \text{(adenyl-AA}_1\text{) Enz}_1 + \text{PP}$$

Not long afterward the existence of this reaction was confirmed by Hoagland *et al.* (1956), who also showed that the activation enzymes precipitate at pH 5.2 and found preliminary evidence that separate enzymes catalyze the activation of different amino acids. Simultaneously Berg (1956) partially purified a specific, methionine-activating enzyme from yeast, DeMoss *et al.* (1956) found a leucine-specific enzyme in *E. coli*, and Davie *et al.* (1956) purified a tryptophan-specific enzyme from beef pancreas (mol. wt. 70,000–90,000). The latter system was used by Kingdon *et al.* (1958) to isolate and identify the product of the reaction, adenyl tryptophan, which was found to remain closely bound to the tryptophan-activating enzyme.

In 1957, Hoagland *et al.* discovered still another cofactor in the rat liver cell-free system: this was a low molecular weight (ca. 25,000) RNA present in the soluble fraction, precipitating with the pH 5 enzymes, and entirely distinct in its physical and metabolic properties from ribo-somal RNA. Since the soluble RNA (sRNA) acquired some isotopic label after incubation with ATP and ^{14}C-leucine, it was postulated that this RNA fraction acts as an acceptor of "activated" amino acids.

$$\text{(adenyl-AA}_1\text{) Enz}_1 + \text{sRNA}_1 \rightleftharpoons \text{AA}_1\text{-sRNA}_1 + \text{AMP} + \text{Enz}_1$$

Again confirmation for this second reaction was obtained soon after by Hoagland *et al.* (1958), who demonstrated that amino acids bound to sRNA are indeed used as precursors for protein synthesis by rat liver microsomes.

The same two-step reaction scheme was found by Berg and Ofengand (1958) in extracts of *E. coli*, where it could be shown that one valine-specific enzyme catalyzes both the amino acid activation and the transfer of amino acid to sRNA. Zachau *et al.* (1958) showed that the amino acid is held to sRNA by a 3'-ester linkage with a terminal adenosine group. Although there are more than 20 different sRNA species, corresponding to the different amino acids and amino acid-activating enzymes (aminoacyl RNA synthetases), all sRNA molecules end in a 3'-cytosine-cytosine-adenosine sequence; in fact, if these three nucleotides are removed experimentally, binding of the amino acid cannot occur. Synthesis of the terminal C-C-A sequence is catalyzed by a single, soluble enzyme employing cytosine and adenosine triphosphates as precursors. It should also be noted that the AMP by-product in the transfer reaction is released from the adenyl amino acid rather than from the RNA (Fig. 14-1).

The significance of the sRNA-amino acid complexes was accounted for independently by Crick, who had predicted on theoretical grounds that some type of nucleic acid adapter molecules must occur in the mechanisms of protein synthesis. This conclusion followed from the absence of any simple steric correspondence between polynucleotide and polypeptide chains, such that the nucleotide sequences could be imagined to specify amino acid sequences directly. If the amino acids were not assembled on the surface of a nucleic acid "template," then they might be oriented by means of short RNA adapter molecules; these adapter molecules could assemble at specific sites on a nucleic acid template by their complementary nucleotide sequences, and at the same time could transport specific amino acids by binding them in terminal positions. This general scheme has now been fully confirmed. sRNA–amino acid complexes can be isolated from a wide variety of organisms, where they are shown to be necessary intermediates in the processes of protein synthesis. Furthermore, there is at least one specific sRNA for each amino acid, and binding of different amino acids to their own sRNA's is catalyzed via ATP activation by different aminoacyl RNA synthetases (Fig. 14-1). In elegant experiments carried out by Chapeville *et al.* (1962) and Ehrenstein *et al.* (1963), cysteine was converted to alanine while complexed with the specific cysteine sRNA; as a result, polypeptide chains were synthesized *in vitro* which contained alanine at specific sites where cysteine should have been. These experiments provide direct proof that "recognition" of specific amino acids during protein synthesis is mediated through the sRNA component. In order to denote this function, the terms "transfer RNA" or "adapter RNA" are often used instead of "sRNA."

By the early 1960's it was clearly established that two distinct kinds of RNA participate in the mechanisms of protein synthesis: (1) amino acid-specific transfer RNA's, and (2) ribosomal RNA. It was natural to

assume that the ribosomal RNA might provide the template on which
transfer RNA's orient, but this was more or less contradicted by a general similarity in base composition among ribosomal RNA's from a
variety of species. Consequently it remained for Brenner *et al.* (1961) to

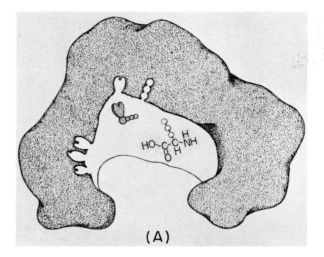

(A)

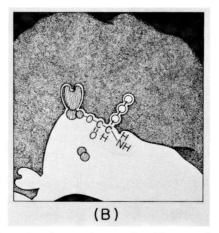

(B)

Fig. 14-1. Diagram illustrating the reactions catalyzed by an aminoacyl RNA synthetase.
In (A) and (B) an amino acid is adenylated at the expense of ATP, with pyrophosphate as
a byproduct; in (C) and (D) the specific adenyl amino acid is coupled to the adenyl end of a
specific transfer RNA molecule, with AMP as a byproduct.

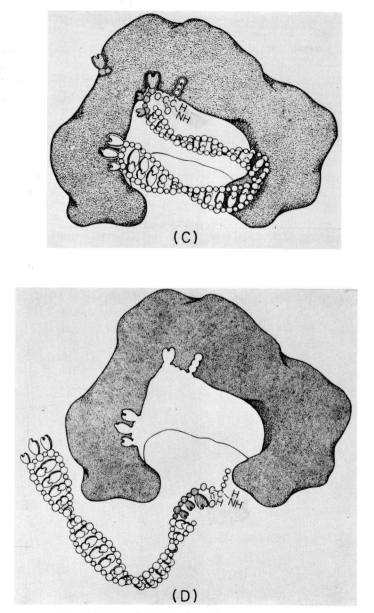

Fig. 14.1 (C) and (D). For legend see opposite page.

demonstrate that, after infection of *E. coli* with the bacteriophage T4, no new phage-specific ribosomes are synthesized, but a phage-specific RNA is formed which attaches to the preexisting *E. coli* ribosomes. This specific phage RNA is formed from the virus DNA by a DNA-dependent RNA polymerase reaction, and it is therefore the only RNA which contains information about viral DNA base sequences. The discovery of this third RNA fraction, known as "template" or "messenger" RNA, was strikingly confirmed *in vitro* by Nirenberg and Matthaei (1961), who defined a cell-free system from *E. coli* capable of synthesizing protein, but requiring ATP, twenty amino acids, and three RNA fractions (ribosomal RNA, transfer RNA, and a template RNA). When artificial poly U was used as the template RNA in this system, it synthesized a protein containing only phenylalanine residues, thereby providing the first example of a specific correspondence between one polynucleotide sequence and one polypeptide sequence.

The concept which has developed from these experiments is that ribosomes provide a more or less unspecific mechanism for assembling polypeptide chains, while information concerning specific peptide sequences is conferred by a single-stranded, high molecular weight messenger RNA; sRNA's, on the other hand, function to orient specific amino acids in their proper sequence according to the base sequence of the messenger RNA. These relationships are summarized by the equation:

$$n(\text{sRNA-AA}) + \text{ribosome} + \text{mRNA} \xrightarrow[\text{ATP}]{\text{GTP}} \text{protein-mRNA-ribosome} + n(\text{sRNA})$$

Transfer RNA

Analysis of base ratios in the sRNA fraction very early revealed a number of unusual features, including; (1) the ratios of A:U and G:C are near unity, suggesting a high proportion of internal hydrogen-bonding and formation of DNA-like helical segments; (2) there is a preponderance of G-C pairs, the ratio of AU:GC being only about 0.7; (3) most or all sRNA's have a guanosine residue at the 5' end, while all sRNA's have a C-C-A nucleotide sequence at the opposite (3'-amino acid) end; (4) a number of "odd" bases occur predominantly in the sRNA fraction, including 5-ribosyluracil (pseudouridine, abbreviated ψ), dihydrouridylic acid, 2-methyladenine, 6-methylaminopurine, 1-methylguanine, 5-methylcytosine, and thymine; (5) the base ratios and compositions of mixed sRNA's are remarkably similar from a wide variety of sources, including *E. coli*, yeast, rat liver, pea seedlings, *Euglena*, and other species. Representative base compositions for *E. coli*, yeast, and other sRNA's are given in Table 14-1. These soluble RNA's make up 10–20% of the total RNA content in yeast and *E. coli* (most of the remainder being ribosomal RNA).

In an early physical analysis of *E. coli* transfer RNA molecules, Tissieres (1959) reported a sedimentation coefficient of 4 S, corresponding to a molecular weight of about 25,500 and a chain length of 80–90 nucleotides. Hypochromicity studies (Chapter 12) also confirmed that a large proportion of the bases participate in intrastrand hydrogen bonding, the helical content being estimated at about 76% from optical density data and 82% from hydrogen exchange analysis. Englander and Englander (1965) have calculated that in an sRNA containing 70 nucleotides, only about 8 "common" bases and 6 "odd" bases are not in helical configurations. That the preponderance of G-C pairs includes long GC sequences, which melt at a slightly different temperature from the rest of the base pairs, has been inferred by Felsenfeld and Cantoni (1964) from a melting analysis of pure serine sRNA.

Since transfer RNA's are among the smallest of naturally occurring nucleic acids, they have been used for detailed base sequence analysis in much the same way that insulin was used for early amino acid sequence studies. As a result, the first complete nucleotide sequence for a native nucleic acid was reported for yeast alanine sRNA by Holley *et al.* (1965); this alanine sRNA consists of a chain of 77 nucleotides (mol. wt. 26,600), which includes the following bases: 8 A, 12 U, 25 G, 23 C, 2 ψ, 1 T, 1 I, 1 methyl-I, 1 methyl-G, 1 dimethyl-G, and 2 dihydro-U (Fig. 14-2). Methylation of the "trace bases" is thought to occur after the polynucleotide chain has been synthesized.

More recently Madison *et al.* (1967) have published a complete sequence for yeast tyrosine sRNA (78 nucleotides), and Zachau *et al.* (1967) have sequenced yeast serine sRNA (85 nucleotides). From comparative studies of these and other partially sequenced sRNA's, some notable

Table 14-1

NUCLEOTIDE COMPOSITION OF sRNA'S FROM VARIOUS SOURCES (MOLE % OF IDENTIFIED NUCLEOTIDES AND NUCLEOSIDES)[a]

Source	G	A	C	U	Ψ	T	MG	MA	MC	pGp	Nucleosides
Yeast	29.2	21.1	26.4	16.1	4.6	1.3	—	—	—	1.2	1.3
E. coli	32.1	20.3	28.9	15.0	2.1	1.1	0.1	0.4	—	—	—
Wheat germ	29.7	21.8	23.6	19.2	2.6	—	—	—	—	1.9	1.3
Silk worm	28.3	19.3	26.1	19.3	3.3	1.3	0.5	—	0.4	1.5	—
Rabbit liver	31.1	16.6	27.8	15.9	4.3	—	2.4	0.6	—	—	1.1

[a] From Miura (1967).

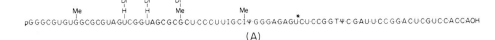

(A)

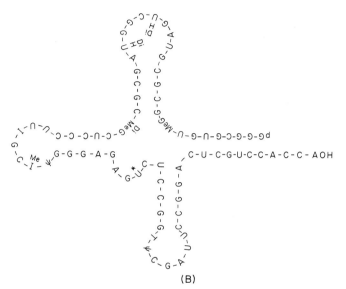

(B)

Fig. 14-2. (A) Base sequence of alanine-sRNA from yeast. (B) A possible folding configuration for alanine-sRNA, which places the presumptive anticodon (I-G-C) at one end and the coupling sequence (C-C-A) at the other end. From Holley *et al.* (1965).

similarities in the positions of "odd" bases and probable helical regions have emerged. For example, the 3'-terminal pApCpCpA-OH sequences of these molecules remain unpaired, and seem to act as flexible, single-stranded attachment sites for the amino acid. However, several other nucleotides at the 3'-end engage in helix formation with complementary nucleotides at the 5'-end (Fig. 14-2). The intermediate parts of these molecules seem to be folded in a "cloverleaf" pattern, with three separate helical regions (Fig. 14-2). An "anti-codon" nucleotide triplet, for correct recognition between the sRNA and messenger RNA, seems to be located at a single-stranded loop on the second of these helical regions. For example, experiments to be discussed later in this chapter indicate that the messenger RNA sequences for alanine are pGpCpX (Table 14-3), and according to the "wobble hypothesis" proposed by Crick (1966), these messenger codons probably correspond to the sRNA anticodon CpGpIp, involving residues 36-37-38 of yeast alanine sRNA. The sequence G-T-Ψ-C-G has also been found in several transfer RNA's, but its significance is not understood.

Even though all transfer RNA's end in a C-C-A base sequence, Ishida and Miura (1965) have shown that the terminal sequences next to this trinucleotide are specific for each amino acid sRNA from a given organism; furthermore, the sequences differ among corresponding sRNA's from different organisms (e.g., leucyl RNA from yeast, rat, and E. coli). Nevertheless, cross-reactions can occur in some cases between the sRNA of one organism and the "activating enzyme" (amino-acyl RNA synthetase) of another organism. For example, Benzer and Weisblum (1961) found cross-reactions using enzymes and acceptor RNA's from E. coli and yeast, but they also found incompatibilities which depended on the particular amino acid sRNA's and the particular organisms being compared. The situation is somewhat complicated by the fact that the same organism often contains two or more sRNA's for the same amino acid, and there is evidence that heterologous enzymes may "recognize" one of these types but not the other. For instance, Bennett et al. (1965) have isolated four distinct leucine-accepting sRNA's from E. coli and have shown that only two of these can be "charged" with leucine by aminoacyl RNA synthetases from yeast. The basis of transfer RNA specificity for (1) the appropriate activation enzyme and (2) the appropriate position on messenger RNA, remain to be elucidated; two entirely different molecular sites may be involved.

Ribosomes

The key to effective protein synthesis in most *in vitro* systems is the isolation of functional ribosomes, and consequently these complex particles have been extensively investigated by a variety of physical and chemical techniques. At present it is clear that ribosomes from different sources differ somewhat in mass, base composition and RNA/protein ratio, but there is nevertheless a general similarity in substructure and other functional relationships. In the spectrum of ribosome types, the two extremes are represented by ribosomes from the bacterium *E. coli* and from mammalian tissues such as rat liver or rabbit reticulocytes (Fig. 14-3).

Ribosomes were first isolated from *E. coli* by Tissières and J. D. Watson (1958), who found that ribosomal RNA alone accounts for 22% of the total dry weight in rapidly growing cells (90% of total RNA). Since the ribosomes also contain about 37% protein, it can be estimated that under optimum growth conditions the intact RNP particles comprise over one-third of the total bacterial dry mass. No substances other than

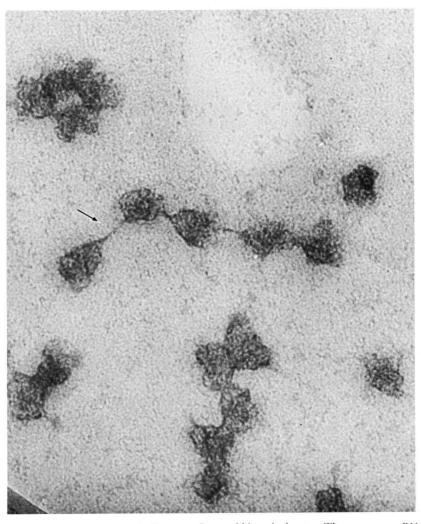

Fig. 14-3. Ribosomes and polyribosomes from rabbit reticulocytes. The messenger RNA strand, presumably coding for hemoglobin, is clearly visible in the extended polyribosome (arrow). 470,000×. From Slayter *et al.* (1963).

RNA and protein seem to be present in the RNP particles, at least within an accuracy of 1–2%. Characteristically the intact ribosomes of *E. coli* sediment with a Svedberg coefficient of 70 S, corresponding to a total molecular weight of 2.6×10^6, and they are resistant to digestion with ribonuclease. However in a low Mg^{++} concentration these ribosomes separate into two components, one with a sedimentation coefficient of

51 S (mol. wt. 1.8×10^6) and the other with a coefficient of 32 S (mol. wt. 800,000); this dissociation is reversible if Mg^{++} is restored, the reconstituted ribosomes being fully functional in protein synthesis.

Although the larger subunit is about twice the mass of the smaller, Spahr and Tissières (1959) found that the protein:RNA ratio and base compositions of both particles are almost identical to one another (Table 14-2). It is notable that this base composition does not show the A = U, G = C relationship of double-stranded nucleic acids, since the most abundant bases are guanine and adenine (purine:pyrimidine = 1.3). Experiments carried out by Kurland (1960) showed that the smaller (30 S) ribosomal subunits contain a single RNA strand sedimenting at 16 S and having a molecular weight of about 560,000 (corresponding to 63% of 800,000). The larger (50 S) RNP subunits contain RNA strands sedimenting at 23 S (mol. wt. 1.1×10^6). Since the base composition is similar in the two types of RNA, it was suggested that the 23 S chain might be a dimer of two 16 S chains; however, Yankofsky and Spiegelman (1963) have demonstrated by DNA-RNA "hybridization" (annealing) experiments that the base sequences in the two are sufficiently different to prevent them from competing for the same sites in *E. coli* DNA. Recently Takanami (1967) has reported that the 5'-terminal nucleotide sequence is pGpGpUp . . . for the 23 S compound and pApApApUpGp . . . for the 16 S one. Since both ribosomal RNA's do form RNase-resistant hybrids with DNA from the cells of origin, they both are apparently synthesized in an RNA polymerase reaction from the *E. coli* chromosome; at the same time, the 16 S and 23 S components seem to be derived from different genetic loci.

Tissières and Watson originally detected the 30 S and 50 S ribosomal subunits from changes in the ultracentrifugal sedimentation constants when the Mg^{++} concentration was varied. Later however, Huxley and Zubay (1960) succeeded in observing the subunit structure of *E. coli* ribosomes directly with the electron microscope; especially after negative staining, a conspicuous cleft is visible which divides each ribosome into a larger, dome-shaped segment (diameter 140–160 Å) and a smaller, more irregular, and somewhat flattened segment (70 Å by 160–180 Å). The smaller subunit, corresponding to the isolated 30 S particles, appears to fit on the flat surface of the larger (50 S) subunit in the manner of a "cap," and the combination of the two constitutes a 70 S particle with a diameter of about 140–180 Å. After positive staining with uranyl acetate, a folded RNA thread can be detected in the ribosome, and this RNA has a fairly high degree of intrastrand base pairing; thus hypochromicity studies by Doty (1962) place the helical content at about 78%. These investigations suggest that each ribosomal subunit consists of a specifically folded ribonucleoprotein fiber, in which protein subunits adhere to a long RNA strand. Direct confirmation for this model has been obtained by Spirin *et al.* (1963) and Spirin (1964), who were able to induce unfolding of both the 30 S and 50 S subunits to form flexible nucleoprotein strands about 30–40 Å in diameter; after unfolding these RNP fibers still contain 40% protein, and under appropriate experimental conditions they can fold up again to reconstitute intact ribosomes. Hart (1965) has also observed such unfolding, estimating 7000 Å as the fiber length in the 50 S component; his electron micrographs resolve much detail regarding the precise pattern of folding.

In addition to the 16 S and 23 S components of ribosomal RNA, three new RNA species have since been described. One of these is a 5 S soluble RNA which was first reported by Rosset and Monier (1963) in *E. coli* ribosomes. At first the 5 S RNA was thought to be a precursor of 4 S transfer RNA, but Galibert *et al.* (1966) have recently concluded that it is a new RNA component of the ribosome; the complete nucleotide sequence has been worked out by Brownlee *et al.* (1967), who found that the "odd" bases of transfer RNA are lacking in 5 S RNA. Furthermore Knight and Darnell (1967) have detected this component in a 1:1 ratio with the larger (28 S) ribosomal RNA of mammalian cells. Two other ribosomal RNA species are a 45 S and a 35 S particle first reported by Scherrer and Darnell (1962) in human (HeLa) cells. These larger particles have been shown by Scherrer *et al.* (1963) and Girard *et al.* (1965) to be precursors of the vertebrate 16 S and 28 S ribosomal RNA's. According to a scheme supported by these authors and by Penman *et al.* (1966), vertebrate ribosomal RNA's are first synthesized in the nucleolus as very long RNA strands (45 S), which are then cleaved into a 16 S

Table 14-2

BASE COMPOSITIONS OF RIBOSOMAL RNA'S FROM VARIOUS SPECIES

Source	A	U	G	C
E. coli 30 S[a]	24.6	21.0	31.6	22.8
50 S	25.6	22.1	31.4	20.9
70 S	25.0	21.4	31.5	22.1
Pea embryo[b]	24.3	22.0	31.4	22.3
Yeast	25.9	27.4	27.7	18.9
Rat liver	18.6	20.4	31.9	29.0
Thymus nucleus RNP particles[c]	20.4	18.6	32.7	28.2

[a] From Spahr and Tissières (1959).
[b] From Huang and Bonner (1965).
[c] From Pogo *et al.* (1962).

ribosomal subunit and a 35 S particle; the latter is eventually converted in some unknown way to a 28 S ribosomal subunit, either before or during its passage through the nuclear envelope to the cytoplasm (see Chapter 17).

In mammalian cells, including the rat liver system first isolated *in vitro*, the ribosomes are considerably larger than those of *E. coli*, and they generally resist dissociation into subunits at low Mg^{++} concentrations. Ribosomal RNA's from vertebrate cells also exhibit slightly higher sedimentation coefficients than those from *E. coli* (usually reported in the range 16–18 S and 28 S). The base composition of the RNA, while similar in various mammals, differs notably from that of *E. coli* by containing much more cytosine and less adenine (Table 14-2). It is not known whether important differences in the protein synthetic mechanisms accompany these differences; however, in the experiments of Ehrenstein *et al.* (1963), it was shown that an sRNA derived from *E. coli* can function successfully with rabbit reticulocyte ribosomes.

According to Tashiro and Yphantis (1965), intact guinea pig liver ribosomes sediment at 77 S, corresponding to a molecular weight of 5.0×10^6; other ribosomes from yeast, pea seedlings, and rat liver also generally fall in the range 3.6–4.6×10^6 molecular weight, 77–80 S sedimentation constant, and 230 Å diameter. Although it is now known that subunits do exist in these larger ribosomes, the number, relative sizes, and interrelations of the components are not yet entirely worked out. In their guinea pig liver preparations, Tashiro and Siekevitz (1965) found evidence that each ribosome is composed of one large subunit (47 S, mol. wt. 3.2×10^6) and one small subunit (32 S); they could not determine the molecular weight of the small particles directly, but since the larger ones account for about two-thirds of the mass of the entire ribosome, an analogy is suggested with the two-thirds:one-third division of *E. coli* ribosomes. Nevertheless, the 47 S subunit of liver ribosomes (mol. wt. 3.2×10^6) is considerably larger than the entire *E. coli* ribosome (mol. wt. 2.6×10^6). Pea seedling ribosomes (80 S) have been shown to consist of two 26 S particles combined with two 40 S particles; according to Bayley (1964), each 26 S subunit is an elongate granule 210–250 Å long and 90 Å across, while the 40 S subunit is disklike, about 210–250 Å in diameter and 80 Å thick.

These larger ribosomes contain a higher content of protein than bacterial ribosomes; for instance, Ts'o *et al.* (1958) determined a protein content of 60% for pea seedling particles and 55% for those from rabbit reticulocytes (compared to 37% for *E. coli*). However, the amino acid compositions of ribosomal proteins from bacteria, plants, and mammals are very similar in their high content of both basic and acid residues. Crampton and Petermann (1959) noted a high proportion of lysine and arginine (over 30%) in rat liver RNP particles, as well as indications that the protein molecules are of low molecular weights; both these properties are reminiscent of histones. Another histonelike characteristic found by Butler *et al.* (1960) in the proteins of rat liver microsomes is a high proportion (40%) of N-terminal proline and alanine residues. The proteins of *E. coli* ribosomes have been analyzed by Waller (1964), who detected at least 24 components by starch gel electrophoresis; most of these seem to be basic proteins with N-terminal residues that are predominantly alanine and methionine. However, the content of acid side chains is also high, especially in some fractions; in fact, the total content of basic and acid groups together exceeds 37%.

Although some authors reserve the term "histone" for basic proteins associated with DNA, the possibility has not been excluded that the same protein molecule may establish a salt linkage at different times with either DNA or RNA. Furthermore, it appears that both ribosomes and histones are synthesized in the nucleolus, at least in some cells. The degree of similarity or identity between ribosomal proteins and DNA-linked histones is not yet clear, but the possibility of a direct relationship exists. The primary enzymatic activity associated with ribosomes is a high specific GTPase, which plays an undetermined role in the transfer of amino acids from sRNA to nascent protein. Although RNase activity is also commonly found, this is now regarded as due to a contaminating, nonribosomal enzyme.

In addition to the well-known cytoplasmic ribosomes of macro-organisms, it has been established that protein-synthesizing RNP particles occur in the nuclei and in the chloroplasts of some cells. Frenster *et al.* (1960) were the first to recognize nuclear RNP particles in 0.14 M NaCl extracts of calf thymus nuclei, showing them to be capable of incorporating leucine-^{14}C in a cell-free system. The physical properties of the nuclear ribosomes were further investigated by Pogo *et al.* (1962) and by Wang (1963), who determined the base composition of the RNA (Table 14-2) and found that the intact ribosomes sediment at 72 S; after removal to Mg^{++}-free medium, they dissociate into 45 S and 33 S components. The particles are about 200 Å in diameter and they contain 40% protein, which is largely basic with 29% arginine, lysine, and histidine. In most respects, including their requirements for protein synthesis, these nuclear ribosomes resemble the cytoplasmic ribosomes in the same cells.

With respect to chloroplast ribosomes, Clark *et al.* (1964) have found that leaves of the Chinese cabbage contain two distinct classes of RNP particle, one sedimenting at 83 S (cytoplasmic) and the other at 68 S (chloroplast); in the green unicell *Euglena*, Eisenstadt and Brawerman (1964) also reported 70 S cytoplasmic ribosomes and 60 S chloroplast ribosomes. Both intact chloroplasts and isolated chloroplast ribosomes are able to carry on protein synthesis *in vitro*, provided that sRNA's and supernatant fractions are added back. According to Boardman *et al.* (1966), the smaller chloroplast ribosomes also dissociate reversibly into 50 S and 35 S subunits, in a way that is highly reminiscent of *E. coli* ribosomes. If bacterial and mammalian ribosomes really represent two distinct classes of RNP particle, then it would appear that both classes occur together in photosynthetic cells.

Messenger RNA and Its Relationship to Ribosomal and Transfer RNA

The concept that ribosomes are essentially unspecific instruments for polypeptide assembly and that they require an information-bearing "messenger RNA" to specify amino acid sequences, was largely introduced by Brenner *et al.* (1961). Previously it had been thought that the ribosome itself must serve as a template in protein synthesis, and this implied that the formation of new types of protein, for example after phage infection of *E. coli*, would require an initial synthesis of new ribosomes. The key experiment of Brenner *et al.* involved marking the

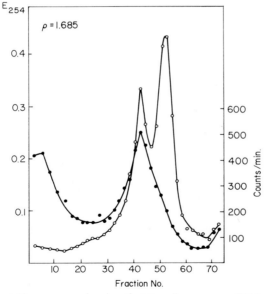

Fig. 14-4. Ultracentrifuge curves showing that "new" messenger RNA is associated with "old" ribosomes during protein synthesis in phage-infected *E. coli* cells. The new messenger RNA is located by radioactive labeling with ^{32}P (black circles); the radioactivity peak coincides with a peak of "heavy" ribosomes density-labeled by growing bacteria in an $^{15}N^{13}C$ medium before infection (white circles). The major peak in the UV curve (white circles) represents standard ribosomes from cells grown on unlabeled medium. From Brenner *et al.* (1961).

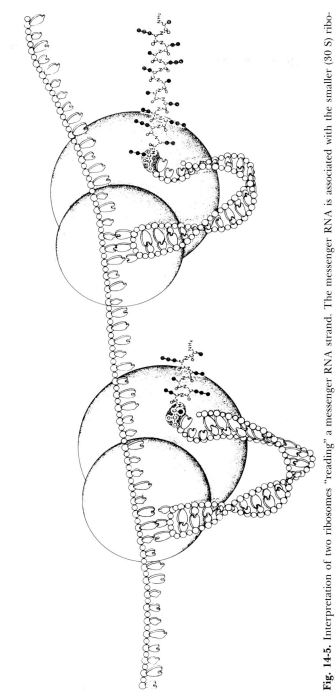

Fig. 14-5. Interpretation of two ribosomes "reading" a messenger RNA strand. The messenger RNA is associated with the smaller (30 S) ribosomal subunit, while the developing polypeptide chain is associated with the larger (50 S) subunit. New amino acids are added to the carboxyl end of the polypeptide chain one at a time. Each precursor amino acid is brought to the site of synthesis as an adenyl ester on the C-C-A end of a specific transfer RNA molecule. The anticodon of the transfer RNA recognizes a codon triplet in the messenger RNA, permitting it to insert the appropriate amino acid in the polypeptide chain.

"old" ribosomes of uninfected bacteria with the heavy isotopes ^{15}N and ^{13}C, while labeling the "new" RNA of the infected bacteria with radioactive ^{32}P; after ultracentrifugation, all the new radioactive RNA was found to be associated with the heavy "old" ribosomes, while no new ribosomes were synthesized at all (Fig. 14-4). Brenner could also show that the new RNA is characterized by a short half-life, and at low Mg^{++} concentrations this RNA separates from the ribosomes. In melting-annealing experiments, Hall and Spiegelman (1961) demonstrated that the base sequences of the new RNA component are complementary to those of the phage DNA. Finally, the "old" *E. coli* ribosomes have been shown to be active in synthesizing "new" phage proteins.

It was the development of Nirenberg and Matthaei's (1961) cell-free system for protein synthesis, however, that unequivocally demonstrated the role of messenger RNA. This system, derived from *E. coli*, has the unique property of requiring three RNA components—sRNA, ribosomes, and a third, template RNA. When an artificial poly U strand is used as template, the protein synthesized is a polyphenylalanine chain; on the other hand, with a tobacco mosaic virus RNA, this system synthesizes protein highly similar to native TMV protein (as determined from serological, chromatographic, and other properties). Using this *E. coli* system, Takanami and Okamoto (1963) found that in the presence of Mg^{++}, the poly U template molecules become structurally bound both to 70 S ribosomes and to pure preparations of the 30 S ribosomal subunits. Since no binding occurs with 50 S subunits, the smaller component evidently contains the site where the messenger RNA normally attaches. By contrast, Gilbert (1963) found that if the ribosomes are dissociated during synthesis, the new polyphenylalanine chains remain attached to the larger, 50 S subunits; this linkage, furthermore, is mediated by a covalent, amino acyl bond with an sRNA molecule (Fig. 14-5). The discovery that the messenger attaches to the smaller component and the nascent polypeptide to the larger suggests that during synthesis each transfer RNA molecule must first be admitted to the 30 S messenger site for recognition, and must then be passed to the 50 S peptide-linking site for incorporation (Fig. 14-5). Confirmation that the complex between a 30 S particle and an artificial messenger is able to recognize and bind specific amino acyl sRNA's has recently been reported by Pestka and Nirenberg (1967). The number of sRNA residues bound to each ribosome during active synthesis has also been estimated by Wettstein and Noll (1965), who found evidence for (1) one polypeptide-linked sRNA, (2) one "free" sRNA, and (3) between zero and one aminoacyl sRNA. The single free sRNA is not tightly bound and is regarded as occupying an exit site after contributing its amino acid to the growing polypeptide chain; on the other hand, the remaining two (amino acid-linked) sRNA molecules are irreversibly complexed.

In the physical relationship between a ribosome and a messenger RNA strand, one serious difficulty is the fact that the messenger may be 33,000 Å long (as in TMV), while the ribosome itself is only about 180–240 Å in its greatest dimension. This steric problem suggested that a ribosome may "read" its messenger strand sequentially, and good evidence has now accumulated to confirm this supposition. For instance Takanami *et al.* (1965), using f2 bacteriophage messenger RNA complexed with *E. coli* ribosomes, digested the uncomplexed parts of the messenger with RNase; they could then recover the remaining (complexed) messenger segments for analysis of base ratios. Under conditions of no protein synthesis, all the ribosomes complex with the f2 RNA at one specific place, which has a distinctive base ratio (not the 3′-OH end of the strand); when protein synthesis is induced, on the other hand, that part of the messenger found complexed to the ribosome shows a different base composition, demonstrating directly that ribosome and messenger strand move relative to one another during synthesis.

Just as reading of the messenger RNA strand is sequential, so also the synthesis of the polypeptide chain proceeds sequentially. This has been demonstrated most clearly with another cell-free system derived from rabbit reticulocytes by Schweet *et al.* (1958), in which almost all the protein synthesized is hemoglobin. Both the α and β chains of hemoglobin have valine as the N-terminal residue, but Bishop *et al.* (1960) found that during short-term *in vitro* synthesis in the presence of valine-^{14}C, very little of this amino acid is incorporated into the N-terminal positions. This finding suggested that the N-terminal end might be the first part of the chain to be synthesized, a conclusion which was firmly established by Dintzis and his collaborators (Dintzis, 1961; Naughton and Dintzis, 1962). The design of Dintzis' experiments involved adding tritium-labeled leucine to the hemoglobin synthesizing system in a "pulse" of controlled duration; the distribution of labeled leucine in different parts of newly completed α-hemoglobin chains was than analyzed in terms of the pulse length. After a very long pulse, labeled leucine is found evenly distributed in all parts of the α-polypeptide; however, with very short pulses, label is expected only in those parts of the molecule synthesized *last*, and Dintzis found this to be the C-terminal end. Pulses of intermediate length resulted in labeling of more peptides sequentially in an order now known to correspond to the amino acid sequence of the rabbit α-hemoglobin chain. Consequently these experiments established that the hemoglobin polypeptide chains are synthesized sequentially, beginning with the N-terminal amino acid and proceeding linearly to the C-terminal end. Synthesis of the complete

α chain (141 amino acids) requires about 7 minutes at 15°C or 1.5 minutes at 37°C (approximately two amino acids per second).

The mechanism by which an amino acid is actually transferred from sRNA to a peptide linkage in protein has been found to include two separate reactions, each catalyzed by a different soluble enzyme. Arlinghaus *et al.* (1964) succeeded in isolating these two enzymes from the cell-free rabbit reticulocyte system, demonstrating that one is essentially a "binding enzyme," whereas the other functions as a peptide synthetase. In their experiments, the rabbit reticulocyte system was adapted from hemoglobin synthesis to the synthesis of polyphenylalanine using a poly U template. In the presence of the binding enzyme, ribosomes containing dipeptide chains (Phe-Phe) took up one molecule of phenylalanyl-sRNA each, but no tripeptide was formed; in the presence of the peptide synthetase, on the other hand, the tripeptide (Phe-Phe-Phe) was synthesized, but no further reaction occurred. Arlinghaus's evidence indicates that normally both enzymes are bound to the ribosome and that during protein synthesis they act alternately, one amino acid at a time. These authors also found that the specific requirement for GTP, first noted by Hoagland *et al.* (1957), for the transfer of amino acids from sRNA to protein, is characteristic of the binding reaction rather than the peptide synthetase reaction. Although the exact role of the GTP is not known, the products of the reaction are GDP and orthophosphate (rather than GMP and pyrophosphate), and guanosine is apparently not incorporated into any RNA fraction. In cell-free systems, about 50 molecules of GTP are hydrolyzed per amino acid transferred, so that the relationship between the two processes is obscure.

The concept which has developed from these detailed experiments is that the appropriate "charged" aminoacyl sRNA molecule is first "recognized" by the ribosome–mRNA complex by binding at a coding site and is then permitted to displace the previous C-terminal sRNA by formation of a peptide bond between its amino group and the polypeptide terminal carboxyl (Fig. 14-5). The displaced sRNA is "spent," and thereafter returns to the medium for recharging (via the exit site). Although not all the details of energy flow during this process have been worked out, it has long been known that polymerization of amino acids to form a polypeptide chain is an endergonic process, requiring 2–4 kcal per peptide bond. Evidently this endergonic synthesis is coupled with the exergonic hydrolysis of ATP (7 kcal/mole) by way of the amino acid adenylation (or activation) step. The two intermediate compounds, aminoacyl adenylate and aminoacyl-sRNA, both equal or exceed the energy transfer potential of ATP. For example tryptophan adenylate can react with pyrophosphate to re-form ATP, and in similar fashion aminoacyl-sRNA reacts with AMP and pyrophosphate to reconstitute

ATP. The overall equilibrium constant for the two-step reaction

$$\text{valine} + \text{ATP} + \text{sRNA} \rightleftharpoons \text{valine-sRNA} + \text{AMP} + \text{PP}$$

is about 0.32, indicating that the valine-sRNA is at a slightly higher energy level than ATP.

In the scheme outlined above, a special problem is presented by the first amino acid to be incorporated into a new polypeptide chain (N-terminal residue). Although the first amino acid-sRNA may be bound at the recognition site in the usual way, there is no pre-existing polypeptide-sRNA to receive it at the condensing site. The manner in which this steric and biochemical difficulty is solved probably plays an important role in the initiation of protein synthesis. Recently it has been found that N-terminal amino acids are often substituted at their α amino ends with formyl or acetyl groups. In fact, Marcker and Sanger (1964) have discovered a special enzyme system which formylates methionine after it has been linked to its sRNA (generating N-formyl methionyl-sRNA). Most recently Leder and Bursztyn (1967) have demonstrated that such N-formyl methionine is incorporated preferentially at the N-terminal site of proteins synthesized *in vitro,* whereas nonformylated methionine is used at intermediate positions in the chain. According to Marcker *et al.* (1967), two different types of methionine-sRNA are involved, only one of which can undergo the formylation reaction.

An interesting feature of the messenger RNA-ribosome relationship is the varying degree of stability of the messenger strands in different cells. For bacterial and viral messengers, one of the first properties detected was a high turnover rate, which in *Bacillus subtilis* corresponds to a half-life of only 2.5 minutes for the entire mRNA complement (Levinthal *et al.,* 1962). However in rabbit reticulocytes and rat liver the messenger RNA's appear to be stable, with half-lives extending over many days. Scott and Bell (1964) have studied the survival times of mRNA in various tissues of the chick embryo by using actinomycin D to inhibit the RNA polymerase reaction (shutting off synthesis of mRNA) and observing the decline in protein synthesis. They found that many or most cell types have relatively short-lived messengers, but that the cells of the ocular lens and of the down feather primordia are able to continue protein synthesis for over 24 hours without renewing their messengers. It has also been estimated that the half-life of messenger RNA in human (HeLa) tumor cells is about 3 hours. Generally speaking, messenger stability seems to be inversely correlated with the degree of cell specialization. Thus in bacterial cells, which must shift their protein synthesizing machinery rapidly to make first one type of protein and then another, stable messenger molecules would be a disadvantage; on the other hand, stable messenger is likely to permit higher efficiency in a rabbit reticulocyte, which synthesizes almost nothing but hemoglobin. In *E. coli* the mRNA fraction makes up only about 3% of the total RNA (ribosomal RNA comprising some 90%); the extraordinarily high turn-over in this minor fraction may be partly due to digestion of the (single-stranded) messengers by ribonuclease or polynucleotide phosphorylase.

Polyribosomes

In 1962 Marks *et al.* discovered that most of the amino acid incorpora-tion during hemoglobin synthesis is associated (both *in vivo* and *in vitro*) with a ribosome fraction sedimenting faster than 100 S. This observation was confirmed and extended by Warner *et al.* (1962), who found most of the amino acid incorporation in a 170 S peak, which they could show by electron microscopy contained primarily pentamers of the 78 S ribo-somes (Fig. 14-3). After brief digestion with RNase, the pentamer peak disappears while the monomer peak increases, showing that the aggre-gate is held together by a single-stranded RNA. In Slayter's high resolu-tion electron micrographs, this 10–20 Å nucleic acid fiber can actually be seen to connect the ribosomes (Fig. 14-3). Although the pentamers are the most common aggregates in mammalian reticulocytes, groups of 2, 3, 4, and 6 can also be isolated as minor peaks in the ultracentrifuge, most of them showing protein-synthesizing activity. Evidence that the RNA connecting strand is in fact messenger RNA has been presented by Gierer (1963), who noted that the addition of artificial poly U to a cell-free reticulocyte system stimulates both phenylalanine incorporation (as in *E. coli*) and the formation of aggregates. Takanami and Okamoto (1963) have also observed polyribosome formation on poly U strands in the *E. coli* system.

The concept that has developed from these experiments is that a messenger RNA molecule of sufficient length may be used as template by several ribosomes at once; each ribosome is thought to begin reading the message at the same place, but as it proceeds sequentially along the RNA strand it may be closely followed by another ribosome synthesizing the same type of polypeptide at a slightly earlier stage of completion (Fig. 14-5). Warner *et al.* (1963) have attempted to calculate the relation-ship between the number of ribosomes in a polyribosome group and the theoretical length of the messenger RNA strand: on the assumption that three messenger nucleotides are required to specify one amino acid (to be discussed later), they estimated that the messenger RNA for hemo-globin should be about 1500 Å long (146 amino acids, 438 nucleotides, and 3.4 Å per nucleotide); since neighboring ribosomes have a center-to-center spacing of 300–350 Å, a 1500 Å hemoglobin messenger would have just room enough for five linked ribosomes. Polyribosomal groupings have now been studied in a number of different systems where the number of ribosomes in a cluster does appear to be approximately proportional to the expected length of the messenger. Some examples of larger polysomes include 30–50 ribosome clusters in an *E. coli* β-galactosidase synthesizing system (protein mol. wt. = 125,000), clusters of about 60 in polio-infected HeLa cells, and as many as 100 during collagen synthesis in chick embryos (collagen mol. wt. = 360,000).

A number of other very admirable investigations support the polyribosome concept outlined above. For example, Hardesty *et al.* (1963) showed that the attachment of ^{32}P-labeled single ribosomes to polyribosome groups is correlated with the initiation of protein synthesis, and that their detachment from polyribosomes is correlated with the completion and release of polypeptide chains. In Hardesty and Schweet's cell-free reticulocyte system, the largest ribosome aggregates disappear first as protein synthesis ends, followed in order by successively smaller polysome classes. That reticulocyte polyribosomes contain exactly one nascent polypeptide chain per ribosome has also been shown by Warner and Rich (1964). More recently, Williamson and Schweet (1965) have carried out experiments showing that the chain length and N-terminal amino acid of each ribosome's nascent polypeptide chain can be influenced by the ribosome's position on the messenger RNA strand. They achieved this by treating rabbit reticulocyte polyribosomes with puromycin, which causes the growing hemoglobin chains to detach from the ribosomes; if the puromycin was then removed protein synthesis resumed, but the first polypeptides synthesized were shorter than native hemoglobin chains and they also lacked the native N-terminal residues of hemoglobin. Williamson and Schweet interpreted this to mean that, following the puromycin-induced detachment of incomplete polypeptides, each ribosome resumed synthesis according to its intermediate position on the messenger RNA; such a conclusion was reinforced by the fact that the N-terminal residues of the "short" polypeptides were of random type, rather than uniformly valine (as in native hemoglobin). The authors point out that since the N-terminal residue in the native protein *is* always the same, ribosomes normally must always begin "reading" the messenger RNA at the same place—presumably one specific end of the strand. Recently Guest and Yanofsky (1966) have presented genetic evidence that a messenger RNA strand is read from the 5' to the 3' end, corresponding to polypeptide synthesis from an N-terminus to a C-terminus.

The existence of polyribosomes *in vivo* in rabbit reticulocytes and other cells has been confirmed by thin-section electron microscopy, and Marks *et al.* (1963) have established that in the intact reticulocyte during the peak of hemoglobin synthesis, 80–90% of the ribosomes are in clusters; as expected, the proportion of polyribosomes to single ribosomes decreases progressively as hemoglobin synthesis ends. The polysomes of reticulocytes seem to float freely in the cytoplasm, but in other tissues they are bound to the membranes of the endoplasmic reticulum (which are absent in reticulocytes). In Chinese cabbage leaves, both the 83 S cytoplasmic ribosomes and the 68 S chloroplast ribosomes have been found to occur as polyribosomes; in fact, according to Clark *et al.* (1964), the formation of polysomes in this plant is induced by sunlight.

The Genetic Code

The concept that nucleic acid molecules might store and transmit "information" in the form of specific nucleotide sequences was a direct corollary of Watson and Crick's (1953) base pairing model of DNA. That this information would be directly expressed in protein structure was also predicted by the one gene-one enzyme concept which developed from Beadle and Tatum's analysis of nutritional mutants in *Neurospora*. However, in visualizing a precise mechanism by which nucleic acid information might be related to protein structure, an important obstacle was encountered in the fact that proteins contain about twenty different kinds of amino acid, whereas nucleic acids contain primarily four different kinds of nucleotide. Gamow (1954) was one of the first to suggest that a special coding system must exist, and he pointed out that the minimum coding ratio would be three nucleotides for one amino acid (since two nucleotides provide only 16 different combinations).

For about eight years the analysis of possible coding systems proceeded largely from indirect evidence and theoretical inference. The major point that was settled in this period was the question of whether the code could be "overlapping" or not; i.e., assuming that three nucleotides specify one amino acid, can the same nucleotide form part of two or more different triplets? As noted by Brenner (1957), an overlapping code would restrict the possible amino acid sequences in natural polypeptides, whereas a careful analysis of known sequences shows that no such restrictions exist; furthermore, in an overlapping code a single nucleotide change (mutation) would be expected to alter two or more neighboring amino acids at once. Since single amino acid substitutions are found in hemoglobin and TMV mutants, the overlapping code could be eliminated as a possibility.

A second problem was whether the code would have to be "punctuated"; i.e., assuming that the information is contained in a long series of nonoverlapping nucleotide triplets, how does the protein-synthesizing mechanism know where one triplet ends and the next begins? A simple type of punctuation would be provided by a reading frame code, i.e., one in which the mechanism begins reading at a fixed point and reads every three nucleotides until it comes to the end of the polynucleotide chain; in that case it would be theoretically possible for any combination of three nucleotides to code for an amino acid, and since there are 64 possible combinations ($4 \times 4 \times 4$) but only 20 amino acids, there would be a chance of degeneracy in the code (i.e., two or more different triplets coding for the same amino acid). By contrast, Crick *et al.* (1957) proposed a remarkable coding scheme based on purely mathematical considerations, in which no punctuation would be necessary but no degeneracy would be permissible either. In their system only 20 triplets would be meaningful, while the remaining 44 would be "nonsense" triplets; Crick showed that the meaningful triplets could be so selected that they might be placed in any order side-by-side along a polynucleotide chain, yet could never be confused with overlapping nonsense triplets (which might happen if the mechanism began to read, for example, on the second instead of the first nucleotide). It was regarded as significant that mathematical restrictions dictate that *no more* than 20 meaningful triplets can be devised in this way. Despite the mathematical brilliance of this particular coding scheme, it is now clear that the genetic code in reality is both degenerate and based on a reading frame mechanism.

Strong evidence that the "message" is read in threes from a fixed point was obtained by Crick *et al.* (1961) from an analysis of induced and spontaneous mutations in bacteriophage T4. Artificial mutations were induced by treating the phage DNA with acridine, which is believed to act by adding or deleting one base pair. It was then possible to detect many additional, spontaneous mutations by their ability to "suppress" the acridine mutation, leading to restoration of wild-type phage. Approximately 80 mutations were found, all occurring in a highly localized region of the phage chromosome and all having the property of either suppressing the acridine mutation or suppressing the suppressors. Crick devised a tentative scheme to explain these observations, in which all mutations must belong either to a + class or a − class, one class consisting of mutations caused by an "extra" base pair, the other containing mutations caused by a "missing" base pair. He was then able to support this scheme by showing that most combinations of + with − mutations lead to wild type, but that any two + or any two − mutations together remain mutant in phenotype. This suggests that if a mutation is due to a missing base pair, it can be effectively repaired by adding one new base pair nearby; it cannot be repaired, however, by deleting a second base pair. Taken together, the data suggest that the loss of a single base pair disrupts reading of the entire message (rather than of a single amino acid), and this implies that the reading mechanism does in fact operate sequentially from a fixed point, being unable to recognize individual parts of the message except by reference to the "origin."

A key experiment carried out by Crick *et al.* (1961) with these T4 mutants was designed to show whether the protein synthesizing mechanism actually reads the nucleotides by threes. Although on theoretical grounds three nucleotides are expected to be the minimum coding unit, in practice the code might be based on sets of four or more, or even on a combination of pairs, triplets, quartets, etc. In order to test this point, + and − mutations were combined in threes (+++ or −−−). The hypothesis was that, even though a missing nucleotide might not be corrected by deleting another base pair (−−), it could be approximately corrected by deleting two additional base pairs (−−−); in this case the effect would be equivalent to deleting one entire triplet, and even though a few wrong amino acids might be built into the chain between the mutation sites, most of the message could be read correctly. Provided that the bulk of the polypeptide chain is synthesized normally, then it is possible that no mutant phenotype will be detectable. When Crick combined + or − mutations in threes, he did in fact observe that wild-type phages were regenerated, and he could therefore conclude that the nucleotide sequence is read either in triplets or in some simple multiple of three nucleotides. Later Crick (1963) further confirmed this conclusion by determing that combinations of four or five + mutants are inactive, whereas six + mutants together give wild type.

Direct experimental analysis of the coding relationship between a polynucleotide messenger and a polypeptide product became possible in 1961, when Nirenberg and Matthaei (1961) introduced their template-dependent system for cell-free protein synthesis. In this *E. coli* system, an artificial poly U strand was found to specify the synthesis of a poly-phenylalanine chain, suggesting that the coding triplet for phenylalanine must be pUpUpU. Other artificial template RNA's could be synthesized (by means of Ochoa's polynucleotide phosphorylase system), and it was found that templates containing uracil together with a second type of base stimulate incorporation of several amino acids (including phenylalanine). For example a poly UC strand containing 5 uracil:1 cytosine leads to incorporation of phenylalanine, leucine, serine, and proline, but no other amino acids. From this observation it may be postulated that each of these amino acids is "coded" by one of the eight UC triplets: UUU, UUC, UCU, CUU, UCC, CUC, CCU, and CCC. Based on experiments with poly U, the first of these could be assigned to phenylalanine, and similarly poly C was found to dictate the incorporation of proline, leading to an assignment of CCC to this amino acid. The other UC triplets could be assigned from the *ratios* of incorporation of different amino acids, as compared with the calculated ratios of various triplets in 5:1 poly UC. For instance, if it is assumed that the sequence of U and C in the artificial template is random, then the probability of a UUU triplet is about 0.58 ($5/6 \times 5/6 \times 5/6$), while the probability of a 2U1C triplet is only 0.116 ($5/6 \times 5/6 \times 1/6$); the ratio UUU/2U1C is then expected to be 5:1, and since the observed incorporation ratio of phenylalanine to serine was about 4.4:1, serine could be assigned a 2U1C triplet. Unfortunately this method provided no way to distinguish between triplets of identical base composition but different base sequence (e.g., pUpCpC, pCpUpC, and pCpCpU).

During the early 1960's, these techniques were extended simultaneously to other artificial templates with different base compositions and ratios, e.g., poly UA (5:1), poly UG (5:1), poly UAC (10:1:1), poly UCG (10:1:1), and poly UGA (10:1:1). Although the ratios of amino acids incorporated with different primers often varied markedly from expectation, there was sufficient internal consistency to provide confidence that a specific "coding system" was operating. Thus if serine was incorporated with a poly UC template, it was also incorporated with a poly UCA template, and in about the proportion expected for UC triplets. By 1962, Matthaei, Nirenberg, and co-workers had proposed the base composition of code triplets for 15 amino acids, while Ochoa and his co-workers had independently proposed base composition triplets for 19 amino acids (Speyer *et al.*, 1962). Although the data of the two laboratories were not in perfect agreement, the correspondence was reasonable, and it was already clear that several amino acids are coded by more than one triplet (i.e., the code is degenerate). It was also established that some amino acids are not incorporated except in the presence of templates containing 3 different types of base; since no amino acids required 4 different bases, this supported the concept of a triplet code. However these early experiments suffered from two great disadvantages: (1) the sequence of nucleotides in each triplet could not be distinguished, so that a code of 1U2C (for example) might be assigned to three different amino acids coded by UCC, CUC, and CCU;

and (2) the standard for almost all code assignments was phenylalanine incorporation, which was thought to be dictated only by UUU. This meant that only U-containing templates could be used, and therefore very little could be inferred about the 27 possible triplets that do not contain uracil. Furthermore, information about the 37 uracil triplets was biased by the then-unknown fact that phenylalanine incorporation is dictated by both pUpUpU and pUpUpC.

These disadvantages were overcome in an elegant technique introduced by Nirenberg and Leder (1964). The method is based on the discovery that *binding* of specific aminoacyl-sRNA's to the ribosome is itself dictated by messenger RNA independently of peptide synthesis. In a mixture of ribosomes, Mg^{++}, amino acyl sRNA's and poly U, for example, phenylalanyl-sRNA specifically and irreversibly complexes with the ribosomes, and this effect can be detected very simply by using ^{14}C-labeled phenylalanyl-sRNA, filtering out the ribosomes from the uncomplexed (soluble) aminoacyl-sRNA's at the end of the reaction, and measuring the radioactivity of the filter residue. Nirenberg determined the minimum messenger length which can dictate specific binding in this reaction and reported that it is the trinucleotide, thus providing direct support for the concept of a triplet code. Dinucleotides, oligodeoxynucleotides, and oligoribonucleotides with 3′ terminal phosphates are all inactive; only ribonucleotides with 5′ terminal phosphate or no terminal phosphate have activity. This rapid assay technique made it practical to test each of the 64 possible trinucleotides individually for ability in specifying the binding of one or another of the 20 aminoacyl-sRNA's ($20 \times 64 = 1280$ possible combinations); for the first time, it became possible to discriminate between the effects of RNA code words having identical base compositions but different base sequences.

The initial application of this technique by Nirenberg and Leder (1964) confirmed that the triplet pUpUpU specifies phenylalanine, pCpCpC specifies proline, and pApApA specifies lysine. Each response is highly specific for only one aminoacyl-sRNA out of approximately 20 tested. In subsequent reports, Leder and Nirenberg (1964a,b) further confirmed that triplets having identical base compositions (2U1G) but different base sequences are able to code specifically for different amino acids; in this study pGpUpU was found to be specific for valine, pUpGpU for cysteine, and pUpUpG for leucine. One corollary of this fact is that the reading of the messenger RNA strand must make sense in one direction only.

The first instances of degeneracy in the binding code were found by Bernfield and Nirenberg (1965), who tested the eight possible triplets expected in a poly UC template (known to stimulate incorporation of phenylalanine, serine, leucine, and proline). It was discovered that binding of phenylalanyl-sRNA is induced by *both* pUpUpU and pUpUpC; similarly the code words for serine include both pUpCpC and pUpCpU, and for proline pCpCpC and pCpCpU. In all these instances of degeneracy, the two alternative triplets are identical except for the substitution of one pyrimidine base for the other (U or C) at the 3' end. In addition to revealing this specific pattern of degeneracy, the same study detected the first potential "nonsense" triplets, since pCpUpU and pCpUpC did not induce notable binding by any aminoacyl-sRNA. However, since none of the eight UC triplets had much influence on leucine-sRNA (whereas poly UC induces both binding and incorporation of leucine), the authors suggested that CUU and CUC may act as leucine code words only when they occur in nonterminal parts of a messenger polynucleotide; this hypothesis has since been confirmed.

At present all the 64 possible trinucleotides have been tested for coding activity with the 20 aminoacyl-sRNA's, both by Nirenberg and his co-workers (1965) and by Soll, Khorana, and their collaborators (1965). The pattern of degeneracy observed earlier, in which $C = U$ for the 3' nucleotide, has been found to include interchangeability of the two purine bases also (i.e., $A = G$ in the 3' position); thus the code words for lysine have been reported as pApApG and pApApA. Alternative (or degenerate) code words have been found for all the amino acids except methionine and tryptophan. As suggested much earlier by Eck (1963), the 64 triplets approximate 32 pairs, both members of which specify the same amino acid; these pairs are identical except in the 3' terminal nucleotide, where one purine replaces the other, or alternatively one pyrimidine replaces the other. Also in a fair number of instances, four alternative code words have been found for one amino acid, all identical except that any of the four bases can occupy the 3' position (i.e., $C = U = A = G$). In these cases, although the code may be read by three's, only the first two nucleotides seem to contain specific information (Table 14-3).

The fact that messenger RNA really is read three nucleotides at a time has now been established by Khorana and his co-workers (Nishimura *et al.*, 1965) from an analysis of polypeptides synthesized in the *E. coli* cell-free system with template RNA's of regularly alternating base sequence. For example with a poly UC messenger (UCUCUCUC), they have found that a polypeptide is made which contains serine and leucine in regular alternation (Ser-Leu-Ser-Leu); on *a priori* grounds alone, this requires that the coding unit must contain an odd number of bases (3, 5, 7, etc), thereby excluding double triplets as a possible coding unit. Furthermore, since the trinucleotide UCU is known to specify serine, this result confirms that CUC acts as a code word for leucine when it occupies nonterminal positions. In similar fashion, poly UG (UGUGUG) dictates synthesis of a copolymer between cysteine (UGU) and valine (GUG); poly AC (ACACAC) dictates a copolymer between threonine (ACA) and histidine (CAC); and poly AG (AGAGAG) dictates a copolymer between glutamic acid (GAG) and arginine (AGA, which also seems to be an "internal codon," since the trinucleotide does not influence

Table 14-3
AMINO ACID ASSIGNMENTS FOR 64 TRIPLET CODONS[a,b]

| 5'-Nucleotide | Middle Nucleotide | | | | 3'-Nucleotide |
	pU	pC	pA	pG	
pU	Phe	Ser	Tyr	Cys	pU
	Phe	Ser	Tyr	Cys	pC
	Leu	Ser	Ochre	?	pA
	Leu	Ser	Amber	Try	pG
pC	Leu	Pro	His	Arg	pU
	Leu	Pro	His	Arg	pC
	Leu	Pro	Gln	Arg	pA
	Leu	Pro	Gln	Arg	pG
pA	Ileu	Thr	Asn	Ser	pU
	Ileu	Thr	Asn	Ser	pC
	Ileu	Thr	Lys	Arg	pA
	Met	Thr	Lys	Arg	pG
pG	Val	Ala	Asp	Gly	pU
	Val	Ala	Asp	Gly	pC
	Val	Ala	Glu	Gly	pA
	Val	Ala	Glu	Gly	pG

[a] The 5'-nucleotide of any given triplet is read from the left vertical margin, the middle nucleotide from the top horizontal margin. Most degeneracy is in the 3'-nucleotide, read along the right vertical margin. From Morgan *et al.* (1966).

[b] The assignments not underlined are on the basis of binding experiments only. Doubly underlined assignments are from binding data and have been confirmed by cell-free polypeptide synthesis using completely defined polymers. Singly underlined assignments are deduced from incorporation experiments with defined polymers but gave essentially no binding.

binding of arginine-sRNA). The possibility of a coding unit made up of 5 or 7 nucleotides has been excluded by using a nucleotide sequence which follows the pattern AAGAAGAAGAAG; this RNA chain dictates the synthesis of three different homopolymer proteins: (1) polylysine (AAG); (2) polyglutamic acid (GAA); and (3) polyarginine (AGA). Evidently the type of homopolymer synthesized depends on which nucleotide is read first, a "frameshift effect" that can be accounted for only if the chain is read from a fixed point sequentially and three nucleotides at a time.

Although most of the trinucleotides induce specific binding of only one aminoacyl-sRNA, some cases exist in which the code appears to be "ambiguous," i.e., the same triplet influences binding of two or more different amino acids. An example is the trinucleotide pApCpA, which Nirenberg's group found to induce binding of lysine-sRNA as well as threonine-sRNA. Since this ambiguity is not observed with a long-chain copolymer ACACAC (which incorporates only threonine alternately with histidine), it may be in part an artifact of the trinucleotide technique. Leucine has also been a difficult coding problem ever since the early cell-free incorporation studies, when it was noted that almost all the artificial messengers induce some leucine incorporation. This includes poly U, the original template which is famous for dictating synthesis of polyphenylalanine, but which also induces a small percentage of leucine-sRNA binding and leucine incorporation. Interestingly enough, the trinucleotide pUpUpU does not show this ambiguity, being specific for phenylalanine-sRNA. The code words which have now been established for leucine fail to fit exactly into the pairwise scheme to which most of the other amino acids conform; in particular, they show degeneracy at the 5' end, where U = C in the triplets pUpUpG and pCpUpG (Table 14-3). Arginine is also remarkable in possessing six codewords, four of which constitute a typical quartet while the other two differ in containing A instead of C at the 5' end. On the whole the impression is that the middle nucleotide is the most informative one in the triplet, followed in order by the 5' nucleotide and finally the 3' nucleotide.

The exact significance of degeneracy, or alternate code words, in the mechanisms of protein synthesis is not completely understood. However, it appears likely that this phenomenon accounts for many instances in which the DNA of closely related organisms differs widely in base composition without accompanying differences in protein amino acid composition. Such striking "degeneracy" serves to emphasize that, although the detailed rules which relate polynucleotide sequences to protein sequences may conveniently be called a "code," they are not so much a code as a physicochemical mechanism that depends for its operation on the specificity of several enzymatically catalyzed reactions. It is evident that the base sequences of DNA have no meaning except in relation to a specific set of aminoacyl-sRNA's, which are synthesized by specific aminoacyl RNA synthetases and are then admitted to the ribosomal peptide synthetase site by an enzyme–mRNA–ribosome complex. The specificity of the system as a whole cannot exceed that of the enzyme components which operate in it to recognize different sRNA's and which also play an essential part in recognizing different aminoacyl-sRNA's at the ribosomal binding site. The fact that the enzymes themselves are probably synthesized from a DNA-RNA "code" does not alter the fact that the code has meaning only when it is translated by other enzymes.

At present it is not yet clear to what extent the observed degeneracy of the code involves separate sRNA molecules with specific but slightly different coding triplets. It can be asked, for instance, whether the six arginine codons correspond to six different arginyl-sRNA molecules, or whether there is only one arginyl-sRNA which responds to any of the six messenger triplets; available evidence suggests that the truth lies somewhere between these two extremes. For example, the leucine-sRNA of E. coli includes five different fractions, some of which do not respond to the pUpUpG leucine code word. On the other hand, in the alanine-sRNA from yeast (for which the complete nucleotide sequence is known; Fig. 14-2), it appears that the sequence pIpGpC constitutes the anticodon for the alanine code words XpCpGp, and that the inosine residue acting as a 5' anticodon end, may pair relatively unspecifically with various 3' triplet ends in the messenger. Crick (1966) has proposed in his "wobble hypothesis" that the first two bases of an sRNA anticodon hydrogen bond specifically with the first two bases of the mRNA codon (in antiparallel), but that the third base can undergo unusual base pairings (=wobble). In his theory, the inosine residue of alanine sRNA may pair with either U, C, or A in a messenger codon; this would then account for three of the four degenerate alanine codons, but would require an additional sRNA to recognize the GCG code word. It appears that most organisms possess a set of at least 40 different transfer RNA's. Available evidence indicates that the messenger RNA is read from the 5' end toward the 3' end, and that the 5' end corresponds to the N-terminus of the polypeptide (Guest and Yanofsky, 1966).

Only 3 of the 64 possible nucleotide triplets are not assigned in E. coli, but these appear to have little or no influence on the binding of any specific aminoacyl-sRNA (Table 14-3). Although UGA may represent "nonsense," a special significance is likely for the triplets UAA and UAG, which Brenner et al. (1965) believe are involved in the amber and ochre mutants of bacteriophage T4. Since the effect of one amber mutant is to produce partial fragments of the polypeptide chain which makes up the phage head protein, Brenner has speculated that UAA and UAG are "terminator" triplets, signaling the end of a given polypeptide and inducing detachment of the protein chain from the ribosome. Direct evidence for this conclusion has been obtained by Takanami and Yan (1965), who compared the release of nascent polypeptides from the ribosomes to the supernatant using different template RNA's in the *E. coli* cell-free system. They found that the polypeptide chains are not released if poly U or poly UC are used as messenger, whereas template RNA's which contain both U and A do induce chain release. Consequently the triplets UAA and UAG may represent a special punctuation in the code, i.e., the period ending the "sentence."

Considerable speculation has been devoted to the question of whether the code is universal, i.e., does a given triplet specify the same aminoacyl-sRNA in all organisms? Available evidence is restricted to very few examples, but it favors quite consistently the idea that the code is universal for the most part. Poly U, for instance, induces synthesis of polyphenylalanine in cell-free systems derived from both *E. coli* and rabbit reticulocytes. Furthermore, when RNA from tobacco mosaic virus is used as template in the *E. coli* system, it synthesizes proteins that are very similar to native TMV protein (though apparently differing in minor respects). An indication of universality is also obtained by examining amino acid replacements in mutant forms of human hemoglobin; Smith (1962) lists the following known replacements:

Glu—Val	Asn—Lys
Glu—Lys	Gly —Asp
Glu—Gly	Lys —Asp
Glu—Gln	His —Tyr
Glu—Ala	His —Arg
Val—Glu	Ser —Thr
	Thr—Asn

In all but one instance (Lys—Asp) these changes can be accounted for by a single base transformation (mutation) between triplets assigned to amino acids in the *E. coli* cell-free system (Table 14-3); consequently the evidence suggests that the code is the same in human beings and in the bacteria which inhabit human intestines. A particularly convincing point is that single base changes in the *E. coli* glutamic acid triplet (pGpApX) can give rise to only 6 possible amino acid substitutions; of these, five (but no unexpected substitutions) occur in human hemoglobin.

15

THE ORGANIZATION OF GENETIC MATERIAL IN MICROORGANISMS

We are reminded again of the first principle of genetics, that we cannot recognize genes directly but only their difference. In turn, we should not insist on genes as self-reproducing units, but as units or markers of a more complex self-reproducing system.

J. LEDERBERG *1956*

In this and later chapters, an attempt will be made to integrate the classical cytology of DNA-containing structures (viruses, bacterial nucleoids, mitotic chromosomes, interphase nuclei) with the functional data of formal genetics. This subject is best approached from the direction of microbial genetics, in which a causal relationship between purely genetic phenomena and the physical structure of the DNA molecule is already well established. Since both the techniques and the observed phenomena of bacterial and viral genetics are multitudinous and complex, a complete review of these subjects cannot be provided in this chapter. However, investigations will be described which provide essential insights into the organization of DNA both in microorganisms and in higher forms.

Biochemical genetics traces its origin to the pioneer experiments of Beadle and Tatum (1941), who worked with the mold *Neurospora,* and became the first to isolate metabolic or nutritional mutants. These mutant forms could be detected by their inability to grow on a "minimal medium" which would support the growth of wild-type fungi; growth became possible for the mutants only after the addition of one or more nutritional factors, such as vitamin B_6, tryptophan, histidine, or other specific metabolites. After a detailed biochemical analysis of the synthetic pathways blocked by such mutations, Beadle and Tatum concluded that a single gene change often corresponds to the loss or inactivation of a specific enzyme—a concept that became famous as the "one gene–one enzyme" hypothesis. At about the same time, Avery *et al.* (1944) focused attention on DNA as the genetic material by showing that the active factor in genetic transformation of the bacterium *Pneumococcus* is DNA rather than protein; this experiment laid the groundwork for later demonstrations of DNA constancy in the nuclei and chromosomes of plants and animals. At present the one genetic system that is understood in broadest detail is that of the bacterium *E. coli,* which has been subjected both to extensive genetic analysis and to biochemical dissection into various cell-free systems for *in vitro* DNA replication, RNA transcription, and RNA-directed protein synthesis (Chapters 13 and 14).

Genetic Organization of Bacteria

Physical Arrangement of the Genetic Material

The intact *E. coli* cell is a cylindrical or capsule-shaped object approximately 2 μ long and 0.8 μ in diameter, which is enclosed by a plasma membrane and an external mucosaccharide cell wall (Fig. 15-1). The cells

404

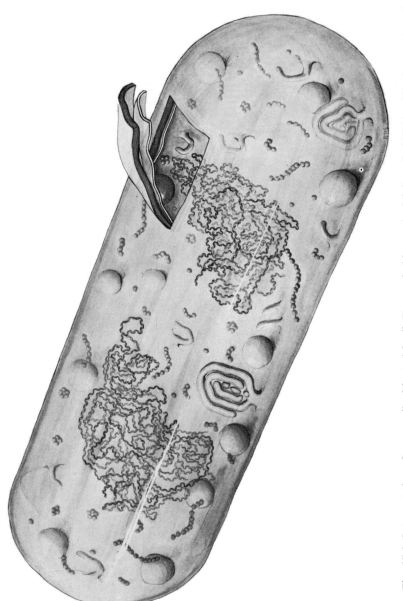
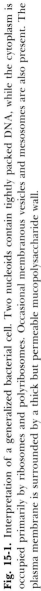

Fig. 15-1. Interpretation of a generalized bacterial cell. Two nucleoids contain tightly packed DNA, while the cytoplasm is occupied primarily by ribosomes and polyribosomes. Occasional membranous vesicles and mesosomes are also present. The plasma membrane is surrounded by a thick but permeable mucopolysaccharide wall.

can survive and even divide after removal of the outer cell wall, but the naked spheroplasts are very sensitive to osmotic conditions and require a laboratory controlled environment. Internally, the contents of the cell are distributed between a dense, ribosome-rich cytoplasm and two or more "nucleoids," each containing DNA but no ribosomes. Although the latter are often compared to the nuclei of higher cells, they are not membrane-enclosed and are probably more comparable to mitotic chromosomes than to nuclei. Specialized cytological structures such as mitochondria, centrioles, and endoplasmic reticulum do not occur in *E. coli*. Cell division is also carried out without the formation of a mitotic spindle, yet the nucleoids segregate equally to the daughter cells in a manner similar to the anaphase chromatid separation in higher cells; division is accomplished by development of a septum across the center of the bacterium, comparable in some respects to the telophase septation in plant cells. One or more mesosomes, fingerlike invaginations of the plasma membrane, are usually present (Fig. 15-1), and Fuhs (1965) has shown that these come into direct contact with the nucleoids. The mesosomes are sometimes found in polar positions, as if anchoring the daughter nucleoids, but during cell division they occur in the vicinity of the developing septum; consequently it has been speculated that they may be part of the mechanism responsible for nucleoid segregation.

Abbo and Pardee (1960) showed that under optimum growth conditions, synchronized cells of *E. coli* are able to synthesize DNA continuously and at constant rate throughout a 30-minute life cycle; each time the DNA content doubles the cells divide, and the next round of DNA synthesis begins immediately. Since the rate of replication, the number of nucleoids per cell, and the absolute amount of DNA per cell vary somewhat with nutritional conditions and temperature, it has been difficult to determine a characteristic "haploid" DNA content. However this problem has been partially clarified recently by experiments of Lark and Lark (1965) and Lark and Bird (1965), who have pulse-labeled *E. coli* nucleoids with thymine-^{3}H and followed the distribution of labeled units by autoradiography during subsequent generations. In cells grown on glucose medium (generation time 40 minutes), the thymine is halved between daughter cells at both the first and second divisions, after which those cells that are labeled exhibit no further decrease in the amount of label; this indicates that in the parent cell thymine is incorporated into four equal units, corresponding to two independently replicating chromosomes (or nucleoids). On the other hand, in cells grown on succinate medium (generation time 70 minutes), a similar thymine pulse labels only two units in the parent cells, while only half as much thymine is incorporated. Lark and Lark (1965) have accounted for this effect by showing that at slow growth rates the two chromosomes replicate alternately instead of simultaneously. When they are replicating simultaneously, the amount of DNA per cell is equivalent to a molecular weight of 8.4×10^9, whereas during alternate replication the amount is only 7.0×10^9. From these data it can be estimated that the amount of DNA in a single, nonreplicating chromosome must be equivalent to a molecular weight of 2.8×10^9, or about 1400 μ of Watson-Crick molecule.

The fact that this DNA replicates by a semiconservative mechanism was first shown by the *in vivo* experiments of Meselson and Stahl (1958), who used heavy ^{15}N to distinguish "old" from "new" DNA in the ultracentrifuge. *Escherichia coli* were first thoroughly labeled with ^{15}N by growing them for several generations on an appropriate medium, then they were transferred to a normal ^{14}N medium and their DNA prepared at intervals for centrifugation in a cesium chloride density gradient. The newly synthesized "light" DNA first appeared in hybrid molecules of intermediate density, which increased in amount during the first generation until all the DNA was hybrid; not until the second generation did DNA appear in which both strands were "light," but even at the end of two generations half of all the DNA still had the "hybrid" density (Fig. 15-2). These observations show that the original ^{15}N-labeled DNA molecules are not dispersed, but are conserved as single polynucleotide chains (i.e., the original double-helix is semiconserved; see Chapter 13). A similar relationship has since been demonstrated for DNA synthesized *in vitro* with *E. coli* DNA polymerase.

In Meselson and Stahl's experiment, it was evident that those parts of the bacterial DNA which have replicated once do not begin synthesis again until all the DNA has completed its first replication. Subsequently Bonhoeffer and Gierer (1963) isolated high molecular weight Watson-Crick molecules from *E. coli* and measured the *in vivo* rate at which 5-bromouracil-^{14}C (a thymine analog) appears in individual molecules. They found that the equivalent of 36×10^6 molecular weight DNA can be synthesized in one molecule after 10 minutes, corresponding to about 1.8 μ of Watson-Crick molecule per minute. Of even greater interest, this rate corresponds closely to the total rate of DNA synthesis per nucleoid in whole cultures under the same conditions. Consequently the authors concluded that all the DNA synthesis in a single nucleoid is localized at one molecular site or "growing point"; a corollary of this fact is that different parts of the DNA in one nucleoid must reach the synthesis site at different times, i.e., sequentially. The rate of DNA synthesis is relatively slower in the presence of 5-bromouracil, but Bonhoeffer and Gierer estimated that the normal replication rate in nutrient medium at 37°C must be about 50 μ per minute. Direct confirmation

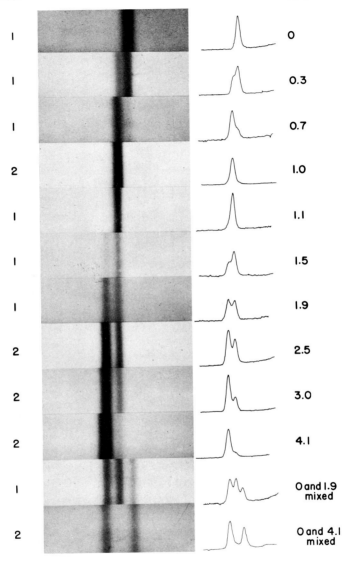

Fig. 15-2. Changes in the density patterns of bacterial DNA after transfer from an ^{15}N medium to an ^{14}N medium. After one generation all the DNA becomes half-light, shown by a leftwards shift in the single ultracentrifuge peak. After two generations, half the DNA is fully light and the rest is half light. Even after three or four generations a small, half light component persists, demonstrating that the original ^{15}N-labeled DNA strands are conserved, but are paired in the double helix with ^{14}N strands. Consequently the original DNA molecules are said to be semiconserved. From Meselson and Stahl (1958).

that DNA replicated at any given time in one generation is replicated at the same time in the next generation was obtained by Lark *et al.* (1963); in their experiments, *E. coli* at random points in the replication cycle were first pulse-labeled with thymine-^{3}H, then labeled again at various intervals with bromouracil. Regardless of the different phases of synthesis, all cells produced double-labeled DNA about one generation later.

The first evidence that all the DNA in a single nucleoid may be present as a long continuous Watson-Crick molecule was presented by Kleinschmidt *et al.* (1962, 1963), who ruptured bacterial cells on the surface of a Langmuir trough, picked up the cells on electron microscope grids, shadowed them with metal, and examined them. Electron micrographs of cells prepared in this way show many long loops of DNA, but free ends and other special configurations are absent; this lack of free ends suggests that all the DNA is present as one or two very long molecules. Subsequently Cairns (1963a,b) confirmed this conclusion with very elegant autoradiograph experiments, in which *E. coli* were allowed to incorporate thymidine-^{3}H, then very gently lysed and their contents exposed on an autoradiographic emulsion. The result showed continuous chains of labeled DNA 1100–1400 μ long (Fig. 15-3), many of which were in the form of circles. By presenting the bacteria with "pulses" of thymidine-^{3}H for 3 minutes or 6 minutes, Cairns further showed that: (1) DNA synthesis proceeds around these circles at a constant rate of about 20–30 μ per minute; (2) both "daughter strands" are labeled equally and simultaneously at the site of synthesis; and (3) this site exhibits the configuration of a "replication fork," as predicted by the Watson-Crick model (Chapter 12). Since there is good correspondence in length and replication rate between the individual molecules observed by Cairns and those predicted from gross chemical analysis, the evidence is very strong that each chromosome of *E. coli* is a single, circular Watson-Crick molecule over a millimeter long, and that DNA replication proceeds sequentially around this molecule at constant rate like a toy train on a circular track. At the point of synthesis, the two polynucleotide strands of the parent molecule continuously unwind, each forms the template for construction of a complementary strand, and the hybrid daughter molecules then immediately rewind. This unwinding-rewinding requires a "swivel point" somewhere in the circumference of the DNA circle, which may be provided by a very short, single-stranded region or break. When replication has proceeded completely around the circular DNA "track," the daughter molecules are free to separate and begin a new round of synthesis (Fig. 15-3B).

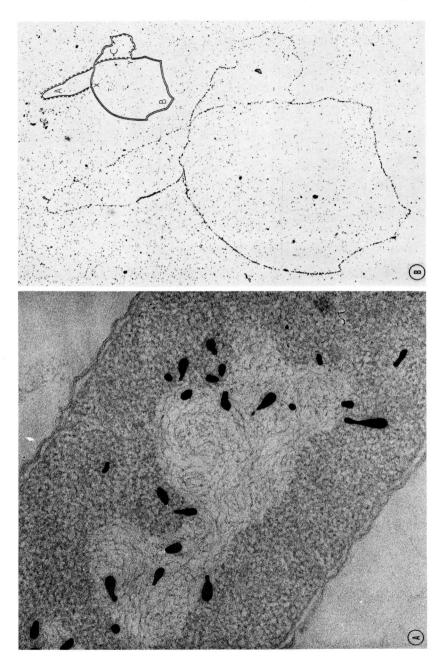

The exact three-dimensional arrangement by which 1100–1400 μ of DNA are packed into a single nucleoid about 1 μ long has not yet been completely established. In thin-sectioned *E. coli* cells, the appearance of the nucleoids varies considerably with different fixatives, but micrographs generally suggest the presence of longitudinally oriented, parallel filaments (Fig. 15-3A). Cross sections usually cut the DNA in about 500–900 individual strands, which led Kellenberger (1961) to propose that the single long molecule is folded back and forth several hundred times; provided that clumping of the parallel DNA strands is avoided during fixation, the individual 20 Å filaments seem to be evenly spaced at about 100 Å intervals, and according to Fuhs (1965) they do not show evidence of supercoiling (Fig. 15-3). The close packing of DNA filaments in itself may be sufficient to exclude the 200 Å ribosomes from the nucleoid; in fact many large protein molecules are probably excluded also. According to X-ray diffraction studies by Wilkins and Zubay (1959), a large part of *E. coli* DNA is not combined with protein, so that neutralization of the DNA phosphates is presumably brought about by polyamines, Mg^{++}, and other small cations. That the exact pattern of DNA packing varies from cell to cell, or at different stages of DNA replication, is not only possible but likely; according to Fuhs (1965): "The nuclear patterns observed in a large number of cells of *B. subtilis* and *E. coli*, resting and growing, are different from cell to cell, and in most cases are complicated and difficult to analyze."

Recently Ryter and Jacob (1963) have found that the nucleoids of *E. coli* often have a point of contact with the plasma membrane, either directly or by way of a mesosome (or plasmalemmasome). Since other experiments show that the tightly folded DNA chain replicates at only one site, it has been suggested that this site may be localized at the plasma membrane. Such a possibility seems plausible because other enzyme systems, including the enzymes of oxidative phosphorylation, are known to be present in the bacterial cell membrane. Ganesan and Lederberg (1965) have recently found that, after homogenization and centrifugation of *Bacillus subtilis*, nascent DNA labeled with thymidine-^{3}H tends to centrifuge down with the membrane and cell wall fraction, while older DNA remains in the supernatant; about 25% of the total assayable

---

Fig. 15-3. (A) Thin-section autoradiograph, showing DNA packed in the nucleoid of *E. coli*; black silver grains show the location of thymidine-^{3}H incorporated into DNA. Ca. 100,000×. From Schnös and Caro, by permission. (B) Autoradiograph of DNA isolated from *E. coli* and spread in extended form on a glass slide. The molecule (or chromosome) is circular, about 1100 μ in circumference, and is replicating at a fork. 100×. From Cairns (1963b).

DNA polymerase activity is also found in the membrane fraction. Ryter and Jacob (1963) have further suggested that the mesosomes play a role in segregating daughter chromosomes as DNA synthesis proceeds. Apparently two different modes of segregation can occur, depending on nutritional factors: thus Lark and Bird (1965) have found that during growth on glucose medium, when both nucleoids replicate simultaneously, the segregation is reductional (i.e., the two replicates of one chromosome remain in the same daughter cell). On the other hand, when the two nucleoids replicate alternately (as with succinate medium), segregation is equational and the two replicates of any given chromosome go to different daughter cells; the latter process is directly comparable to mitotic division in higher cells.

That the *E. coli* chromosome contains a special site, or initiator region, where DNA replication begins and ends was first suggested by Maaløe and Hanawalt (1961). Subsequently their hypothesis was supported by Lark *et al.* (1963), who found that DNA replication in *E. coli* starved for arginine or other amino acids always stops at a characteristic site; for instance, cells that are first starved for 60 minutes, then resupplied with amino acids in the presence of thymine-^{3}H (a 9-minute pulse), then allowed to grow for several generations, starved again, and finally refed in the presence of bromouracil, show the appearance of double-labeled DNA soon after the onset of synthesis. These observations show that a specific protein synthesis "event" is necessary for DNA replication in *E. coli*, and this event takes place in the same part of the molecule during each generation. Later Pritchard and Lark (1964) discovered that thymine starvation also induces DNA synthesis to begin at the same initiator site, even when synthesis is already in progress at another randomly located growing point; under these conditions, *two* replication forks proceed sequentially around the chromosome, one behind the other. This experiment has special theoretical importance, since it shows that the number of replication forks does not necessarily correspond to the number of Watson-Crick DNA molecules, e.g., in the chromosomes of macroorganisms. Pritchard and Lark could show that the thymine-sensitive site coincides with the amino acid-sensitive site by demonstrating that thymine starvation can substitute for amino acid starvation in the "double-labeling" experiment. They also found that the requirement for amino acids is correlated with the beginning of a new cycle of DNA synthesis, rather than with the ending of a previous cycle. Only DNA synthesis induced by thymine deficiency is inhibited by chloramphenicol (which prevents protein synthesis), suggesting that two different proteins function at the initiator site (Lark and Lark, 1964; Lark, 1966).

BACTERIAL GENETICS

Bacterial Genes and the DNA Molecule

The discipline of genetics represents a particular approach, or set of techniques, which exploits two fundamental properties of the hereditary material: the capacity to mutate and the capacity to show spontaneous linear recombination. The great triumph of bacterial and viral genetics has been the unequivocal demonstration that both these properties are inherent in the physical structure and chemical function of the DNA molecule. Within the domain of microbial genetics, a mutation is understood to be one of several possible alterations in DNA nucleotide sequences; similarly genetic recombination is an exchange of segments between DNA molecules, the frequency of which depends partly on the number of nucleotides between markers and partly on the particular mechanism responsible for the transfer. The gene itself is now defined in ultimate terms as that part of a DNA molecule which specifies a single polypeptide chain (Edgar *et al.*, 1964). These principles are accepted as a matter of course by microgeneticists, yet they are by no means so clearly established for the chromosomes of plants and animals. Nevertheless, it will be the thesis of later chapters (Chapters 17 and 18) that these same principles are universally applicable.

For many decades it was accepted by microbiologists that bacteria are asexual organisms, reproducing by simple fission to produce clones of identical cells. Not until 1946 was it discovered by Lederberg and Tatum that recombination of mutants can occur occasionally between two different strains of *E. coli*, implying a process of conjugation and sexual exchange; later it was demonstrated that one strain always acts as the genetic donor (male) and the other as recipient (female). Extensive analysis of recombination frequencies has established that all genetic markers in *E. coli* are linked, implying that each nucleoid contains only a single "chromosome." The mechanism by which this chromosome is transferred from the donor cell to the recipient was investigated by Wollman and Jacob (1955), who mechanically interrupted conjugation at different intervals after the initial mixing, then examined the genetic constitution of recipients as a function of conjugation time. It was discovered that within any given strain, genetic markers are always passed to the recipient cells sequentially, at a given rate and in a given order. At 37°C, transfer of the entire chromosome requires about 100 minutes, and if mating is interrupted by mechanical shearing at an earlier time, then the recipient cell is diploid for only a part of the genome (referred to as a merozygote).

That the *E. coli* chromosome is equivalent to a DNA molecule was suggested by early experiments of Jacob and Wollman (1958), in which ^{32}P was used to label DNA in the donor strain but not the recipient cells; the genetic effects of atomic decay from ^{32}P to ^{32}S were then analyzed both before and after conjugation. The authors found that during ^{32}P decay, various genetic markers progressively lose their capacity to be transferred during conjugation; furthermore, the rate of this loss for any given gene is proportional to its recombination distance from the "origin" of the chromosome (i.e., from the first gene to be transferred). Since ^{32}P decay is thought to cause breaks in the polynucleotide chains, this result implies that the genetic recombination distance is directly proportional to the number of phosphate atoms along the DNA backbone. In fact, Jacob and Wollman were able to estimate that 1 minute of chromosome transfer during conjugation corresponds to about 20 genetic recombination units and to approximately 4×10^4 DNA nucleotide pairs (corrected estimate, equivalent to 13.6 μ of DNA). Although the first gene to be transferred differs from one strain to another, there are great similarities in the *order* of gene exchange; for example, in one strain the order might be: T L Az T_1 Lac T_6 Gal λ; and in another: T_1 Az L T B_1 etc. A comparison of these sequences among several different strains led Jacob and Wollman (1958) to conclude that all of them are variants of the same basic arrangement, and further that this arrangement is best represented as a circle. Breaking the circle at different points gives different chromosomal "origins" without fundamentally changing the gene order. This scheme was the first circular linkage map ever detected, a fact which led the authors to maintain the cautious viewpoint that a circular gene map does not necessarily imply a circular chromosome. Nevertheless, Cairn's (1963a,b) discovery by autoradiography that the DNA of *E. coli* occurs in the form of a very long, circular Watson-Crick molecule has now brought Jacob and Wollman's (1958) genetic data into pleasing harmony with physical-chemical data. Both the genetic and the biochemical facts confirm that the *E. coli* chromosome corresponds to a single, circular molecule of DNA.

Further confirmation comes from genetic experiments which have demonstrated that the genes, like the DNA molecule, are replicated in sequence. This was shown for *E. coli* by Nagata (1963), who found that the exact sequence of gene replication is specific for each strain and is related to the position of the chromosome origin and terminus. Simultaneously, Yoshikawa and Sueoka (1963) achieved an even more direct demonstration of sequential gene replication in *Bacillus subtilis*. Their experiments were based not on conjugation but on a system of genetic recombination similar to the DNA-induced transformation first studied in *Pneumococcus* by Avery *et al.* (1944). The authors simply compared the frequency of transformation for different genetic markers derived from bacteria in rapid (exponential) growth and in stationary growth; on statistical grounds, it was expected that a culture of cells in random stages of replication (exponential growth) would contain more copies of those genes which replicate earlier in the life cycle; this relationship would not be expected for control cells in stationary growth. Yoshikawa and Sueoka found, in fact, that the various genes could be arranged linearly according to their transformation frequencies during rapid growth, and that the resulting "map" corresponded to (and even predicted) the order of genes as determined from cross-over experiments. They could conclude that gene replication begins near the adenine gene and proceeds in sequence to completion near the methionine and isoleucine genes.

That genetic recombination in *E. coli* involves a direct transfer of double-stranded DNA segments from one type of chromosome to another has been demonstrated by Siddiqi (1963). The DNA of a virus-sensitive cell line was labeled with thymidine-^{3}H and these bacteria then acted as conjugation recipients for the unlabeled chromosomes of a virus-resistant strain. Recombinant progeny DNA was recognized by its property of virus-resistance together with the presence of thymidine-^{3}H. Siddiqi found that 5–6.5% of the recipient cells were recombinants, and that these contained 4–5% of the total parental isotope; this result showed that essentially all the recombinant chromosomes contained DNA segments from the labeled parent strain, and that double-stranded DNA segments had been transferred to the recombinants (corresponding to a so-called "break-rejoin" mechanism). More recently Forro (1965) has followed the distribution of thymidine-^{3}H among progeny cells during several generations and has measured the deviation from 100% conservation of DNA polynucleotide strands; he estimated the number of dispersive events (break-rejoin) as about 0.5–0.7 per chromosome per generation.

In addition to sexual conjugation and direct DNA transformation, bacteria are capable of a third mechanism of DNA exchange which involves transfer of *bacterial* DNA by a *virus* carrier. The first such "transduction" system was demonstrated by Zinder and Lederberg (1952); subsequently viral transduction has been extensively exploited by Demerec and his collaborators to analyze chromosomal structure in the bacterium, *Salmonella,* and Yanofsky has also employed this technique in elegant experiments with *E. coli* and phage P1 (described below).

The Gene Concept

During the first half of the 20th century, the units of genetic mutation, recombination and function were regarded as the same hypothetical structure, called the "gene." The existence of any given gene could be detected only if it occurred in two or more alternate forms, known as alleles, and the process by which one allele arose from another was called mutation. In a diploid cell heterozygous for two linked genes, recombination (or crossing-over) between the two loci could usually be measured at a characteristic rate between 0% and 50%; furthermore, when the rates of recombination were compared among three linked genes, they were usually found to be additive, i.e., if A and B recombine 10% of the time, and B and C recombine 4% of the time, then A and C are expected to recombine either 14% or 6% of the time (depending on whether C is on the near or far side of B). These relationships suggested that the genes must be strung out in a linear array, like beads on a string, with a frequency of recombination determined by the distances separating them. In the special case of the *Drosophila* giant salivary chromosomes, Painter (1933) and Bridges (1936) were actually able to demonstrate that cytologically visible bands coincide with the positions of specific genes as determined from recombination distances (or cross-over maps). For these chromosomes Pontecorvo (1952) could estimate that one recombination unit (1% recombination) corresponds to about 6 μ of actual chromosome length.

In the early system of concepts, a given gene was specified by two properties: first, by its locus or position in the cross-over map; and second, by the influence of its various alleles in determining specific phenotypic variations. On the basis of these two properties, a new mutation might be regarded as an entirely new gene or as a different allele of a known gene. For instance after a cross between two homozygous mutants, the offspring could be either (1) all mutant or (2) all wild type; in the first case, the two mutations would be regarded as alleles, and in the second case as different genes. The conclusions from this experiment could then be checked by testing for cross-over recombination between the two mutations: true alleles are supposed to occupy the same locus in homologous chromosomes and should show no recombination, whereas some percentage recombination is expected between different genes, however closely linked. In practice the two tests usually coincide. However, during the 1940's concern arose about various mutations that were found to act as alleles in their effects on the phenotype but at the same time showed a low frequency of recombination. Such instances are now regarded as representing recombination *within* a gene, but at that time the concept of the gene as an indivisible unit forced the conclusion that there must be two or more closely linked genes which were acting as "pseudoalleles." This explanation, in turn, raised the question of why recombinants of genotype xy/++ (cis configuration) should exhibit the wild phenotype when the original pseudoallelic hybrids of genotype x+/+y (trans configuration) possessed a mutant phenotype (hence pseudoalleles). This puzzle was referred to as "position effect" and implied that the two mutations could function normally if they were present in the same chromosome but not if they were on different homologous chromosomes of the same cell. Early investigations of position effects in *Drosophila* by Lewis (1945) and by Green and Green (1949) showed that genes exhibiting such effects are linked within about 0.02–0.09 recombination units.

In these early investigations, the detection of rare genetic recombinants was limited by the laborious techniques available; for example, Green and Green (1949) had to examine 12,900 *Drosophila* fruit flies in order to recover 7 recombinants. Fortunately the discovery of mutations in bacteria and viruses, together with systems for inducing genetic recombination among them, soon made it possible to detect one recombinant among 10^8 microbes. The basic technique involves crossing two mutant forms, neither of which is able to grow without a nutritional supplement, and plating the progeny on a minimal medium (lacking any supplement); of the millions of bacteria present, only recombinant wild-type cells can survive. This type of experiment vastly increased the "resolving power" of genetic techniques, and soon led to the demonstration that a small percentage of recombination occurs *as a rule* between functional alleles; furthermore, such low-order recombination is usually (but not always) accompanied by a "position effect." The inevitable conclusion, that the unit of gene function is not the same as the units of gene mutation and recombination, was first put forward by Benzer (1955), whose experiments with the virus T4 will be described in the next section; he demonstrated that at least 244 separate mutation sites occur within the same (rIIA) "gene," all able to act as functional alleles when present in separate chromosomes, yet exhibiting a low percentage of recombination and producing wild type when present in the same chromosome. From these experiments, Benzer proposed that the term "gene" should be discarded and replaced by new terms for the units of function (cistron), of mutation (muton) and of recombination (recon). He estimated that the units of mutation and recombination are in the order of one to several DNA nucleotide pairs.

Further elucidation of the coding relationship between DNA, RNA, and protein, which has emerged largely from experiments with bacterial cell-free systems (Chapters 13 and 14) has now provided an even more specific conception of genetic mutation and recombination. In *E. coli*, for instance, the chromosome is a single Watson-Crick DNA molecule containing 4×10^6 nucleotide pairs; of these, a large fraction serve to code specific polypeptide amino acid sequences, every three nucleotides dictating one amino acid. Different nucleotide triplets often code for the same amino acid, different amino acids often function effectively at the same site in a polypeptide chain, and different polypeptides often co-operate as dimer or polymer aggregates (Chapters 12 and 14). These relationships lead to the following expectations:

1. The *E. coli* DNA molecule or chromosome is functionally differentiated into different regions which code for different polypeptides; each such region corresponds to a "gene."

2. Alteration of a single nucleotide pair will produce a genetic effect (i.e., an observable mutation) provided that the alteration leads to an amino acid substitution and that the amino acid substitution either partially or completely changes the functional properties of the polypeptide.

3. The *maximum* number of mutation sites in a gene is limited by the number of nucleotide pairs in the gene, which is expected to be three times the number of amino acids in the polypeptide.

4. All mutations within the same triplet are expected to direct amino acid substitutions at the same polypeptide site; since the code "degeneracy" is greater for the third (3′) nucleotide of the triplet, the latter nucleotides will give rise to amino acid substitutions less often than the others.

5. At a given nucleotide site the maximum number of alternative mutations, producing different amino acid substitutions at the same polypeptide site, is four (corresponding to four possible nucleotide pairs).

6. Mutations at different sites in the same gene are expected to have the same linear order as the corresponding amino acid substitutions in the polypeptide (colinearity).

7. Two homologous chromosomes, each containing a mutation in a different gene, can complement one another if they are present in the same cell, since each is able to code for the polypeptide which the other

lacks; the cell is therefore wild-type and in the old terminology the two mutations are nonallelic.

8. Two homologous chromosomes, each containing a mutation at a different site in the same gene, usually cannot complement one another when they are present in the same cell since neither is able to code for the complete, wild-type protein; the cell is therefore of mutant phenotype and, in the old terminology, the two mutations are alleles. (In some cases *intra*-allelic complementation has been observed, but the effect is believed to depend on compensation between the two mutant polypeptide chains when they form functional dimers or polymer aggregates.)

9. Genetic recombination (crossing-over) between two homologous chromosomes is a property of polynucleotide chains and occurs with approximately the same linear frequencies both between and within genes. In both cases, recombination produces one double-mutant chromosome and one wild-type chromosome (the latter accounting for position effect, i.e., a wild-type phenotype in cis but not trans configuration).

Although not all of these expectations have been critically demonstrated, many of them are now well established and the bulk of available evidence supports the remaining ones (discussed in the next section).

Single Nucleotide Pairs as Units of Mutation and Recombination

A conclusive demonstration of colinearity between a series of closely linked gene mutations and the corresponding amino acid substitutions of a polypeptide chain has been achieved in bacteria by Yanofsky and his collaborators (1964). Random mutations were first induced in *E. coli* with ultraviolet irradiation, and those mutations were selected which led to loss or inactivation of tryptophan synthetase activity. Early in the work Yanofsky found that activity of this enzyme depends on two polypeptide chains, both of which can be isolated by column chromatography and analyzed with respect to amino acid composition. However, only the "A protein" and its corresponding "A gene" have been extensively studied. The A protein itself consists of a single polypeptide chain with 280 residues (mol. wt. 29,000), within which a detailed sequence has been worked out for approximately 75 amino acids. From the many available tryptophan synthetase mutations, a detailed recombination map has also been worked out for 16 "A gene" mutations that cause specific amino acid substitutions in the 75 residue region. Since several mutations produce substitutions in the same amino acids, the 16 DNA sites correspond to only 9 polypeptide sites. However, as shown by Yanofsky, the linear order in the two series is exactly the same.

The fact that the gene mutations are colinear with the amino acid substitutions implies that each mutation is a local change in the DNA polynucleotide sequence that codes the polypeptide chain (Chapter 14).

The minimum units of mutation are presumably no larger than the minimum units of recombination, and in the *E. coli* chromosome the latter can be estimated by several methods. The simplest is based on the fact that the chromosome contains about 4×10^6 nucleotide pairs and exhibits approximately 2000 recombination units; this means an average recombination of 0.0005% per nucleotide pair. Although the *E. coli* conjugation system would permit detection of much lower recombination frequencies, the minimum map distance reported between any two mutations is, in fact, 0.0005% (Jacob, cited by Clowes, 1964). The transduction method employed by Yanofsky is less precise in establishing such standard recombination frequencies, but Henning and Yanofsky (1962) found two mutations separated by 1/625 to 1/2500 of the total map length of the A gene (tryptophan synthetase); since the A protein contains 280 amino acids, the A gene is expected to contain 840 nucleotide pairs, and 1/840 of the total recombination would therefore correspond to one nucleotide pair. Henning and Yanofsky also showed that these two, closely linked mutations produce amino acid substitutions at the same site in the 280-residue polypeptide chain, one inducing a substitution of glutamic acid for glycine and the other replacing the same glycine with arginine; this result is in accord with theoretical expectation, implying that both mutations occur in the same nucleotide triplet.

Even more impressive is the discovery that recombination between such closely linked mutations also leads to new and specific amino acid substitutions; for instance in a cross between two mutant strains, one containing the arginine substitution and the other containing a comparable valine substitution, recombinant types were isolated which contained either serine or the original glycine at the same site (Yanofsky, 1963). The effects of the original mutations, as well as the subsequent recombinations, can be understood best in terms of the triplet code recently elucidated by Nirenberg *et al.* (1965), and the overall relationship requires that the mutations and the recombinations both occur at the level of single nucleotide pairs. Thus:

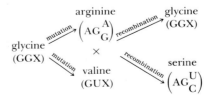

Yanofsky (1964) has also studied various back mutations or reversions, which partially or completely restore the activity of a mutant A protein. He finds that only a fraction of these reversions actually return the glycine residue to its original site in the polypeptide chain, and even these are not necessarily true "back mutations" (i.e., mutations that restore the original DNA nucleotide sequence). Other reversions act by producing a new specific amino acid substitution at the mutant site, thereby altering the inactive polypeptide chain to another mutant form which possesses partial or full enzymatic activity. Still other reversions seem to be mutations at entirely different sites in the same gene, which by themselves produce an inactive polypeptide, but in combination with the first mutation are able to compensate for one amino acid substitution with a second one elsewhere in the molecule. All these effects are consistent with the known relationships between the primary structure of proteins, such as hemoglobin and myoglobin, and their corresponding functional capacities (Chapter 12). The specific substitutions observed are also consistent with Nirenberg's amino acid code, and like the natural amino acid substitutions observed in mutant hemoglobin, they provide evidence that simple mutations correspond to single nucleotide changes. The following substitutions have been observed at a single polypeptide site in tryptophan synthetase:

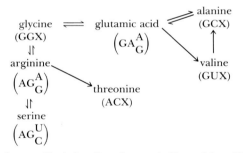

In one example studied by Brody and Yanofsky (1963), a limited amount of mutant A protein was restored to the wild-type amino acid sequence by a mutation in an entirely different gene (suppressor mutation); this could be explained in terms of known mechanisms of protein synthesis by postulating that the second mutation alters the specificity of an sRNA molecule or of a corresponding amino acyl RNA synthetase enzyme. Thus an altered DNA "message" may still signify the original amino acid sequence, provided that there is a compensating change in the mechanism of translation (i.e., the code book). Such suppressor mutations underscore the fact that the "information" of a DNA nucleotide sequence depends entirely on the system that translates the polynucleotide message into a specific polypeptide chain.

Functional Organization of Bacterial Chromosomes

Viral transduction experiments by Demerec and his colleagues have shown that the bacterium *Salmonella*, like *E. coli*, contains but a single chromosome which is characterized by a circular recombination map. In fact, at least 59 genes are homologous between *E. coli* and *Salmonella*, and these corresponding genes have very similar positions in the two recombination maps. Demerec's (1955) earlier genetic analysis in *Salmonella* contributed significantly to the realization that all microbial genes contain multiple mutation sites and exhibit intragenic recombination. Beyond this, at the level of multiple gene interactions, *Salmonella* revealed still another feature of chromosome structure; this is the tendency for different genes, directing the synthesis of metabolically related enzymes, to occur as clusters in localized parts of the chromosome.

The classic example of clustered genes is a series of 8 distinct loci concerned with biosynthesis of histidine in *Salmonella*; these genes are all closely linked and they correspond to 10 linked reactions mediated by separate enzymes, all of which are necessary for the synthesis of histidine. Over a thousand different histidine mutants have been mapped by transduction techniques, from which Ames and Hartman (1963) have concluded that the sequential order of the genes is E-F-A-H-B-C-D-G, while the order of corresponding enzyme reactions is G-E-A-H-F-B-C-B-D-D. Although the correspondence is not perfect, it is surprising that there should be any correspondence at all, since it is known that the homologous genes in the fungus *Neurospora* are not even linked. Recently Demerec (1964) has estimated that the genetic map of *Salmonella* contains about 130 genes, of which 87 are known to affect biochemically related reactions; of these, at least 63 (or 72%) are clustered into 17 functionally related gene groups.

Analysis of the *E. coli* linkage map indicates that a similar topography exists in this species and suggests a likely rationale for such clustering. In particular, a group of mutations has been analyzed by Jacob and Monod (1961a) which affect lactose metabolism in *E. coli* and which can be related to three separate proteins: (1) the enzyme β-galactosidase; (2) a galactoside-permease; and (3) a galactoside transacetylase. Synthesis of these three proteins is directed by three adjacent genes and remains at a very low level in the absence of lactose; however, in the presence of lactose or certain other inducers, the rate of synthesis for all three proteins increases several hundred-fold. Jacob and Monod (1961b) concluded that two distinct kinds of gene or gene mutation control the production of these inducible enzymes; one type is the familiar "structural gene," in which mutations lead to altered amino acid sequences partly or totally inactivating the corresponding enzymes; the other type is a "regulator gene," in which mutations do not alter the protein molecule itself but change the rate of synthesis, or maintain synthesis in the absence of inducer (so changing the inducible enzyme to a constitutive enzyme). As shown by Jacob and Monod (1961a), the regulator gene and three structural genes concerned with lactose metabolism in *E. coli* lie near one another in the same region of the chromosome; in addition, a special region near one of the structural genes has the capacity to respond to the regulator gene and is known as the "operator." Detailed experiments show that the three structural genes are under the control of the same operator, implying that the entire complex represents a functional unit or "operon." In the absence of lactose, the regulator gene produces a repressor molecule which turns off the operator and its three structural genes, preventing synthesis of the corresponding enzymes; in the presence of lactose, the repressor molecules are inactivated, the operator permits the structural genes to participate in messenger RNA synthesis, and enzyme synthesis follows (Fig. 15-4). Gilbert and Müller-Hill (1966) have recently isolated the

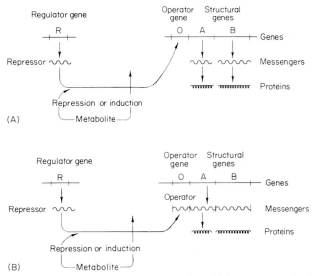

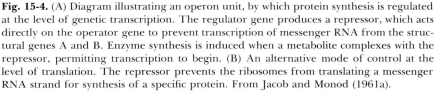

Fig. 15-4. (A) Diagram illustrating an operon unit, by which protein synthesis is regulated at the level of genetic transcription. The regulator gene produces a repressor, which acts directly on the operator gene to prevent transcription of messenger RNA from the structural genes A and B. Enzyme synthesis is induced when a metabolite complexes with the repressor, permitting transcription to begin. (B) An alternative mode of control at the level of translation. The repressor prevents the ribosomes from translating a messenger RNA strand for synthesis of a specific protein. From Jacob and Monod (1961a).

repressor molecule of the β-galactosidase system, showing that it is a protein of 150,000–200,000 mol. wt. Since one cell contains only about 10 repressor molecules per gene, the key to the isolation was the ability of these molecules to bind specifically to an inducer of β-galactosidase synthesis (isopropyl thiogalactoside). It appears that clustering of biochemically related genes in bacteria is a device which provides for coordinated control of the cell's synthetic machinery.

Since the introduction of Jacob and Monod's operon concept, many other examples of joint genetic control have been found. Such examples include the 8 linked histidine genes of *Salmonella*, which respond cooperatively to single mutational events, and whose corresponding enzymes exhibit coordinated increases or decreases in response to histidine starvation. Similar coordinated synthesis, or constant proportion among enzymes, has also been observed by Pette *et al.* (1962) in the glycolytic and respiratory enzymes of locusts and several vertebrates; however, it is not definitely known whether coordinated operon units exist in higher organisms.

Experiments described previously have shown that the *E. coli* DNA molecule contains special sites which variously control both DNA synthesis (replication) and RNA synthesis (transcription). Still another genetic control element of a unique type has been detected as a determinant of sex during conjugation. The capacity to act as a genetic donor (male) during bacterial conjugation was shown by Lederberg (1952) to depend on an autonomously replicating factor, which was called the "F factor" (for fertility). If an F^+ strain is mixed with an F^- strain, the F factor is transferred with almost 100% efficiency, even though only one donor cell in 10^4 actually transfers chromosomal DNA. Furthermore, a single F^+ cell can transform an entire suspension of F^- cells at a rate which requires that the F particle must replicate at least twice as fast as the chromosome itself. Jacob and Wollman discovered a special form of F which induces chromosome transfer at much higher frequency (ca. 1%) and accordingly is designated Hfr; in Hfr strains, the F factor is integrated into the chromosomal linkage group, replicates at the same rate as the chromosomal genes, and during mating is transferred as the last chromosomal marker. In fact, the specific chromosomal site at which the F particle is linked determines the strain-specific "origin" of the chromosome, i.e., the site at which DNA synthesis begins and the genetic marker that will be transferred first to the recipient cells. Subsequent studies (reviewed by Adelberg and Pittard, 1965) have permitted the physical isolation of F particles and a demonstration that they consist of double-stranded circles of DNA which are about 1.9% as long as the *E. coli* chromosome. About 10%

of the particle has an unusual base composition with 44% GC, whereas the remaining 90% resembles the *E. coli* chromosome itself in base composition and (partially) in base sequence. The main insight provided by the F factor is its ability to act as a facultative chromosomal gene, replicating autonomously in some cells and forming an integral part of the chromosome in other cells. Such facultative chromosomal elements have been termed "episomes" by Jacob and Wollman (1958), and other examples, such as temperate bacteriophages, are now known.

Expression of Genetic Information in Bacteria

A variety of investigations have served to confirm that the mechanisms of RNA transcription and ribosomal protein synthesis, as elucidated in cell-free systems, do actually operate in intact bacterial cells. Like DNA synthesis, the manufacture of RNA and protein (including induced β-galactosidase) goes on continuously in synchronized *E. coli* (Abbo and Pardee, 1960); however, the turnover rate for different RNA fractions varies considerably. Levinthal *et al.* (1962) have estimated that the half-life for the total messenger RNA fraction in *B. subtilis* is only 2-1/2 minutes, while ribosomal RNA is much more stable. Nevertheless ribosomal and transfer RNA's, like messenger RNA, seem to be made from a DNA template. Yankofsky and Spiegelman (1963) used the DNA–RNA hybridization technique (Chapter 12) to detect chromosomal base sequences (or genes) complementary to both the 23 S and the 16 S components of ribosomal RNA. In their procedure, isotopically labeled ribosomal RNA was melted (heat-denatured) with homologous chromosomal DNA, then slowly cooled; under these conditions, complementary segments of RNA and DNA form double-stranded hybrid molecules, which can be detected by their resistance to RNase and DNase digestion together with the presence of radioactive isotope. It was found that both the 23 S and 16 S components form hybrids with chromosomal DNA, and since they do not compete for sites, they are evidently coded by different genes.

Electron microscope autoradiography by Franklin and Granboulan (1965) has revealed that a 10-second pulse of uridine-^{3}H is incorporated by *E. coli* primarily in the body of the nucleoid, implying that RNA polymerase is localized there (in contrast to DNA polymerase, which seems to be associated with the cell membrane). Much of the labeled RNA appears in the cytoplasm within 30–150 seconds, suggesting an RNA migration from nucleoid to cytoplasm similar to that which occurs in higher cells (Chapter 17). As noted in Chapter 13, messenger RNA synthesis *in vivo* seems to transcribe only one of the two DNA polynucleotide strands. This was demonstrated by Guild and Robison (1963) in *Pneumococcus*, where the two complementary strands differ significantly in base composition and can be separated by density gradient centrifugation; it could be shown that the genetic expression of the heavier strand is significantly delayed relative to the lighter strand, evidently depending on replicative synthesis of a new complement. Experiments by Spiegelman and his colleagues have also shown that only one strand of double-stranded ϕX174 DNA is transcribed.

That β-galactosidase newly synthesized *in vivo* is bound to the ribosomes has been demonstrated directly by Zipser (1963), and other evidence shows that messenger RNA synthesis accompanies adaptive enzyme induction. Such messenger synthesis does not require DNA replication, but data obtained by Hanawalt and Wax (1964) suggests that each round of DNA replication is also accompanied by a round of transcription; in this way, a low level of β-galactosidase activity is maintained even in the absence of inducer.

Genetic Organization of Viruses

The RNA-containing tobacco mosaic virus was the first virus particle to be obtained in crystalline form (Stanley, 1935), and its physicochemical structure has now been worked out in great detail (described in Chapter 12). However, the TMV system has not yet been employed for experiments in genetic recombination; consequently the virus systems that are most thoroughly understood with respect to genetic organization are those of the bacteriophages T2, T4, and λ, which parasitize *E. coli*. Since these viruses multiply by integrating themselves into the synthetic machinery of a bacterial host, many of the genetic principles which apply to *E. coli* apply equally well to their phages. However, the greater simplicity of the viruses has made it possible in some instances to resolve finer details of genetic organization and consequently to establish more clear-cut proofs.

PHYSICAL ARRANGEMENT OF GENETIC MATERIAL

The T-even coliphages are tadpole-shaped particles of total mass 5×10^{-4} picograms, of which 40% is DNA (2×10^{-4} picograms) and the remainder largely protein. The head of the phage consists of a polyhedral, membraneous sac containing the bulk of the viral DNA and measuring about 950 Å by 650 Å (Fig. 15-5). The head membranes could be isolated as empty "ghosts" by Van Vunakis *et al.* (1958), who found that they consist of a homogeneous protein possessing an N-terminal alanine and a molecular weight of 80,000. Although this head

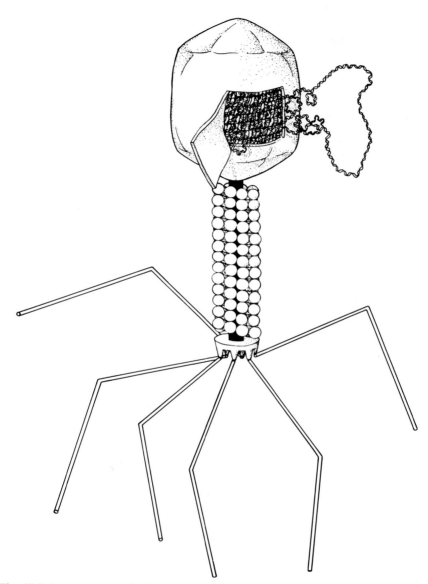

Fig. 15-5. Interpretation of ultrastructure in a T-even bacteriophage. The head contains about 52 μ of DNA helix, probably packed as a coiled coil. A contractile tail sheath consists of 144 protein monomers in a cylindrical array. Specific protein tail fibers provide a mechanism for adhering to the bacterial surface.

protein has the same molecular weight in T2 and T4, it can be distinguished in the two strains by its immunological properties. Finch *et al.* (1964) have studied the fine structure of "polyheads" formed by mutant T4, and have concluded that the head protein subunits are arranged as a helical tube, resembling tobacco mosaic virus in this respect, but differing in that the surface pattern is approximately hexagonal. In addition to the outer membrane and DNA, phage heads possess a lysozyme capable of attacking bacterial cell walls, plus a DNA-associated "internal protein."

The structure of the phage tail is relatively complex and involves several different protein components. The outside consists of a contractile sheath, which in the extended state is 800 Å long, 165 Å in diameter, and has a central opening 70–80 Å across. As noted in Chapter 9, this sheath is composed of 144 identical protein subunits (mol. wt. 55,000), possibly arranged as a helical chain (Fig. 15-5); after maximum contraction, it measures only 350 Å in length and 250 Å in diameter. Inside the sheath is a cylindrical pin or core about 80 Å in diameter with a central hole some 25 Å in diameter. At the head end of the sheath a "collar" is sometimes seen, while at the opposite end there is a flat "end plate" exhibiting the shape of a six-pointed star (Fig. 15-5); finally, attached to each point of the end plate is one of the six long, filamentous tail fibers, each fiber consisting of two protein molecules with molecular weights totaling about 100,000. It is apparent that the complete structure of the virus, while highly ordered, involves no more than 10 or 20 different types of protein, of which 80% consists of "head protein."

The DNA of the T-even phages is unusual because it contains hydroxymethylcytosine (HMC) instead of cytosine, and this HMC is also linked to glucose in a ratio that is characteristic for the particular strain; in T4, for instance, all the HMC is glucosylated whereas only 75% is glucosylated in T2. Phage DNA is very tightly packed into the virus head, where it is equivalent to an 80% solution; the closeness of packing, in fact, exceeds the semicrystalline packing of DNA-protamine in fish sperm (North and Rich, 1961). Such tight packing requires that the negatively charged phosphate groups must be neutralized by cations, and according to Ames and Dubin (1960) this function is normally accomplished by Mg^{++} together with the polyamines spermidine and putrescine (Chapter 13). The neutralizing molecules seem to be taken directly from a pool in the host bacterium, since viral spermidine can be replaced with spermine simply by growing the host bacteria on a spermine medium.

That the DNA of T2 phages consists of a single, long molecule was first suggested by the experiments of Hershey and Burgi (1960), who concluded from controlled shearing experiments that all the T2 DNA molecules are identical in length and chromatographic properties. Soon after, Cairns (1961) showed by autoradiography that T2 DNA can take the form of unbranched rods about 52 μ long, corresponding well with the estimated molecular weight of DNA in each phage (130 × 10^6). Kleinschmidt *et al.* (1962) also obtained impressive electron micrographs of ruptured T2 particles, showing long continuous loops of DNA with an average total length of 49 μ (Fig. 15-6); these micrographs give a good indication of the impressive DNA folding, which permits a molecule some 520,000 Å long to be packed into a phage head less than 1000 Å long.

Although the exact pattern of DNA packing in the T-even phages is not yet clear, several investigations have provided important clues. North and Rich (1961) succeeded in obtaining X-ray diffraction patterns from noncrystalline T2 preparations, and found that the pattern is similar to that of imperfectly oriented DNA. From this it could be concluded that only part of the DNA is oriented parallel to the phage axis, that the DNA remains in the B configuration (Chapter 12), and that it shows evidence of very tight hexagonal packing. There was also an indication that the DNA is organized into crystalline domains about 140 Å across. An analysis of DNA orientation in T4 was carried out by Gellert and Davies (1964), using flow birefringence; from their experiments they concluded that only 9% of the DNA is aligned parallel to the phage axis. From these and other investigations, Kilkson and Maestre (1962) have proposed that the 520,000 Å DNA molecule of T-even phages is coiled into a superhelix 61,000 Å long and 76.7 Å in diameter (an 8.7:1 coiling ratio); this long superhelix is then supposedly wound up in overlapping layers like thread on a spool (Fig. 15-5). Such an arrangement is consistent with the tight packing, and as shown by Maestre and Kilkson (1965) it is also consistent with the birefringence and other physical data.

A related problem is the mechanism by which the DNA is induced to coil up so tightly. Kellenberger *et al.* (1959) have shown that, during the growth of phages in an infected bacterium, the new DNA molecules assume "packed" configurations *before* the new virus particles are completed, i.e., apparently before the DNA becomes enclosed by a head membrane. Since inhibition of protein synthesis with chloramphenicol prevented the folding process, it was postulated that an "internal" protein brings about folding by attaching to the DNA. Later Minagawa (1961) characterized an acid-insoluble internal protein, which is attached to the DNA of phage T2 and accounts for 7% of the total phage protein. Chaproniere-Rickenberg *et al.* (1964) attempted to induce folding of T2 DNA by adding purified internal protein to a DNA solution *in vitro;* although they detected a configurational change, the amount

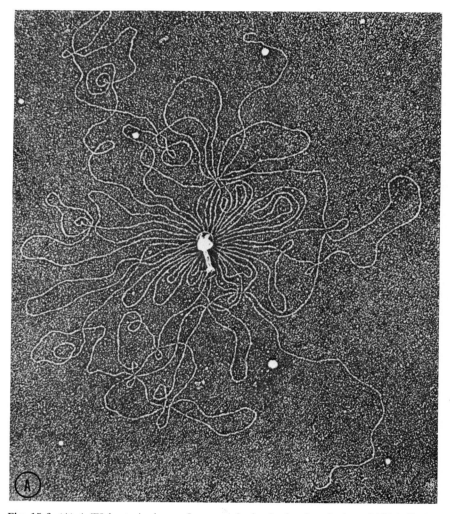

Fig. 15-6. (A) A T2 bacteriophage after osmotic shock, showing the long DNA helix (or chromosome) released from the head; the chromosome is more than 500 times as long as the phage head. 61,800×. From Kleinschmidt *et al.* (1962).

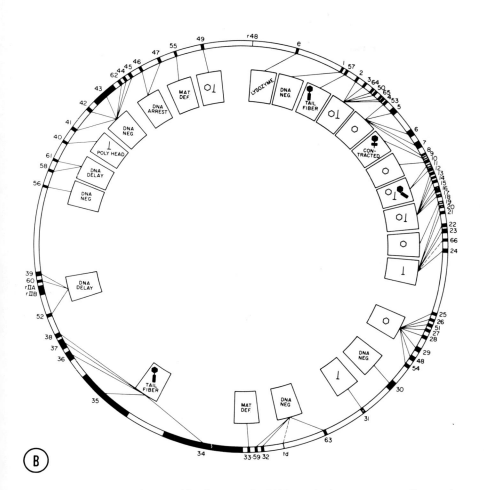

Fig. 15-6. (B) A genetic recombination map for T4 bacteriophage, corresponding to the chromosome shown in (A). The map is circular and shows clustering of genes concerned with DNA synthesis (upper left), head and tail synthesis (upper right), and tail fiber synthesis (lower left). From Edgar and Wood (1966).

of folding was far short of that achieved in the intact virus. Consequently this problem remains to be solved.

That viral DNA molecules can occur in a circular form was first inferred in ultracentrifuge experiments by Fiers and Sinsheimer (1962), using the single-stranded DNA of bacteriophage ϕX174. It was noted that a slower-sedimenting, noninfective ϕX-DNA can be derived from the infective DNA by a single chain break, but that this break does not alter the molecular weight; by contrast, further breakage gives rise to fragments of lower molecular weight. Since enzymatic data also indicated that infective ϕX-DNA lacks free 3′ and 5′ hydroxyls, it was concluded that the faster-sedimenting form is a circular molecule, which is converted to an open chain by a single breakage event. Subsequently Kleinschmidt *et al.* (1963) confirmed by electron microscopy that the double-stranded (replicative) form of ϕX-DNA is a circle of 1.64 μ circumference, while the single-stranded (infective) form is a circle of 1.77 μ circumference. Weil and Vinograd (1963) also found circular DNA molecules in polyoma virus, where the circumference is 1.58 μ (corresponding to a DNA molecular weight of 3.0×10^6). DNA in the temperate coliphage λ also occurs in circular form, with a total length of 17.2 μ (MacHattie and Thomas, 1964); however, in this case infectivity depends on opening of the ring, which according to experiments by Strack and Kaiser (1965), occurs at a specific site. The ends of the open DNA molecule are "sticky," but exposure to a DNA polymerase reaction causes them to lose this property; as correctly interpreted by Kaiser, the two ends of the helix possess short, single-stranded protrusions about 20 nucleotides long, which end in 5′ carbons. The left and right ends are not identical but are complementary to one another (Hershey and Burgi, 1965), and in fact Wu and Kaiser (1968) have recently begun to work out the exact base sequences of the single-stranded ends. A λ DNA molecule enters the host bacterium in its linear form, but shortly afterward the ends cohere, forming a circular molecule. The single-strand breaks at the joining site are then closed covalently by polynucleotide ligase, an enzyme isolated recently by Olivera and Lehman (1967). Finally the completely covalent, circular helix is induced to super-coil by slight changes in the helical twist of the two DNA chains (Bode and MacHattie, 1968). It is clear that the phage λ chromosome is specifically organized for reversible transitions between the circular and open-chain forms of DNA.

Viral Genetics

The foundations of viral genetics were established in the mid-1940's by a group of far-seeing pioneers, including Delbrück, Demerec, Luria, and

Hershey. Of all viruses, bacteriophages were the material of choice, since they permitted a technique in which a weak suspension of virus particles could be plated on a "lawn" of *E. coli* (i.e., a uniform bacterial scum growing on the surface of an appropriate medium in a petri dish). Wherever a single virus fell on the lawn, the ensuing cycle of infection, reinfection and local bacterial lysis produced a clear spot or "plaque." Consequently by this method the number of virus particles in a suspension could be estimated, and by altering the strain of bacteria used for the lawn, mutant phages of restricted host range could be detected. Later on, Hershey (1946) introduced a new type of mutation, in which the average size of the plaques was altered.

The mechanics of phage infection were not well understood until the classic experiments of Hershey and Chase (1952), who showed that osmotic shock separates a phage particle into two major components, one containing almost all the phage DNA and very little protein, the other containing all the protein sulfur. They determined that it is the protein membrane of the phage which protects its DNA from DNase digestion, and that after adsorption of phage to dead bacteria, the viral DNA becomes available to DNase. Finally by labeling the protein component with ^{35}S, or alternatively the DNA with ^{32}P, they demonstrated that almost no ^{35}S is transmitted from the parent phages to their progeny, but that 30% or more of the ^{32}P is transmitted. These experiments showed that during viral infection, it is primarily DNA which enters the bacterium, and consequently it must be DNA which transmits the characteristics of the parent to the offspring. Together with the bacterial transformation experiments of Avery *et al.* (1944), this work by Hershey and Chase helped to establish that DNA possesses the properties of the hereditary material.

The Process of Phage Infection

The events which occur during infection of an *E. coli* cell by a T-even phage have been carefully investigated by many different laboratories, using biochemical, cytological, and electron microscope techniques. The major facts can be summarized as follows:

1. The phage particle attaches to the bacterial cell wall by its tail fibers, which partly determine the host specificity. Thus antisera against phage tails inactivate the particles, whereas antisera against the heads do not (Franklin, 1961).

2. The tail sheath contracts, driving the central hollow pin through the bacterial cell wall in the manner of a hypodermic syringe; this process is accompanied by release of inorganic phosphate from ATP and other high energy compounds contained by the virus.

3. The viral DNA together with its attached "internal protein" is injected into the bacterium through the 25 Å hole in the center of the tail pin. Since the dimension of this hole is only slightly larger than a single, open-chain Watson-Crick helix, the DNA cannot be circular during injection.

4. Synthesis of *E. coli* DNA, RNA, and protein stops immediately; within 1 minute the bacterial nucleoids begin to move toward the cell wall, where they become vacuolate as DNA is depolymerized.

5. Within 2 minutes, messenger RNA molecules appear which have been synthesized from the phage DNA as template. As discussed in Chapter 14, the existence of messenger was first demonstrated in the phage system, where Brenner *et al.* (1961) discovered that preexisting *E. coli* ribosomes are employed for the synthesis of phage proteins. Later Hall and Spiegelman (1961) demonstrated that the phage-induced RNA is specifically complementary to phage DNA. Spiegelman (1963) has also shown that slightly different parts of the T2 DNA molecule are transcribed at different times after infection.

6. Within 4 minutes, phage-specific "early proteins" begin to appear, including a T2 DNA polymerase (Aposhian and Kornberg, 1962), "interior protein" (Minagawa, 1961), an enzyme which converts bacterial cytosine to viral hydroxymethylcytosine, a CTPase, and enzymes which add glucose to HMC after DNA synthesis is complete.

7. Within 6 minutes, phage DNA is in process of replication at about 5 times the usual rate of *E. coli* replication. As first shown by Levinthal (1956), replication of phage DNA proceeds in a semiconservative fashion.

8. Within 8 minutes isolated tail cores, tail sheaths, and tail fibers can be seen in infected cells by electron microscopy.

9. Within 10 minutes phage DNA begins the transition from an extended (vegetative) state to a condensed (particulate) state. At this time, 60% of the protein synthesized in the bacterium is phage "head protein" and synthesis of internal protein has also reached its maximum rate. Soon afterward, the condensed DNA is enclosed by its "head protein" membrane.

10. Within 11 minutes the tail sheaths and "pins" join the phage heads; within 12 minutes the tail fibers are added and the phages are essentially complete.

11. Synthesis of more phages continues until about 20 minutes after infection when the bacterium lyses, releasing 100–200 new virus particles.

Recently Wood and Edgar (1967) have begun a much more detailed, *in vitro* analysis of the self-assembly process by which specific head or tail proteins aggregate in the correct pattern to form a complete phage particle. For example, they have found that a tail core is required for the proper assembly of a contractile tail sheath. Consequently it is clear that the timing of protein synthesis, which provides the core protein before the sheath protein, is an important feature of bacteriophage morphogenesis.

Virus Genes and the DNA Molecule

The experiments of Hershey and Chase (1952), described above, left little doubt that viral nucleic acid is the actual carrier of genetic information. Subsequently it has become clear that, as in bacteria, all DNA viruses investigated thus far possess only a single, long DNA molecule, which corresponds to a single genetic linkage group. The identity between viral "chromosomes" and single DNA molecules has been established most clearly in the temperate phage λ, for which Kaiser and Hogness (1960) were able to show that a 95% pure DNA extract can infect bacteria and give rise to complete phage particles. Later Kaiser (1962) demonstrated that when the intact λ DNA molecule is broken in two, each half transmits a corresponding half of the viral genes. Although λ DNA occurs in circular form, its recombination map is linear—a relationship that might be expected since the DNA is infective only in open-chain form. Transmission of virus characters by a pure nucleic acid extract has also been demonstrated for tobacco mosaic virus; these plant viruses contain linear, single-stranded RNA instead of circular, double-stranded DNA, but nevertheless they exhibit very similar gene-polynucleotide relationships (to be discussed).

Since the coliphages employ *E. coli* ribosomes and other parts of the bacterial synthetic machinery, it might be expected that phage DNA would be coded in a manner similar to bacterial DNA; a great deal of evidence is now available to confirm this supposition. As noted previously, Benzer's (1955) genetic analysis of the rII region in phage T4 was one of the first to demonstrate multiple mutation sites and recombination within a gene. Mutant polypeptide chains corresponding to the rII mutations have not yet been isolated, but mutants can be recognized by their inability to grow on *E. coli* of strain K and by the large plaques they form. Using these characters, Benzer tested several hundred rII mutations for recombination distance and ability to complement one another in trans position. His method was to infect the same bacteria simultaneously with two types of mutant phage (making them effectively diploid for virus characters), then to score the resulting plaques for mutant or wild-type character; the appearance of wild-type plaques represents complementation between the two original mutants, indicating that they affect different polypeptide chains. The progeny viruses (F_1) can then be plated and scored as separate virus particles in order to detect the frequency of genetic recombination (or cross-over). Benzer found that all rII mutations belong to one of two complementation groups (or cistrons), such that mutations within the same group cannot "complement" to produce wild-type plaques in the first generation, but can recombine at low frequencies to produce wild-type in the second generation; mutations in different cistrons, on the other hand, are able to complement in the first generation *and* recombine in the progeny. Although there were other possibilities, Benzer found that noncomplementing mutations also show linear recombination relationships, such that each of the two complementing groups maps in a specific region of the chromosome and therefore corresponds to a "gene." At present over 244 mutable sites have been demonstrated in the "A" gene and 129 in the "B" gene, all showing perfect linearity. Detectable mutations are more frequent at some sites than at others, as might be predicted from known differences in nucleotide code degeneracy (Chapter 14).

Colinearity between a series of phage genetic mutations and a specific amino acid polypeptide sequence has also been demonstrated by Sarabhai *et al.* (1964) for the structural gene controlling T4 "head protein." Their method exploits a type of mutation known as *amber*, which can occur in any part of the genetic map and which, when it occurs in the head protein gene, results in synthesis of partial polypeptide fragments. Sarabhai compared the peptide content of different head protein fragments corresponding to *amber* mutations at 10 different sites in the head protein gene; he found that these fragments could be arranged in a linear order according to their lengths (i.e., peptide contents). Recombination data then gave the linear order of the mutations, which turned out to be the same as the order of peptides. These and other experiments described previously serve to establish that the characteristics of viral "genes" are those expected if genes correspond to segments of a DNA molecule responsible for coding individual polypeptides (as in *E. coli*).

That genetic recombination in T2 is accompanied by a physical transfer of DNA segments was first demonstrated by Hershey and Burgi (1956). Phage DNA in one genetic strain was labeled with ^{32}P, and the viruses were then crossed with unlabeled phages of another genetic type. It was found that 65% of the parental ^{32}P could later be recovered in recombinant progeny exhibiting the genotype of the unlabeled parent. In one major theory of genetic recombination (copy choice), recombinants would not be expected to contain any parental DNA. Consequently Hershey and Burgi's observations indicate a remarkably site-specific breakage and rejoining of DNA molecules from different parents. The exact mechanism of this site-specific recombination is not yet known, but it apparently does not occur in the currently available cell free systems.

Single Nucleotide Pairs as Units of Mutation and Recombination

The unit of recombination in phage T4 can be estimated from the total recombination length of the chromosome (about 2500 map units) and the number of nucleotide pairs in the chromosome (1.5×10^5); by simple division, an average recombination per nucleotide pair can be estimated as 0.016%. In striking correspondence to this, Benzer has found that the smallest recombination between different sites in the rII region is 0.02%, even though a recombination of one in 10^8 could theoretically be detected. Somewhat more sophisticated calculations by Stahl *et al.* (1964) for the lysozyme gene of T4 are in agreement with the conclusion that the units of recombination in phages, as in *E. coli*, are probably single nucleotide pairs; it is noteworthy, however, that the amount of recombination per nucleotide pair is evidently some 40 times greater in phages than in bacteria. Possibly this difference is related to a greater stability of the *E. coli* circular chromosome, as compared with the phage open-chain chromosome.

In viruses it has been possible to carry out very sophisticated experiments in chemical mutagenesis, which serve to confirm that chemical alterations of individual nucleotides have all the properties of classical gene mutations; in fact, chemical mutagenesis promises to be a powerful tool in the analysis of specific DNA nucleotide sequences. Most experiments so far have employed one of three major types of mutagen:

1. The acridine dyes are planar molecules which are able to occupy spaces between and among base pairs in double-stranded DNA; in contrast to many types of mutation, acridine-induced rII mutations do not revert, and consequently they seem to represent deletions of base pairs rather than transitions between A-T and G-C. The two classes of reverting and nonreverting mutations also occur spontaneously, of which the nonreverting characteristically map as extended (multi-site) deletions. By contrast, acridine mutations usually behave as single-site or "point" mutations. There is also a possibility that acridine treatment can sometimes lead to base pair additions, thereby suppressing a previous base pair deletion.

These characteristics of acridine mutations were employed by Crick *et al.* (1961) to demonstrate a direct relationship between single gene mutations and the triplet code. They studied a series of suppressor (+) and antisuppressor (−) mutations in the B gene of the rII region, and found that combinations of three (or six) + mutations, or alternatively three (or six) − mutations, lead to restoration of the wild-type phage. On the other hand, combinations of 2, 4, or 5 acridine mutations still produce mutant type phages (Chapter 14). This result is readily understood if each mutation represents a deletion or addition of one base pair, and if the addition or deletion of three base pairs is less serious than the addition or deletion of one or two. Since the three additions (or deletions) could not all be in the same triplet, Crick's findings also imply that the mutation sites function in a manner that would be predicted if they are "read" sequentially from a fixed point, as in cell-free polypeptide synthesis; in this case a single base pair deletion would disrupt reading of the entire message, whereas three deletions would permit correct reading of most of the message. This same interpretation is supported by a multi-site deletion found in T4 by Champe and Benzer (1962), which removed the end of the A gene and the beginning of the B gene; this deletion had the effect of linking the A and B regions of the chromosome, so that viruses carrying the deletion could no longer complement with A gene mutants. Such observations are all consistent with the concept that a single gene is a DNA segment which codes a single polypeptide, that the genetic code is identical with the triplet code found in cell-free systems by Nirenberg, and that alterations in single nucleotide pairs cause mutations by altering the triplet sequences.

2. Base analog substitutions have been shown to induce mutations in the head protein gene of phage T4. For example, 5-bromouracil is readily incorporated into DNA in place of thymine, forming a base pair with adenine; however during subsequent replications it can occasionally pair with guanine instead of adenine, thereby altering an A-T pair to a G-C pair. Similarly, 2-aminopurine is an analog of adenine, which is believed to cause transformations in both directions between A-T and G-C. Finally, hydroxylamine reacts specifically with cytosine to produce a base analog that pairs with adenine, altering a C-G pair to A-T.

These chemically induced base substitutions have been employed by Brenner *et al.* (1965) to analyze the triplet code words involved in *ochre* and *amber* mutations. For instance, since hydroxylamine does not induce reversions of *ochre,* it can be concluded that the *ochre* DNA triplet does not contain a cytosine-guanine pair; other restrictions lead to the conclusion that the code word for *ochre* is UAA and the one for *amber* is UAG. Since the effect of *amber* is to produce a partial fragment of head protein, it has been concluded that UAG is probably a code for terminating the polypeptide chain (thereby dividing a continuous DNA molecule into different genes). This conclusion is reinforced by the fact that the UAG sequence apparently does not specify any amino acid in Nirenberg's polynucleotide-amino acid code (i.e., it represents a "nonsense" triplet; Chapter 14).

3. Nitrous acid has been found to act as a potent mutagen for tobacco

mosaic virus, which contains RNA rather than DNA. This reagent is a deaminating agent, capable of altering cytosine to uracil and adenine to hypoxanthine (which then pairs with cytosine); its primary effects, consequently, are to change RNA nucleotides from C to U, and from A to G (in effect). It has been shown by Tsugita (1962) that nitrous acid treatment of TMV leads to replacement of proline by leucine, serine by phenylalanine, and other substitutions which are consistent with single nucleotide changes in the amino acid code of Nirenberg. Nitrous acid mutations in TMV also exhibit first-order kinetics, implying that a single deamination event corresponds to a mutation (Mundry and Gierer, 1958). Unfortunately, genetic analysis in the plant viruses has been hindered by a lack of techniques for obtaining and measuring recombination and genetic complementation.

Functional Organization of Bacteriophage Chromosomes

The concept that the T-even bacteriophages possess a circular recombination map was first proposed by Streisinger *et al.* (1964), based on crossover relationships between three mutations which could not be represented on a linear map. At that time relatively few phage genes were known, but the subsequent discovery of two classes of "conditional lethal" mutations has made it possible to fill in the map and confirm its circularity. The key to this success has been provided by the *amber* mutations discovered by Epstein *et al.* (1963), and by the temperature-sensitive (*ts*) mutations explored by Edgar and Lielausis (1964). Phages carrying a *ts* mutation can grow in their hosts at 25°C but not at 37°C, making it possible to maintain the virus line under one set of conditions, and to study the mutant effect under the other set of conditions. Using this approach, Epstein *et al.* (1963) found different *ts* mutations which affect different virus structural proteins; e.g., at 37°C the lysates from infected bacteria may contain heads but no tails, tails but no heads, or various other combinations of phage fragments. An analysis of over 382 *ts* mutations by Edgar *et al.* (1964) revealed that the T4 chromosome contains at least 49 genes arranged in circular order (Fig. 15-6), and with notable functional groupings (as in *E. coli*). Genes affecting the synthesis of "early proteins" and enzymes necessary for DNA replication are grouped in one part of the map, while genes affecting the tail and head structural proteins are in other parts. Since the 52 μ DNA molecule of the T-even phages seems to exist only in an open-chain form, it is puzzling that the recombination map should be circular. This problem has been investigated by Foss and Stahl (1963) and by Streisinger *et al.* (1964), who have concluded that a small number of genetic loci are present in duplicate at the two ends of the chromosome. It can be shown that recombination between corresponding genes in the terminal parts of the chromosome leads to circularity in the overall recombination map.

Champe and Benzer (1962) found experimental evidence that, as in *E. coli*, only one strand of the T4 DNA molecule is transcribed into messenger RNA; the base analog 5-fluorouracil was used to replace uracil during mRNA synthesis, and this had the effect of substituting cytosine for uracil in the triplet code words. It was found that this treatment reverses the mutant phenotype of some, but not all, rII mutations. Correlations between genetic reversion of specific mutants by 2-aminopurine and phenotypic reversal of the same mutants by 5-fluorouracil suggested that, of all mutant A-T pairs, only about half produce a U-containing message; this would correspond to expectation if the thymine member of the A-T pair is in the "sense" strand about half the time, and in the complementary "nonsense" strand the other half of the time. Strangely enough, 5-fluorouracil does not produce mutations in tobacco mosaic virus, even when it replaces 40% of the uracil.

The messenger activity of another RNA virus, the phage MSϕ2, has been investigated by Ohtaka and Spiegelman (1963) in a cell-free system derived from *E. coli*. This virus contains RNA of molecular weight one million, which codes for at least three proteins, including a coat protein and an RNA-dependent RNA polymerase (Chapter 13). The virus "message" is therefore clearly polycistronic, yet the authors found that even *in vitro* the rate of protein synthesis differs for the various cistrons (or genes) of the same RNA strand. Evidently there is a built-in control mechanism, which permits one part of the messenger RNA strand to be read more frequently than other parts.

16

SYNTHESIS IN NUCLEATED CELLS

1. THE CYTOPLASM

It seems likely that a high concentration of nucleic acids is the basis of the generally noted basophily of embryonic tissues. .,. . The presence of pentose nucleotides in high concentration in rapidly dividing tissues is probably thus a general phenomenon.

T. O. CASPERSSON AND J. SCHULTZ *1939*

The findings here presented are compatible with our general hypothesis [that] the digestive enzymes are synthesized by the attached RNP particles, transferred across the limiting membrane into the cavities of the endoplasmic reticulum, segregated temporarily into intracisternal granules, and finally packed and stored in the form of mature zymogen granules.

P. SIEKEVITZ AND G. PALADE *1958*

The clearest and most reliable understanding of protein and nucleic acid synthesizing mechanisms has been obtained from experiments with cell-free systems (Chapters 13 and 14). Nevertheless, such isolated systems are only simplified models of the synthetic process as it occurs in living cells, and they usually lack important structural restraints or regulatory mechanisms that are clearly essential for long-term viability. Macromolecular synthesis in higher cells is typically associated with conspicuous organelles and structural changes that have long intrigued the cytologist. The recently elucidated biochemical mechanisms have now made it possible to reinterpret this important area of cytology, and such a reinterpretation constitutes the subject of this and the following chapter.

At the structural level cell synthesis is most conspicuous both in glandular tissues, which are specialized for intensive production of one or very few species of molecule, and in embryonic tissues, which exhibit a rapid and generalized process of growth. During the last part of the 19th century, many cytologists noted that such tissues are characterized by intense basophilic staining both in the nucleus and in the cytoplasm. The term "ergastoplasm" was coined by Garnier (1897) for localized regions of the cytoplasm showing a strong affinity for basic stains; in the cell bodies of neurons, similar basophilic regions were also referred to as "Nissl substance," and in this instance the affinity for basic stains was very early understood to be due to the presence of nucleic acid, which binds such stains in salt linkages. Berg (1920) also called attention to the fact that the amount of cytoplasmic basophilia is highly variable and becomes notably reduced in the cells of starved animals.

Earlier investigations of cytoplasmic synthesis were greatly hampered by confusion regarding the chemistry of nucleic acid, particularly the lack of a distinction between RNA and DNA. The existence of two classes of nucleic acid in all cells was not understood until after the work of Feulgen and Rossenbeck (1924), who detected the presence of "thymus nucleic acid" in the nuclei of plants. Caspersson and Schultz (1939) were the first to infer that "pentose nucleotides" (RNA) are the basis for cytoplasmic basophilia, basing their studies on gross chemical analysis combined with UV microspectrophotometry at the 2600 Å nucleic acid absorption maximum. The isolation of a specific RNase by Kunitz (1940) provided a method for contrasting the intracellular distribution of RNA and DNA, by comparing basophilic staining before and after RNase digestion. This method was exploited very early by Brachet (1940), who confirmed Caspersson's conclusion about RNA in the cytoplasm and also demonstrated that the nucleolus is rich in RNA. An entirely different approach was pioneered by Claude (1938, 1941), who

442

attempted to characterize the various cytoplasmic inclusions by homogenizing tissues in mass and separating the homogenates into different centrifugal fractions. After removal of larger fragments, nuclei, and mitochondria, a fraction was obtained which contained "submicroscopic particles" or microsomes, estimated to be about 600–2000 Å in diameter and unusually rich in RNA; subsequently the microsomes were shown by Hultin (1950), Siekevitz (1952), and others to be active in protein synthesis. Thus the classic correlation between basophilia and cell synthesis was extended to successive correlations between basophilia and RNA, between RNA and the microsome fraction, and between the microsome fraction and protein synthesis.

By good fortune these advances coincided with the introduction of thin-section electron microscopy, which soon made possible a much more precise characterization of cytoplasmic morphology. Even before the introduction of ultrathin sectioning, Porter *et al.* (1945) used the electron microscope to examine unsectioned tissue culture cells and described a "lacelike reticulum" in the cytoplasm. During the late 1940's this newly discovered system of cytoplasmic tubules, sacs, and lamellae was reported in a variety of different cell types and came to be called the endoplasmic reticulum (Porter and Thompson, 1948). When thin-sectioning was introduced in the early 1950's, Palade and Porter (1954) systematically established an identity between the endoplasmic reticulum as recognized in unsectioned cells, and various types of membrane-enclosed tubules and cisternae found in the cytoplasm of sectioned cells (Fig. 16-1). They also noted that in some instances the outer surfaces of the vesicles are covered with small granules 150–200 Å in diameter (first described by Dalton *et al.*, 1950), and in other cases they are without granules or "smooth." In cells which are synthesizing proteins very actively, the granular (or "rough") ER often increases enormously, so that the cisternae become closely packed together and assume concentric forms surrounding the cell nucleus (Fig. 16-1). In this state the endoplasmic reticulum can sometimes be distinguished *in vivo* by phase contrast microscopy (Fawcett and Ito, 1958). In starved animals, on the other hand, Fawcett (1955) showed that the rough ER is considerably reduced or absent.

As information developed concerning both cytoplasmic fine structure *in situ* and the characteristics of the microsome fraction *in vitro*, these two lines of research were integrated in an important study by Palade and Siekevitz (1956). These authors examined both intact rat liver cells and rat liver microsomes with the electron microscope, concluding that the microsome fraction is identical with the rough endoplasmic reticulum and that the rough ER is identical with the ergastoplasm

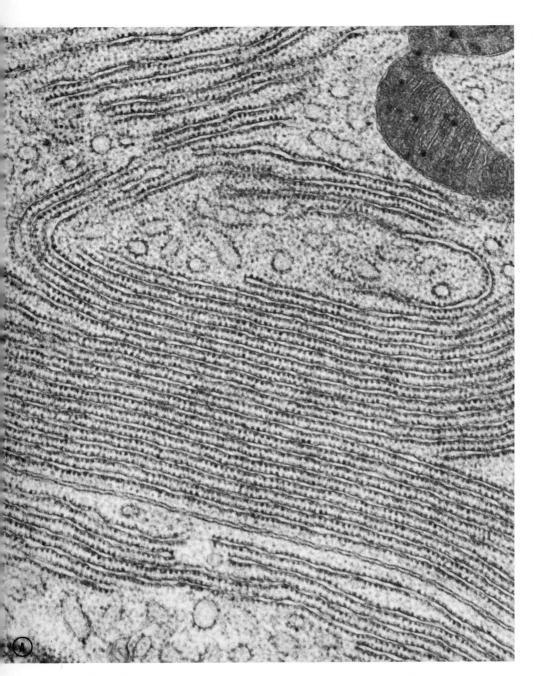

Fig. 16-1. (A) Rough endoplasmic reticulum from bat pancreas, showing ribosomes attached to typical lamellar membranes, 70,000×. From S. Ito, by permission.

444

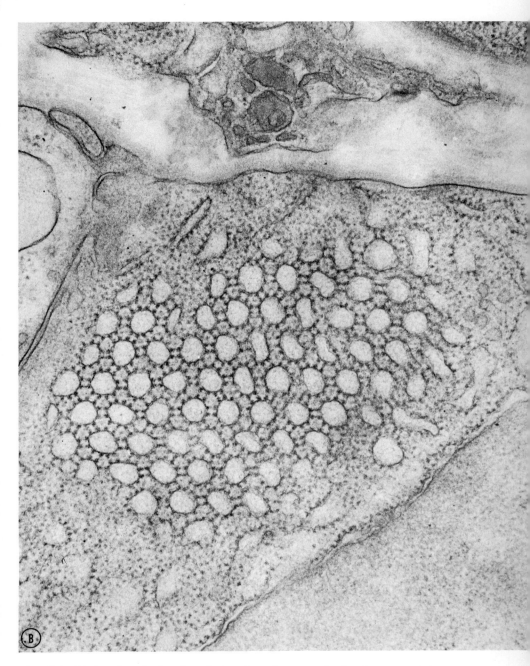

Fig. 16-1. (B) Rough endoplasmic reticulum from bat stomach, showing unusual, hexagonally packed tubules, each surrounded by 12 ribosomes. Note that the tubule contents differ in density from the surrounding ground plasm. 60,000×. From Ito and Winchester (1963).

of classic light microscopists. Furthermore, by examining preparations after RNase treatment, they showed that most of the RNA associated with microsomes is contained in the granules, which subsequently have come to be known as ribonucleoprotein (RNP) particles or ribosomes. Later studies have made it clear that the ribosome particles and the membraneous endoplasmic reticulum are two distinct structures, which are often found in association with one another, but sometimes not. In mammalian reticulocytes, in embryonic tissues, and in bacteria such as *E. coli*, the ribosomes act as sites of protein synthesis in the complete absence of endoplasmic reticulum. By contrast, other tissues such as mammalian testicular interstitial cells, contain an abundant smooth ER which is largely lacking in ribosomes. The structure and function of ribosomes, as well as their mutual association into polyribosomes, have been extensively discussed in Chapter 14; in this chapter the endoplasmic reticulum and its derivatives will be described. In summary, it may be stated that the cytoplasmic basophilia, or ergastoplasm, of classic authors represented concentrations of RNA-containing ribosomes, which occur both in association with endoplasmic reticulum and as free polyribosomes. In both states, ribosome aggregates are the immediate sites of cellular protein synthesis and tend to be most abundant in cells which are actively growing or producing glandular secretions.

The Endoplasmic Reticulum

The tubular, vesicular, or cisternal membrane systems of the endoplasmic reticulum are found most abundantly in the cytoplasm of mature, differentiated cells; they are often absent in eggs and in many embryonic or undifferentiated cells. In essence, this system represents an intricate arrangement of membrane-bounded spaces, which always have a distinct inside and outside. As observed in isolated microsomes by Palade and Siekevitz (1956), the vesicles also have the properties of osmometers, showing that the ER membranes are semipermeable. A single ER membrane is typically about 50–60 Å in width and shows the "unit membrane" structure described by Robertson (1959), i.e., two osmiophilic layers separated by an osmiophobic layer. In addition, almost all the lipid of isolated microsomes is associated with the membranes (i.e., the deoxycholate-soluble fraction), and this consists primarily of phospholipids (especially lecithin and cephalin) plus cholesterol, as is usual for membraneous cell structures (Chapter 10).

The shape and size of the membrane-enclosed ER spaces varies considerably from one cell type to another. Many cells, in fact, possess two distinct forms of ER which are in continuity with one another (Fig. 16-2): the first is a latticelike system composed of tubules 500–1000 Å in diameter, the membranes of which are not associated with ribosomes (smooth ER); the second is a system of platelike, flattened cisternae 400–500 Å in width, to which ribosomes adhere on the *outside* surfaces (rough ER). The close relationship between these two systems is indicated not only by the continuity of their membranes in regions of contact, but by Fawcett's (1955) observation that the reappearance of rough ER in liver cells of rats that have been starved and refed begins with the appearance of smooth, tubular ER (together with free cytoplasmic ribosomes). As

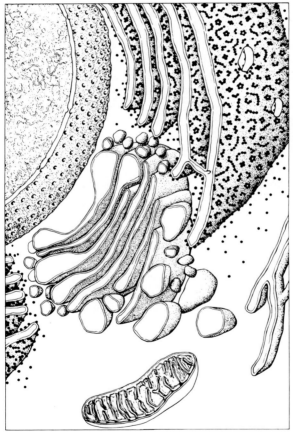

Fig. 16-2. Interpretation of endoplasmic reticulum (ER) and Golgi ultrastructure. Polyribosomes line the outer surfaces of the rough ER vesicles, but are lacking from the Golgi membranes and the smooth ER (bottom right). The Golgi apparatus has a "forming face" nearest the nuclear envelope, and a "maturation face" opposite.

might be expected, rough ER predominates in cells which are actively synthesizing proteins, whereas smooth ER is prominent in cells whose metabolism is geared to nonprotein types of synthesis (Christensen and Fawcett, 1961).

In the classic cytology of secretory cells, it was commonly observed that the secretory product takes the form of visible cytoplasmic particles, or secretory granules. For instance in the exocrine pancreatic cells of vertebrates, digestive enzymes are synthesized and accumulated as zymogen granules, which often become quite numerous before being released in successive cycles. Siekevitz and Palade (1958) used differential centrifugation to isolate zymogen granules about 6000 Å in diameter from guinea pig pancreas and demonstrated that these granules possess very high proteolytic and RNase activity; the same authors (1958) then succeeded in isolating "intracisternal granules" (about 1000–4000 Å in diameter) from the ER of the same cells. These intracisternal granules possessed enzyme activities nearly equal to those of the completed zymogen granules, indicating that the newly synthesized enzymes are deposited in the ER before being formed into zymogen granules. Finally, Siekevitz and Palade (1958) succeeded in showing that these cells incorporate ^{14}C-labeled leucine first in the attached ribosome fraction (outside the ER membranes), then in the intramicrosomal spaces (inside the ER membranes), and finally in the zymogen granules themselves. These observations make it clear that the endoplasmic reticulum, at least in guinea pig pancreatic cells, functions as a depot and transport system for nascent proteins. The protein molecules are first synthesized on the ribosomes at the outside surface of the endoplasmic reticulum, after which they enter the interior of the ER, are formed into intracisternal granules, and finally are released as membrane-enclosed zymogen granules. Evidence reviewed by Palade (1961) also suggests that the Golgi apparatus participates in this process, possibly by "packaging" the intracisternal granules in a surrounding membrane.

Porter (1964) has demonstrated essentially this same sequence during the secretion of collagen fibers by vertebrate fibroblasts. These cells possess a very extensively developed endoplasmic reticulum and a widely distributed Golgi system. If they are exposed to a pulse of ^{3}H-proline (which is incorporated primarily into collagen in these cells), then examined in electron microscope autoradiographs, the label is found first in the cisternae of the endoplasmic reticulum, then in the Golgi spaces, and finally in the extracellular collagen. There is evidence that the collagen-containing Golgi vesicles migrate to the cell surface, fuse with the plasma membrane, and discharge their contents in a process which is essentially a reversal of pinocytosis. This finding is all the more intriguing because a relationship between "true" pinocytosis vesicles and the ER spaces has been demonstrated in rat intestinal cells by Palay and Karlin (1959). In their experiments, fasted rats were fed with corn oil, their intestinal cells were fixed at time intervals, and the corn oil droplets were then detected and localized by their osmiophilic "staining" properties. After 20 minutes the fat droplets were found primarily in pinocytosis vesicles beneath the brush border, but after 60 minutes they were found distributed inside the endoplasmic reticulum and in the Golgi spaces.

From these investigations it seems clear that the ER functions as an intracellular transport system, both for nascent proteins and at least sometimes for lipids. Still another type of transport is suggested by the fact that, in cells containing both ER-attached and unattached ribosomes, it is the attached ribosomes which are most active in protein synthesis; this suggests that the ER may provide a pathway for messenger RNA to move from the nucleus to the cytoplasmic ribosomes. Continuities between the ER and the nuclear envelope have often been reported, and Ernster *et al.* (1962) have confirmed earlier observations that the ER membranes themselves contain about 25% of the total microsomal RNA (the remainder being accounted for by ribosomes). Membrane-bound messenger RNA has also been reported recently in sporulating bacteria by Aronson (1965). Rough ER cisternae cut in tangential sections show that the attached ribosomes are in the form of polyribosomal circles and chains, implying an association with messenger RNA strands (Fig. 16-2; see Bonnett and Newcomb, 1965).

Beyond the general transport function of the ER, there is impressive evidence that a number of specific enzymes are bound to the reticulum membranes in rat liver, and may actually constitute a structural part of the ER in the same way that oxidative enzymes form a structural part of the mitochondrial membranes (Chapter 7). NADH-cytochrome c reductase activity, which was first reported in rat liver microsomes by Hogeboom (1949), has been shown by Ernster *et al.* (1962) to be associated with the microsomal membranes rather than with the ribosomes or the vesicle contents. The function of this electron carrier is not known, since microsomes do not contain cytochrome c; however they do contain a distinctive cytochrome b_5. Also associated with the microsomal membranes are NADH diaphorase, glucose-6-phosphatase, and Mg^{++}-activated ATPase. Essner and Novikoff (1962) have shown cytochemically that the ER rapidly hydrolyzes UDP, GDP, and IDP, besides exhibiting thiaminepyrophosphatase activity; a direct electron microscope cytochemical demonstration of ATPase activity has also been provided by Wachstein and Fernandez (1964). Since most of these enzymatic activities are associated with energy transfer or release, there is a strong suggestion that the endoplasmic reticulum engages in dynamic energy-requiring processes. One of these processes is apparently the *de novo* synthesis of lipids and phospholipids, which has been shown to occur in isolated microsomes (Siekevitz, 1963).

Significant clues concerning other processes mediated by the endoplasmic reticulum have been obtained from comparative observations of the abundance of "smooth" ER in different cell types. For instance in mouse liver cells, a rapid buildup of glycogen occurs just before birth followed by a rapid decline due to increased glucose-6-phosphatase activity. Peters *et al.* (1963) have shown that the depletion of glycogen is accompanied by an increase in the amount of tubular ER in glycogen-rich areas of the cytoplasm, and Rosen (1964) has confirmed cytochemically that the tubular ER in these cells (like the rough ER) possesses glucose-6-phosphatase activity. It therefore appears that the ER membranes in these cells function in glycogenolysis. Still another activity of the endoplasmic reticulum has been found in the interstitial cells of mammalian testes, where a smooth, tubular ER is extremely abundant and fills most of the cytoplasm (Christensen and Fawcett, 1961). Lynn and Brown (1958) showed that microsomes derived from testicular tissue have the ability to catalyze the oxidation of progesterone to testosterone and acetic acid. This oxidation involves four enzymes, all of which are found to be more active in a particulate (or membrane-bound) state; furthermore, their activity is destroyed by lipase (which hydrolyzes lipids) but not by trypsin or RNase.

Smooth ER is abundant in striated muscle fibers, where it is generally called "sarcoplasmic reticulum" and where Porter and Palade (1957) found that the vesicles are arranged metamerically in close relationship to the contractile sarcomeres (Fig. 8-1). Hasselbach and Makinose (1962) have shown that isolated sarcoplasmic reticulum (microsomes) carry-on an extremely active, ATP-dependent uptake of calcium ions from solution (i.e., active transport into the ER spaces); in this process, calcium may be concentrated inside the vesicles as much as 1400-fold. Though it is not known whether the ER carries out active transport in other types of cell, it is tempting to speculate that the membrane-bound ATPase found by Ernster *et al.* (1962) in rat liver microsomes may function in active transport like the membrane-bound ATPase of the plasma membrane (Chapter 11).

At present the manner of origin of the endoplasmic reticulum is not definitely known; the most concrete hypothesis is that the ER is "budded" off from the nuclear envelope. Continuities between the nuclear envelope and ER have often been reported, and Barer *et al.* (1959) found evidence that the nuclear envelope re-forms from ER-like vesicles after cell division. An identity is also suggested by Essner and Novikoff's (1962) discovery that both the nuclear envelope and the ER membranes catalyze hydrolysis of UDP, GDP, and IDP, and by the fact that in rat liver cells both membranes have glucose-6-phosphatase activity. In pancreatic and other cells, ribosomes are attached to the outside membrane of the nuclear envelope. A possible objection to this concept is Fawcett's (1955) observation that, in fasted and refed rat liver cells, new ER seems to appear first near the cell periphery.

The most notable structural difference between the ER and the nuclear envelope is the presence of numerous conspicuous annuli, about 500–1000 Å in diameter, in the nuclear envelope. Such annuli are not generally seen in the endoplasmic reticulum, but cytoplasmic membranes known as "annulate lamellae" occur in invertebrate and vertebrate oocytes, spermatocytes, and some types of somatic cell. These were first described by Afzelius (1955) and named by Swift (1956), both of whom noted a striking morphological similarity to the nuclear envelope. Merriam (1959a) also concluded from his electron microscope analysis that the annulate lamellae of echinoderm eggs arise by proliferation from the nuclear envelope, and that 150 Å ribosome-like particles are associated with these membranes. Rebhun (1956) also established an identity between basophilic regions in the oocytes of clams and snails, and geometric arrays of annulate lamellae. More recently Kessel (1963) has confirmed that the annulate lamellae of salamander oocytes arise by budding from the nuclear envelope. The function of these lamellae and the question of whether they represent an intermediate stage in the formation of endoplasmic reticulum, have not yet been settled.

The Golgi Apparatus

Although the Golgi complex was first discovered by Golgi (1898) in the neurons of owls and cats, it was not accepted as a universal organelle in plant and animal cells until the development of thin-section electron microscopy during the early 1950's. At that time, Dalton and Felix (1953) became the first to describe its characteristic fine structure, reporting that it consists of three major constituents: (1) flattened, membrane-enclosed cisternae; (2) dense vesicles about 600 Å in diameter; and (3) large, apparently empty vacuoles (Fig. 16-3). Like the smooth endoplasmic reticulum, the elements of the Golgi apparatus are sacs enclosed by a 60 Å unit membrane and they lack attached ribosomes; several

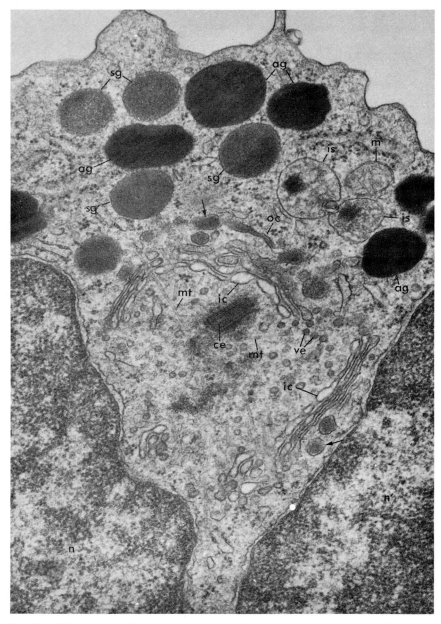

Fig. 16-3. Thin-section of a leukocyte, showing the centrosome complex lying in a pocket of the nucleus (n,n′). The complex consists of a centriole pair (ce) surrounded by vesicles of the Golgi apparatus (ve, ic); in addition, microtubules (mt) radiate out from the centrioles to the outer cytoplasm. The large dense granules near the cell surface (sg, ag) are primary lysosomes, which are believed to develop from the Golgi vesicles. 40,000×. From Bainton and Farquhar (1966).

authors, in fact, have detected apparent continuities between the Golgi membranes and the membranes of the ER, and some investigators regard the Golgi complex as a differentiated part of the ER. Morphologically, however, the Golgi apparatus is a distinctive, disk-shaped organelle, the membranes of which tend to lie closer to one another than those of the ER (Fig. 16-2). The spacing between Golgi cisternae is typically about 115 Å, and the intracisternal space is about 60–90 Å. Cunningham *et al.* (1966) have studied the fine structure of Golgi complexes isolated intact from onion stem tissues; they find that there is an extensive system of anastomosing tubules 200–400 Å in diameter, which surrounds the central membranous elements. Typically the Golgi complex lies near the nuclear envelope in close proximity to the centriole pair (Fig. 16-4). In mammalian leukocytes a system of radiating microtubules arises from the centrioles, traverses the Golgi membranes, and extends into the cytoplasm (Fig. 16-3); this entire complex constitutes the centrosome, which is visible *in vivo* by phase contrast microscopy and within which a radial streaming of cytoplasmic particles is conspicuous.

During the era of light microscopy there was a great deal of uncertainty regarding the occurrence and function of the Golgi complex. This was partly due to the difficulty in staining it, which generally depended on its ability to reduce silver or osmium ions, and partly to the use of different names for the same structure as it was found in different types of cell. For instance, in spermatids and plant cells the term "dictyosome" was often used, and there was divided opinion as to whether the dictyosome was homologous with the Golgi apparatus of neurons. Despite this confusion, it was recognized that the Golgi complex tends to be more prominent in cells that are synthetically active, and sometimes seems to increase in total amount during synthesis. As has been established by electron microscopy, some cells do possess multiple sets of Golgi complexes. Bowen (1929) also reported an apparent relationship between the dicytosome of spermatids and the development of the sperm acrosome (a caplike structure at the anterior end of the mature spermatozoan); this study tended to support the concept of the Golgi apparatus as a synthetic organelle.

At the present time, electron microscopy has confirmed several instances in which the Golgi system participates conspicuously in cell synthetic activities. In fact, Whaley *et al.* (1964) have pointed out that the Golgi complex typically shows a structural polarity, such that one surface seems to be a "forming face" composed of flat, empty sacs, and the opposite side is a "maturation face" where the sacs become bloated and rounded out with unspecified contents. Bowen's early light micro-

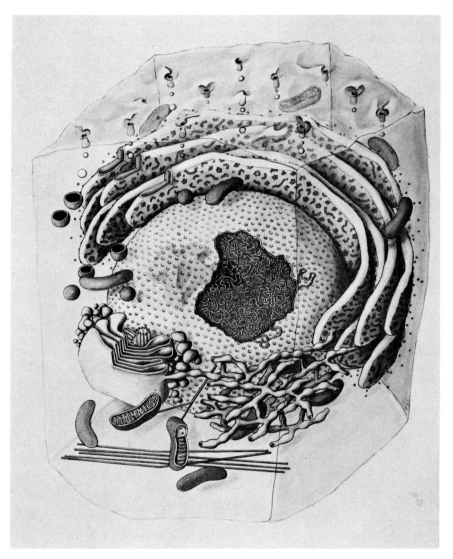

Fig. 16-4. A generalized eukaryote cell. The nucleus consists of a nuclear envelope with hexagonally arranged annuli, enclosing a mass of chromatin fibers. Rough ER is typically lamellar, while smooth ER is typically tubular. Mitochondria are sometimes connected to the nuclear envelope by microtubules. A Golgi complex lies near the nucleus, partly enclosing a pair of centrioles. The plasma membrane exhibits active pinocytosis (top).

scope observations on spermatids were confirmed and extended by Burgos and Fawcett (1955), who found that in differentiating cat spermatids the Golgi apparatus becomes entirely reorganized, and one or more enlarged Golgi vacuoles develop a dense, proacrosomal granule. Both granule and vacuole then continue to enlarge until the mature acrosomal vesicle has been completed. An even more striking example has been studied by Slautterback and Fawcett (1959) and Slautterback (1961) during the differentiation of cnidoblasts in the polyp *Hydra*. Each cnidoblast is able to develop a highly complex, capsule-enclosed nematocyst, which possesses a triggering device and a harpoon-like stinging barb. Differentiation begins with a striking increase in the total amount of rough ER in the cytoplasm; more or less simultaneously, one of the Golgi vacuoles becomes enormously enlarged, apparently filling up with a structureless fluid. The inside wall of the vacuole is gradually reinforced by a thick capsule, and somewhat later the barbed sting and associated complex structures of the nematocyst suddenly and spontaneously condense from the structureless contents (Fig. 9-6). This process is surely one of the most startling and still mysterious events that has been described at the electron microscope level.

In a few systems it has been possible to identify the contents of the Golgi vacuoles. As previously noted, the newly synthesized collagen of fibroblasts or digestive enzymes of exocrine pancreatic cells enter the endoplasmic reticulum spaces, and it has been shown by electron microscope autoradiography that these proteins eventually penetrate the Golgi vacuoles; in all probability such vacuoles contribute the limiting membranes of the zymogen granules. A similar "packaging" of hydrolytic enzymes by the Golgi membranes seems to give rise to primary lysosomes in some cells. This conclusion was suggested by Novikoff *et al.* (1964) when they found by electron microscope cytochemistry that acid phosphatase activity is concentrated in some but not all Golgi vacuoles. Bainton and Farquhar (1966) have now confirmed that in rabbit leukocytes two different kinds of primary lysosome are formed in this manner: at one stage, dense azurophile granules about 8000 Å in diameter arise from the concave face of the Golgi, whereas at another stage less dense "specific granules" about 5000 Å in diameter arise from the opposite, convex face (Fig. 16-3).

In some cases the Golgi complex seems to be involved in the synthesis of nonprotein secretions. For example the secretion of norepinephrine by neurosecretory cells can be followed very precisely in thin sections because the raw product (norepinephrine) is electron dense and appears black in the electron microscope. Exploiting this fact, Sano and Knoop

(1959) demonstrated that norepinephrine-containing secretory granules form first from Golgi vacuoles. More recently Neutra and Leblond (1966) have reported that glucose-^{3}H is incorporated into mucus glycoprotein by the Golgi apparatus of intestinal goblet cells. The diversity of these synthetic relationships has led to the concept that the Golgi complex may represent a packaging area, in which newly synthesized materials are accumulated from the endoplasmic reticulum, possibly with the simultaneous removal of water, and then are discharged as membrane-enclosed particles.

With respect to the chemical composition of the Golgi apparatus, early centrifuge experiments showed that this structure has a relatively low density, moving to the centripetal pole in the manner of lipid-rich components. Later Kuff and Dalton (1959) succeeded in isolating a bulk "Golgi fraction" from homogenized rat epididymis tissue, and confirmed that this fraction is rich in phospholipid. The isolated Golgi fraction also showed acid phosphatase activity, which may have been due to an involvement of the Golgi system in the formation of primary lysosomes; according to cytochemical observations of Novikoff and others, lysosome formation may not be an invariable activity of the Golgi. Bulk isolation of the Golgi complex from onion stem tissue has also been achieved by Cunningham *et al.* (1966).

There has as yet been no clear demonstration concerning the manner of origin of the Golgi apparatus; however the most likely possibility is that it arises as a differentiation of the endoplasmic reticulum. Numerous observations of structural continuity between the ER and Golgi membranes have been reported, and Essner and Novikoff (1962) showed that both types of membrane possess thiaminepyrophosphatase activity. It has been suggested that there may be a dynamic process of membrane flow, in which the ER membranes are proliferated from the nuclear envelope and then continually transform into Golgi membranes, which are continually used up in the formation of lysosomes or secretory granules. Such a membrane-flow hypothesis would provide a very effective mechanism to account for the rapid transport of particles and molecules through the ER and Golgi spaces.

Cytoplasmic Synthesis Associated with Other Organelles

Although the endoplasmic reticulum, ribosomes, and the Golgi apparatus are the most conspicuous organelles of cytoplasmic synthesis, recent investigations have shown that comparable synthetic machinery operates in chloroplasts, mitochondria, and possibly centrioles. All the latter structures, when isolated in bulk from fractionated cells, are capable of carrying on protein synthesis. In addition, chloroplasts and mitochondria are known to contain DNA of characteristic types, and both of these carry on DNA-dependent RNA synthesis. Detailed discussions of synthesis associated with chloroplasts, mitochondria, and centrioles can be found in Chapters 5, 7, and 9. In addition, the interrelationship of cytoplasmic and nuclear synthesis is dealt with in Chapter 17.

17

SYNTHESIS IN NUCLEATED CELLS

2. THE INTERPHASE NUCLEUS

. . . the nucleus alone suffices for the inheritance of specific possibilities of development.

E. B. WILSON *1896*

. . . in 1885 [Rabl concluded] that the chromosomes lose neither their identity nor their grouping at the close of the division, but are only lost to view by branching out and anastomosing to form the framework of the resting nucleus.

E. B. WILSON *1925*

The presence of a membrane-enclosed nucleus is a constant feature in plant and animal cells, a fact which was first emphasized by Schleiden and Schwann (1839) soon after Brown (1833) first described and named the nucleus in the cells of orchids. During the last half of the 19th century the nucleus received intensive cytological study in the same period when Miescher (1871) was pioneering the isolation of nuclei in bulk for biochemical analysis. A gradual sophistication of nucleic acid biochemistry occupied the early decades of the 20th century, until by the early 1940's it was understood that the nucleus has a notably rich DNA content and the cytoplasm is rich in RNA. These discoveries set the stage for the first serious investigation of DNA as the material basis of heredity.

The concept of DNA inheritance was introduced for debate by the discovery of Avery *et al.* (1944) that *Pneumococcus* extracts capable of inducing inherited transformations in bacteria seemed to owe their activity to DNA rather than to protein. Soon afterward the same idea was extended to plant and animal tissues largely through the discovery that the amount of DNA per chromosome set is remarkably constant in a given species. Boivin *et al.* (1948) were the first to postulate that the genetic material should be constant in amount per nucleus and to show by extraction of bulk isolated nuclei that DNA fulfills this criterion. Almost simultaneously Mirsky and Ris (1949) succeeded in adapting Feulgen staining of DNA for quantitative microspectrophotometry, permitting them to demonstrate cytochemically that the amount of DNA *in individual nuclei* is approximately constant per chromosome set. For example the DNA amount in haploid sperm nuclei and diploid somatic nuclei of the same species is found to be in a ratio of $1:2$; furthermore, the absolute amounts of DNA per nucleus are not diminished by starvation, in marked contrast to the effects on RNA content. Swift (1950a) confirmed this DNA constancy for plant tissues, where he found classes of nuclei containing 2, 4, 8, 16, or 32 times the haploid DNA amount. In growing tissues, Swift (1950b) also found nuclei containing DNA amounts intermediate between the exact ploidy classes, which he correctly interpreted as nuclei at an intermediate stage of replicating their DNA before cell division.

The average haploid amount of DNA may be considered as a constant characteristic for a given species (although variations up to $\pm15\%$ would go undetected in most microspectrophotometric techniques). As first noted by Mirsky and Ris (1951), this haploid DNA amount varies widely from one species to another in a way that is not obviously related to the complexity of the organisms. For example, they determined that the amount of DNA per diploid nucleus in the salamander *Amphiuma* is about 168 picograms (one picogram = 10^{-12}g), whereas many birds con-

459

tain no more than 2.4 picograms. In the plant *Tradescantia,* according to Van't Hof and Sparrow (1963), the diploid DNA content is about 59 picograms. A review by Vendrely (1955) indicates that most terrestrial vertebrates (reptile, bird, mammal) have diploid DNA contents of 6 picograms or less, whereas aquatic vertebrates (fish and amphibians) have much higher amounts. In nondividing human diploid cells, Leuchtenberger *et al.* (1954) determined the DNA content as 5.6 picograms, equivalent to approximately 174 cm of Watson-Crick DNA molecule.

Within a given species, there is sometimes a proportionality between the DNA content (or ploidy) of the nuclei in different tissues and the corresponding nuclear volumes. This was first noted by Boveri (1905) in haploid, diploid, and tetraploid sea urchin larvae, where it was found that the surface areas of the nuclei are directly proportional to the chromosome number; Van't Hof and Sparrow (1963) also noted a linear relationship between DNA content and nuclear volume across six genera of plants. In other cases, however, this relationship is not observed. Such volume-mass proportionalities, when they occur, imply a tendency toward a constant intranuclear DNA concentration; when the proportionality is absent, wide differences in DNA concentration can be found between the nuclei of different tissues or species. An extreme case is represented by the sperm nuclei of trout, in which the DNA-protamine complex accounts for 91% of the dry weight of the nuclei, whereas in liver cells the DNA-chromatin accounts for only about 64%, and the DNA alone for 18% of the total dry weight.

Among the other components of the interphase nucleus, RNA was demonstrated cytochemically by Brachet (1942) both in the nucleolus and in chromosomes. Not long afterward, Mirsky and Pollister (1946) showed that RNA-protein complexes can be extracted free of DNA with 0.14 M NaCl; these early investigations made it clear that intranuclear RNA occurs, but that it is quantitatively a fairly minor constituent. In rat liver cells less than 5% of the nuclear dry mass is RNA, and of the total cellular RNA, 85–90% is found outside the nucleus. Despite its restricted amount, the intranuclear RNA is distributed among several fractions, including the nucleolus, the chromatin, and the nuclear sap (Table 17-1). RNA is easiest to stain in the nucleolus because it is relatively concentrated there, but in terms of percent dry mass, only about 3–5% of isolated nucleoli is accounted for by RNA.

As might be expected from the above data, the greatest part of the nuclear dry mass in somatic cells consists of protein. Early chemical analyses of nuclei isolated in aqueous media tended to underestimate the nuclear protein content because a great deal of material was leached out by the suspension medium; however, after techniques were introduced for fractionating cells and isolating their nuclei in nonaqueous media (e.g., cyclohexane-carbon tetrachloride mixtures), ratios of intranuclear protein to DNA were found in the order of 2.8 (calf thymus) to 7.3 (horse liver; Allfrey et al., 1952).

Nuclei in different tissues often vary widely in volume while preserving a constant diploid DNA content; such variations sometimes reflect a tendency toward a constant nucleocytoplasmic volume ratio, such that larger cells have larger nuclei and vice versa; in other cases, synthetically active cells often develop enlarged nuclei with greatly expanded, convoluted surfaces. These adjustments in nuclear volume generally do not involve a diminution in intranuclear protein concentration, implying that the total protein mass increases with the size of the nucleus. The percentage of total cell mass accounted for by the nucleus has been estimated by Allfrey et al. (1952) to vary from 5% in beef heart to 61% in calf thymus. In this respect the nuclear protein fraction differs from DNA, which typically remains constant in amount in all tissues (unless somatic polyploidy occurs), and which must therefore diminish in concentration as nuclear volume and mass increase.

Fractionation of intranuclear proteins began with the pioneer studies of Mirsky and Pollister (1942, 1946) on histones, nonhistone proteins, and their complexes with DNA. As refined by Mirsky and Ris (1948), the technique involved isolation of nuclei in 0.14 M NaCl, followed by extraction of chromatin (DNA, histone, and DNA-linked nonhistone protein) with 1–2 M NaCl; after this treatment, some nonhistone protein and RNA remained as an insoluble residue. Subsequently the use of nonaqueous media for isolation of nuclei revealed that still another protein and RNA fraction had been extracted by the 0.14 M NaCl (Table 17-1). In modern refinements of the sequential extraction technique, it is possible to recognize several major classes of intranuclear protein:

1. Soluble "nuclear sap" proteins extractable in 0.14 M NaCl
2. Sedimentable ribonucleoprotein particles extractable in 0.14 M NaCl
3. Basic histones, extractable with DNA in 1–2 M NaCl (subfractionation of different histones has been discussed at length in Chapter 12).
4. Nonhistone proteins linked to DNA and extractable with DNA in 1–2 M NaCl
5. Nonhistone proteins not linked to DNA and insoluble in all concentrations of salt. Most or all of this fraction is "acid protein," extractable with 0.05 N NaOH (Steele and Busch, 1963).

The percent dry weight accounted for by these fractions in liver nuclei, together with their relative contents of DNA and RNA, are listed in Table 17-1.

By far the best-known component of intranuclear protein is the histone fraction, which makes up about 20% of the dry weight of liver nuclei. In the terminology employed by many authors, the histones are

Table 17-1

FRACTIONATION OF ISOLATED LIVER NUCLEI
BY DIFFERENTIAL EXTRACTION[a]

Fraction	Percent dry weight		
		Fraction	
	Nucleus	DNA	RNA
0.14 M NaCl	17.0	1.5	3.4
0.10 M Tris	5.3	6.8	10.9
2.0 M NaCl-1	54.0	31.1	5.2
2.0 M NaCl-2	10.0	12.2	5.1
0.05 N NaOH	5.6	0.3	8.9
Residual	2.2	0.0	0.6

[a] From Steele and Busch (1963).

defined as basic proteins linked to DNA, and this linkage is primarily by ionic bonds between negatively charged phosphates and positively charged basic amino acid side chains. A remarkable quantitative correspondence between histones and DNA was first demonstrated cytochemically by Alfert *et al.* (1955) in rat thyroid nuclei, and confirmed in rat liver and tissue fibroblast nuclei by Bloch and Godman (1955). These authors measured the amount of DNA in individual nuclei by microspectrophotometry after Feulgen staining, and then measured the amount of histone in the same nuclei by microspectrophotometry after fast green staining. It was found that cells containing polyploid amounts of DNA also contain polyploid amounts of histone, and that in nuclei preparing for cell division, both the DNA and histone contents double more or less synchronously. These findings subsequently were confirmed for various plant species in a cytochemical analysis by Rasch and Woodard (1959) and an autoradiographic study by De (1961). The close quantitative correlation between DNA and histone has also been supported through direct chemical analyses by Davison and Butler (1956) and Crampton *et al.* (1957), who found that the ratio of total basic amino acids in histone to total DNA phosphate in the same cells is close to 1 (actually about 0.9). Correspondingly the total mass of histone extractable from a given tissue is usually nearly the same as the mass of DNA present (Table 17-2).

In addition to the histones, the DNA-complexed proteins include a major nonhistone fraction, which accounts for 27% of all the DNA-associated protein in calf thymus nuclei. Although this fraction is not as well characterized as the histones, it certainly includes RNA polymerase, the enzyme responsible for mediating transcription of genetic information from DNA to RNA. Weiss (1960) first demonstrated that the RNA polymerase of rat liver, calf thymus, and ascites tumor nuclei is an "aggregate enzyme" which can be extracted with the DNA in 1 M NaCl, but resists purification from the chromatin; similar properties are exhibited by the RNA polymerase of pea seedlings (Huang et al., 1960). DNA polymerase, the other major enzyme of nucleic acid synthesis, is usually a much more soluble enzyme, but Littlefield et al. (1963) have shown that this enzyme moves from the soluble to the particulate fraction during DNA synthesis in mouse fibroblasts. It is difficult to imagine that DNA polymerase would not form part of the DNA-linked protein during replication, and there is direct evidence for such a linkage in bacteria (Chambon, DuPraw, and Kornberg, 1968). In addition to polymerases, the DNA-associated fraction apparently includes NAD synthetase and nucleoside triphosphatase, both of which are extracted in 1 M NaCl but not in 0.14 M NaCl (Busch, 1965). The newly discovered histone acetylases also appear to be DNA-linked, and there is a phosphoprotein fraction which constitutes up to 15% of the DNA-linked nonhistone protein (Frenster, 1965b). The native complex of DNA with its many types of histone and nonhistone protein (as well as a small amount of RNA) is commonly referred to as "chromatin," and it is notable that the percent dry weight composition of the chromatin fraction (1 − 2 M NaCl soluble) is very similar in a wide variety of plant and animal tissues (Table 17-2).

The soluble, or "nuclear sap," proteins extractable in 0.14 M NaCl are often quantitatively the most important fraction of intranuclear protein, but they are probably also the most variable from one tissue to another. Some of these proteins may actually have little or no significance for nuclear function, e.g., hemoglobin, which Stern et al. (1952) found inside the nuclei of avian erythrocytes. On the other hand, the soluble enzymes of anaerobic glycolysis, including aldolase, PGAD, enolase and pyruvate kinase have been shown by McEwen et al. (1963) to contribute to the energy metabolism of interphase calf thymus nuclei. Other enzymes which are present and conspicuous inside nuclei are

Table 17-2
CHEMICAL COMPOSITIONS OF VARIED CHROMATINS[a]

Source of chromatin	Content, relative to DNA, of				Template activity (% of DNA)
	DNA	Histone	Nonhistone protein	RNA	
Pea embryonic axis	1.00	1.03	0.29	0.26	12
Pea vegetative bud	1.00	1.30	0.10	0.11	6
Pea growing cotyledon	1.00	0.76	0.36	0.13	32
Rat liver	1.00	1.00	0.67	0.043	20
Rat ascites tumor	1.00	1.16	1.00	0.13	10
Human HeLa cells	1.00	1.02	0.71	0.09	10
Cow thymus	1.00	1.14	0.33	0.007	15
Sea urchin blastula	1.00	1.04	0.48	0.039	10
Sea urchin pluteus	1.00	0.86	1.04	0.078	20

[a] From Bonner *et al.* (1968).

adenosine deaminase, guanase, and the enzymes of the monophosphate shunt (glucose-6-phosphate dehydrogenase, etc). It was discovered by Frenster *et al.* (1960) that the 0.14 M NaCl extract of calf thymus nuclei includes ribonucleoprotein particles which, like cytoplasmic ribosomes, are active in protein synthesis both *in vivo* and *in vitro;* associated with these nuclear ribosomes are the enzymes of protein synthesis, including specific amino acyl RNA synthetases (Chapter 14). However, according to Busch such RNP particles may be absent or rare in liver nuclei.

Besides DNA, RNA, and protein, calf thymus and other nuclei contain significant amounts of cofactors, precursor molecules, and various salts. NAD, ATP, and acetyl-CoA are present, as well as the other nucleoside mono- and triphosphates (AMP, GMP, CMP, and UMP) and the intermediate metabolites of glycolysis and the citric acid cycle (Chapter 6). A significant nuclear uptake of amino acids has also been demonstrated (Naora *et al.*, 1962). Finally, sodium and potassium ions appear to be actively transported into the nuclei of frog oocytes, where they reach concentrations 2–3 times greater than in the cytoplasm; there is evidence that sodium functions to neutralize a fraction (about 10%) of charged DNA phosphate groups.

The Ultrastructure of Interphase Nuclei

THE NUCLEAR ENVELOPE

The nucleus is essentially a membrane-enclosed space, within which is preserved the major component of cellular DNA, together with DNA-associated proteins. Consequently, the nature and properties of the nuclear envelope are of primary importance in further defining the composition of the intranuclear space, as well as the dynamic interchange which occurs between nucleus and cytoplasm. In this respect, the nuclear envelope stands in the same relationship to the nucleus as the plasma membrane to the cell as a whole.

During the era of light microscopy, relatively few facts could be established concerning the nuclear envelope. It was determined, however, that isolated nuclei exhibit osmotic phenomena, e.g., swelling in hypotonic media (Holtfreter, 1954). In intact cells, micrurgical puncture of the nuclear envelope also leads to rapid shriveling of the nucleus and death of the cell; in fact, the cell's difficulty in "healing" its nuclear envelope stands in sharp distinction to the behavior of the plasma membrane, which has an outstanding ability to repair itself after penetration by a microneedle. Centrifugation of interphase cells, followed by staining of the nuclei, reveals that the DNA contents in many cells resist displacement from the inside of the envelope, suggesting some form of attachment between the chromatin and the surrounding membrane (Merriam, 1961b). The most extreme case of this type was reported by Brenner (1953), who found that even 150,000 g failed to dislodge prophase chromosomes from their nuclear envelope. The reality of the envelope as a permeability barrier was also demonstrated in elegant experiments by Feldherr and Feldherr (1960), who injected fluorescein-labeled γ-globulin into young oocytes of the cecropia moth, and found that these fluorescent molecules strikingly fail to penetrate the nuclear envelope and the intranuclear space.

The first electron microscope description of the nuclear envelope was published by Callan and Tomlin (1950), whose investigation just preceded the introduction of thin-sectioning techniques; consequently they worked with intact nuclear envelopes stripped from the large "germinal vesicles" of amphibian oocytes. In these membranes, very conspicuous circular structures or "annuli" could be seen, each of which was about 400–500 Å in diameter with a center-to-center spacing of 1000–1300 Å. From their micrographs, Callan and Tomlin concluded that the nuclear envelope consists of two proteinaceous membranes, the outer of which contains 400 Å "pores" and the inner of which lacks pores, accounting for the impermeability of the envelope as a whole.

After the introduction of thin-sectioning methods, the concept of a double membrane structure was confirmed by Hartmann (1953), who described two concentric, osmiophilic layers enclosing the nuclei of rat neurons; each dense line measured 80–120 Å in width and the two membranes were separated from one another by a variable space 100–150 Å across (giving a total envelope thickness of about 350 Å). Subsequently

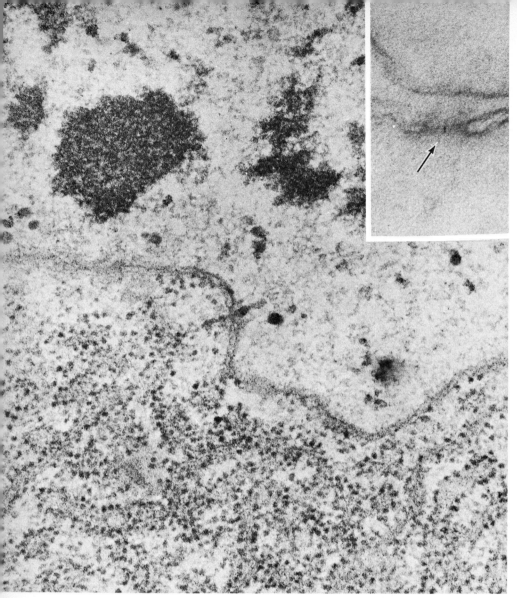

Fig. 17-1. Thin-section of a *Chironomus* salivary cell, showing an RNP particle passing from the nucleus (top) to the cytoplasm (bottom) through an annulus (center). 80,000×. From Stevens and Swift (1966). Inset: particles of colloidal gold, injected into the cytoplasm of an *Amoeba*, are found passing from cytoplasm to nucleus through the exact center of an annulus (arrow). 184,000×. From Feldherr (1962).

many investigators have confirmed that typical nuclei are enclosed by two concentric unit membranes, and that specialized circular structures —the annuli—are arranged hexagonally in this double envelope (Fig. 17-3). In addition, a thin fibrous layer is sometimes appressed to the inside of the inner membrane, particularly in vertebrate cells (Fawcett, 1966; Fig. 17-6). The exact substructure of an annulus, and the relationship of the annuli to the inner and outer nuclear membranes, is not yet settled; however, an octagonal symmetry has been observed recently in negative stained annuli from newts, starfish, and pea seedlings studied

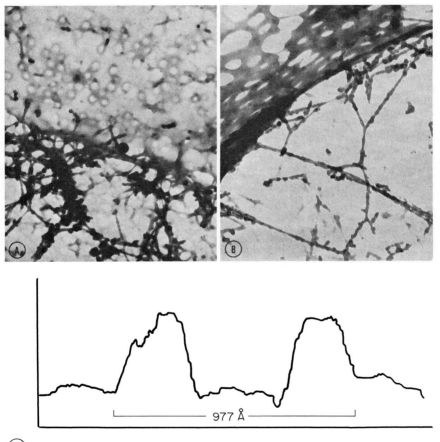

Fig. 17-2. (A) Stretched nuclear envelope from a honey bee embryonic cell, showing the annuli as light circles outlined by dense rings; chromatin fibers are seen near the bottom margin of the envelope. 30,800×. Micrograph by DuPraw. (B) The same type of preparation as (A) but digested briefly with trypsin; the annuli are preferentially digested with trypsin. 58,100×. Micrograph by DuPraw. (C) The mass distribution in a single annulus selected from the electron micrograph in (A); the rim of the annulus has been scanned transversely in two places, showing the dry mass as two peaks enclosing the electron light center. From DuPraw and G. F. Bahr (unpublished).

by Yoo and Bayley (1967) and Gall (1967). This 8-fold symmetry seems to be due to eight spheroid particles, each 70–80 Å in diameter, which lie in a ring within each annulus.

The notion that annuli represent large pores through the nuclear envelope was introduced by Bretschneider (1952) in an early review article, and was supported by Hartmann (1953) in his pioneer thin section study of nuclei in rat neurons. In thin-sectioned material, the inner and outer nuclear membranes often seem to meet at the edges of each annulus (Fig. 17-1, inset). At the annulus center a variety of materials have been observed by different investigators, including: (1) a thin diaphragm or "annulus membrane" (Afzelius, 1955; Merriam, 1961); (2) amorphous, electron-dense material; (3) RNP granules (Gall, 1954; Stevens and Swift, 1966); (4) plasm continuous with the nucleus on one side and the cytoplasm on the other (Hartmann, 1953; Whaley *et al.*, 1960); (5) ultrastructural granules or tubules (Yoo and Bayley, 1967). Although some or all of these conditions may occur in different tissues, the osmotic properties of typical nuclei and the well-established role of the envelope as a semipermeable barrier to large and small molecules, require that the annuli must be special structures of selective permeability (rather than holes).

The problem has been partially resolved by recent elegant experiments of Feldherr (1965), which indicate that the annuli are in fact the sites of temporary or permanent openings in the envelope, but that such openings are much smaller than the annuli themselves. In these experiments, colloidal gold particles of 25–170 Å diameter were coated with polyvinylpyrrolidone (PVP) and injected into the cytoplasm of *Amoeba proteus;* after intervals of 3 minutes, 10 minutes, or 24 hours, the amoebae were prepared for thin-section electron microscopy and the distribution of gold particles was analyzed in terms of particle size. Feldherr found that gold particles up to 85 Å diameter pass through the nuclear envelope within 3 minutes, whereas particles 89–106 Å in diameter enter much more slowly; particles of larger diameter rarely can enter the nucleus at all. Since the apparent diameter of the "pores" in *Amoeba* is 640 Å, it is clear that not all of this area represents an opening in the envelope; in fact Feldherr (1962) has found that gold particles in process of passing through an annulus are typically confined to the exact center, implying that a narrow channel exists there (Fig. 17-1). The size of the channel can be estimated from the maximum diameter of gold particles which pass through (106 Å), plus 20–40 Å added diameter due to the PVP coat (i.e., a total diameter of 125–145 Å).

In a refinement of the above technique, Feldherr (1964) has also shown that the annuli of frog oocytes are sites of binding for colloidal gold particles coated with PVP (negatively charged), poly-L-proline (neutral), or poly-L-lysine (positively charged). The negative and neutral particles tend to bind around the periphery of the annulus, whereas the positive particles are found over the center of the annulus and seem to bind to a lesser extent. On the basis of these experiments, Feldherr has suggested that passage of particles through the annuli may involve a process of binding and membrane flow akin to micropinocytosis (Chapter 10). Such a mechanism would account for the penetration of relatively large gold and ferritin particles into the nucleus, and at the same time it would provide a mechanism for selective uptake, active transport, and the semipermeability required to explain osmotic swelling of nuclei.

Intact nuclear envelopes from honey bee embryonic cells have been studied by DuPraw (1965a), who could compare the dimensions and arrangement of annuli in unstretched or stretched envelopes, or in envelopes partially digested with trypsin (Fig. 17-2). Envelopes that are relatively unstretched show annuli packed hexagonally with a center-to-center spacing of about 800 Å and with electron-light centers varying around 150 Å in diameter; in this configuration no space can be seen between the rims of adjacent annuli, and the inside diameter of each annulus has almost the dimension predicted for the central canal in the experiments of Feldherr (1965). However, when the envelope is stretched, the hexagonal arrangement of annuli is lost and variable expanses of membrane become visible between neighboring annuli (Fig. 17-2A); at the same time the annuli themselves expand to a varying degree, often attaining outside diameters of 1200 Å or more, and they are raised in a craterlike relief both on the inside and the outside surfaces of the envelope. The fact that these annuli can assume widely different diameters (Fig. 17-2A) suggests that in life they may exhibit sphincterlike contraction or relaxation responses.

Digestion of stretched envelopes with weak trypsin solution preferentially attacks the annuli (Fig. 17-2B), causing large gaps to open in the membrane and suggesting that the annulus proper contains more basic proteins than the matrix between the annuli (since trypsin preferentially hydrolyzes peptide bonds involving arginine and lysine). A similar conclusion is suggested by Feldherr's (1964) observation that negatively charged gold particles bind more profusely to frog oocyte annuli than positively charged ones (basic proteins would be expected to carry a net positive charge at neutral pH). That the nuclear envelope as a whole is primarily proteinaceous, being entirely dispersed by prolonged digestion with trypsin or other proteases, is an observation on which most authors are agreed. Digestion with RNase or DNase has little effect on the structural integrity of the nuclear envelope (Merriam, 1961a; DuPraw, 1965a).

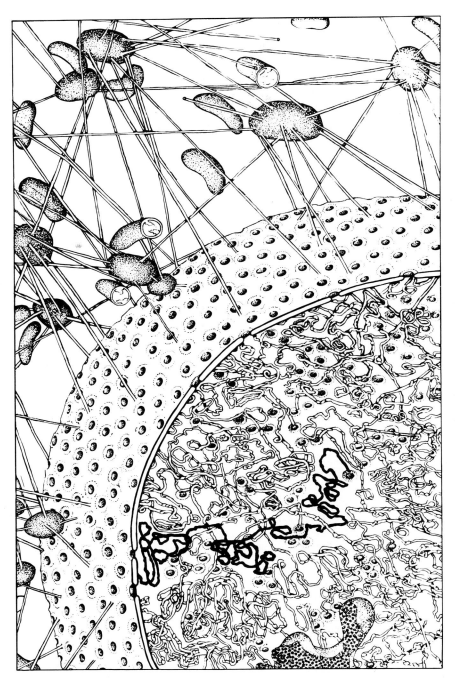

Recently a quantitative technique of electron microscopy, introduced by Bahr and Zeitler (1965), has been applied by DuPraw and Bahr to analyze the distribution of dry mass in honey bee annuli. In this method, the relative proportion of dry mass can be inferred from the degree of electron scattering from different parts of the structure; the result is a curve representing the mass distribution in a cross-section of the annulus, including opposite sections of the rim together with the electron-light center (Fig. 17-2C). The curve illustrated in Fig. 17-2 was derived from a slightly expanded annulus, with an outside diameter of 977 Å, an inside diameter of 359 Å, and a rim width of 285–334 Å; no mass attributable to a central membrane could be demonstrated in this specimen. However, several unstretched annuli have been found to exhibit a central electron density significantly higher than background and amounting to about 22–34% of the density in the annulus rim. At the same time the annulus rims were found to have a maximum electron density about 60–80% as great as the electron density of a nearby chromatin fiber 293 Å in diameter. If both the annulus rim and the fiber are treated as cylinders of identical diameter, this would mean that the density in gm/ml is only 80% as great in the annulus as in the chromatin.

Considerable variability has been observed in the size, frequency, and perhaps the permeability of annuli from one species to another. Weiner et al. (1963) compared the electrical resistance and annulus distribution of nuclear envelopes in toad oocytes and Drosophila salivary glands. They estimated that the hexagonally packed annuli account for 11–12% of the total nuclear surface in both types of cell; however the salivary gland envelopes present a strong diffusion barrier which is capable of sustaining a resting potential of 15 mV, whereas the oocyte envelopes provide essentially no diffusion barrier at all. Statistically significant differences in the average outside diameters of annuli in different genera of echinoderms were reported by Afzelius (1955), who measured average values from 757 Å to 1067 Å. A comparison of annulus size and distribution in immature and mature frog oocytes has also been published by Merriam (1962), who found that the immature cells have 34.6 annuli per square micron compared to only 25.0 per square micron for mature oocytes. Nevertheless individual annuli are larger in immature cells, exhibiting outside diameters of 1450 Å, compared to an average outside diameter of 1338 Å in mature oocytes. No evidence could be found that new annuli

---

Fig. 17-3. An interpretation of nuclear ultrastructure in honey bee embryonic cells. One chromatin fiber, possibly equivalent to a single chromosome, has been defined in black, and terminates at the inside margin of an annulus. The nuclear envelope also serves for structural orientation of extranuclear particles, which are attached to the envelope by cytoplasmic fibers.

Fig. 17-4. In honey bee embryonic cells, the chromatin fibers are firmly attached to the nuclear envelope at the edges of annuli. An unbroken attachment is seen at the arrow, and broken fiber ends are visible on other annuli. 94,700× From DuPraw (1965a).

ever arise as "miniatures" and subsequently enlarge to the typical diameter; rather the annuli appear to develop at full size by some still unknown process. According to Stevens and Swift (1966), RNP particles in elongate configurations pass through the nuclear envelope by way of the annuli (Fig. 17-1). Another possible mechanism to permit the passage of ribosomes or much larger particles out of the nucleus is suggested by observations of "blebbing" and other types of separation or fusion between the nuclear membranes and membranous vesicles in the cytoplasm. Gay (1956) found that the nuclear envelopes of *Drosophila* salivary gland cells at a particular developmental stage begin to form outpocketings or "blebs," which apparently pinch off as cytoplasmic vesicles. Palade (1956), Whaley *et al.* (1960), and later authors have also noted continuities between the nuclear envelope and endo-plasmic reticulum, suggesting that ER vesicles may be budded from the nuclear envelope.

In cells which are carrying on active cell division, it is well known that the nuclear envelope fragments or entirely disappears during the mi-totic prophase, permitting free mingling of intranuclear components with the cytoplasm. According to Merriam (1961b), this dissolution re-quires only about 2 minutes in *Chaetopterus* eggs, a rapid effect that can be mimicked with trypsin solutions (Merriam, 1961a). With respect to the re-formation of the nuclear envelope after telophase, Barer *et al.* (1959), Merriam (1961b), and others have concluded that it develops from an accumulation of vesicles resembling endoplasmic reticulum, which at first lie in irregular contours very close to the telophase chro-mosomes, then fuse into a continuous membrane, and finally expand into the usual spheroid form. Merriam has suggested that the envelope itself is closely akin to endoplasmic reticulum at all stages, and that the formation of annuli may be induced by the nearby chromatin.

However, a few cases are known in which at least part of the nuclear envelope appears to arise inside the nucleus, where it is unlikely to owe its origin to the ER. The most clear-cut example has been described by Afzelius (1963b) in the dinoflagellate *Noctiluca,* where the nuclear envelope is unusually thin (150 Å) and lacks annuli. In the nucleo-plasm just beneath the envelope there are several thousand small vesicles, the membranes of which possess approximately 80 annuli each; these vesicles apparently fuse with the overlying envelope from time to time, discharging their contents into the cytoplasm. New annulated vesicles are then presumably produced in the nucleoplasm. In *Amoeba proteus* too, it has been shown by Greider *et al.* (1956) and by Pappas (1956) that the usual annulated nuclear envelope is reinforced on the nucleoplasm side by a specialized "honeycomb" layer about 2800 Å thick; each of the honeycomb hexagons terminates at its outside end in a typical annulus.

Aside from its function as a barrier to macromolecules and cytoplas-mic organelles, the nuclear envelope clearly acts as a "keystone" to main-tain the relative positions of cytoplasmic organelles and preserve the mechanical integrity of the cell. Many authors have reported attach-ments of cytoplasmic organelles to the outside of the nuclear envelope; according to Merriam (1961), for instance, yolk granules, mitochondria, and vesicles are attached by long strands to the nuclear envelopes of oocytes in *Rana pipiens* and *Chaetopterus.* Similar attachments have been detected in mouse liver cells by Barton (1961). In honey bee embryonic cells, DuPraw (1965b) has demonstrated an extensive system of cytoplasmic fibers about 185 Å in diameter, which bind cytoplasmic granules to one another and to the nuclear envelope (Fig. 9-7). On the inside of the envelope, the chromatin also forms structural attachments (Fig. 17-4), which may serve to hold the interphase chromosomes in fixed positions relative to one another.

THE INTERPHASE CHROMATIN

Early thin-section studies of interphase nuclei were both puzzling and disappointing, because they failed to reveal any sign of discrete interphase chromosomes, or indeed any indication of molecular order that might account for the precise genetic functions of the nucleus. The nuclei in some of the first studies looked surprisingly empty or "watery," a result of inadequate fixation; in other instances, nuclei seemed to contain a uniform mass of dispersed granules or fiber segments. One of the best early electron micrographs was published by Bretschneider (1952), who illustrated a system of irregular tangled interphase threads about 80–300 Å in diameter. Not long afterward, Ris (1955) described the structure of unsectioned chromosomes and interphase nuclei as based on fibers approximately 250 Å in diameter; in a later analysis based on sectioned material, Ris (1956) emphasized that the nuclear contents of lilies, onion roots, *Tradescantia, Triturus,* and rats consist primarily of a system of long 200 Å microfibrils; in sectioned material only the cut ends of these fibrils can be observed, but in unsectioned material they are seen to be at least several microns in length. The transition from the interphase to the metaphase state seemed to be based primarily on a tighter packing of the previously loose fibers. Ris also noted that the cut ends of the fibers exhibit an electron-light core or center, which he speculated might contain DNA.

These morphological observations were remarkably in accord with the earlier biochemical demonstrations by Mirsky and Pollister (1946) and Mirsky and Ris (1948) that extracted interphase chromatin reprecipitates in the form of very long fibers. Nevertheless, Ris's observations on the fine structure of interphase nuclei did not receive the acceptance they deserved, in part because it was unclear how so irregular a mass of fibers could function in the precise manner required of the genetic material; there was also a clear possibility that the interphase fibers might represent some type of precipitation artifact. In the meantime, other investigators reported a wide range of dimensions for chromatin fibers as seen after thin-sectioning; for instance, Gay (1956) noted fibers 200–500 Å thick in *Drosophila* salivary cells, whereas Kaufmann and McDonald (1956) reported 125 Å fibers in *Drosophila* salivary and

Tradescantia chromosomes. Hay and Revel (1963) also described a mesh-work of 50–75 Å filaments in the nuclei of cells from regenerating salamander limbs. More recently Ris and Chandler (1963), Gall (1963b), DuPraw (1965a,b, 1966), and others have returned to a study of un-sectioned nuclei, using refined techniques introduced by Kleinschmidt *et al.* (1962) and Anderson (1951); after this type of whole-mount preparation, typical nuclei are found to contain "bumpy" fibers whose diameters vary from less than 200 Å to more than 300 Å, apparently reflecting an irregular twist along the axis of the fiber (Figs. 17-4 and 17-5A). That these long threads do indeed represent structures present in the living state is supported by the observation that many of the indi-vidual chromatin fibers are attached to the nuclear envelope specifically at the edges of annuli (Fig. 17-3, 17-4); when the envelope is stripped off during preparation, the broken ends of these attached fibers can still be found adhering to their annuli, a fact that leaves little room to doubt the reality of either the attachments or of the fibers themselves (Fig. 17-2).

The substructure of the 200–300 Å interphase fibers has stimulated a certain amount of controversy. After calling attention to these struc-tures, Ris himself came to the conclusion that each 200 Å fiber consists of two 100 Å fibers, and that each of these in turn consists of two 40 Å fibers representing single DNA-protein molecules (Ris, 1959; Ris and Chandler, 1963). However, such a multiple strand structure could not be confirmed by DuPraw (1965a), Gall (1966) or others. In fact, DuPraw (1965a,b) has demonstrated that individual interphase fibers of honey bee embryonic cells, after brief digestion in trypsin, show single trypsin-resistant cores of the dimension expected for *one* Watson-Crick DNA molecule (Fig. 17-5B,C); segments of undigested fiber alternate with these cores like the beads on a string. After further digestion with DNase, the trypsin-resistant filaments are removed and only protein-aceous fragments remain (Fig. 17-5D). These experiments provide direct evidence that a one-to-one relationship exists between individual 230 Å

Fig. 17-5. [See following two pages for illustrations.] (A) Undigested chromatin fibers from a honey bee embryonic cell. Note the bumpiness, which suggests an irregular helical twist. 105,600×. (B) Chromatin fibers from a honey bee embryonic cell after brief digestion in trypsin. Each 230 Å fiber consists of a single, trypsin-resistant DNA filament packed into a proteinaceous, trypsin-sensitive sheath. 100,800×. (C) Part of a honey bee embryonic nucleus after brief trypsin digestion, showing the nuclear envelope with annuli preferen-tially digested, and the beads-on-a-string appearance of the partially digested chromatin fibers. 36,700×. (D) A preparation identical to that in (C), but further digested with DNase. The nuclear envelope remains, but the trypsin-resistant filaments of the chromatin fibers are preferentially digested by DNase. 16,400×. All micrographs from DuPraw (1965a).

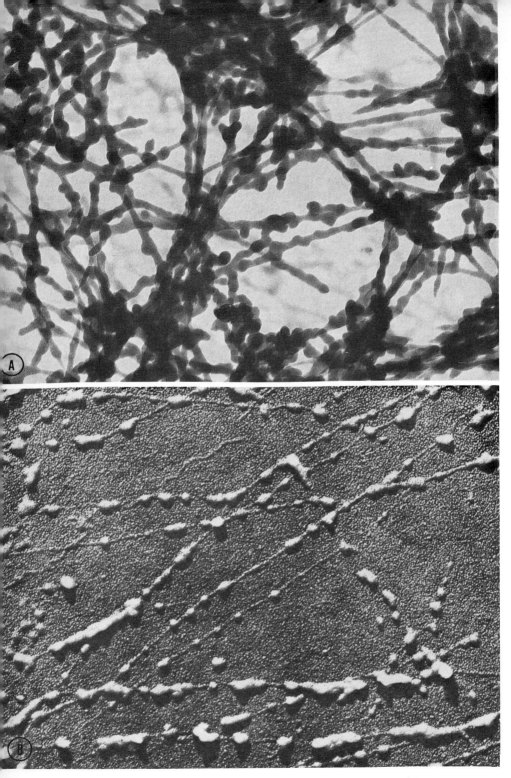

Fig. 17-5. (A) and (B). For legend see page 475.

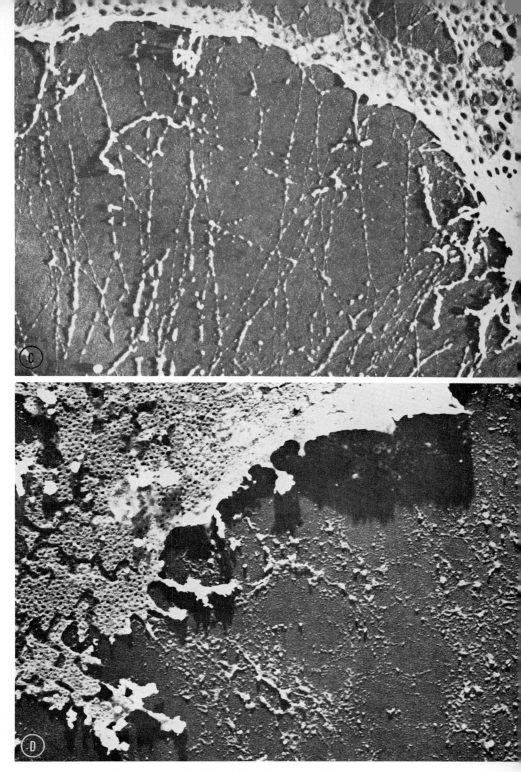

Fig. 17-5. (C) and (D). For legend see page 475.

chromatin fibers and long single Watson-Crick molecules (Chapter 12). More recently Ris (1966b) himself has confirmed these results by digesting chromatin fibers from newt erythrocytes with Pronase (a protease); accordingly, in his latest interpretations Ris (1966a,b) has abandoned the idea that one 200 Å fiber contains four side-by-side DNA helices.

DuPraw and Bahr (1968) have recently succeeded in measuring the dry mass per unit length of human chromatin fibers, by determining the amount of electron scattering relative to polystyrene spheres of known mass (Bahr and Zeitler, 1965). Their data permit them to exclude models of chromatin structure based on one, two, or four relatively extended DNA helices in each 230 Å fiber. As described in Chapter 12, the mass of one extended DNA molecule (3.26×10^{-22} gm/Å) represents only about $\frac{1}{200}$ the mass of a 230 Å fiber (ca. 6×10^{-20} gm/Å). Since chromatin isolated from a wide variety of sources contains about 30% DNA by dry weight (Table 17-2), the packing ratio of total helix length per unit length of 230 Å fiber must be at least 56:1. A less exact estimate of 13:1 (DuPraw, 1966a) was suggested earlier by rough volumetric estimates of fiber length compared with microspectrophotometric determinations of DNA content. Inasmuch as X-ray diffraction data exclude a crystalline hexagonal packing of DNA in nucleohistone (Chapter 12), these high packing ratios probably reflect a coiled coil arrangement of DNA.

Further insights about the structure of single chromatin fibers have been obtained by measuring the electron scattering in transverse scans of fibers dissected with weak trypsin (DuPraw and Bahr, 1968). Such fibers spring apart into alternating segments of thick and thin fiber, the thick regions showing diameters similar to those of undigested fibers (200–300 Å) while the thin regions have diameters of about 35–60 Å (Fig. 17-5). It has been found that the thinner (type A) subfibrils have a higher density and a more symmetrical mass distribution than the thicker (type B) fibers (Fig. 12-13). The evidence suggests a model of chromatin structure in which a type A fibril represents a single DNA molecule wrapped with protein in the manner of polyarginine (Fig. 12-12); this type A fibril is then induced to supercoil by addition of more protein, generating a type B fiber (Chapter 12). In the type A fibril the packing ratio of helix length to fiber length is between 1 and 10, while the DNA/protein ratio is about 50:50; by contrast, the packing ratio in a type B region must exceed 50:1, while the DNA/protein ratio is only about 30:70, accounting for the lower density of the fiber. As noted previously, both histones and such enzymes as RNA polymerase, NAD synthetase, and nucleoside triphosphatase are typically coextracted with DNA from interphase nuclei; the evidence indicates that these functional proteins form part of the type B chromatin fibers, and DuPraw (1965) has suggested that the units of nuclear structure should be conceived as one-dimensional (filamentous) enzyme arrays comparable to the two-dimensional (membranous) arrays of mitochondria and chloroplasts (Chapters 5 and 7).

The interphase chromatin filaments are known to be extremely long, in fact so long that it has not yet been possible to determine their maximum dimensions. For instance, Solari (1965) employed electron microscopy to measure DNA molecules at least 50–93 μ long in sea urchin sperm, while Huberman and Riggs (1966) used autoradiography to demonstrate continuous DNA molecules up to 1.8 mm long from Chinese hamster cells. The latter report somewhat exceeds the 1 mm DNA molecules detected by Cairns (1963c) in human (HeLa) cells. DNA fibers up to 2.2 cm long have been reported from human lymphocyte nuclei by Sasaki and Norman (1966). Assuming that such long DNA molecules replicate sequentially by unwinding at one or more forks (like the *E. coli* chromosome), it might be expected that nuclei in process of DNA synthesis would contain forked chromatin fibers. Such forked fibers have actually been observed in nuclei from embryonic stages actively incorporating DNA precursors (DuPraw, 1965a).

In many species, one or more metaphase chromosomes (particularly the sex chromosomes) fail to assume the extended interphase condition, but are found more or less permanently condensed in the interphase nucleus. This condition has sometimes been termed "heteropycnosis," and chromosomes exhibiting such behavior were referred to by Montgomery (1904) as "heterochromosomes" (in contrast to the more conventional "euchromosomes"). Later Heitz (1928) called attention to the fact that the same chromosome may contain both heteropycnotic and nonheteropycnotic regions, and following Montgomery, he coined the term "heterochromatin" to designate those regions that remain condensed during interphase (the remainder comprising "euchromatin"). Since heteropycnotic regions often appear to contain fewer genetic loci, the concept developed that heterochromatin and euchromatin represent two entirely different kinds of chromosomal material. Nevertheless, electron micrographs of heteropycnotic chromosomes indicate that they are composed of type B chromatin fibers identical in appearance to those of nonheteropycnotic chromosomes; they differ in that these fibers remain in a tightly folded state during interphase. More direct experimental evidence, to be discussed in Chapter 18, confirms that heterochromatin is not a unique kind of chromatin, but a differentiated state of chromatin associated with a condition of tight folding.

In accord with these concepts, thin-sectioned interphase nuclei often

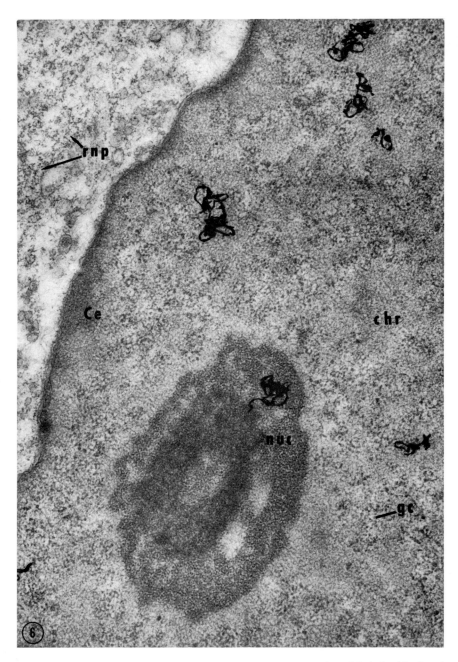

Fig. 17-6. Thin-section autoradiograph of a salamander nucleus labeled with thymidine-³H. DNA synthesis is associated with diffuse regions in the chromatin fiber mass (chr), and is not confined to any one part of the nucleus. Note some incorporation of DNA precursor in the nucleolus (nuc). 23,900×. From Hay and Revel (1963).

contain regions of condensed as well as diffuse chromatin fibers; the condensed regions are often visible in living cells by phase contrast microscopy and have been referred to as "chromocenters" by classical light microscopists. By means of electron microscope autoradiography, Hay and Revel (1963) demonstrated that the *in vivo* incorporation of DNA precursors (thymidine-^{3}H) occurs almost exclusively in the diffuse chromatin, a finding that implies that all the chromatin enters a diffuse state at one time or another during interphase DNA replication (Fig. 17-6). That the diffuse chromatin is also the primary site of incorporation for RNA precursors (uridine-^{3}H) has recently been demonstrated with calf thymus nuclei by Littau *et al.* (1964). In the thymus nuclei, many conspicuous masses of condensed (or repressed) chromatin are present, which Frenster (1965a) has shown by electron microscopy are structurally continuous with the diffuse chromatin fibers; Littau *et al.* (1965) have also demonstrated by selective removal of lysine-rich (but not arginine-rich) histones, that the condensed chromatin can be transformed reversibly into a diffuse fiber meshwork. Using sonication of isolated thymus nuclei, Frenster *et al.* (1963) were able to separate the condensed and diffuse chromatin phases as bulk fractions, finding that up to 80% of the nuclear DNA is normally in the condensed phase; by contrast, only 17% of the nuclear RNA is in this fraction. Since lysine-rich histones occur in both fractions in about the same proportion (20% of the total histone), it is not clear how these histones are involved in bringing about condensation of the interphase chromatin. Nevertheless, the fact that a histone fraction does play a role in this condensation is significant in view of the evidence discussed previously that type A and B chromatin fibers supercoil and fold by virtue of their association with histones (Chapter 12).

NUCLEOLI

The occurrence of one or more conspicuous, dense granules within a nucleus was first noted by Fontana in 1781. Later Schleiden and Schwann (1838) supposed that nucleoli arise spontaneously from a structureless blastema and develop into nuclei (or cytoblasts), which in turn develop into cells. Some decades later, after the demise of the cytoblast theory, the cytologists of the late 19th century were able to note a general relationship between the presence and size of nucleoli and the relative activity of various cells in protein synthesis (Montgomery, 1898). It was established, for example, that nucleoli are typically absent or inconspicuous in sperm cells, early cleavage cells, muscle fibers, leukocytes, and during mitosis in most cells, corresponding in each instance to a stage or tissue which exhibits little or no protein synthesis; by contrast, the nucleoli of neurons, secretory cells, and advanced embryonic stages are relatively prominent. Lagerstedt (1949) also noted that the nucleoli of rat liver cells become diminished during starvation but increase again after refeeding, paralleling the same kinds of change in the cytoplasmic basophilia. In living cells, the formation of clear, intranucleolar vacuoles can sometimes be observed, which in time-lapse films may exhibit a cyclical activity, first expanding and then extruding their contents into the nucleoplasm. In plants, diurnal changes in nucleolar volume have been noted by Fischer (1934), who also found that when leaf tissues are experimentally damaged, the nucleoli in nearby cells increase from 3.6 μ in diameter to 7.1 μ.

The presence of RNA in nucleoli was first detected cytochemically by Brachet (1940). Later Vincent (1952) carried out a detailed biochemical analysis of nucleoli isolated in bulk from starfish oocytes; he found that his preparations consisted primarily of proteins rich in glutamic acid, poor in basic amino acids and containing 1% tightly bound phosphate. Only about 5% of the nucleolar mass in starfish oocytes consists of RNA, and similar values have since been confirmed for the nucleoli of several other cell types. Starfish nucleoli are very dense (sp. gr. about 1.35) with a dry mass of 85% in small, nonvacuolate ones and 40% in larger, vacuolate nucleoli. Isolated nucleoli from pea embryos have also been analyzed by Stern et al. (1959), who found that the nucleolar RNA equals about 10% of the mass of nucleolar protein, 20% of the total nuclear RNA, and 1.6% of the total cell RNA. The nucleoli of guinea pig liver, isolated in bulk by Maggio et al. (1963), account for about 6–11% of the nuclear mass and contain 11–17% of the nuclear RNA (RNA = 4% of nucleolar dry weight).

Numerous studies of nucleolar ultrastructure are consistent with the concept that these organelles are sites of synthesis and assembly of ribosomes. DeRobertis (1954), soon after the introduction of thin-section electron microscopy, observed masses of dense particles on both sides of the nuclear envelope in frog and earthworm neurons, which led him to suggest a nuclear origin for the newly discovered ergastoplasm particles (ribosomes). In a similar study of ovarian nurse cells in the bug *Rhodnius*, Anderson and Beams (1956) called special attention to the fact that the nucleolus consists of tightly packed 200 Å granules, which resemble the granules in the nuclear sap and cytoplasm; they also found apparent continuities between nuclear and cytoplasmic material through openings in the nuclear envelope. As summarized more recently by Marinozzi and Bernhard (1963), most nucleoli contain two distinct parts: (1) a region of dense, ribosome-like granules 150–200 Å in diameter, and (2) a region of fibrillar elements 80–100 Å in diameter. In plant cells, dipteran salivary glands, and amphibian oocytes, the fibrillar region constitutes a central core in the nucleolus (pars amorpha), while the granules form a more peripheral "shell"; on the other hand, in most vertebrate cells, the greater part of the nucleolus is granular, while the fibrillar part occurs in the form of a tortuous thread or nucleolonema (Fig. 17-6). RNA is present in both parts of the nucleolus, and most data are consistent with the hypothesis that the fibrillar RNA is an immediate precursor of the granular RNA. It may be recalled that cytoplasmic ribosomes are also composed of threadlike RNA strands tortuously folded into the configuration of the spheroid ribosome (Chapter 14). Since nucleoli are not membrane enclosed, they tend to disperse readily, and according to Holtfreter (1954), the presence of Ca^{++} ions is essential in maintaining nucleoli intact.

In its base composition, nucleolar RNA also shows a close correspondence to the base composition of cytoplasmic (ribosomal) RNA in the same cells. Edström (1960; Edström and Beermann, 1962; Edström and Gall, 1963) has been able to determine the base compositions of RNA's from nucleoli isolated by hand from spider oocytes, chironomid salivary glands, and amphibian oocytes; in each case he found a striking correspondence between the RNA's from nucleoli and from the cytoplasm, both of which differ in base composition from the RNA of the nucleoplasm (Table 17-3). Maggio et al. (1963) also found that the base composition of RNA in nucleoli isolated from guinea pig liver is characterized by a high guanine content (50 moles percent), together with low cytosine and adenine, resembling the base composition of mammalian ribosomes and sRNA.

In his studies with plant chromosomes, Heitz (1931) became the first to note that nucleoli have a constant relationship to specific chromosomes (*Nukleolenchromosomen*), and consequently tend to be constant in number and position for a given species. This concept was confirmed and elaborated by McClintock (1934), who demonstrated that the nucleolus in maize is associated with a specific chromosomal locus, which she called the "nucleolus organizing body." Diploid cells possess two nucleolus organizers and develop two nucleoli, whereas triploid cells have three organizers and develop three nucleoli (although some or all of these bodies may fuse together later in interphase). McClintock also observed that, after certain types of genetic translocation, one nucleolus organizer can be divided unequally between two nonhomologous chromosomes, so that the diploid cells in this case develop two large and two small nucleoli. Similar effects were observed by Beermann (1960) in genetic crosses between sibling species of the fly *Chironomus*; one of these species

Table 17-3

Correspondence in Base Composition between
Nucleolar and Cytoplasmic RNA's
from Different species[a]

Source	A	G	C	U
Spider oocyte				
Nucleolus	25.2	29.8	22.9	22.2
Cytoplasm	25.1	30.2	21.9	22.9
Chironomid salivary				
Nucleolus	30.6	20.1	22.1	27.1
Cytoplasm	29.4	22.9	22.1	25.7
Triturus oocyte				
Nucleolus	21.8	27.6	27.8	22.7
Cytoplasm	20.9	30.2	27.5	21.4

[a] Determined by Edström (1960), Edström and
Beermann (1962), and Edström and Gall (1963).

(*C. tentans*) exhibits two nucleolus organizers and the other (*C. pallidivittatus*) has but a single organizer which does not correspond to either of those in *C. tentans*. By appropriate crosses it is possible to obtain hybrid offspring which vary in the number of nucleolus organizers from six (homozygous for all three organizers) to none. Although the anucleolate individuals die as embryos, the presence of a single nucleolus organizer (or even a "partial" one) is sufficient to ensure normal development. It appears therefore that all three nucleoli are functionally equivalent.

These cytogenetic analyses have been clarified in recent years by sophisticated biochemical experiments indicating that (1) both the 28 S and 18 S components of ribosomal RNA are synthesized in the nucleolus; (2) this synthesis proceeds by a DNA-dependent reaction which is sensitive to actinomycin D inhibition (RNA polymerase reaction); (3) the nucleolus organizer region of the chromosome contains the DNA cistrons (or genes) which code for both ribosomal RNA's; and (4) a single nucleolus organizer may possess 130 or more copies of each ribosomal cistron (genetic redundancy). The most advanced analysis is that of Ritossa and Spiegelman (1965), who studied the annealing of ribosomal RNA's to denatured DNA (Chapter 12) from several mutant stocks of *Drosophila;* these mutants vary in the number of nucleolus organizers present on the X and Y chromosomes (from one to four), and correspondingly the authors found that the amount of DNA complementary to ribosomal RNA is proportional to the number of nucleolus organizers (Fig. 17-7). Furthermore the total amount of this ribosomal DNA in a haploid chromosome set is much greater than would be necessary to code for one 28 S and one 18 S subunit; it amounts to 0.27% of the entire genome, equivalent to about 130 copies of each cistron. The data suggest that all these copies lie near one another, probably in a continuous DNA segment. Since the 28 S and 18 S components do not compete for DNA sites, they must be coded by different DNA regions.

Similar results have been obtained for the toad *Xenopus*, a species in which Brown and Gurdon (1964) first clearly demonstrated that the nucleolus is necessary for synthesis of cytoplasmic ribosomes. Their experiments were carried out with a homozygous mutant that lacks normal nucleoli, a condition that is lethal at the tadpole stages; however if such anucleolate individuals are exposed to RNA precursors for 48 hours, then homogenized and fractionated for ribosomal and transfer RNA, it is found that the amount of incorporation into ribosomal RNA

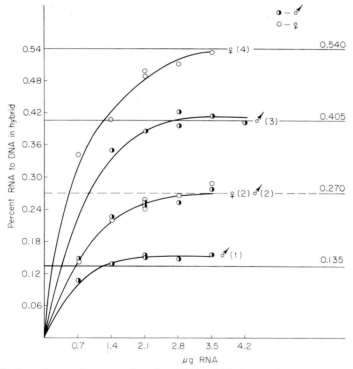

Fig. 17-7. Experiment demonstrating that DNA which is complementary to ribosomal RNA is associated with the nucleolus organizer in *Drosophila*. The proportion of ribosomal RNA which can be hybridized to DNA *in vitro* is a function of the number of nucleolus organizers in the particular *Drosophila* strain. The four curves correspond to strains with one, two, three, or four organizers. From Ritossa and Spiegelman (1965).

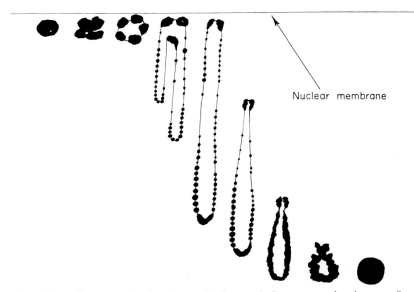

Nuclear membrane

Fig. 17-8. Transformations in the ring nucleoli of axolotl oocytes as they increase from 1 mm to 1.9 mm diameter (left to right). From Callan (1966).

(both 28 S and 18 S) is less than 5% the level in normal control embryos. By contrast, the synthesis of sRNA and messenger RNA appears not to be diminished at all. More recently Wallace and Birnstiel (1966) have shown by DNA-RNA annealing experiments that the anucleolate homozygotes have little or no DNA complementary to ribosomal RNA, while heterozygotes have an amount intermediate between anucleolate and normal individuals; they therefore suggest that the anucleolate *Xenopus* mutation represents a deletion for DNA coding ribosomal RNA. They calculate that normal *Xenopus* cells may contain up to 1600 copies of each cistron (28 S and 18 S).

These sophisticated analyses of nucleolar organization have been matched by the discovery that the vertebrate ribosomal RNA's (16–18 S and 28 S) are first synthesized in the form of a much larger 45 S particle. This rapidly labeling 45 S component was first reported by Scherrer and Darnell (1962) in human (HeLa) cells, and the same authors later showed (1963) that the 45 S particles are converted into 35 S, 16 S, and 28 S RNA's. More recently Penman *et al.* (1966) and Gall (1966b) have obtained evidence that the 45 S precursor particles are localized in the nucleoli of HeLa and salamander cells. Cleavage of the 45 S precursor produces a 16 S ribosomal subunit, which enters the cytoplasm, and a 35 S precursor which remains in the nucleolus; subsequently the 35 S precursor is converted into a 28 S ribosomal subunit either before or during its passage through the nuclear envelope to the cytoplasm (Fig. 17-1).

It is now known that nucleolar synthesis in some cells, especially amphibian oocytes, is associated with the presence of an extrachromosomal nucleolar DNA. This DNA was first found by Miller (1964, 1966), who was able to isolate the fibrous cores of *Triturus* nucleoli in 0.025 *M* KCl, and found that they opened out into circular beaded "necklaces." The axial strand holding the circles together is only 30 Å wide, it is fragmented by DNase but not proteases, and it attains lengths up to 200 μ. Evidently this nucleolar DNA, like mitochondrial DNA, has the form of closed circles. The exact origin and role of nucleolar DNA in synthesis remain to be clarified, but at present it appears that the nucleolar DNA is synthesized by specific chromosomal loci at an earlier stage, and that several hundred DNA circles then form the basis for a like number of nucleoli in each *Triturus* oocyte nucleus (Fig. 17-8). These hundreds of nucleoli line the inside of the nuclear envelope, and do not appear to retain any connection with the chromosomes. However Miller (1966) has reported that each nucleolus possesses a long, membranous tubule 500–5000 Å in diameter and up to 25 μ in length, which is attached at a characteristic position on the side nearest the nuclear envelope. Nucleolar DNA is also thought to occur in oocytes of the insect *Tipula*.

Although synthesis and assembly of ribosomes is undoubtedly a function of some or all nucleoli, it appears that other processes occur as well. As reported by Vincent (1958), starfish oocyte nucleoli contain NAD and the enzyme NAD synthetase, as well as nucleoside phosphorylase, latent RNase and weak acid phosphatase activity. There is also good evidence for two distinct RNA fractions, one of which turns over more rapidly than the other and is associated with a minor N-terminal histidine protein; evidence to be discussed in the next section indicates that this fraction represents newly synthesized transfer RNA. The presence of histones in nucleoli was inferred from microspectrophotometric evidence by Caspersson (1950) and has now been confirmed for the nucleoli of pea seedlings by Birnstiel and Flamm (1964), who also found nonhistone basic proteins. Electrophoresis of extracts from isolated beef pancreas nucleoli has led Poort (1961) to conclude that there are at least five nucleolar proteins, two of which have isoelectric points considerably higher than pH 8.

In most dividing cells, the nucleoli disappear as the nuclear envelope disintegrates during prophase; their later reappearance at telophase seems to be a rather complex process, the significance of which has not yet become entirely clear. Specifically, a number of small dense bodies or pronucleoli form at several loci on different chromosomes, and these subsequently migrate together or merge into the one or two nucleoli characteristic of the species. This process suggests that the nucleolus may have a multiple genetic origin and may not be entirely synthesized *in situ* at the nucleolus organizer. In the *Chironomus* hybrids studied by Beermann (1960), those embryonic cells which entirely lacked a nucleolar organizer (and were therefore destined to die before hatching) typically contained many small, spheroid bodies instead of a single, irregularly shaped nucleolus. The salivary gland cells of the fly *Sciara* also contain about 20 small nucleoli instead of the single nucleolus of related genera such as *Drosophila* and the chironomids. Conceivably the pronucleoli may represent deposits of messenger RNA transcribed from various active chromosomal loci for attachment on nucleolar ribosomes. Alternatively, they may simply be remnants of the original nucleoli which disperse during prophase and may attach randomly or nonrandomly to the metaphase chromosomes. Evidence for the presence of messenger RNA in nucleoli, and for synthetic activity in the nucleolus itself as well as in the nucleolus organizer, will be discussed in the next section.

Synthesis in Interphase Nuclei

A very extensive literature has developed around the details of intranuclear synthesis, both in isolated, cell-free nuclei and in different kinds of intact cell. The techniques employed most frequently are either: (1) monitoring of net synthesis by quantitative chemical analysis, or (2) measuring the turnover in protein or nucleic acids by means of isotopically labeled precursor molecules. Needless to say, many different relationships have been found in the kinds and relative rates of nuclear synthesis, depending on the physiological state of the cells and their particular mode of specialization. Nevertheless, the majority of studies fit the pattern that would be predicted from the coding relationships determined for DNA, RNA and protein in biochemical systems. Of the three types of macromolecule, DNA itself is the most metabolically stable but shows a replicative synthesis in proliferating cells prior to cell division; RNA, by contrast, has a much more rapid turnover rate, and there appear to be several classes of RNA synthesis, corresponding to ribosomal RNA, sRNA and messenger RNA's. In some cells there is evidence that all RNA is synthesized inside the nucleus in association with DNA, and that newly synthesized RNA then moves into the cytoplasm to participate in protein synthesis. Although protein synthesis in the cytoplasm quantitatively outweighs that in the nucleus, several intranuclear protein fractions exhibit high metabolic turnover; however, the DNA-associated histones are distinctly more stable than most other nuclear proteins. Intranuclear protein synthesis is also RNA-dependent and occurs in association with RNP particles. Perhaps a typical relationship exists in adult rat liver cells, which according to Revel and Hiatt (1964) synthesize the equivalent of their own protein content every 6 days or less, renew their RNA about every 25 days, and replicate on the average less than once a year.

DNA Synthesis

Prior to the introduction of quantitative microspectrophotometry as a technique for determining the DNA content of single nuclei, it was generally supposed that the synthesis of chromosomal DNA occurs very rapidly during the prophase of mitosis when the chromosomes become visibly double. However, this classic scheme was refuted by the investigations of Pasteels and Lison (1950) and Swift (1950b), who found that the DNA contents of individual somatic nuclei actually double during the interphase preceding mitosis (Fig. 17-9). A more precise subdivision of the cell cycle was then introduced by Howard and Pelc (1953), who distinguished a D period (prophase to telophase), a G_1 period (telophase to beginning of DNA synthesis), an S period (time of DNA synthesis), and a G_2 period (end of DNA synthesis to prophase). More recently

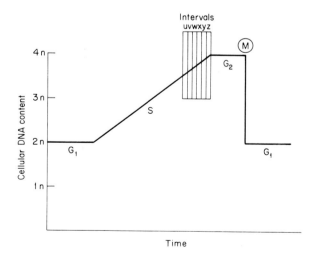

Fig. 17-9. Graph representing the cell cycle, including the G_1, S, G_2, and M (or D) periods. It is sometimes possible to subdivide the period of DNA synthesis (S), depending on which specific chromosomes are still undergoing replication (intervals u-z). From German (1964).

evidence has been found that a small amount of DNA synthesis occurs during G_2 and prophase in some cells (Kihlman and Hartley, 1967; Ito *et al.*, 1967). In duration, the G_1 period in human amnion cells is the most sensitive to environmental factors (Sisken and Kinosita, 1961); by contrast, the S and G_2 periods show a relative constancy, requiring about 9.5 and 1.4 hours, respectively. Cellular DNA synthesis tends to follow the rule that, once it has begun, it does not stop until the nuclear DNA content has approximately doubled. Although ordinarily the completion of DNA replication is followed shortly by mitosis, in many species and tissues DNA doubles successively without cell division, giving rise to polyploid somatic cells that contain DNA in geometric proportion to the diploid amount (2, 4, 8, 16, 32, etc).

Van't Hof and Sparrow (1963) have noted a direct linear correlation between the absolute DNA content of nuclei across six genera of plants, and the minimum mitotic cycle times; this relationship implies some degree of constancy in the *rate* of DNA synthesis in nuclei differing widely in absolute DNA content. At the same time, several authors have also demonstrated in plant, animal, and protozoan nuclei that DNA synthesis is focalized, i.e., it does not occur simultaneously in all parts of the interphase chromatin. If cells are exposed to a 10- or 15-minute "pulse" of thymidine-^{3}H during the S phase, then autoradiographed at metaphase, the labeled DNA is found concentrated in some chromosomal regions but may be absent from others. The trend to a constant rate, together with evidence for focalized synthesis, indicates that individual segments of DNA in nucleated cells replicate sequentially by a mechanism similar to the moving replication fork found in *E. coli* by Cairns (1963a) and others (Chapter 15).

Indeed, a clear demonstration of sequential DNA replication has been achieved for the macronucleus of *Euplotes*, a ciliate protozoan; in this organism the macronucleus is ribbon-shaped, about 140 μ long and 8 μ wide, and DNA synthesis occurs over a period of 8–10 hours. During the S period, two visible "reorganization bands" appear at either end of the macronucleus, which gradually move toward one another until they meet at the center (Fig. 17-10). Gall (1959) has shown that DNA synthesis in these nuclei is confined to a small region near the trailing edge of each reorganization band; behind the bands, the DNA content has doubled, whereas in front of the bands synthesis has not yet begun. As discovered by Roth (1957) and Prescott (1962), each band actually has two distinct parts, an "anterior" region in which interphase RNA and protein are partially removed from the chromatin, and a "posterior" region in which DNA synthesis is confined to a transverse line less than 0.5 μ wide (Fig. 17-10). The fine structure of the bands has also been examined by Kluss (1962), who found that in the region of DNA syn-

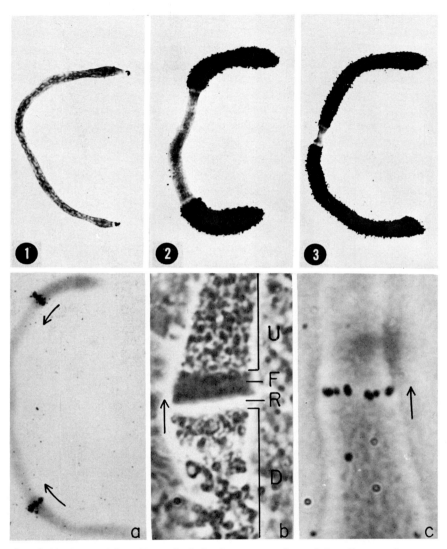

Fig. 17-10. Sequential DNA synthesis in the macronucleus of the ciliate *Euplotes. Top:* autoradiographs of isolated macronuclei exposed continuously to thymidine-³H for increasing lengths of time; incorporation begins at the two ends of the macronucleus and proceeds symmetrically toward the center. *Bottom:* figure (a) is an autoradiograph of a macronucleus pulse-labeled with thymidine-³H for 20 minutes; all DNA synthesis is confined to two narrow "reorganization bands." Figure (b) is a phase contrast micrograph of one reorganization band in a living cell, showing that it is divided transversely into forward (F) and rear (R) zones. Figure (c) is an autoradiograph of one reorganization band after pulse-labeling for 2 minutes, showing that all DNA synthesis is confined to the rear zone of the band. From Prescott (1962, 1966).

thesis the 150 Å chromatin fibers are transformed to a "dispersed" state.

In the slime mold *Physarum polycephalum*, Braun *et al.* (1965) have demonstrated that DNA which replicates during the first half of one S period also replicates during the first half of the next S period, suggesting a sequential replication mechanism. In their experiments, thymidine-^{3}H was used to label DNA during the last half of DNA synthesis in one nuclear cycle, and 5-bromodeoxyuridine was used to label DNA during the first half of the next nuclear cycle. Since the bromodeoxyuridine-labeled DNA molecules were found not to contain tritium, it could be concluded that "late DNA" is distinct from "early DNA" from one cycle to the next. Experimental analyses of DNA synthesis in plants and animals have also shown that each interphase chromosome has a characteristic pattern (and sometimes rate) of DNA synthesis. In human leukocytes, German (1964) found that long chromosomes tend to continue DNA synthesis later in the S period than do short chromosomes; nevertheless there were some notable exceptions to the rule, such as the heterochromatic X-chromosome, which typically does not begin replication until late in the S period. Several authors have also found evidence that DNA synthesis may sometimes be sequential *within* a given interphase chromosome. The most frequently detected sequential pattern is one in which the DNA near the chromosome ends (telomeres) replicates early, while the DNA near the centromeres replicates late. Autoradiographic evidence for such a pattern was found in various genera of plants by Taylor (1958b), Lima-de-Faria (1959), and Pelc and LaCour (1960), while a similar "early telomere-late centromere" pattern has been reported in some human and other mammalian chromosomes by Stubblefield and Mueller (1962), Moorhead and Defendi (1963), German (1964), and Hsu (1964). Such telomere to centromere patterns resemble the bipolar sequential replication carried out by *Euplotes* macronuclei (Fig. 17-10).

Several laboratories have recently estimated the exact rate of synthesis at individual replication forks as they move along DNA helices in mammalian nuclei. For example Cairns (1966), after determining the rate of replication in the bacterium *E. coli* as 20–30 μ per minute, used the same autoradiographic method to estimate a rate of only 0.5 μ per minute in human (HeLa) cells. More recently Taylor (1968) has studied incorporation of ^{3}H-labeled bromodeoxyuridine by Chinese hamster chromosomes, estimating a maximum rate of 2 μ per minute at any given site. From these data, plus the total duration of the S period, it is possible to estimate the minimum number of replication forks in a single mammalian nucleus. For example, the total length of DNA helix in a human diploid nucleus is 174 cm (p. 460); a single replication fork moving at 2 μ per minute during an S-period of 10 hours could replicate only about 1200 μ of helix (and possibly much less). The minimum number of replication forks should therefore be in the order of 1450 per diploid human nucleus (174×10^4 μ divided by 1200 μ). Preliminary evidence indicates that these sites are distributed along relatively few very long DNA molecules, with lengths of 2.2 cm or more (Cairns, 1966; Sasaki and Norman, 1966). Because of the unwinding problem (Chapter 12) it is likely that each replication fork begins with a single strand break in the double helix, which may be induced by an endonuclease; this single strand break can then act as a swivel for unwinding of the helix in one or both directions (Vinograd and Lebowitz, 1966).

The number of replication forks per chromosome is not yet known, but it probably depends on the total helix length in the chromosome. For example, an average *Tradescantia* chromosome contains about 166 cm of DNA helix (2000 cm total distributed among 12 chromosomes), and replicates within an S period of 10.8 hours (Van't Hof and Sparrow, 1963); at a rate of 2 μ per minute per replication site, this would require about 1280 replication sites per chromosome. On the other hand, smaller chromosomes containing less than a centimeter of DNA would be able to replicate in the same time at many fewer sites, which in some cases might correspond to two replication forks proceeding sequentially from either end toward the middle (as in *Euplotes*). DuPraw (1965c) has proposed such a scheme for the tiny chromosomes of honey bees (Fig. 18-12), and more recently Holliday (1966) has obtained genetic evidence for this pattern of replication in the small chromosomes of the fungus *Ustilago*. In Holliday's work, ultraviolet irradiation of synchronized cells at different times in the S period induces mitotic crossing-over between different sets of genetic markers; the fact that genes near the chromosome ends are sensitive to UV earlier than genes near the centromeres indicates that these genes replicate first.

The length of time required to replicate a set of chromosomes can vary greatly in different tissues containing the same chromosomal complement. In the cleavage nuclei of many embryos a very rapid mechanism of DNA replication permits repeated mitosis at intervals of only a few minutes. For instance, the nuclei of *Drosophila* embryos, which contain about 30 cm of DNA, carry out a sequence of many, apparently normal mitotic replications, each of which requires only 10 minutes; on the other hand the same chromosome complement requires several hours to replicate in *Drosophila* salivary cells. Additional features of interphase DNA synthesis will be discussed later in relation to the structure of mitotic chromosomes (p. 579).

HISTONE SYNTHESIS

Since the basic histone proteins are physically complexed with DNA, are quantitatively proportional to DNA in haploid, diploid, and polyploid nuclei, and exhibit unique properties which influence nuclear function in still unknown ways, the place and manner of their synthesis have a special significance altogether different from that of most other intra-nuclear proteins. As first shown cytochemically in rat liver and fibroblast cells by Bloch and Godman (1955), the synthesis of histone usually occurs during the S period simultaneously with DNA synthesis. Further-more, in nondividing cells incorporation of labeled amino acids into the histone fraction has a lower rate than for any other nuclear protein, a metabolic stability paralleling that of DNA itself (Allfrey *et al.*, 1955). In the *Euplotes* macronucleus, Gall (1959) found that doubling of the histone content accompanies the local doubling of DNA as the two re-organization bands move through the nucleus, and subsequently Pres-cott (1962) confirmed that the reorganization bands are sites of rapid, localized histidine incorporation (as well as thymidine-^{3}H incorpora-tion). Since neither RNA nor RNA synthesis seems to occur in the bands, it has been suggested that histone manufacture may be uniquely inde-pendent of an RNA template. Reid and Cole (1964) have suggested a similar conclusion for the lysine-rich histones of calf thymus nuclei; they found that this histone fraction is synthesized by isolated thymus nuclei, requiring Na^+ ions and an energy source, but that the histone synthesis is insensitive to RNase.

These findings have led some authors to speculate that the histones may be synthesized directly on DNA as a template, by a mechanism totally different from the more usual ribosomal-messenger RNA system. This theory is rendered unlikely, however, by the discovery of Flamm and Birnstiel (1964) that the histone fraction of tobacco cells continues to incorporate amino acids at the normal rate even when DNA synthesis is experimentally blocked. It appears that histone synthesis and DNA synthesis, though usually coupled by some unknown mechanism, are basically independent processes which can be uncoupled by appropriate methods. Birnstiel and Flamm (1964) have also observed that in pea seedling and tobacco nuclei a significant amount of histone synthesis seems to occur in the nucleolus. After a 40-second pulse of ^{14}C-labeled amino acids, incorporation into nucleolar histone is 2.5 times greater than into nucleoplasm histone; later on the ratio becomes nearly re-versed. This suggests that histones made in the nucleolus are not merely associated with nucleolar chromatin, but are "exported" to other parts of the nucleus. Many questions still remain to be answered regarding the sites and mechanisms of histone synthesis.

cytidine in terminal linkages and binds leucine-^{14}C with an alkali-labile bond (all properties of sRNA). Soon afterward, Sirlin *et al.* (1961) found that chironomid nucleoli at early developmental stages incorporate pseudouridine, a relatively rare nucleotide which is characteristically found in the sRNA fraction (Chapter 14). The pattern of incorporation is a very remarkable one, in which label appears first in the part of the nucleolus nearest the nucleolus organizer, then migrates outward to the nucleolus periphery. Essentially the same pattern was observed for the four common ribonucleotides, but these continued to be incorporated at later stages after uptake of pseudouridine had ceased. More recently Sirlin *et al.* (1965) have been able to inhibit RNA synthesis in the chromatin while permitting nucleolar RNA synthesis to proceed; by labeling the newly synthesized nucleolar RNA and fractionating it on a sucrose density gradient, they have been able to confirm that *both* transfer RNA's and ribosomal RNA's are made in chironomid nucleoli. Since the nucleolus is a major site of ribosome and sRNA synthesis, the occurrence in nucleoli of messenger RNA derived from other parts of the chromatin should not be surprising. In fact, the messenger RNA fraction isolated from calf thymus nuclei by Sibatani *et al.* (1962) was associated with the nucleolar RNA.

The sensitivity of nucleolar RNA synthesis to inhibitors such as actinomycin D, which are known to be relatively specific for the RNA polymerase reaction, indicated that this synthesis proceeds from a DNA template. Although some earlier authors maintained that the nucleolus proper does not contain DNA, Miller (1964, 1966) has demonstrated a ring-shaped nucleolar DNA in amphibian oocyte nucleoli. An electron microscope autoradiographic study by Granboulan and Granboulan (1964) has also revealed that enough chromatin occurs inside the nucleoli of monkey kidney cells to incorporate appreciable amounts of thymidine-^{3}H; this intranucleolar chromatin is morphologically continuous with the external, "nucleolus-associated chromatin." Biochemical evidence for intranucleolar DNA comes from the experiments of Ro *et al.* (1964), who are the first to demonstrate RNA synthesis in nucleoli *after* isolation. They obtained RNA synthesis by cell-free rat liver nucleoli, which exhibit the typical requirements of the RNA polymerase reaction (Mg^{++} and all four ribonucleotides); of greatest significance, RNA synthesis is 95% inhibited if the preparations are treated with DNase. More recently LaCour and Crawley (1965) have demonstrated that a rapid pulse of uridine-^{3}H is incorporated *first* in the nucleolonemata of plant cell nucleoli; this suggests that the irregular, thread-like nucleolonema is the site of intranucleolar chromatin, RNA polymerase, and the fibrillar product RNA of the nucleolus.

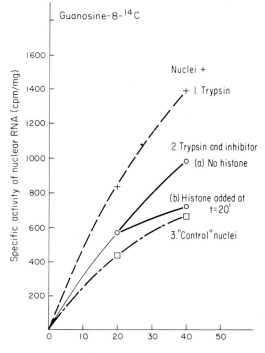

Fig. 17-11. The influence of histones on RNA synthesis in isolated thymus nuclei. Curve 1 shows that extensive histone removal with trypsin greatly enhances RNA synthesis relative to control nuclei (curve 3). Curve 2b shows that replacement of histones once again reduces RNA synthesis to the level of the controls. From Allfrey *et al.* (1963).

THE INFLUENCE OF HISTONES ON RNA SYNTHESIS

As noted previously, most of the DNA in calf thymus nuclei appears not to be involved in interphase synthesis; it has also been shown that native chromatin from plant and animal cells is only partially active as a primer in the RNA polymerase reaction (Table 17-2). Since the basic histone proteins are closely associated with DNA in native chromatin, a possible role for histones as selective inhibitors of RNA transcription was proposed very early. Initial supporting evidence for such a role comes from the fact that addition of histones to cell-free RNA polymerase systems leads to marked reduction in the reaction rates (Chapter 13).

At the level of intact nuclei, the most elaborate analysis of histone effects on RNA synthesis has been carried out with isolated calf thymus nuclei by Allfrey, Mirsky, and their collaborators. It was found by Allfrey *et al.* (1963) that addition of total histone or specific histone fractions to a cell-free preparation of thymus nuclei strongly inhibits nuclear RNA synthesis; furthermore the effect is reversible and it is more pronounced with arginine-rich histones than with lysine-rich histones. Removal of histones from these nuclei leads to a rate of RNA synthesis far in excess of the control rate (Fig. 17-11). With the discovery that RNA synthesis occurs predominantly in the diffuse chromatin and is nearly absent in the compact chromatin, an effort has been made to detect some difference in the concentration or state of various histones in the two types of chromatin. Littau *et al.* (1965) determined that selective removal of lysine-rich histones from whole nuclei transforms the compact chromatin into a diffuse state; Frenster (1965b) also discovered that the diffuse chromatin has a notably lower DNA melting temperature (81°C) than the compact fraction (86°C). Nevertheless neither lysine-rich histone, arginine-rich histone, nor RNA polymerase seem to differ quantitatively between the repressed and active chromatin.

A possible "histone switch" mechanism has recently been found, however, which is based on minor changes in chemical state of histones. Although relatively little histone synthesis occurs in isolated thymus nuclei, it was discovered that specific histone acetylases are present in the chromatin, and that these catalyze the addition of terminal acetyl groups from acetyl-CoA to histone (as in the N-terminal acetyl-alanine histone; Chapter 12). This led Allfrey *et al.* (1964) to the discovery that histones which are artificially acetylated lose much of their inhibitory effects on RNA synthesis. Although such acetylated histones still form complexes with DNA, they apparently stop interfering with DNA template activity during the RNA polymerase reaction. Following on these discoveries, it was then determined that the histones of the diffuse (or active) chromatin fraction are acetylated to a much greater extent than those of the repressed fraction. The full relationship between repression of RNA synthesis and condensation of chromatin is not yet clear, since Frenster (1965b) has also found differences in the RNA and non-histone proteins of the active and repressed chromatin fractions; specifically, there is twice as much nonhistone protein in the active fraction, five times as much RNA, and four times as much phosphoprotein. Frenster (1965c) has demonstrated a fundamental antagonism between these polyanions (which promote RNA synthesis) and polycations such as histone (which are inhibitory). In pea nuclei, an unusual class of histone-bound RNA's has also been found by Bonner *et al.* (1968), which could play a role in conferring specificity on histone inhibition.

INTRANUCLEAR SYNTHESIS OF NONHISTONE
PROTEINS, NUCLEAR PHOSPHORYLATION, AND
ACTIVE TRANSPORT AT THE NUCLEAR ENVELOPE

The first type of synthesis to be demonstrated in isolated nuclei was the
synthesis of (nonhistone) proteins, which Allfrey (1954) found would
occur in his calf thymus preparations provided that α-ketoglutarate was
added as an energy source. His earliest observations showed that the
incorporation of alanine-^{14}C by these nuclei was sensitive to DNase
digestion rather than to RNase, and that it required Na$^+$ ions. Further
sophistication of the cell-free technique revealed that the requirement
for sodium ions is part of an active transport mechanism by which free
amino acids are moved from the medium into the nuclei. Uptake of
amino acids by isolated nuclei is inhibited at low temperatures or by
2,4-dinitrophenol, in the same way as active transport at the plasma
membrane. This amino acid uptake also depends on Na$^+$, but once the
amino acids have entered the nucleus the sodium requirement in protein
synthesis is abolished. On the other hand, the requirement for DNA in
protein synthesis is due to the DNA-dependence of the intranuclear
system for generating ATP. In the absence of sufficient ATP, protein
synthesis comes to a stop because ATP-activation of amino acids is required (as in cytoplasmic protein synthesis). Unlike the absolute DNA-
dependence of RNA and DNA synthesis, both of which approach zero
as DNA content approaches zero, protein synthesis is only partially
dependent on DNA content. The requirement for DNA in protein synthesis can also be satisfied by adding back many other kinds of large
polyanion.

The existence of an intranuclear system for generating ATP by oxidative phosphorylation was first shown by Osawa *et al.* (1957), who were
able to distinguish this system from mitochondrial oxidative phosphorylation because it is sensitive to DNase and is not inhibited by calcium
ions, methylene blue, or (as found later) carbon monoxide. Subsequently
McEwen *et al.* (1963) showed that in isolated thymus nuclei, intranuclear
phosphorylation depends on nuclear enzymes of glycolysis (aldolase,
pyruvate kinase, lactic dehydrogenase) and on enzymes of the citric
acid cycle (isocitric, succinic, and malic dehydrogenases). They also
showed that AMP, ADP, and ATP cannot enter these nuclei to any great
extent from the medium (or presumably from the cytoplasm), but appear to be degraded rapidly to the nucleoside and free bases, which do
enter. Since ATP is not exchanged between the nucleus and cytoplasm,
and since cytoplasmic phosphorylation (unlike nuclear phosphorylation)
is sensitive to carbon monoxide, McEwen *et al.* (1964) could demonstrate

that exposure of intact cells to carbon monoxide suppresses cytoplasmic protein synthesis without affecting nuclear protein synthesis. However, both nuclear and mitochondrial phosphorylation are inhibited by cyanide and by 2,4-dinitrophenol. At present it is not known why oxidative phosphorylation in the nucleus requires DNA or other large polyanions; since succinic dehydrogenase is an insoluble enzyme, it may depend for normal functioning on ordered molecular arrays similar to those thought to occur in mitochondria. The most obvious structures capable of supporting ordered molecular arrays inside the nucleus are not membranes, but the protein sheaths of the 230 Å chromatin fibers; as shown by DuPraw (1965a), the structural integrity of these chromatin fibers does depend on DNase-sensitive filaments which are probably single Watson-Crick molecules. It should be noted that the enzymes of the pentose phosphate shunt also occur in thymus nuclei, but that generation of CO_2 (and presumably NADH) by this system is not sensitive to DNase.

By 1957 Allfrey *et al.* had found that isolated thymus nuclei also carry out RNA synthesis (see above), and that an early inhibition of RNA production does inhibit protein synthesis, suggesting that the latter is not entirely independent of RNA. Subsequently Frenster *et al.* (1960) found that a large part of the protein synthesis in thymus nuclei is associated with ribosome-like RNA particles, which function in a system requiring sRNA's, amino acid-activating enzymes, and other cofactors similar to those of cytoplasmic protein synthesis (Wang, 1963). In thymocytes these nuclear ribosomes are evidently most abundant in the nuclear sap, since they are readily extracted from the nuclei by neutral buffers or 0.14 M NaCl. However, in many cells it is the nucleolus which is the most conspicuous site of ribosome-like particles, and correspondingly an active protein synthesis occurs in some (but evidently not all) nucleoli. Sirlin (1960), for example, has found that leucine is uniformly incorporated throughout the nucleoli of chironomid salivary cells, in contrast to the "centrifugal" pattern of RNA synthesis in the same nucleoli (i.e., RNA incorporation beginning near the nucleolus organizer). An even more striking situation exists in pea seedlings, where Birnstiel *et al.* (1962) found that short pulses of leucine-^{3}H label the nucleoli first and that only later does labeled protein appear in the chromatin; they suggested, in fact, that the nucleolus may export protein to the chromatin. Later Birnstiel and Hyde (1963) discovered that even isolated pea nucleoli are able to incorporate amino acids *in vitro*. Birnstiel and Flamm (1964) have recently characterized some of the proteins synthesized in pea seedling and tobacco nucleoli as histone and nonhistone basic proteins. At least one fraction of these proteins is virtually identical in amino acid composition to the ribosomal structural proteins, suggesting that both the RNA and protein components of cytoplasmic ribosomes may be made in nucleoli. Although the nucleoli of starfish and frog oocytes also exhibit active protein synthesis, many somatic cells seem to lack a nucleolar protein synthetic mechanism (even though RNA continues to be turned over).

It seems likely that the synthesis of most nuclear proteins, as in cytoplasmic protein synthesis, depends on the assembly of ribosomal, messenger, and transfer RNA's, together with corresponding ribosomal proteins, aminoacyl RNA synthetases, and of course amino acids. The evidence suggests that in different tissues the major sites of assembly, and therefore of intranuclear polypeptide synthesis, may be either the nucleolus, the nucleoplasm, the chromatin, or any combination of these. In the last analysis these differences probably depend on variations in intranuclear transport phenomena. For example, in pea seedlings it appears that RNA is synthesized primarily in the chromatin, is then transported to the nucleolus, where it participates in synthesis of proteins for transport back to the chromatin; in insect salivary cells, on the other hand, the most active RNA synthesis is in the nucleolus itself, and there is evidence that ribosomes find their way not only to the cytoplasm, but to localized sites in the chromatin. The particular proteins synthesized probably depend in large part on the specific requirements of the species or tissue. Allfrey *et al.* (1955) observed that in several mouse tissues, the turnover in DNA-linked, nonhistone proteins is much higher than the histone turnover, and tends to approximate the turnover rate for cytoplasmic proteins in the same cells; similarly Mirsky and Ris (1951) found wide variations in the percentage of DNA-linked nonhistone proteins of various tissues, the proportion tending to be greater in cells with a higher cytoplasmic mass. Recently an active but atypical form of protein synthesis has been found by Wang (1965) associated with the acidic proteins, RNA and DNA that remain after thorough extraction of isolated thymus nuclei with saline solutions ("residual nucleus"). This residual synthesis is RNA dependent, but surprisingly it is not stimulated by adding ribosomal RNA, sRNA, or artificial messengers such as poly U.

Nucleocytoplasmic Exchange

It is clear that the broad features of synthesis in intact cells approximate the relationships expected between DNA as the genetic material, RNA as the transcribed carrier of genetic information, and specific proteins as the functional molecules of the cytoplasm (i.e., enzymes, contractile elements, structural proteins, etc.). This represents a system of concepts which predicts that DNA and RNA will be synthesized in the nucleus, that RNA will pass to the cytoplasm, and that cytoplasmic RNA will direct the synthesis of specific proteins. Although much evidence has been cited to support these simpler expectations, there remain a number of very fundamental questions which have not yet been answered, and which, when they have been answered, are sufficiently potent to turn the entire system of concepts upside down.

Considering first the problem of genetic information, it may be asserted that the sequences of nucleotide pairs in the DNA molecule cannot *by* *themselves* "mean" anything. Like a series of dots and dashes in a telegraph wire, their significance depends on how they are translated, on the meaning that is assigned to them, or specifically, on the system that responds to these sequences by providing a particular amino acid at a particular site in a particular polypeptide chain. It is apparent that the exact operation of the system depends on the properties of certain proteins, such as aminoacyl sRNA synthetases which are responsible for binding a given amino acid to its corresponding sRNA, or on the ribosomal binding enzyme which admits a given aminoacyl-sRNA to the ribosome. In a very real sense these protein components of the total system contribute to the meaning of the nucleic acid components, and it is by no means obvious that the information content of these proteins is wholly conferred upon them by those nucleic acids that mediated their synthesis. Even the replication of DNA and the transcription of RNA depend on specific catalysis by the proteins DNA and RNA polymerase, whose contribution to the information required for synthesis remains to be determined at a submolecular level (Chapter 13).

As a practical problem at the cell level, it need only be pointed out that the nuclei of many early embryonic cells are functionally identical, completely interchangeable, yet that the fates of individual nuclei during the differentiation of tissues such as muscle, nerve, and so on depends on unknown types of "extranuclear" (or cytoplasmic) information. Clearly an interaction between nucleus and cytoplasm occurs, but the role of the cytoplasm is still only poorly understood. Whereas the function of nucleic acids in the nucleus has been studied for nearly 100 years, the presence of DNA in chloroplasts, mitochondria, nucleoli, and centrioles has only begun to receive attention. For the most part it is not yet known how extranuclear DNA is related to intranuclear DNA, what part the plasm plays in regulating the replication and transcription of intranuclear DNA, whether such critical enzymes as DNA and RNA polymerase, aminoacyl sRNA synthetases, the ribosomal binding enzyme, or histone acetylases are made in the cytoplasm or the nucleus, and to what extent the cytoplasm and nucleus are autonomous in regulating quantitative synthesis of different proteins from available RNA messengers. Until these and many similar questions are answered, the present state of information does not permit us to decide whether nucleic acids "dictate" the synthesis of proteins, whether proteins "dictate" the synthesis of nucleic acids, or whether (as is most likely) the entire "master–slave" conception is only an artificial construction. With respect to the synthesis of DNA, RNA, and proteins inside the nucleus, several specific questions may be asked: (1) Is all cytoplasmic (and nuclear) RNA synthesized in the nucleus? (2) Are all nuclear proteins synthesized inside the nucleus? (3) Are any cytoplasmic proteins synthesized inside the nucleus? (4) To what extent does DNA synthesized in the nucleus enter the cytoplasm and cytoplasmic organelles? (5) Insofar as DNA, RNA, and proteins move between the nucleus and cytoplasm, does this transfer take place in both directions or only one? (6) To what extent are the differences between differentiated cells, such as muscle and nerve cells, maintained by nuclear or cytoplasmic factors? None of these questions has as yet been completely resolved.

The most direct methods that have been developed for investigating questions such as these are, first, simple comparison of nucleated and anucleate cells or cell fragments; and second, transplantation of nuclei between cells, permitting an experimental recombination of different nuclei with different cytoplasms. The earliest and simplest experiments of this type involved cutting or constricting protozoans into two or more parts, only one of which contained a nucleus; according to Hughes (1959), such microdissection began as early as 1783, and became relatively popular during the 1880's; the most frequent result was that the nucleated parts lived while the anucleate fragments eventually died. Nevertheless completely anucleate fragments sometimes survived a surprisingly long time, up to several months in the large unicellular alga *Acetabularia* (Hämmerling, 1934). Furthermore, a very fine cytoplasmic strand was generally sufficient to convey the nuclear "influence" to distant bits of plasm. These early experiments showed that, whatever the role of the nucleus, its presence is not continuously required for survival, but it is necessary for long-term growth and reproduction.

During the 1950's it became possible to refine the same type of experiment by monitoring protein and RNA synthesis in anucleate cell fragments. The earliest labeled isotope experiments by Brachet and Chantrenne (1951) revealed that protein synthesis continues for some weeks in enucleated *Acetabularia*, in contrast to net RNA synthesis which ceases immediately (Hämmerling, 1959). Prescott later investigated whether anucleate fragments of *Amoeba* (1959) or *Tetrahymena* (1962) could synthesize RNA at all, i.e., whether all the RNA in these cells is made in the nucleus. Intact protozoans were cut into nucleate and enucleate halves, incubated with labeled RNA precursors, and autoradiographed. Prescott found that, provided care is taken to prevent false uptake by bacteria or yeast in cytoplasmic food vacuoles, anucleate halves do not synthesize RNA, whereas nucleate halves synthesize very actively; it appears, therefore, that the nuclei are the exclusive source of cytoplasmic RNA in these cells. Pulse experiments with *Tetrahymena* have also shown that labeled RNA appears in the nucleus within 1.5 minutes, but does not enter the cytoplasm for about 12–15 minutes. Anucleate *Acetabularia* generally continue synthesis to a much greater extent than anucleate *Amoeba*, a result that can now be understood at least partly in terms of the DNA, RNA, and associated synthetic system present in *Acetabularia* chloroplasts (Naora *et al.*, 1960). However, according to Keck (1963) even chloroplast protein synthesis falls off eventually, suggesting that all the cytoplasmic components are ultimately dependent on the nucleus. Keck's experiments have shown, in addition, that individual species of protein, such as acid phosphatase, invertase, or phosphorylases, stop being synthesized at different times after enucleation. The simplest explanation for this result is that the messenger RNA's for each protein differ in half-life and disappear at different rates after removal of the nucleus.

Micrurgical transplantation of nuclei was attempted as early as 1886; not until much later, however, did Hämmerling (1943) succeed in producing viable recombinations between various nuclei and cytoplasms by grafting together nucleated or anucleate fragments from different species of *Acetabularia* (Chapter 20). The first successful experiments involving direct micro-manipulation of nuclei were reported by Lorch and Danielli (1950); they used a method in which the recipient amoeba is first enucleated by simply pushing its nucleus out through the plasma membrane with a blunt microneedle; a donor amoeba is then placed next to the recipient, and its nucleus is pushed across both membranes, thus renucleating the recipient with a foreign nucleus. Using a similar technique, Goldstein and Plaut (1955) were able to transfer nuclei from amoebae containing ^{32}P-labeled RNA into unlabeled cells; they found that, whereas all the label was still in the nuclei 5 hours after the transplant, in 12 hours considerable labeled RNA had appeared in the cytoplasm. If a labeled nucleus was transferred into an *intact* amoeba still containing its own unlabeled nucleus, labeled RNA appeared in the recipient's cytoplasm, but not in the recipient's nucleus. These experiments provide direct evidence that RNA synthesized in the nucleus moves to the cytoplasm, but that this movement occurs in one direction only.

A somewhat different result was obtained when nuclei containing isotopically labeled *protein* were transferred into intact, unlabeled amoe-

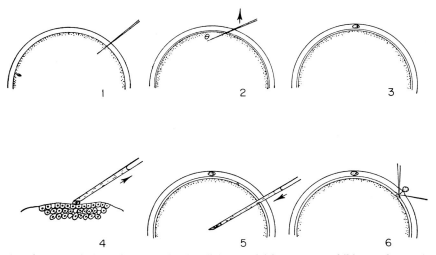

Fig. 17-12. Technique for transplanting living nuclei between amphibian embryos. An egg is artificially activated by pricking with a glass needle (step 1), and shortly afterward the egg pronucleus is removed (steps 2 and 3). A single cell from a blastula or later embryonic stage is then picked up in a micropipette (step 4) and injected into the enucleate egg (steps 5 and 6). From Briggs and King (1955).

bae. In this experiment, Goldstein (1958) found that 90% of the labeled nuclear proteins became distributed between the two nuclei, and that very little protein accumulated in the cytoplasm. Later Goldstein (1963) determined that a characteristic ratio of 2.6 to 1 establishes itself within 5 hours after transplantation between the amount of label in the transplanted nucleus and the labeled protein that migrates into the recipient nucleus. From these and other experiments (Prescott, 1963) it appears that about 40% of the labeled nuclear proteins do not migrate, but that the remainder are able to migrate randomly out of one nucleus and into the other (contrasting with the one-directional migration of RNA). Since the same 2.6 to 1 ratio is observed after labeling with leucine-^{3}H, arginine-^{3}H, tryptophan-^{3}H, or methionine-^{3}H, neither the migrating nor nonmigrating proteins correspond exactly to a histone fraction.

Still another elegant experiment indicates that both types of protein are synthesized in the cytoplasm. In this test, *enucleated* amoebae were incubated with leucine-^{3}H, then the precursor was "washed out" with unlabeled leucine and the cells were renucleated from unlabeled donors; after 24 hours the nuclei were then transferred a second time into intact, unlabeled cells and permitted to equilibrate with the recipient nuclei. It was found that not only did the unlabeled nuclei acquire labeled proteins from the cytoplasm, but some of these proteins migrated to the recipient nuclei in the usual 2.6 to 1 ratio. It appears, therefore, that in

Amoeba both migrating and nonmigrating nuclear proteins are synthesized in the cytoplasm. During mitosis both these proteins leave the chromosomes and become distributed through the cytoplasm, but they
return to the nuclei at the next interphase.

In 1952 Briggs and King introduced the first successful nuclear transplant technique involving nuclei from an advanced multicellular organism; their method was based on the egg of the common laboratory
frog, *Rana pipiens*, which may be activated parthenogenetically and enucleated by removing the egg pronucleus with a microneedle. If such an
enucleated egg is injected with a single diploid nucleus from an *R. pipiens*
blastula cell, normal development often ensues, leading eventually to
a typical adult frog (Fig. 17-12). This experiment demonstrates that the
functional capabilities of at least some blastula nuclei are not permanently altered in any way from those of the original zygote nucleus. In
experiments of the same design, Briggs and King subsequently tested
the morphogenetic capacities of nuclei from various gastrula stages,
from different germ layers, and even from fully differentiated tissues. In
almost all cases, a certain proportion of transplanted nuclei proved
capable of supporting advanced development. In fact in the toad
Xenopus, for which a similar nuclear transplant technique was developed
by Fischberg *et al.* (1958), Gurdon (1962) has found that at least 4% of
nuclei from the differentiated gut cells of hatched tadpoles are able to
act as cleavage nuclei, giving rise to normal adult frogs. To a first approximation, then, it may be concluded that some types of cell differentiation do not necessarily involve permanent alterations in the nucleus;
such differentiation must be either entirely a function of cytoplasmic
elements, or else depend on temporary nuclear changes induced by cytoplasmic elements.

By contrast, the *percentage* of nuclei capable of supporting the full

Table 17-4
LOSS IN THE CAPACITY OF ENDODERM NUCLEI TO SUPPORT DEVELOPMENT WHEN
TRANSPLANTED FROM SUCCESSIVELY LATER EMBRYONIC STAGES TO ENUCLEATED EGGS[a]

| | | Percent of cleaving eggs showing | | |
| | | --- | --- | --- |
Stage of donor	No. recipients initiating normal cleavage	Normal larva	Abnormal advanced embryo	Early gastrula arrest
Early gastrula	57	**77**	13	10
Late gastrula	79	20	**53**	27
Neurula	25	4	24	**72**

[a] From Briggs and King (1959).

range of normal development declines as the differentiation of tissues becomes more advanced (Table 17-4). This loss of capacity seems to be more marked in *Rana* than in *Xenopus*, it is usually associated with the appearance of chromosomal aberrations in transplanted nuclei, and at present it is not entirely clear to what extent this effect is due to technical difficulties, such as damage to the nuclei during transplantation. Nevertheless, in some instances the nuclear changes exhibit a high degree of specificity; for example, Briggs and King (1959) found that nuclei from frog endoderm cells will support advanced development, but these embryos possess overly developed endoderm derivatives and underdeveloped mesoderm and ectoderm derivatives. DiBerardino and King (1965) have also obtained advanced embryos from eggs containing transplanted adenocarcinoma nuclei, but these embryos were defective in various ways, e.g., lacking eyes. Recently Smith (1965) has contrasted the developmental capacity of somatic endoderm nuclei with that of germ cell nuclei from the same embryos, finding that 40% of eggs cleaving with germ cell nuclei develop into normal tadpoles, whereas none of the eggs receiving endoderm nuclei yield normal tadpoles. In *Xenopus* also, Gurdon (1962) noted that 7 out of 27 adult frogs derived from advanced gut nuclei were normal in appearance but reproductively sterile.

That such changes in nuclear capacity may be partly or entirely irreversible is shown by a "serial transplant" experiment introduced by King and Briggs (1956). In this method a single nucleus is transplanted from an advanced tissue cell into an enucleated egg, the egg is permitted to replicate to a multicellular blastula stage, then one to many daughter nuclei are transplanted from the blastula back into individual enucleated eggs; blastulae from these second-generation embryos may then be used for another generation of transplants, the experiment being repeated for as many generations as desired (Fig. 17-13). When different embryos containing "sister nuclei" are permitted to complete development, the result is usually a "clone" of almost identical embryos possessing identical abnormalities if these are present. As shown by King and Briggs in *Rana*, the severity of abnormalities associated with differentiation does not decline even though the nuclei undergo dozens of replications in undifferentiated egg cytoplasm. On the other hand, some partial reversal of abnormalities has been observed in *Xenopus*, where the abnormalities also seem to be less specific. Since some nuclei from differentiated cells are not changed, it is not clear why others should be changed, or what mechanisms may be involved. Aside from possible experimental damage, Markert and Ursprung (1963) have found that nuclear changes of this kind may be induced experimentally by injecting frog zygotes with protein components from the nuclear or cytoplasmic fractions of adult frog liver. The "globulin + albumin" fraction is somewhat more effective than the histone fraction in producing developmental arrest at a blastula stage; nuclei from such arrested embryos will also support cleavage mitosis if transplanted back into enucleated eggs, but even after 7 generations of back-transfers, these nuclei will not support development past the blastula stage.

That differences intrinsic to the chromatin play a role in the functional differentiation of tissues has been shown in elegant experiments by Bonner *et al.* (1963). Using a combination of cell-free RNA and protein synthesizing systems from *E. coli*, these authors tested the template activity of native chromatin from two types of pea plant tissue: (1) pea cotyledons, which synthesize a characteristic pea seed reserve globulin; and (2) pea buds, which do not synthesize this globulin *in vivo*. Bonner

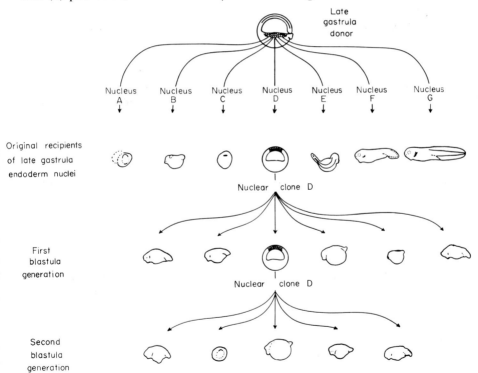

Fig. 17-13. Technique for serial transplantation of nuclei and development of genetically identical "clone" embryos in amphibia. In the first stage, different donor cells are used to initiate development in enucleated eggs; when the recipient embryos reach a blastula stage, they may be used as donors for a second generation of transplants. The same cycle may be repeated for an indefinite number of generations. From King and Briggs (1956).

et al. were able to demonstrate that cotyledon chromatin *in vitro* does direct the synthesis of reserve globulin, whereas bud chromatin does not. This difference in the chromatin was shown to depend on the DNA-linked proteins.

The recombination of nuclei and cytoplasm from different species was first achieved by Hämmerling (1943) in grafting experiments with the unicellular alga *Acetabularia*. He found that the characteristics of the nucleocytoplasmic "hybrid" individuals eventually become those of the nuclear parent, but that this change is not necessarily immediate; in fact, his experiments clearly demonstrate that *Acetabularia* accumulates species-specific substances in the cytoplasm, the synthesis of which depends on the nucleus but which can direct a highly specific type of morphogenesis in the absence of the nucleus (or in the presence of a foreign nucleus). These morphogenetic substances arrange themselves in a gradient, with the region of highest concentration most distant from the nucleus; Werz and Zetsche (1963) found that the gradient could be directly visualized by labeling with either serine-^{14}C or uracil-^{14}C, suggesting that the materials in question contain both protein and RNA.

Lorch and Danielli (1950) were the first to transplant nuclei micrurgically between two species, *Amoeba proteus* and *A. discoides*, which differ in nuclear size, pseudopod morphology, rate of multiplication, antigens, and other characteristics. They found that nucleocytoplasmic hybrids between these two species are able to survive, and occasional individuals (less than 1%) may even give rise to long-term clones. However, the size of the nucleus alters within 24 hours to that characteristic of the cytoplasmic species, and pseudopod morphology also tends to be cytoplasmic (with some nuclear influence eventually appearing). By contrast, the rate of multiplication and the range of antigens are determined by the nucleus. The most remarkable discovery was that the cytoplasmic influence on the characteristics of the hybrids did not diminish even after six years, when the clones had undergone a geometric series of at least 600 successive replications. When the nuclei and cytoplasms of the hybrids were then tested for compatibility with pure parent strains, Danielli (1958) found that both nucleus and plasm had changed during their association together, and were no longer compatible with either parent type. Thus a *proteus* nucleus that had been in a *discoides* plasm for five years could no longer function in either a *proteus* or a pure *discoides* plasm; conversely, the originally *discoides* plasm after its association with a *proteus* nucleus could not function with either a *discoides* or *proteus* nucleus. These results were not due to experimental damage since control transplants gave 95% viability.

After the introduction of amphibian nuclear transplant techniques, Briggs and King (1955) were able to investigate the developmental capacity of nuclei which were genetic hybrids between *R. pipiens* and *R. catesbeiana*. Although hybrid embryos become arrested at a gastrula stage, nuclei transplanted from these embryos into enucleated *R. pipiens* eggs are able to support normal development again to a gastrula stage. Thus the developmental arrest does not result from an impairment in the ability of the nuclei to replicate, but from their inability to function in a foreign cytoplasm. Later experiments by Moore (1958, 1960) have demonstrated that amphibian nuclei, like *Amoeba* nuclei, undergo an irreversible change when they replicate in a foreign cytoplasm. In Moore's experiments, diploid or haploid nuclei of *R. pipiens* were permitted to go through cleavage replications in *R. sylvatica* eggs, then micrurgically transferred back to enucleated eggs of *R. pipiens*; it was found that, although such *pipiens* nuclei are able to support development of *pipiens* eggs to a gastrula stage, they have lost the capacity to support later development in a normal fashion. This loss of capacity is associated with severe chromosome anomalies, and it cannot be restored even after five generations of serial transfers in *pipiens* cytoplasm. Very similar results were obtained by Gurdon (1962) in experiments recombining nuclei and cytoplasm of *Xenopus laevis* and *X. tropicalis;* in this case, the changes in the nuclei showed a high degree of specificity with respect to the time of developmental arrest, they were complete after 8 nuclear replications in the foreign cytoplasm, and they could not be reversed even after 70 replications in native cytoplasm. Additional research employing nuclear transplant techniques has been reviewed recently by Gurdon (1964).

Experiments such as these have clearly established that cytoplasmic components are able to cause functional changes in nuclei which the nuclei themselves are unable to reverse; such changes, furthermore, are sufficiently delicate so that the altered nuclei retain a considerable reproductive capacity. The nature of the effective cytoplasmic materials is not yet known, but various possible components include membranous precursors of the nuclear envelope, protein components of the chromatin fibers (e.g., RNA polymerase), or the DNA itself. The latter alternative has been favored by Moore (1962), who emphasizes that cytoplasmic deoxypolynucleotide chains may be used as chromosomal precursors in early amphibian embryos, and if so, it would be expected that the nucleus of one species would be unable to replicate normally in the cytoplasm of another. The presence of high polymer DNA in the cytoplasm of frog eggs and oocytes has been well established by Hoff-

Jorgensen and Zeuthen (1952), Grant (1958) and others, who found that such DNA amounts to over 1000 times the DNA mass in a single diploid nucleus. As noted previously, the rate of DNA replication during embryonic cleavage is so extraordinarily rapid that it may well depend on incorporation of already polymerized DNA segments. Grant (1958) was able to show directly that the cleavage nuclei of *R. pipiens* do not incorporate ^{32}P, and B. C. Moore (1963) also found that injected thy-midine-^{3}H is incorporated less actively during early cleavage than by later blastula cells. Whether cytoplasmic DNA can account for the extra-nuclear effects observed in *Amoeba* remains to be seen, but alternative possibilities in this case are the cytoplasmically synthesized nuclear proteins detected by Goldstein (1963).

With the recent discovery that specific DNA's are present in chloro-plasts (Chapter 5), mitochondria (Chapter 7), and possibly in centrioles (Chapter 9), it has become legitimate to inquire whether all of these DNA's replicate as autonomous cytoplasmic components or whether some of them are derived ultimately from DNA synthesized in the nucleus. Numerous instances have been reported in which DNA-con-taining material is seen to pass from the nucleus into the cytoplasm. As reviewed by Beers (1963), such "chromatin extrusion" occurs regularly in several genera of ciliate protozoa. Boveri (1910) also described a remarkable process of chromosome elimination during embryogenesis in the roundworm *Ascaris;* in the presumptive somatic cells of these embryos, the large chromosomes of the zygote fragment transversely into some 30 small chromosomes, plus several large masses from the ends of the chromosomes. Although the small chromosomes possess individual attachments to the mitotic spindle, the terminal masses are lost from the spindle and enter the cytoplasm. By contrast with the somatic cells, these changes are not observed to occur in the presumptive germ cells. Geyer-Duszynska (1959) has also reported a comparable orderly process of chromosome elimination in embryos of the sawfly.

Although such chromatin extrusion certainly occurs, its significance is not entirely understood; at the same time, there is impressive evidence that, at least in some organisms, particular structures or chemical com-ponents of the cytoplasm are partly or entirely independent of the nucleus. For instance, the experiments of Danielli (1958) with nucleo-cytoplasmic hybrids of *Amoeba* showed that the cytoplasm retains auton-omous characters independently of the nucleus for at least 600 suc-cessive generations. Independent extranuclear inheritance of some chloroplast characters is also well established, and the base composition of chloroplast DNA differs significantly from that of nuclear DNA (Chapter 5). In yeast and *Neurospora*, mitochondrial DNA replicates autonomously and influences the inheritance of at least some mito-chondrial characters (Chapter 7).

In ciliate protozoans there is also clear evidence that, while the specificity of macromolecules is determined by DNA, the manner in which these molecules are assembled into cytoplasmic organelles is regulated by the preexisting patterns of structure in the cytoplasmic cortex. Sonneborn (1963), for example, has studied abnormal *Parame-cium* in which one row of cilia is reversed in anterior-posterior polarity; by special microgenetic techniques it is possible to replace the nuclei of such individuals with nuclei from normal cells, yet the reversed polarity persists for 400 generations. In the ciliate *Stentor*, as well, elegant micrur-gical experiments have been carried out by Tartar (1961), in which bits of cortex or nuclei from different individuals or different regions of a single cell were recombined in various ways. These experiments clearly demonstrate that certain regions of the cortex determine or "induce" the pattern of cell morphology and that the nucleus is no more able to im-pose its character on a foreign cortex than the cortex can dictate its specificity to a foreign nucleus (Tartar, 1953). In these examples, as in the differentiation of embryonic tissues, the plasm clearly possesses "information" of its own, which is indispensable for the development and normal functioning of the intact cell. The exploration of this cyto-plasmic information, its mode of transmission, and its interaction with polynucleotide information, deserves to be elucidated in much greater detail. The analysis of plasmic determiners operating during embryonic development will be discussed further in Chapter 20.

18

ORGANIZATION OF GENETIC MATERIAL IN EUKARYOTIC CHROMOSOMES

Our function is not to provide confirmatory morphological evidence for old concepts, but to define a new morphological background against which old and new physiological data will be interpreted in the future.

G. E. PALADE *1956*

In contrast to the division of microorganisms, cell division in nucleated cells is accompanied by impressive morphological and physiological changes, including cessation of DNA, RNA, and protein synthesis, fragmentation of the nuclear envelope, condensation of several or many bipartite chromosomes, development of an elaborate mitotic apparatus, and orderly alignment of chromosomes on a metaphase plate. The occurrence of these events was discovered in the 1870's and provided some of the earliest insights into the nature of the genetic mechanism. Yet almost a century later there is greater uncertainty about the structure and organization of DNA in eukaryotic chromosomes than in those of bacteria or viruses. The prevailing academic confusion is not so much a product of insufficient data, but of an enormous and confused literature, in which for any given observation a precisely opposite "anti-observation" can be found. A second difficulty has been the illogical sequence of discovery, which provided enormous cytogenetic detail long before the molecular basis for cytogenetic events could be understood. Speculative interpretation of these data gave rise to a plethora of theories and associated jargon which continue to plague student thought long after their usefulness has been outmoded. The present chapter does not seek to achieve a balanced review of available observations, but attempts rather a creative reinterpretation of old and new observations in terms of recently discovered molecular mechanisms.

At the level of light microscopy, an accurate description of chromosomal events during the division of both plant and animal cells was summarized by Flemming (1880; see translation, 1965), who recognized that the metaphase chromosomes arise by a condensation of threadlike elements in the interphase nucleus; in fact, the term "mitosis" which Flemming coined for these chromosomal events refers specifically to their threadlike nature. About the same time, Van Beneden (1883) noted the occurrence of a characteristic, linear pattern of chromomeres in *Ascaris* chromosomes, i.e., a "beads-on-a-string" structure which was precisely duplicated in the daughter chromatids. Boveri (1888) further analyzed the relationship between the metaphase chromosomes and the interphase nuclei of *Ascaris* embryos, showing that the nuclear envelope develops with outpocketings corresponding to the ends of the large chromosomes. Even during interphase when the metaphase chromosomes are no longer visible, the number and position of these "pouches" corresponds to the number and position of chromosomes in the particular species or strain; each outpocketing also marks the place where a chromosome will reappear at the next prophase. Sometimes one or two chromosomes establish an entirely separate "micronucleus," which has the typical, structureless appearance of the main nucleus at inter-

515

phase, but at prophase gives rise again to the original one or two chromosomes. These observations, which were the first to suggest that the metaphase chromosomes retain their individuality and relative positions even when they become invisible at interphase, were later abundantly confirmed in other organisms. In fact, whenever it is possible to distinguish different chromosomes by their morphologies, it is found as a rule that individual chromosomes tend to occupy characteristic positions on the metaphase plate and that this position is maintained from one cell division to the next. This is true in hemipteran insects studied by Wilson (1909), and it has also been noted recently in human leukocytes by Miller *et al.* (1963). In Wilson's study, the genetic continuity of individual chromosomes was further confirmed by the presence of small "accessory chromosomes" (or m-chromosomes), which were shown to be distributed unequally and randomly to the daughter cells; nevertheless, wherever an m-chromosome goes, it continues to replicate autonomously and exhibits the usual condensation-decondensation cycle of the other chromosomes.

The exact nature of the change that occurs when interphase chromatin condenses to form the metaphase chromosomes, or conversely when the chromosomes become invisible at telophase, has been poorly understood until very recently. One early concept was based on observations of coils and coiled-coils in metaphase chromosomes, which suggested that condensation involves a tighter and tighter supercoiling of a long, thin thread. An alternative possibility was suggested by Ris and Mirsky (1949), who found evidence that isolated chromosomes can "swell up" to several times their metaphase volumes, suggesting a type of gel hydration reaction. However, recent analysis of nuclear ultrastructure by electron microscopy and other techniques (Chapter 17) has established that interphase chromatin is composed of long bumpy fibers 200–300 Å in diameter. Since such fibers cannot be resolved with the light microscope, they are invisible as individual units; nevertheless when they become more closely packed, e.g., in interphase heterochromatin or metaphase chromosomes, the aggregates as a whole become visible. Most *in vivo* transitions between visible and invisible chromatin states can be accounted for very simply by alterations in the tightness of folding of such chromatin fibers (Fig. 18-1). Furthermore, the observed ultrastructure of metaphase chromosomes is entirely consistent with the same concept (to be discussed).

It was noted fairly early that the number of chromosomes in a given cell is characteristic for the species, yet may vary markedly between closely related species. *Ascaris megalocephala* for instance possesses only four chromosomes, a property which made it a very useful object in

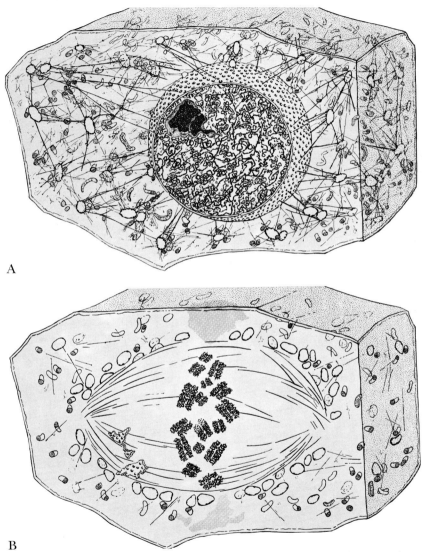

A

B

Fig. 18-1. An interpretation of the relation between interphase organization (A) and meta-phase organization (B) in honey bee embryonic cells. At interphase the chromatin fibers are diffusely arranged inside a nuclear envelope, while at metaphase the same fibers fold tightly into discrete chromosomes lying free on the mitotic spindle. From DuPraw (1965c).

the analysis of meiosis during the 1880's; on the other hand, related species of *Ascaris* such as *A. lumbricoides* have diploid numbers in the order of 30 or 40. These and many similar examples indicate that chromosomes may undergo fusion or fragmentation during evolution without seriously altering the genetic characters of the organism; it appears that the sum total of genetic material is much more important than the number of packets into which it is divided. In higher organisms, a haploid number of one chromosome is known to occur only in a particular subspecies of *Ascaris megalocephala* (*A. m. univalens*), whereas the upper limit in haploid chromosome number is in the order of 100–127 for certain crustaceans and 120 for a particular species of fern. The great majority of animals have haploid numbers less than the 23 chromosomes of the human complement (Makino, 1951).

Chromosome size is difficult to characterize, since very marked differences occur in various tissues of the same organism, as well as in the same cell during prophase and metaphase. It was early observed that the diameters of chromosomes in a given cell at a given time are approximately the same, whereas the lengths may differ by a factor of 2, 3, 4, or more. Among human chromosomes, the largest are about 0.6 μ in diameter and in the order of 10 μ long, while the shortest may approximate 1 μ spheres. The total length of the 46 human chromosomes (laid end-to-end) has been estimated as about 220 μ by Osgood *et al.* (1964); similarly the total length of 14 chromosomes in diploid wheat is about 172 μ (Bhaskaran and Swaminathan, 1960), and of 10 chromosomes in sorghum about 61–70 μ (Nirula *et al.*, 1961). The most massive chromosomes are, of course, the polytene chromosomes of dipteran salivary gland cells, which attain lengths exceeding 400 μ and diameters of 4–5 μ. In other tissues of the same flies, the smallest chromosomes are only 0.2 μ long. The delicate lampbrush chromosomes of amphibian oocytes also exhibit lengths attaining 500–800 μ. Since the smallest known chromosomes are at the limit of light microscope resolution, it is entirely possible that even smaller chromosomes may someday be detected with the electron microscope.

In many species, all the chromosomes are of about the same size and shape, making it difficult or impossible to characterize individual ones. For this reason, it was not until 1903 that Sutton discovered the 23 chromosomes of the lubber grasshopper constitute 11 pairs plus an accessory chromosome. Only after the recognition of homologous pairs did it become possible to interpret meiotic tetrads correctly, and to relate the events of meiosis to the phenotypic ratios of Mendelian genetics (Sutton, 1903). Later McClintock (1929) achieved a very exact characterization of the 10 chromosome pairs in *Zea mays*, and the four chromosome pairs of *Drosophila melanogaster* were even more precisely mapped by Painter

(1933) and Bridges (1942). From these studies it became clear that the most important modes of chromosome variation are:

1. The position of the kinetochore (or centromere), i.e., the primary point of attachment between a chromosome and the spindle tubules; at this point there is usually a noticeable constriction or gap in the chromosome body (primary constriction). Chromosomes in which the kinetochore is at a midpoint along the length of the chromosome tend to form V-shapes at anaphase (the kinetochore leading the way toward the spindle pole), and are designated as *metacentric*. On the other hand if the kinetochore is somewhat nearer to one end, the chromosome tends to form a J-shape at anaphase and is referred to as *submetacentric;* in this case, the ratio of length between the long and short arms of the chromosome is an important characteristic. Finally, if the kinetochore is at one end, the chromosome preserves a rod-shape at anaphase and is designated as *acrocentric* or *telocentric*.

2. The linear pattern of beadlike or heavily staining regions, known as chromomeres, is also highly characteristic. Although the most detailed expression of such patterns is that found in the banded giant salivary chromosomes, less extensive chromomere patterns have been mapped in lampbrush chromosomes, in the prophase chromosomes of *Zea mays*, and in a few other species. Chromomere linearity is an important cytological characteristic of chromosomes.

3. The distribution of heterochromatic regions in the chromosome is relatively specific. It was noted by Montgomery (1904) that certain chromosomes sometimes persist in a condensed state during interphase; these he designated as heterochromosomes, distinguishing them from the more typical euchromosomes. Later Heitz (1928) pointed out that different parts of the same chromosome often behave as heterochromatin or euchromatin, respectively. Aside from the tendency to remain in a condensed state, heterochromatic regions are characterized by a markedly lower crossing-over frequency, by a low frequency of genetically active loci, and by a tendency to replicate later in the S period than euchromatic regions. In *Drosophila* and some other species heterochromatic segments typically occur on either side of the kinetochore, and they may also be distributed over a large percentage of the total chromosome mass.

4. The presence and pattern of visible coils along the chromosome arms can sometimes be mapped. Especially in large chromosomes, a right- or left-handed helical structure can usually be demonstrated by appropriate treatment (Fig. 18-6); the number of gyres per arm and the diameter of the coiled unit represent useful, though somewhat variable, chromosome characteristics (Ohnuki, 1965).

5. The positions of various special structures, such as the nucleolus,

Feulgen-positive satellites (attached to the chromosome arms by invisible connections) or various irregular knobs, constrictions, and bends are often useful. These features do not always occur, but when they do they are valuable in characterizing a particular chromosome pair.

In many species, the most readily recognizable chromosomes are those associated with sex determination, the so-called X and Y chromosomes. Henking (1891) first described the X-chromosome in an insect, where its tendency to lag behind the other chromosomes (autosomes) at anaphase made it an "X" quantity. Later Wilson and his students clearly established a correlation between maleness, femaleness, and the occurrence of the X (and Y) chromosome. In XO sex determination the X chromosome is the only unpaired element in one sex, while it is entirely lacking in the other; in XY sex determination, a pair of X's is present in one sex but the X and Y in the other sex often resemble two unpaired chromosomes. Among mammals (including man) the female is the XX individual, and in this case the two X chromosomes are distinguishable because one becomes heterochromatic while the other remains euchromatic. As a result, the heterochromatic X is clearly visible during interphase in female but not male cells, where it is sometimes referred to as a "Barr body" or as "sex chromatin." In a manner typical for heterochromatin generally, the Barr body replicates much later in the S period than its partner does. Such conspicuous karyotypic differences between males and females played an important part in establishing the chromosome theory of heredity, and during the early 20th century the association of certain Mendelian traits with the sex chromosomes also provided a key for demonstrating that the genes reside in the chromosomes.

In a few instances, it has been well established that differences in chromosome morphology between different tissues of the same individual are the result of different functional states of the chromosomes. For example, the giant chromosomes of dipteran salivary glands are actually interphase structures, which occur in cells that are neither dividing nor preparing to divide, but which support active RNA and protein synthesis. On the other hand, the more typical metaphase chromosomes of mitosis and meiosis are metabolically inert, representing temporary structures characteristic of the dividing cell. In many respects the structural modifications associated with cell division represent a type of cell differentiation, and it has also been suggested that differences between mitosis (in somatic cells) and meiosis (in germ cells) should be regarded as a special type of tissue differentiation. The most obvious differences occur during the prophase, when homologous chromosomes pair (or synapse) in meiosis but not mitosis; synapsis evidently leads both to genetic recombination (crossing-over) and to chromosome reduction in the haploid gametes, and it is associated with a special proteinaceous structure, the synaptinemal complex, which occurs only during part of the meiotic prophase. So far as the metaphase chromosomes are concerned, available evidence indicates that their organization is essentially similar in both mitosis and meiosis.

The Chemistry of Chromosomes

Data regarding the chemical constituents of metaphase and related chromosomes comes from several sources, including cytochemistry, autoradiography, experimental inhibition of chromosomal replication, and gross analysis of chromosomes isolated in bulk. These various approaches are consistent in showing that DNA, RNA, and protein all contribute to the chromosomal mass. As far as DNA is concerned, the history of chromosome cytology is closely entwined with a gradual elucidation of DNA structure and function (Chapter 17); during the late 1940's, Mirsky and Ris (1949) established cytochemically that the amount of DNA per chromosome set is approximately constant for a given species, and it is now understood that all higher cells contain DNA masses that are equivalent to Watson-Crick molecules many centimeters or even meters long.

The most convenient measure for DNA per nucleus is the picogram (10^{-12} gm), which is equivalent to about 31 cm of double helical DNA molecule. From this relationship, it can be estimated that human diploid cells contain about 174 cm of DNA (5.6 picograms), *Trillium* cells contain about 37 meters (120 picograms), and *Drosophila* salivary glands (polyploid) contain about 91 meters (293 picograms). It is not yet entirely clear how these great lengths of DNA filament are divided into discrete molecules. The history of published reports concerning DNA molecular weights in higher cells shows a general trend from estimates of many, small molecules (mol. wt. 10^6) to fewer and fewer large molecules (mol. wt. 10^9 or more); this situation obviously represents continued improvement in isolation techniques rather than any change in the properties of native DNA. It is interesting that the same trend occurred in molecular weight estimates for bacterial DNA, which is now known to be one continuous strand over a millimeter long. Recently Solari (1965) has isolated continuous DNA molecules 50–93 μ long from sea urchin sperm, and Cairns (1966) has reported continuous lengths of labeled DNA about 500 μ long from human HeLa cells. Huberman and Riggs (1966) have extended Cairns' autoradiographic finding, reporting in-

Table 18-1
QUANTITATIVE PROPERTIES OF HUMAN CHROMOSOMES[a]

Chromosome	% of diploid absorbance at 257 mμ per unit chromatid	Absolute mass of DNA per unit chromatid $(10^{-13}gm)$	Total mass of chromatid at metaphase $(10^{-13} gm)$	Length of DNA helix per unit chromatid (cm)	Maximum length of 230 Å interphase fiber per unit chromatid (μ)	% of chromatid DNA in long arm
1	4.19	2.35	15.7	7.3	1306	53
2	3.74	2.09	13.9	6.5	1161	60
3	3.32	1.86	12.4	5.8	1033	56
4-5	2.90	1.62	10.8	5.0	900	70
6-X-12	2.45	1.37	9.1	4.3	761	66
13-15	1.79	1.00	6.7	3.1	556	83
16	1.39	0.78	5.2	2.4	433	60
17-18	1.44	0.81	5.4	2.5	450	66
19-20	1.12	0.63	4.2	1.9	350	60
21-22	0.82	0.46	3.1	1.4	256	79

[a] Based on data of Rudkin (1967), Leuchtenberger *et al.* (1954), and DuPraw and Bahr (1968).

corporation of thymidine-³H in continuous DNA strands 1.6–1.8 mm long in Chinese hamster cells. A DNA molecule 1.6 mm long has a molecular weight exceeding 3×10^9, and is approximately 160 times longer than the longest metaphase chromosome in a Chinese hamster cell.

The distribution of total DNA among the various chromosomes of a given cell has also been investigated by means of high resolution cytochemical methods. Rudkin (1967) employed a UV microspectrophotometer to determine the percentage DNA content of various human chromosomes, (Table 18-1), and similar measurements have been made for Chinese hamster chromosomes by Carlson *et al.* (1963) in Caspersson's laboratory. From Rudkin's data, it appears that chromosomal DNA content is approximately proportional to chromosomal size, and that the largest chromosome (No. 1) contains an amount of DNA equivalent to 7.3 cm of Watson-Crick molecule (0.0419×174 cm). Since the chromosome itself is less than 10 μ long, it is clear that the DNA must be very tightly packed.

An important insight concerning the organization of DNA in individual chromosomes was first obtained by Taylor *et al.* (1957), who exposed root cells of the broad bean *Vicia faba* to thymidine-³H and followed the fate of the labeled DNA through subsequent cell cycles by autoradiography. They found that in the first division after labeling the thymidine-³H is equally distributed between each pair of metaphase chromatids, but that at the second division, only one chromatid of each pair contains label (Fig. 18-5); Prescott and Bender (1963a) were able to confirm this result for Chinese hamster and human leukocyte chromosomes, and the latter authors also extended their observations to four cell generations, showing that single labeled chromatids continue to appear at each metaphase. However the proportion of labeled chromatids declines by about 50% in each generation. These observations show that, although the DNA of the chromosome is divided equally between its chromatids at the first generation, it is conserved thereafter in individual units which can be recovered 4 or more generations later. In order to account for the segregation at the first division, it is necessary to conclude that a single interphase chromosome before its replication (i.e., an anaphase chromatid) contains two conserved DNA units. Evidence to be discussed later strongly suggests that these two conserved units correspond to the two polynucleotide chains of the Watson-Crick DNA molecule, and that the semiconservative distribution of the total chromosomal DNA is based on the semiconservative replication of the double helix itself (Chapter 13).

The earliest information concerning the protein components of chromosomes was developed by Mirsky and Ris (1948, 1951), who claimed to have isolated chromosomes in bulk by homogenization of interphase nuclei from various adult tissues. In terms of more recent and sophisticated concepts, which have been developed by Mirsky and Ris among others, their early data actually referred to interphase chromatin and have already been discussed in that context (Chapter 17). Nevertheless these investigations served to call attention to two classes of chromosomal protein, the histones and the residual proteins, which subsequently have been demonstrated in metaphase chromosomes by cytochemical techniques. The amount of histone is generally correlated with the amount of DNA, to such an extent that in the banded salivary gland chromosomes Swift (1964) found that histone staining reveals a pattern nearly identical to DNA staining. Nonhistone or acidic proteins are also present in salivary gland chromosomes, and the presence of detectable tryptophan in mitotic chromosomes of *Vicia* and *Allium* confirms that "residual" nonhistone proteins occur in dividing chromosomes as well. The early concept fostered by Mirsky and Ris was that metaphase chromosomes contain two distinct compartments, a residual protein "backbone" and a set of DNA-histone molecules held together on the protein skeleton. This conception is still frequently encountered, even though the authors themselves have subsequently shown that the nonhistone fraction includes a variety of proteins, some linked to DNA and some not. Furthermore, electron microscopy of sectioned and unsectioned chromosomes has consistently shown that chromosomes do not contain a protein core in the original sense of Mirsky and Ris, anymore than they possess individual chromosomal membranes.

The proteins of Chinese hamster metaphase chromosomes could be labeled by Prescott and Bender (1963b), who used a mixture of ^{3}H-labeled lysine, leucine, histidine, proline, tyrosine, and phenylalanine. The authors then followed the fate of the chromatid proteins for four cell generations, comparing the autoradiograph patterns with the semi-conservative pattern exhibited by DNA in the same chromosomes. It was found that the fate of chromatid proteins is markedly different from that of DNA and that, although labeled proteins are distributed equally between chromatid pairs in the first metaphase, by the fourth generation all the radioactive protein has left the chromosomes. Prescott and Bender also labeled chromosomal RNA, which exhibited a behavior similar to the proteins and was entirely lost from the metaphase chromosomes by the third generation. From these experiments they could conclude that the only "permanent" macromolecule in a typical chromosome, capable of persisting through many cell generations, is DNA itself.

Although RNA synthesis is reduced or absent in metaphase chromosomes, a number of reliable investigators have found that RNA is present. Brachet (1942) was one of the earliest to detect RNA both in chromosomes and in the nucleolus, and Kaufmann et al. (1948) used a combination of pyronin staining before and after RNase digestion to demonstrate RNA in the mitotic chromosomes of onion and lily root-tip cells. Jacobson and Webb (1952) also found cytochemical evidence that metaphase-anaphase chromosomes in human and mouse tissues differ in RNA content from prophase or telophase chromosomes in the same cells; it appeared that the metaphase-anaphase chromosomes pick up a "charge" of ribonucleoprotein which leaves the chromosomes at telophase and enters the cytoplasm (or possibly the nucleolus). More recently LaCour (1963) has used ^{3}H-adenosine labeling in combination with RNase to demonstrate RNA in metaphase chromosomes of *Trillium*, and has also found that in *Vicia faba* the nucleolar RNA becomes labeled during early prophase, then appears on nearby chromosome segments in late prophase when the nucleolus disintegrates. Most of the available evidence suggests that RNA in metaphase chromosomes is not a primary structural component, but represents an adventitious inclusion, possibly bound at the chromosome surface (Huberman and Attardi, 1966).

Attempts to use specific enzyme digestion to demonstrate the intra-chromosomal relationships of DNA, RNA, and protein have given somewhat contradictory results. RNase generally has little or no effect on chromosomal integrity. However, much of the DNA in *Drosophila* salivary chromosomes is also resistant to DNase digestion, probably because it is protected by a protein coat; by contrast, trypsin digestion of histones causes rapid dispersal of both the giant salivary chromosomes and amphibian oocyte lampbrush chromosomes. Using lampbrush chromosomes, Callan and MacGregor (1958) could distinguish the effects of trypsin and pepsin, which disperse the chromosomes by digesting a proteinaceous surface coat, from the effect of DNase, which causes *breaks* and scissorlike fragmentation of the axis and lateral loops. Gall (1963a) analyzed the kinetics of DNase fragmentation in these chromosomes, concluding that integrity of the loops depends on two digestible units (i.e., one double helix), while the axis contains four units (two double-helices). It is not entirely certain how typical lampbrush chromosomes may be, since they occur only in meiotic prophase and they support a very active synthesis of both RNA and proteins. In fact, Izawa *et al.* (1963) measured a protein/DNA ratio of 550 and an RNA/DNA ratio of 9 in isolated lampbrush chromosomes, indicating that DNA comprises less than 0.2% of the chromosomal mass. Nevertheless, the general picture in these chromosomes is that DNA alone is responsible for linear continuity, while much of the protein functions to hold the DNA in its specific pattern of folding.

This same conclusion is strongly indicated for typical metaphase chromosomes by a variety of experiments in which metabolic inhibitors are used to impair DNA or protein synthesis during interphase; afterward the effect on chromosome structure is studied at metaphase (Kihlman, 1966). This approach was pioneered by Hsu and Somers (1961), who used 5-bromodeoxyuridine (BUdR) to replace thymidine in the DNA of ascites tumor and Chinese hamster chromosomes. They found that this alteration in DNA structure produces breaks in the chromatids, which tend to be localized at special sites. For instance, 86% of all breaks in chromosome 1 of the Chinese hamster occur at a particular secondary constriction, while other breaks are found at the centromeres and telomeres. Even in chromosomes that are not broken, the primary and secondary constrictions tend to be markedly elongate, suggesting that the condensation process has been upset. Since bromodeoxyuridine would be expected to produce its greatest effects in regions where A-T nucleotide pairs are most abundant, Somers and Hsu (1962) later investigated the effects of hydroxylamine (HA) treatment, which is thought to affect cytosine and C-G pairs. As might be predicted, they found that chromosome regions sensitive to BUdR are not unusually sensitive to HA, and vice versa (Fig. 18-2). Their analysis indicates that the telomeres

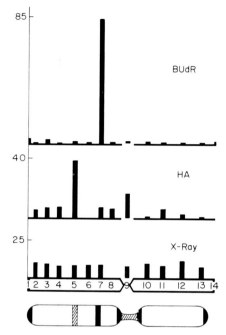

Fig. 18-2. Relative frequency of damage induced by 5-bromodeoxyuridine (BUdR), hydroxylamine (HA) and X-irradiation in 14 subzones of Chinese hamster chromosome 1. The BUdR-sensitive segment is thought to be rich in A-T base pairs, while the HA-sensitive segments (including the centromere) may be C-C rich. From Somers and Hsu (1962).

and some other regions of Chinese hamster chromosomes tend to be rich in A-T pairs, while the centromeres are relatively rich in C-G pairs. X-irradiation, which would not be expected to discriminate between such regions, does in fact produce randomly distributed chromosome breaks. Similar experiments have been carried out in *Vicia faba* by Taylor *et al.* (1962) and by Kihlman (1962), who used fluorodeoxyuridine as a specific inhibitor of thymidylate synthetase; they found that the resulting impairment in thymidine metabolism produces chromosomal lesions and fragments just before DNA synthesis becomes blocked altogether. The same type of fragmentation has also been observed in human leukocyte chromosomes by Kihlman *et al.* (1963) after treatment with fluorodeoxyuridine or alternatively with deoxyadenosine (which inhibits formation of deoxyriboside precursors from ribonucleosides) or with cytosine arabinoside (which inhibits deoxycytidine metabolism).

By contrast with the effects of inhibiting DNA metabolism, inhibition of protein synthesis usually does not fragment the chromosomes, but leads to alterations in the condensation process. Stern and Hotta (1963) examined the effects of ethionine and 5-methyltryptophan (amino acid analogs), as well as azaguanine and chloramphenicol (altering the mRNA-ribosome relationship); in *Trillium* none of these reagents affects the integrity of mitotic or meiotic chromosomes, but most of them result in uncoiling or relative extension of some chromosomal segments. The tryptophan analog 5-methyltryptophan is unusual in promoting a *higher* degree of condensation. One bizarre effect which these authors noted was a tendency for the normal chromosome complement to establish 1 to 5 separate nuclei at interphase, a process which did not prevent the chromosomes from condensing and carrying out a normal mitosis at the next cell division. Stubblefield has observed the same effect in Chinese hamster cells after colcemid treatment, and has shown by autoradiography that one or more of these multiple "subnuclei" may replicate somewhat later than the others. Under these conditions, one or more segments in some chromosomes remain uncondensed or elongate at metaphase, and Stubblefield established that these uncondensed regions correspond to the late-replicating parts of the normal chromosome complement. The exact significance of these results is not yet clear, but it appears that some local event during the late S or G_2 periods is necessary to ensure proper chromosome condensation. Since in Stubblefield's experiments the uncondensed chromosome regions *did* become labeled with thymidine-^{3}H, it would seem that this event is not merely DNA synthesis; more likely it involves the attachment of specific proteins to DNA. Arrighi and Hsu (1965) have shown that molecules which would be expected to compete for attachment sites on DNA, such as actinomycin D or polylysine, interfere with condensation of metaphase chromosomes. Allfrey and Mirsky (1964) have also observed that addition of histone fractions or polylysine causes retraction (or condensation) of lampbrush chromosome loops.

Following the pioneer efforts of Mirsky and Ris (1948), bulk isolation of metaphase chromosomes has now been achieved by workers in several laboratories, including Chorazy *et al.* (1963), Somers *et al.* (1963), Cantor and Hearst (1966), Salzman *et al.* (1966), and Huberman and Attardi (1966, 1967). The morphology of such isolated chromosomes is generally well preserved, although it has been difficult to eliminate minor contaminants such as interphase chromatin and ribosomes. One of the more interesting generalizations to come out of this work is that metaphase chromosomes tend to be stabilized in acid solutions (around pH 3–4), suggesting that acid proteins are important structural elements. Chorazy *et al.* (1963) also found that pepsin and RNase are without effect on isolated mouse chromosomes, while trypsin, chymotrypsin, and DNase all cause marked disintegration.

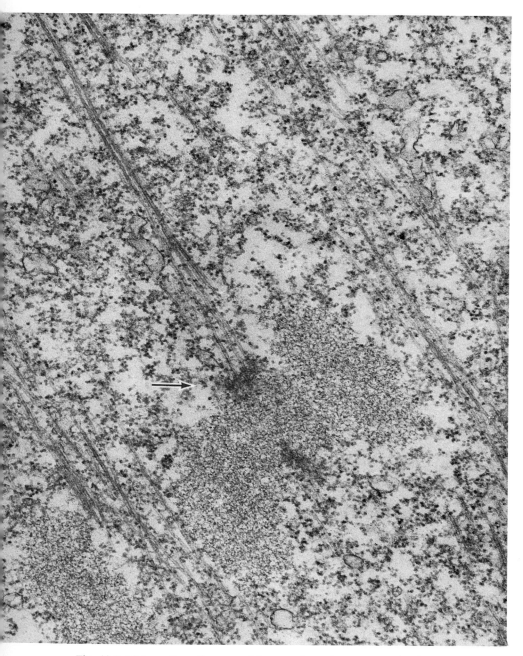

Fig. 18-3. Thin-section of a sea urchin metaphase chromosome, showing spindle micro-tubules inserted at two, oppositely directed kinetochore granules (arrow). Note the fibrous ultrastructure of the chromosome. 48,000×. From Harris (1965).

Table 18-2
Composition (% Dry Weight) of Metaphase Chromosomes
Isolated in Bulk by Various Laboratories[a]

	HeLa 1	HeLa 2	HeLa 3	Mouse ascites
DNA	15.7	20	15	13.5
RNA	10.4	14	12	13.5
Protein (total)	73.9	66	74	68.3
Acid soluble	31.4	17	44	—
Acid insoluble	42.5	49	30	—

[a] Based on a table by Salzman et al. (1966).

The composition of isolated metaphase chromosomes, as reported by various laboratories, is shown in Table 18-2. A surprising feature is that the percentage of DNA is only about half that found in interphase chromatin from a wide variety of sources (Table 17-2), indicating that each unit chromatid has about twice the dry mass at metaphase that it has at interphase; this appears to be due to a relatively higher content of acid insoluble protein and (ribosomal) RNA at metaphase. Recently Huberman and Attardi (1967) have succeeded in separating a "large chromosome fraction" from a "small chromosome fraction" by differential centrifugation of isolated human (HeLa) chromosomes. They could show, for example, that the ribosomal cistrons are confined to the small chromosome fraction.

Chromosome Ultrastructure

Thin-sectioned electron micrographs of nuclei and chromosomes generally reveal little more than a random configuration of chromatin fibers, which vary in diameter and are more closely packed at metaphase than during interphase (Fig. 18-3). The lack of apparent order in such micrographs has been both disappointing and suspicious, since the very orderly behavior of chromosomes in mitosis, meiosis, and during genetic function implies some very precise organization. This apparent contradiction could not be resolved until the demonstration, by bacterial and viral geneticists, that DNA is able to function autonomously in the form of single Watson-Crick molecules with lengths in the order of a millimeter or more. In both E. coli and bacteriophage viruses, such long, single DNA molecules are packed in highly folded or coiled arrangements, which under the electron microscope show no obvious orderliness (Chapter

15). Nevertheless in both cases the essential activities of the genetic material, i.e., replication and transcription, seem to depend primarily on the intactness of the long DNA chains with their specific sequences of nucleotide pairs, rather than on any specific paracrystalline geometry.

Ris (1955, 1956) was the first to suggest that long fibers about 200 Å in diameter are the fundamental units of structure in all plant and animal chromosomes. His earlier electron microscope studies were based on sectioned mitotic and meiotic chromosomes from the lily, onion, salamander, and rat, in all of which he observed 200 Å fibers apparently twisted around one another into bundles. Later Ris (1959, 1961; Ris and Chandler, 1963) pioneered techniques for studying *unsectioned* chromosomes and nuclei, which served to confirm this essentially fibrous chromosome ultrastructure. Evidence that such 230 Å chromatin fibers exist *in vivo* has been obtained by DuPraw (1965a), who studied the ultrastructure of unsectioned nuclei and chromosomes from honey bee embryonic cells. In these cells the individual chromatin fibers are firmly attached to the nuclear envelope at the edges of the annuli (Figs. 17-3 and 17-4); if the nuclear envelope is stripped away from the chromatin during preparation, the chromatin fibers break and the ruptured ends can still be found dangling from the annuli (Fig. 17-4). These observations provide strong evidence, not only that the chromatin-annulus attachments are real, but that the chromatin fibers exist as such in the living nucleus.

The substructure of the individual 200–300 Å fibers has been subject to some controversy (Chapters 12 and 17). In his earliest work with sectioned chromosomes, Ris (1955) found that the cut ends of these fibers resemble doughnuts with an electron-light center, suggesting that each fiber might contain a central core of DNA surrounded by protein. Later Ris (1959; Ris and Chandler, 1963) investigated the morphology of isolated chromatin which he digested in acids and other reagents; this work led him to reinterpret the substructure of 200 Å calf thymus chromatin fibers, which he reported to contain two 100 Å fibers coiled around each other; each 100 Å fiber in turn appeared to consist of two coiled 40 Å fibrils. A difficulty with the micrographs supporting this 4-strand concept was that the fibers were not seen in relation to any other cell structure, so that the possibility could not be eliminated that the isolated fibers had undergone secondary aggregation during their digestion with the various reagents. When DuPraw (1965a) found that the chromatin fibers of honey bee embryonic cells are individually attached to their nuclear envelopes, he used this system to study the effect of brief trypsin digestion on fibers still structurally bound to the annuli; under these conditions, secondary aggregation or tangling is minimized and it can be seen that each 230 Å fiber contains a *single* trypsin-resistant filament with the dimensions of a Watson-Crick helix (Fig. 17-5). Segments of undigested 230 Å fiber alternate with these trypsin-resistant filaments like beads on a string, and after further digestion with DNase the filaments are specifically digested, leaving behind recognizable nuclear envelopes (Fig. 17-5). Recently Ris (1966b) has confirmed the effects of protease digestion on chromatin fibers and has abandoned his 4-strand model. Consequently, the bulk of available evidence supports the view that there is a one-to-one correspondence between single chromatin fibers and single DNA helices.

Other evidence indicates that the DNA filament has the form of a

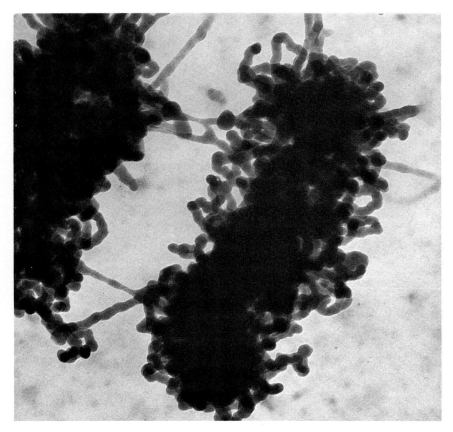

Fig. 18-4. An unsectioned metaphase chromatid from a honey bee embryonic cell. Tightly folded type B chromatin fiber is the primary structural component. Comparison of electron scattering by cross-sections of the chromatid and its individual fibers shows that the cross-sectional mass is equivalent to that of 223 fibers (DuPraw and Bahr, 1968). The total length of type B fiber is estimated at 300–500 μ, packed into a chromatid 1.36 μ long. 79,560×. Micrograph from DuPraw (1965c).

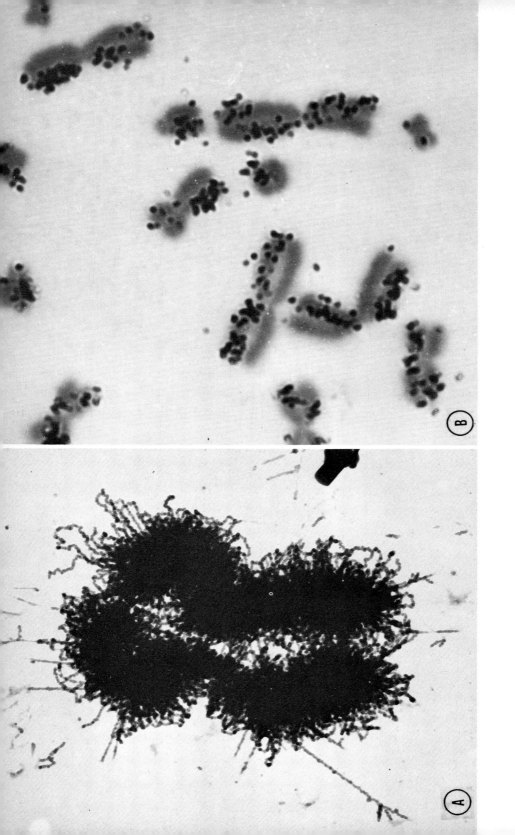

coiled coil inside the 200–300 Å fiber. For example, the cross-sectional mass distribution in trypsin-dissected fibers reveals two different structures (Fig. 12-13): (1) 35–65 Å (type A) fibrils, characterized by a symmetrical mass distribution and a relatively high density; and (2) less symmetrical 200–300 Å (type B) fibers, which seem to be built up by supercoiling of single type A fibrils (Chapters 12 and 17). For a 230 Å (type B) chromatin fiber, electron scattering measurements by DuPraw and Bahr (1968) have shown that the dry weight is about 6×10^{-20} gm/Å; since gross chemical analysis has also established that DNA is 30% or more of chromatin dry weight (Table 17-2), each micron of 230 Å interphase fiber must average about 1.8×10^{-16} gm of DNA, corresponding to 56 μ of Watson-Crick helix (56:1 packing ratio). Although the percentage of DNA in *metaphase* chromosomes is considerably less than 30% (Table 18-2), this is not due to less DNA but to more acid protein and ribosomal RNA-protein linked to the chromosome (Salzman *et al.*, 1966). It is expected that the total fiber length will remain constant or diminish at metaphase (fiber contraction), in which case the greater chromosomal mass should be detectable as a greater *average* diameter in metaphase fibers than in interphase fibers. This prediction has been borne out for human chromosomes, where the average diameters of metaphase fibers exceed 300 Å, while the average interphase diameter is in the range 230–250 Å (DuPraw, 1966a). Very high DNA packing ratios evidently occur in metaphase fibers. For example, the highly contracted chromosome 1 shown in Fig. 18-5A has a ratio of chromatid mass to fiber mass sufficient for only about 600 μ of fiber (about half the length expected at interphase; Table 18-1); the corresponding DNA length is 7.3 cm, requiring an average packing ratio of about 122:1 (compare with the 520:1 ratio in a bacteriophage head). Ratios such as 56:1 and 122:1 cannot be achieved in a 200–300 Å fiber by any simple secondary coil, and it may be concluded that some form of coiled coil occurs.

The arrangement of type B fibers in the metaphase chromosomes of honey bees and human beings has been analyzed by DuPraw (1965a,c, 1966). Honey bee chromosomes, because they are extremely small and rod-shaped, are especially suitable for whole-mount electron micros-

---

Fig. 18-5. (A) A highly contracted human chromosome 1 isolated intact from mitotic liver cells. This specimen exhibits an electron scattering mass of 30.8×10^{-13} gm (for two chromatids; see Table 18-1), of which 52% is in the long arms. The mass of each chromatid is equivalent to about 600 μ of the chromatin fiber drawn out at bottom left, indicating that the contracted fiber has a DNA packing ratio greater than 100:1. 26,200×. Micrograph by DuPraw. (B) At the second metaphase after labeling with thymidine-³H, all the labeled DNA is segregated to one chromatid of each chromatid pair (except for occasional reciprocal exchanges between sister chromatids). This phenomenon provides evidence that all the chromatin fiber in one chromatid is an integral unit. From Marin and Prescott (1964).

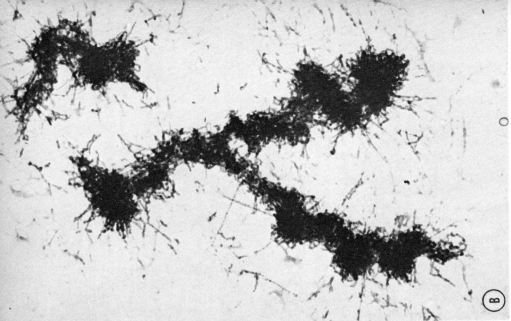

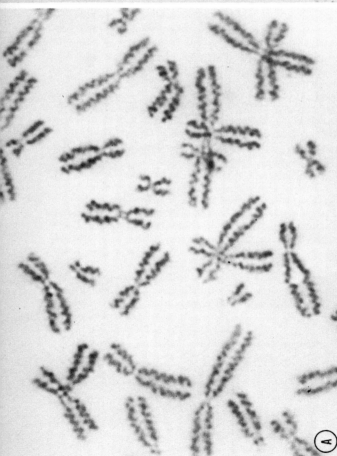

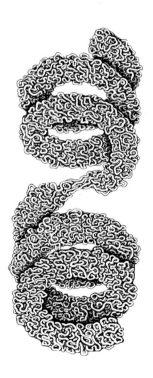

copy, and they seem to consist of nothing other than 200–300 Å chromatin fibers folded in an apparently irregular pattern (Fig. 18-4). In order to establish that the irregularity of the fiber pattern is not due to preparation artifacts, DuPraw (1966a) applied the same techniques to human chromosomes, which possess recognizable shapes and dimensions. The chromosomes of human liver and leukocyte cells were found to preserve their characteristic forms during preparation, yet in these chromosomes too, irregular chromatin fibers seem to be responsible for essentially all the chromosomal mass (Fig. 18-5). In addition, the larger human chromosomes exhibit a pattern of macrocoiling which is not observed in the tiny honey bee chromosomes (this coiling is also visible with the light microscope; Fig. 18-6). By comparing the maximum volume of a given chromosome with the volume of a unit length of chromatin fiber, DuPraw (1965c) could estimate that the *maximum* fiber length in a typical honey bee chromatid (Fig. 18-4) is only 544 μ. For the same honey bee chromatid, DuPraw and Bahr's (1968) electron scattering measurements have now revealed that the cross-sectional mass is equivalent to that of 223 type B chromatin fibers (i.e., single fibers scanned in the same chromatid); similar measurements for the sister chromatid give a value equivalent to 282 type B fiber segments. Consequently both the volumetric and the electron scattering data are consistent with a model in which the length of the chromatid (1.36 μ) is made up of a type B fiber folded back and forth 223 to 282 times and with a total length between 300 and 500 μ. (For estimates of fiber lengths in human chromosomes see Table 18-1.) Whole-mount electron microscopy thus indicates that the ultrastructure of metaphase chromosomes during both mitosis and meiosis is based on irregularly folded type B chromatin fibers. A similar fine structure has been demonstrated in unsectioned giant salivary chromosomes by Rae (1966; discussed below).

Thin-sectioned chromosomes, however, are much more difficult to interpret with respect to fiber configurations and dimensions, and there has been wide disagreement among published estimates of the fiber diameters. For instance, Kaufmann and McDonald (1956) reported 125 Å fibers in sectioned *Drosophila* salivary and *Tradescantia* chromo-

---

Fig. 18-6. Quaternary coiling visible with the light microscope occurs in human metaphase chromosomes. (A) Coiling in human chromosomes as seen with a light microscope. 3340×. From Ohnuki (1965). (B) Coiling in a 6-X-12 chromatid pair as seen with the electron microscope. The extended part of the long arm near the centromere (left) contains a cross-sectional mass equaling 27 to 34 type B fibers. 21,800×. From DuPraw (1966a). (C) Interpretation to show how quaternary coiling is superimposed on a folded-fiber chromatid. From DuPraw (1966a).

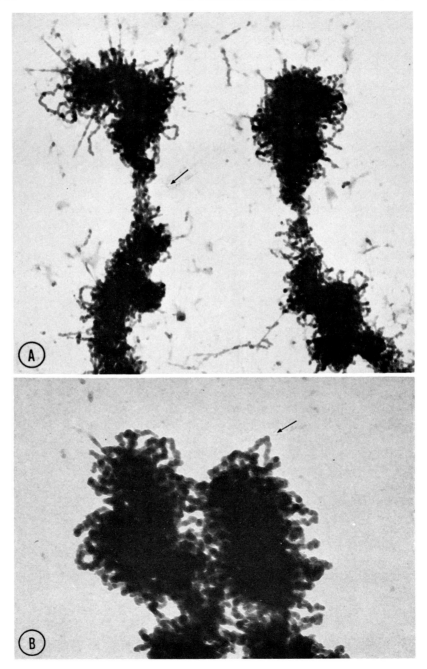

somes, while Gay (1956) measured 200–500 Å fibers in sectioned salivary chromosomes. In thin-sectioned newt erythroblast chromosomes. Davies and Tooze (1964) found evidence for a basic 450 Å thread, and they also observed cylindrical projections extending 0.2–0.6 μ from the chromosome surface (compare with Fig. 18-5). Similar fine projections from the chromosome surface have been reported in thin-sectioned newt fibroblast chromosomes by Barnicot and Huxley (1965). The disparity in fiber dimensions observed by different authors in sectioned chromosomes is probably due in part to the fact that each type B fiber does vary in diameter along its length (i.e., is bumpy), and in part to the varying ability of different investigators to resolve type A subfibrils composing the type B fibers (e.g., see Wettstein and Sotelo, 1965). Most investigators working with unembedded, unsectioned chromosomes are agreed that the external diameters of typical chromatin fibers average about 230–250 Å, with bumps exceeding 300 Å and stretched regions falling below 200 Å.

Both in sectioned and unsectioned chromosomes, the centromere (or kinetochore) regions are composed of fibers similar in appearance and dimensions to those of the chromosome arms. Mota (1962), for instance, concluded that the greater density of the kinetochore in sectioned mouse chromosomes at meiosis is due to the closer packing of chromatinlike fibers. A similar conclusion was reached by Wettstein and Sotelo (1965) for grasshopper meiotic chromosomes. In unsectioned human chromosomes, DuPraw (1965d, 1966a) has shown that the fibers of the centromere region not only are identical in appearance to those of the arms, but are continuous with them (Fig. 18-7). In fact, the only special property of the centromere region in these chromosomes seems to be that the chromatid becomes very narrow at this point, sometimes falling below the limit of resolution of the light microscope. Electron scattering measurements on the centromeres illustrated in Fig. 18-7A indicate that five to seven type B chromatin fibers pass through each centromere from one chromosome arm to the other (DuPraw and Bahr, 1968). In addition, thin sections show the presence of a dense kinetochore granule in the centromere region, which seems to act as a cement to bind the spindle tubules to the chromosome (Figs. 18-3 and 19-2); this material

---

Fig. 18-7. (A) The centromere regions (arrow) in human chromatids of the 4–5 group contain chromatin fibers identical in appearance and dimension with the chromatin fibers of the arms. Measurement of electron scattering in cross-sections of each centromere shows that the number of type B fibers is approximately five (right chromatid) to seven (left chromatid). 26,500×. Micrograph from DuPraw (1966a), quantitative mass determinations by DuPraw and Bahr (1968). (B) The telomeres of human chromosome 16 exhibit fiber loops (arrow) rather than free ends, suggesting that each chromatid is a unit composed of one folded fiber about 300–400 μ long. 44,800×. Micrograph by DuPraw.

has not been seen in whole-mount preparations. The relationship between the centromere chromatin fibers and the kinetochore granule will be discussed again in a later section of this chapter.

That the centromere region shares the general properties of chromatin is indicated by a variety of experimental data. In species with relatively large chromosomes, such as salamanders and higher plants, it has been possible to demonstrate cytochemically that DNA is present in the centromere (Lima-de-Faria, 1958). Furthermore, the centromere follows the same progressive cycle of prophase condensation and telophase decondensation as the rest of the chromosome. Uretz *et al.* (1954) showed that ultraviolet irradiation inactivates the kinetochore region in salamander chromosomes, preventing the normal integration of the chromosome with the spindle mechanism; comparable microbeam irradiation of the arms did not prevent normal chromosomal movements. In maize, McClintock (1938) showed that X-irradiation can fracture the centromere region in such a way that both chromosome parts retain normal kinetochore activity during cell division. Centromere breaks are also induced to some extent when bromodeoxyuridine is used to replace thymidine in DNA, or when DNA cytosine residues are attacked with hydroxylamine (discussed previously). Like the secondary constrictions, the centromere constriction tends to become elongate after bromodeoxyuridine labeling, as though condensation in this region had been impaired. These and other observations are consistent with a concept in which the centromere region (or regions) of a given chromosome are composed of typical chromatin fibers; these may be distinctive, however, in coding for synthesis of special "coupling proteins" that mediate the chromosome-spindle tubule attachments.

The ultrastructure of telomeres has received special attention recently from DuPraw (1966b) and DuPraw and Rae (1966). In both honey bee and human metaphase chromosomes, the telomeres exhibit conspicuous looped fibers (Fig. 18-7), suggesting that the fibers of the chromosome body are continuous with one another and repeatedly folded back and forth. The fact that free ends are rarely seen at the telomeres contradicts the classical idea that each telomere contains the two or four ends of parallel half- and quarter-chromatids. Furthermore, in human or honey bee chromosomes prepared as whole mounts for the electron microscope, the chromatids are never divided into half- or quarter chromatids (Figs. 18-4, 18-5, 18-6, and 18-7).

With respect to the fine structure of heterochromatic regions and chromosomes, it is clear from both sectioned and unsectioned material that heterochromatin is composed of chromatin fibers that are tightly packed but not otherwise unusual in appearance. Ever since the early investigations of Schrader (1921), it has been known that the same set of chromosomes can be euchromatic in one cell and heterochromatic in another. In the mealy bugs studied by Schrader and recently reinvestigated by Brown and Nur (1964), the entire paternal chromosome set becomes heterochromatic during the early embryonic stages in males, whereas in females the paternal chromosomes remain euchromatic. A similar example is provided by the two X chromosomes of mammalian females, one of which becomes heterochromatic in somatic cells but remains euchromatic in germ line cells. As first suggested by Coleman (1943) from his light microscope investigations, it seems that heterochromatin is derived from euchromatin by a permanent or semipermanent state of condensation, a conclusion which tends to be confirmed by ultrastructural studies. In particular, Hay and Revel (1963) concluded that the chromatin filaments of sectioned salamander cells have a similar size and appearance in interphase chromatin, metaphase chromosomes, and in the "chromatin centers" (heterochromatin) at interphase; however, in metaphase chromosomes and chromatin centers the fibers are more tightly packed. The heterochromatic sex chromosomes are also seen, in unsectioned material, to contain fibers identical in appearance to those of the euchromatic autosomes.

It may be concluded that heterochromatin is differentiated from euchromatin by factors, undoubtedly chemical in nature, which do not alter the visible ultrastructure of the heterochromatic fibers. Frenster (1965c) has investigated various biochemical differences between condensed and diffuse chromatin of calf thymus nuclei (discussed in Chapter 17); nevertheless, the exact mechanism of "heterochromatization" remains to be elucidated. Tight folding by itself may account for some of the unusual metabolic properties of heterochromatin; Brown (1966) has summarized these properties as including: (1) absence of RNA synthesis; (2) genetic inertness (possibly identical with property 1); and (3) late DNA replication. Even euchromatin lacks appreciable RNA and DNA synthetic activity during maximum condensation at metaphase and may be regarded as exhibiting a state of (temporary) heterochromatization.

Giant Polytene Chromosomes

The giant chromosomes of dipteran fly larvae were first described by Balbiani (1881), but did not receive serious attention until Painter (1933) showed that the conspicuous pattern of bands (or rings) can be mapped reproducibly. Such banded giant chromosomes occur in the larval salivary glands, midgut epithelium, rectum, and Malpighian tubules of various genera (*Drosophila, Sciara, Rhynchosciara, Chironomus*), where in all cases they are associated with interphase synthesis rather than with cell division. Bridges (1936) carried out a classic series of experiments, in which he demonstrated that various genetic effects in *Drosophila* are correlated with duplications, deletions, or inversions of the banding pattern. Subsequently it has been thoroughly established that the salivary banding pattern of *Drosophila* corresponds precisely to the linear arrangement of genes in a genetic recombination map (Beermann, 1966). According to Burnham's (1962) compilation, the total number of bands in the 4 chromosomes of *D. melanogaster* is about 5149, and they range in length from 0.05 μ (detectable only with the electron microscope) to 0.5 μ apiece. It is also known that several (up to 7) genetic loci can occur within a single cytological band. Stretching of the chromosomes leads to separation of some single bands into two or more separate bands, and sometimes converts a band into an apparent interband region (Swift, 1962).

Although the presence of DNA in the band regions was established very early, a long controversy ensued as to whether DNA occurs in the interbands. In recent years this debate has been settled in the affirmative; continuity of DNA along the whole length of the chromosome has been demonstrated by autoradiography (Beermann and Pelling, 1965), acridine staining combined with DNase (Wolstenholme, 1965), and Feulgen staining (Swift, 1962). Wolstenholme's analysis indicates, in fact, that both DNA and RNA are distributed in all parts of the giant chromosomes of *Chironomus*. Nevertheless the DNA concentration is much greater in the bands than the interbands, and available evidence indicates that most *Drosophila* genes are associated with band regions.

Even under the light microscope a giant chromosome can be seen to contain many parallel longitudinal fibers, which sometimes fray out as banded substrands at the chromosome ends or in expanded regions ("puffs") along the length of the chromosome. That each giant chromosome is equivalent to many replicate metaphase chromatids was first demonstrated by Bauer (1938), who observed in *Lucilia* that the giant chromosomes of ovarian nutritive cells can undergo a separation and contraction of strands to produce many small, metaphase-like chromosomes. Later Swift (1962) employed Feulgen microspectrophotometry to follow the increase in DNA content as the chromosomes increase in size from the first to the third larval molt (instar); he found that this DNA increase occurs in geometric steps similar to the integer DNA contents of polyploid cells, and that in *Drosophila* the chromosomes at maximum size correspond to at least a 1024-ploid condition. Confirmation that the DNA-containing units of early mitotic chromatids persist in polytene chromosomes as fiber-form subunits, and that they extend 400 μ or more from one end of a giant chromosome to the other, has recently been obtained by Beermann and Pelling (1965). They used thymidine-^{3}H to label mitotic chromosomes of *Chironomus* at an early embryonic stage; at a later larval stage, autoradiographs of the fully developed salivary chromosomes revealed the labeled DNA in chains extending from one telomere to the other and exhibiting grain densities compatible with single Watson-Crick DNA molecules (Fig. 18-8). DuPraw and Rae (1966) have developed the concept that such *compound* chromosomes are composed of several hundred *unit chromatids* arranged in parallel register; there is evidence that in other organisms unit chromatids can also be arranged end to end to form a tandemly linked compound chromosome.

The ultrastructure of giant polytene chromosomes was first investigated with thin-section techniques by Beermann and Bahr (1954), who observed numerous fine fibrils in the Balbiani rings of *Chironomus* and estimated that each chromosome contains 1000–2000 separate strands (corresponding to the degree of ploidy). Later Gay (1956) observed strands 200–500 Å in diameter in sectioned *Drosophila* salivary chromosomes; Kaufmann and McDonald (1956) reported somewhat smaller fibrils of 125 Å in the same material. It has been difficult to form a clear concept from sectioned polytene chromosomes regarding the pattern of organization of the fibrils; however Rae (1966) has recently studied unsectioned *Drosophila* chromosomes, and from his micrographs it is clear that the giant chromosomes are composed of bumpy 230 Å chromatin fibers identical in size and appearance to the irregular chromatin fibers of metaphase chromosomes (i.e., type B chromatin fibers; see Fig. 12-13). The individual fibers in band and interband regions are similar in appearance, but the fibers in the bands exhibit a considerable degree of metaphase-like folding and are much more tightly packed (Fig. 18-8). Dry mass determinations by electron scattering have confirmed that the number of 230 Å fibers in a given cross section corre-

---

Fig. 18-8. [See following two pages for illustrations.] (A) Light microscope autoradiograph of two *Chironomus* giant salivary chromosomes labeled with thymidine-^{3}H. A single labeled DNA filament extends the entire length of the chromosome; other unlabeled filaments are believed to lie in parallel with the labeled one, generating the characteristic band-interband pattern. 755×. From Beermann and Pelling (1965). (B) Interpretation of giant chromosome structure, showing four unit chromatids lying in parallel; each fiber contains a single DNA helix, which can spin out locally in a "puff" configuration for genetic transcription. From DuPraw and Rae (1966). (C) An unsectioned *Drosophila* salivary chromosome, showing that both bands and interbands contain 230 Å chromatin fibers. The electron scattering mass in a cross-section near the bottom of the micrograph is equivalent to 1456 type B fibers (DuPraw and Bahr, unpublished). 18,000×. Micrograph from Rae (1966).

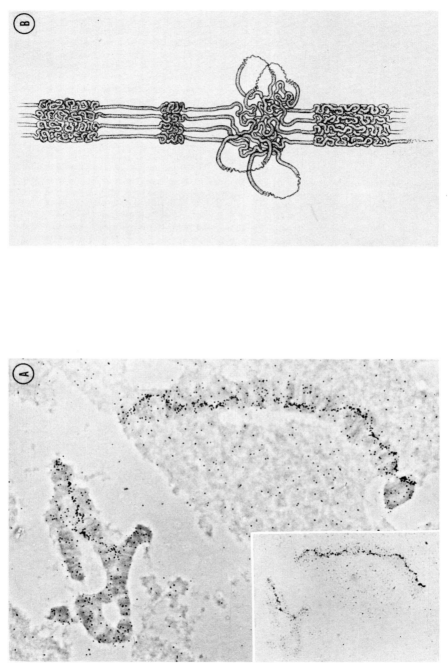

Fig. 18-8. (A) and (B). For legend see page 541.

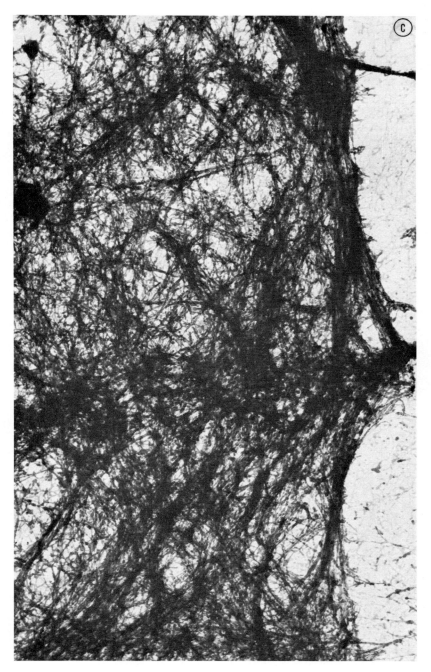

Fig. 18-8. (C) For legend see page 541.

sponds to the ploidy of the giant chromosome, i.e., there is one type B fiber per haploid chromatid unit (Fig. 18-8C).

Since there is separate evidence for a one-to-one relationship between type B chromatin fibers and single Watson-Crick DNA molecules (Fig. 17-5), and since Beermann and Pelling's autoradiographs indicate continuous DNA chains extending from one end of the chromosome to the other, it seems reasonable to conclude from Rae's micrographs that each type B fiber corresponds to a unit chromatid. The unit chromatid is therefore a single nucleoprotein fiber of variable dimensions, configuration, and replication mechanism but definable in general terms as "a single copy of any continuous DNA helix, together with its attached non-DNA components, which is required for the structural integrity of a cytologically recognizable chromosome." This concept implies that *Drosophila* polytene chromosomes are derived from single metaphase chromatids by two steps: first, a partial unfolding or extension of a single type B fiber composing each metaphase chromatid; and second, a progressive replication of each fiber to form a large number of duplicate type B chromatin fibers in parallel register.

One particularly puzzling feature of the giant chromosomes is the presence of a "chromocenter" in which all the chromosomes are joined at their kinetochores, forming a starlike configuration. In males this chromocenter includes the entire Y chromosome, which does not undergo polytenization, and it also includes the heterochromatic regions that typically occur on either side of the kinetochore (pericentric heterochromatin). As has long been known, the mass of this heterochromatin in salivary chromosomes is proportionately much less than in corresponding diploid cells, and Rudkin (1965) has recently been able to account for this on the hypothesis that the centric heterochromatin, like the Y chromosome, does not undergo the polytenic replication exhibited by the chromosome arms. Since in males 33%, and in females 22%, of the entire metaphase chromatin is accounted for by centric heterochromatin, this should lead to discrepancies from the expected 2, 4, 8 progression in DNA content. Rudkin has, in fact, confirmed that the DNA progression in salivary cells is actually 1.63, 3.50, 6.58, 12.6, etc., in very close correspondence to the predicted ratios. It is entirely possible that the lack of replication in the centric heterochromatin and heterochromatic Y results from the state of permanent tight folding in these regions.

Synthesis of RNA in giant salivary chromosomes is associated with an unfolding or spinning out of chromatin fibers at a specific band to produce a local swollen area or "puff" in the chromosome. Beermann and Bahr (1954) studied thin sections of puffed regions and concluded that individual fibers remain continuous across the puff, but that they become extended as short lateral loops. More recently Rae (1966) has observed fraying of 230 Å fiber bundles to form a puff-like configuration in an unsectioned salivary chromosome. This correlation between unfolding of chromatin fibers and activity in chromatin-dependent synthesis seems to be well-nigh universal and will be discussed again later with regard to genetic control mechanisms (Chapter 20).

MEIOTIC PROPHASE AND THE SYNAPTINEMAL COMPLEX

The prophase immediately preceding the first meiotic division is characterized by a number of unusual events which were described in great detail by classical light microscopists. It is traditional to divide this prophase into the following substages:

1. Leptotene, during which the chromosomes are long and thread-like in form, and appear to be unpaired despite the fact that DNA replication has already occurred in the preceding interphase. During late leptotene the ends of all the chromosomes usually attach to the nuclear envelope at a single point near the centriole, and the nuclear contents assume the appearance of a "bouquet."

2. Zygotene, during which homologous pairs of chromosomes establish a point-for-point synapsis, beginning either at the attached ends, at the kinetochore, or elsewhere, and continuing zipper-fashion along the arms. It is at this stage that the synaptinemal complex is first observed in thin-sectioned preparations.

3. Pachytene, during which the homolog pairs (bivalents) appear to grow visibly thicker and the pairs often coil around one another.

4. Diplotene, during which the homologs move apart except at certain points where they seem to be held together by one or more (as many as 12) chiasmata. At this stage the individual chromatids of each homolog become visible, so that the bivalents are recognizable as tetrads. Even under the light microscope it can be seen that each chiasma involves only one chromatid from each homolog; however this is not necessarily the same chromatid for all the chiasmata of a given bivalent.

5. Diakinesis, during which the tetrads visibly coil up to form shorter and thicker chromosomes and the nucleolus detaches or disappears. Since the bivalents are still held together by their chiasmata, they tend to form rather odd shapes, which are not necessarily the same from one generation to the next. Chiasmata originally observed between the kinetochore and the telomere tend to move progressively to the ends of the bivalents (terminalization).

The homolog pairing and chiasmata formation which occur during this prophase have major significance because they lead to the precise reduction division required for formation of haploid gametes, and they also result in a very precise, reciprocal exchange of genetic material

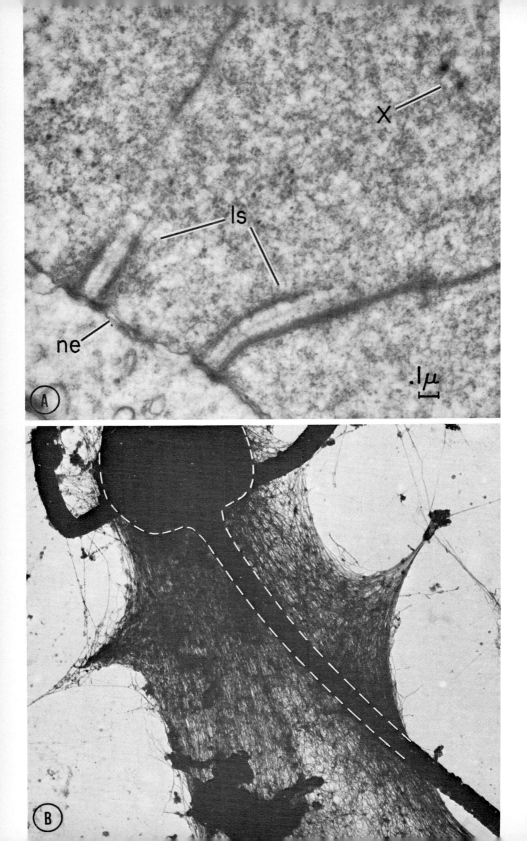

between homologs (crossing-over). The latter process is quite distinct from the physical exchange of DNA between sister chromatids, which is also known to occur during the interphase preceding both mitosis and meiosis.

It was discovered independently by Moses (1956) and by Fawcett (1956) that during zygotene to diplotene each bivalent is associated with a very remarkable structure, now referred to as the synaptinemal complex. A single synaptinemal complex is a ribbonlike object, consisting of two parallel dense rods (each of 450 Å diameter) separated uniformly at a distance of 1000–1200 Å, and connected to a median longitudinal element by transverse fibers (Fig. 18-9). This structure was originally discovered in the males of crayfish, pigeons, cats, and human beings, but it is not present in male *Drosophila,* which have long been known to lack both crossing-over and chiasmata; in other species as well, its presence or absence is closely correlated with the presence or absence of chiasma formation. However, the correlation does not extend to homolog pairing, which does occur in male *Drosophila* and other achiasmate forms.

Although the relationship between the synaptinemal complex and the meiotic chromosomes was unclear for some years, evidence has accumulated to show that the complex is an independent structure, probably formed by self-assembly (spontaneous aggregation) of specific protein molecules. This is best seen in the work of Schin (1965), who has found that grasshopper *spermatids* contain one to several massive "multiple core complexes" exhibiting all the characteristic parts of the spermatocyte synaptinemal complex but in a somewhat modified arrangement. In some cases the multiple core structure is multilayered, as if several single complexes had been stacked on top of one another, while in other cases the layers are rolled up into cylinders or spirals. Regardless of these superficial alterations, the parallel outer rods always occur in pairs with a median central element and regularly disposed cross-fibrils. Schin believes that these multiple core complexes assemble spontaneously from the components of the original synaptinemal complexes, and since they occur in haploid spermatids it is clear that their paired structure is intrinsic, i.e., it does not depend on the presence of paired homologs. This conclusion is supported by studies of triploid

---

Fig. 18-9. (A) Synaptinemal complexes in the nucleus of a rat spermatocyte. Two complexes have been sectioned longitudinally (ls) and show a characteristic termination at the nuclear envelope (ne); another complex has been cut transversely (X), revealing the ribbonlike arrangement of the lateral elements. 50,000×. From Moses and Coleman (1964). (B) Unsectioned bull sperm lysed with a sulfhydryl reducing agent. Tightly woven chromatin fibers have emerged from the head and lie along the flagellum (right). Ca. 16,500×. Preparation by B. Lung, micrograph by DuPraw.

female *Drosophila*, in which the synaptinemal complex is a double structure and does not occur in association with the third, unpaired homolog.

The protein nature of the synaptinemal complex is indicated by various experiments employing specific enzyme digestion or metabolic inhibitors. For instance, Moses and Coleman (1964) found that the complex in rooster spermatocytes seems to be unchanged even after DNase digestion has rendered the cells Feulgen negative. They also found evidence that a basic, arginine-containing protein is a major component of the outer dense rods. Stern and Hotta (1963) have observed various disruptions of meiotic segregation in *Trillium* after administering amino acid analogs or inhibitors of protein synthesis (azaguanine, chloramphenicol, ethionine, and 5-methyltryptophan). Two independent effects were noted: in some instances, chromosome morphology was drastically changed by the appearance of elongate chromosome segments in corresponding regions of both homologs and in other instances, though the chromosome morphology was approximately normal, the segregation of homologs occurred abnormally. Since these two effects could be found either together or separately, Stern and Hotta concluded that the proteins required for chromosome segregation (reduction) are distinct from those involved in chromosome condensation.

The detailed relationship between the synaptinemal complex and the chromatin fibers of the pachytene chromosomes is not yet entirely clear. At a gross level, the two homologs lie along opposite sides of the complex, each one in association with one of the dense outer rods; each homolog seems to consist of an irregular mass of chromatin fiber, with a general aspect similar to that of typical metaphase chromosomes but less folded. The chromatin fibers appear to be attached more or less transversely to the long axis of the complex. However, slight differences in the organization of the synaptinemal complex have been observed by Sotelo and Wettstein (1966) in different species of insect. Whether the DNA of the chromosomes actually spins out into the body of the synaptinemal complex is still unsettled. Further details concerning the mechanism of chiasma formation and crossing-over as mediated by the synaptinemal complex remain to be clarified.

Lampbrush Chromosomes

Lampbrush chromosomes are modified diplotene bivalents, which exhibit lengths in the order of 500–800 μ and which occur in the meiotic prophase of salamander and other vertebrate oocytes. They were first described by Rückert (1892), but have been brought to serious attention largely through the researches of Gall (1952 et seq.) and Callan (1952 et seq.). Although these chromosomes ultimately condense

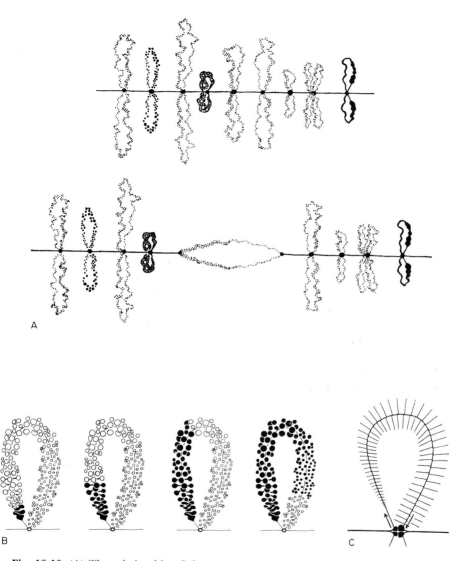

Fig. 18-10. (A) The relationship of chromomeres and loops in an amphibian lampbrush chromosome, as revealed by stretching; each chromomere can be separated into two parts transversely, and two filaments longitudinally. (B) Sequential labeling with RNA precursors on the giant granular loop of chromosome XII, from one to seven days after injection; labeled part shown in black. (C) Interpretation of sequential labeling, suggesting that a DNA filament is spun out from one quadrant of the chromomere, and taken up by another quadrant. All drawings from Callan (1963).

to a typical metaphase configuration and go through cell division, in the oocyte they support an extremely active prophase synthesis of both RNA and protein, which is an integral part of the rapid growth to form an ovum. Each homolog consists of a longitudinal axis, along which several hundred beadlike chromomeres are distributed in a linear array; from each chromomere there emerge two symmetrical lateral loops (one for each chromatid), which are able to expand or contract in response to various environmental conditions (Fig. 18-10). Loop formation reduces the mass of the corresponding chromomeres, implying a spinning out of chromomere material into the lateral strands. The centromeres also have the appearance of elongate Feulgen-positive chromomeres, but they characteristically lack lateral loops.

Since lampbrush chromosomes can be dissected *in toto* from the oocyte nucleus, a variety of experiments may be carried out with the isolated chromosomes. It has been shown, for instance, that individual chromosomes are amenable to stretching up to about 2.5 × their original lengths. With extreme stretching, the chromomeres begin to separate transversely into two halves, so that the paired loops form double-stranded bridges (Fig. 18-10). That the axis between chromomeres is also double can be seen in certain special regions where the two elements separate longitudinally and bear single loops (Callan, 1955). These experiments indicate that each chromomere possesses four quadrants separated by both a transverse and a longitudinal line of division (Fig. 18-10). In fact Callan (1963) regards it as likely that the entire chromatid pair is made up of two continuous strands, which lie parallel to one another in the interchromomere regions, are tightly folded in the chromomeres, and separate as single, unfolded fibers in the loops; each of the two fibers would correspond to one conventional metaphase chromatid. Consideration of this structure led Gall (1956a) to suggest very early that there is a fundamental similarity in the organization of amphibian lampbrush chromosomes and dipteran giant polytene chromosomes; in both cases, very long single fibers correspond to single chromatids and are partly but not completely extended. The substructure of the salivary chromosome "puffs" also bears some similarity to that of the lampbrush lateral loops.

The chemical nature of the two chromatid strands in each homolog has been extensively analyzed both cytochemically, enzymatically, and microchemically. As determined in isolated chromosomes by Izawa *et al.* (1963), protein and RNA contribute a much greater proportion of the total mass than does DNA (which comprises less than 0.2% of the chromosome). Despite this fact, Callan and MacGregor (1958) found that proteases and RNase do not fragment the loops or chromosome axis, but simply strip away a matrix of ribonucleoprotein which coats the loop axes. In striking contrast, DNase rapidly and progressively fragments both the loops and the interchromomere filaments; it seems clear, therefore, that the linear integrity of the chromosome depends primarily or entirely on DNA, and does not involve protein or RNA "links." The kinetics of DNase fragmentation in both the main axis and the lateral loops has been analyzed by Gall (1963a), who concluded that the rate of the reaction is that expected if the loops contain two deoxypolynucleotide chains (one Watson-Crick helix) and the main axis twice this number.

The main axis of a lampbrush chromosome, i.e., the interchromomere strand, is so fine that it is generally not directly resolvable with the light microscope. Its presence and behavior are apparent primarily by its influence in linking the beadlike chromomeres. However, the axis can be resolved in whole-mount preparations studied with the electron microscope. Tomlin and Callan (1951) estimated the axis diameter after drying as 200 Å, and Guyenot and Danon (1953) were able to resolve two parallel strands, each 100–150 Å wide (Fig. 18-10). Since the axis represents two chromatids side by side, these observations suggest that the two strands correspond to two type B chromatin fibers as seen in dipteran salivary chromosomes and metaphase chromosomes of other species. By contrast with the double interchromomere axis, the loop axes have been visualized in the electron microscope as single strands 60–80 Å in diameter (Gall, 1963a), suggesting that they correspond to type A fibrils (Chapter 12). Interesting comparisons may be made between the total length of loops and the estimated total length of DNA in the same chromosomes. According to Callan (1963) there are about 5000 chromomeres in a haploid set, with an average loop length of 50–100 μ; assuming one loop per chromomere, the maximum total length of loops would be about 50 cm. The haploid DNA content on the other hand is about 45 picograms, corresponding to roughly 1400 cm of DNA. Consequently, if the loops represent single, fully extended DNA molecules, most of the total DNA must be folded up into the chromomeres.

Gall (1958) and Gall and Callan (1962) have shown by autoradiography that the loops of the giant lampbrush chromosomes are sites of active incorporation of both uridine-[3]H (indicating RNA synthesis) and phenylalanine-[3]H (protein synthesis). Since the RNA synthesis is inhibited by actinomycin D, it appears to be DNA dependent. In most loops both RNA and protein synthesis occur simultaneously in all parts of the loop, and synthesis seems to be associated with RNase-digestible fibrils extending perpendicularly from the loop axis. An important discovery made by Gall and Callan is that certain specific pairs of loops, such as the giant granular loops on chromosome XII, do not incorporate RNA precursors in all regions simultaneously, but begin incorporation at a localized site near the loop insertion on the chromomere; gradually the labeled area extends out and around the loop at a constant rate over a period of about 10 days, until finally the entire loop is labeled (Fig. 18-10). This phenomenon suggests that the loop axis is slowly moving, spinning out from the chromomere at one end, mediating an initial RNA synthesis, then a progressive protein synthesis, and finally folding back into the chromomere at the other end. The direction of movement in terms of overall chromosome orientation is from the telomere side toward the centromere side, and the fact that the giant granular loops are narrow at their telomere sides and much thicker at their centromere ends supports the concept that synthetic products gradually accumulate during the 10 days that each DNA segment is in the loop.

In fact, most of the lampbrush loops are thicker at one end than at the other (not always the centromere end), and this observation first suggested to Callan and Lloyd (1960) that *all* loops may move in a polarized direction; however, this concept encounters the difficulty that most loops do not show a polarized incorporation of uridine-^{3}H. If the "spinning out" hypothesis is correct, then it would be expected that a length of fiber equal to the total loop length (50 cm) could be spun out about every 10 days; in that case, during the total oocyte growth period of about 200 days, approximately 1000 cm of fiber could move through the loops. This estimate is in the same order of magnitude as the theoretical length of DNA in the same chromosomes (1400 cm). The mechanism of movement can be conceived as a reversible coiling and uncoiling of a type A chromatin fibril in its transitions to and from the more compact type B fiber (Chapter 12). In fact, Allfrey and Mirsky (1964) have shown that arginine-rich histones induce folding or retraction of lampbrush lateral loops.

Recently a lateral loop structure comparable to that of oocyte chromosomes has been observed in the Y chromosome of *Drosophila* spermatocytes. Hess (1967) has described five pairs of loops, each exhibiting a characteristic morphology ("threads," "pseudonucleolus," "tubular ribbons," "clubs," and "noose"); none of these structures occur in XO males (which form immotile sperm) and each is present as two pairs in XYY males (which form unusually long sperm). Since no genes are known to occur in the heavily heterochromatic Y chromosome of *Drosophila*, the origin and synthetic activity of these structures has been carefully investigated. By analyzing Y translocations, Hess (1967) has been able to show that each pair of loops arises from a different region of the Y chromosome, and that all 5 loops are required for development of fertile sperm; in hybrid individuals, the morphology of the loops remains highly specific for each parental type. Meyer and Hess (1965) have also shown that actinomycin causes the loops to collapse and that the effect is reversible. The exact activity of the Y chromosome has been investigated by Meyer (1968), and its function in spermatocytes is evidently comparable to that of other synthetically active chromosomes.

CHROMOSOMES IN SPERMATOZOA

The highly condensed, metabolically inactive state of chromatin in the sperm head is more similar in many ways to the compact condition of metaphase chromosomes than to the more diffuse organization of interphase nuclei. Active research on this question has been carried out primarily with trout and salmon sperm, from which Miescher first isolated the DNA-protamine complex in 1874 (Chapter 12). From this work, the erroneous impression has developed that all sperm contain DNA-protamine and that sperm DNA is always in an extended, semicrystalline state. This is very far from being true. Both biochemically and morphologically, plant and animal spermatozoa fall into many dissimilar classes, and these appear to be partly independent of taxonomic categories. Wilson (1925) has reviewed much descriptive information about male gametes in different phyla, which vary widely in respect to the presence, number and position of flagella, the form of the acrosome, and the shape of the nucleus itself. With respect to the nucleus, it is remarkable that two, fairly distinct classes seem to occur: sperm with highly elongate, almost fiber-form nuclei, and sperm in which the nucleus is round or spheroid.

Biochemically, sperm nuclei fit into at least three classes, depending on whether DNA is complexed with protamine (salmon, herring, trout, rooster, snail, squid), with histones (plants, carp, sea urchins), or with an altogether different, nonhistone, nonprotamine protein (most notably mammals). Vendrely et al. (1960) have contrasted these three situations by comparing the lysine-histidine content of erythrocytes and sperm in three types of fish (since these amino acids are present in histone but not in protamine); their data are given in Table 18-3.

The fact that mammalian sperm contain neither protamine nor histone was known to Miescher as early as 1897. In contrast to the behavior of salmon sperm, mammalian sperm fail to release their DNA-protein during extraction in concentrated salt solutions. Dallam and Thomas (1953) found that the sperm of several mammals (bull, dog, human, ram, boar) contain large amounts of a basic protein that is more complex than protamine but lacks the solubility characteristics of histone; in bull sperm, this protein accounts for 28.7% of the mass, while

DNA is 48% and a membrane-associated lipoprotein is 19.6%. More recently, Bril-Petersen and Westenbrinik (1963) have characterized the basic protein of bull sperm as containing 35% arginine, no lysine or histidine, but 6.3% cysteine; since successful extraction depends on rupturing of S—S bonds, it appears that the cysteine cross-links the protein units and may contribute to the unusual acid insolubility of this basic protein. The same authors found that the molar ratio of arginine to DNA phosphoric acid in bull sperm is about 0.9, implying that most of the arginine residues are in salt linkages with the DNA.

Table 18-3
ARGININE-LYSINE-HISTIDINE CONTENT FOR
ERYTHROCYTES AND SPERM NUCLEI IN
THREE SPECIES OF FISH[a]

	Arginine	Lysine	Histidine
Trout RBC	33.9	63.0	5.0
Sperm	103.0	0.0	0.0
Carp RBC	33.2	64.2	5.0
Sperm	31.2	58.8	5.0
Pike RBC	33.2	68.7	5.0
Sperm	68.7	26.2	2.5

[a] In trout sperm, the replacement of histones by protamine leads to loss of lysine and histidine; this loss is not evident in carp sperm and only partially so in pike sperm. From Vendrely *et al.* (1960).

In sperm containing DNA-protamine, Feughelman *et al.* (1955) showed by X-ray diffraction analysis that the DNA is in the form of extended rods packed in a parallel, hexagonal array (Chapter 12). This relationship had previously been predicted at least for sperm with fiber-form nuclei, since these invariably show negative intrinsic birefringence in polarized light (visible or UV). Although most fibers (e.g., fibrous proteins) show positive birefringence, DNA-protein fibers are unique in exhibiting a negative birefringence relative to the long axis of the DNA; this characteristic is undoubtedly due to the transverse, platelike stacking of Watson-Crick base pairs. Consequently the fact that fiber-form sperm are negatively birefringent relative to the *sperm* axis provides evidence that the DNA is oriented longitudinally and in parallel within the sperm head. From this it might be supposed that there would be a correlation between the extended state of DNA, the fibrous form of the sperm head, the presence of negative birefringence and the occurrence of protamine. However this is not entirely true, since salmon and trout sperm have abundant protamine but spheroid heads. After com-

paring the X-ray diffraction patterns of squid sperm (which are birefringent) and trout sperm (which are not), Wilkins and Randall (1953)
suggested that both types contain the same DNA-protamine units, but
that these are near-parallel in squids while lying in all directions in trout.

In sperm of the snail *Paludina,* Schmidt (1941) found that the negative
birefringence shows a clear spiral pattern, so that in polarized light the
sperm head has a striped or barber-pole appearance. This suggests that
the DNA-protamine molecules, though parallel, are loosely coiled into
a secondary helix. A similar helical pattern is seen in living sperm of the
cave cricket, for which Inoué and Sato (1962, 1966) have carried out a
unique analysis of chromosomal fine structure. Their technique depends on the fact that irradiation of the sperm head with a fine beam of
plane-polarized ultraviolet light destroys the birefringence in irradiated
spots on the nucleus; since this effect is most efficient when the plane
of UV polarization coincides with the plane of the DNA base pairs, it
can be used to detect the exact orientation of the DNA helices. From
their analysis, Inoué and Sato concluded that the chromosomes of cave
cricket sperm are not merely DNA coils, but coiled-coils, i.e., in each
chromosome the 20 Å DNA molecules are wound into a helix 2000 Å
in diameter (0.2 μ), and this in turn is wound into a tertiary helix 8000 Å
in diameter (equaling the diameter of the sperm head). Their data also
indicate that the haploid number of chromosomes lies in single file along
the length of the sperm head, a conclusion that is supported by autoradiograph experiments performed by Taylor (1964) with grasshopper
sperm. In Taylor's work, thymidine-^{3}H was used to label spermatocytes
and sperm; in the spermatocytes it was found that the heterochromatic
X chromosome replicates asynchronously with the autosomes, so that
some spermatocytes contain label only in the X and others are labeled
only in the autosomes. Correspondingly, in the sperm, some cells were
found in which only one short segment of the head was labeled, and
others in which only one short segment was unlabeled. Since the diameter of the sperm head (0.5 μ) is about the same as that of a metaphase
chromatid, it was concluded that the chromosomes lie in tandem. However, the exact position of the X in the line of chromosomes evidently
varies from one cell to the next.

There has been relatively little information concerning the state of
chromosomes in the heads of mammalian sperm until a recent electron microscope analysis by DuPraw's student, B. Lung (1968). A surface
spreading-critical point drying method was used to examine unsectioned
bull and human sperm partially lysed by treatment with thioglycolate.
It was found that the chromatin consists of a closely packed fiber system, rather irregularly arranged, and not dissimilar in aspect to the

chromatin of active interphase nuclei (Fig. 18-9). However, unlike the chromatin of active nuclei, the sperm fibers are much less "bumpy" and they often appear as entirely smooth fibers.

Models of Chromosome Structure

The history of chromosome cytology, which now spans approximately a century, has seen the rise but unfortunately not the fall of innumerable theories of chromosomal organization. Some conceptions have persisted in textbook form long after being discarded in the face of contrary facts by the authors themselves; other theories, first proposed long before the nature of the genetic material could be accurately under- stood, continue to be modified and bolstered by *ad hoc* propositions. If it is indeed the function of observations to replace theories, then the time has come to discard many an older conception in light of newer molecular data. The following discussion will contrast various inter- pretations of chromosome structure that are currently under con- sideration.

Of the modern chromosome models, perhaps the one with the longest tenure is the so-called "protein backbone" model, which traces its an- cestry far into the cytological past and was given an apparently strong biochemical base by the investigations of Mirsky and Ris (1948, 1951). In its simplest form, this concept supposed that a proteinaceous rod or axial filament forms the skeleton of the chromosome, and that DNA- histone molecules are attached to the backbone laterally. Mirsky and Ris (1948) speculated that the backbone is composed of residual (or non- histone) protein which remains as a visible filament after extraction of chromosomal DNA-histone in molar salt solution. Apart from the fact that Mirsky and Ris's observations were based on interphase nuclei, the existence of a residual chromosome per se was challenged fairly early by Pollister (1952); subsequently Ris (1956) himself has led the way to newer conceptions founded on a more precise understanding of chro- mosome fine structure. Among the more critical experiments that make a simple protein backbone theory untenable are: (1) the demonstration that proteases do not fragment the axis of lampbrush chromosomes (whereas DNase causes fragmentation in all parts of the chromosome); (2) Prescott's demonstration by autoradiography that protein molecules are not conserved in Chinese hamster chromosomes (i.e., DNA is the only permanent part of the chromosome); (3) the discovery by Cairns (1966), Huberman and Riggs (1966), and others that the DNA molecules of mammalian chromosomes attain lengths many times that of the chro- mosomes themselves (i.e., in the order of 1.6–1.8 mm). Beyond these facts, neither thin-section nor whole-mount electron microscopy has ever revealed any serious indication of a structural core in metaphase chromosomes. Although the synaptinemal complex during meiotic prophase has been regarded as a core, recent evidence indicates that this structure exists independently of the chromosomes and is related to them as a lateral element rather than as a central core.

The protein backbone concept was advanced by Mirsky and Ris considerably before the Watson-Crick structure of DNA was proposed (1953). After Taylor *et al.* (1957) demonstrated that entire chromosomes show semiconservative distribution of their DNA, Taylor (1957) introduced an ingenious modification whereby a protein backbone could organize many short DNA molecules to form two conserved units per chromatid. This is possible provided that each chromatid possesses two protein backbones, each of which is capable of DNA-like self-replication, and provided that the two polynucleotide chains of each DNA helix are attached terminally to alternate backbones in the same chromatid. A variant of this model postulated a combined protein-DNA backbone in which relatively short DNA molecules would be linked end to end by alternating protein blocks. *A priori* evidence for such a linear alternation of DNA and protein along the chromosome was provided by the alternating band-interband structure of the dipteran polytene chromosomes; however, with the demonstration that DNA occurs in continuous chains through bands and interbands alike, the "tandem linkage" concept lost its most impressive support. The ultimate variant on the protein backbone theme was proposed by Taylor (1963) in his "ladder model" of chromosome structure. This hypothesis attempted to combine the better features of previous protein backbone models into a single unified but rather complex scheme; four different kinds of linker were postulated, which would bind together short DNA molecules in a transverse, ladder-rung arrangement, and which would be capable not only of replicating during chromosomal duplication, but of breaking and re-forming their DNA linkages under different specific conditions. However, a ladder organization has not been found in typical interphase nuclei during the S period nor in intact metaphase chromosomes as seen by electron microscopy; furthermore there is virtually no direct evidence that separate DNA molecules are ever linked in tandem by replicating, non-DNA units composed of protein or any other material. What the evidence does show is that DNA is the only conserved macromolecule in the chromosome, that it is present in all parts of the chromosome, that it is essential to the linear continuity of the chromosome, and that in a chromosome less than 10 μ long a continuous DNA helix can occur which exceeds 1600 μ in length (Huberman and Riggs, 1966). In retrospect, it seems clear that the properties postulated for various types of protein or nonprotein "linkers" are in fact the very properties which distinguish DNA itself.

THE FOLDED FIBER MODEL

Morphological and experimental observations discussed previously have established that the fundamental elements of chromosome structure in plants and animals are long DNA-protein fibers with diameters varying around 230 Å. Nevertheless it has been difficult to fit such DNA-protein fibers into the classic concepts and terminology of light microscope cytology. On the one hand, chromosomes were visualized as containing many duplicate DNA helices lying side-by-side in pairs and pairs-of-pairs to form a ropelike structure (Steffensen, 1959); although such an organization exists in giant polytene (interphase) chromosomes, polytene metaphase chromosomes would not be expected to show a semiconservative distribution of DNA (Fig. 18-5) nor single-hit kinetics for X-ray caused mutations (to be discussed). On the other hand, it was supposed that each chromosome may be composed of a single DNA-protein fiber arranged linearly in coils and coils-of-coils (Swift, 1962); the difficulty in this case is to account for radiation-induced "half-chromatid" breaks and fusions, as well as for light microscope images showing side by side subchromatid strands.

Many of these difficulties have been resolved by a "folded-fiber model" of chromosome structure proposed by DuPraw (1965c, 1966a), in which the chromosomal unit is regarded as a single DNA-protein fiber which is repeatedly folded back on itself both longitudinally and transversely to make up the body of the chromatid (Fig. 18-11). The model defines a "unit chromatid" as a chromatin fiber of variable length, folding configuration and replication mechanism, but corresponding to one continuous Watson-Crick DNA molecule (including possible single-strand breaks). The single DNA helix of the unit chromatid is thought to be wrapped with polypeptides in β-configurations (e.g., very lysine-rich histones) and then supercoiled to make up the 200–300 Å (type B) chromatin fibers (Fig. 18-11). Presumably supercoiling is induced and maintained by cross-linking with α-helical proteins, such as arginine-rich histones. During the interphase S period, the unit chromatid is postulated to replicate sequentially at two or more replication forks, a process that involves local unwinding of the tertiary and secondary helices (Fig. 18-11). Each pair of daughter fibers corresponds to a pair of metaphase chromatids, which are held together by the various unreplicated portions of the fiber, especially in the centromere region (Fig. 18-12A). During prophase and metaphase these two daughter fibers fold up in ways that are reproducible from one generation to the next, but are not otherwise characterized by recognizable order, i.e. the metaphase chromatids are not necessarily linear in organization (Fig. 18-12). At telophase the compact anaphase chromatids unfold but retain their relative positions in the interphase nucleus, possibly by means of attach-

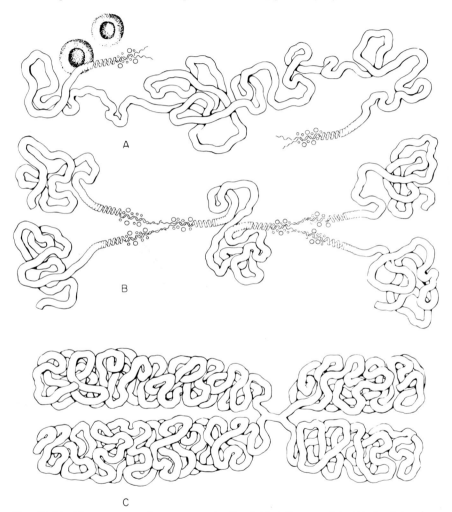

Fig. 18-11. Chromosome ultrastructure in the folded-fiber model. (A) An interphase 230 Å (type B) fiber is composed of a single DNA helix wrapped with protein (type A fibril) and held in a secondary coil by associated proteins. (B) In the simplest case, replication may proceed from either end of the fiber toward the center (telomere to centromere), involving two replication forks. (C) At metaphase the sister fibers fold up as sister chromatids, possibly held together by unreplicated fiber segments in the centromere. From DuPraw (1965c).

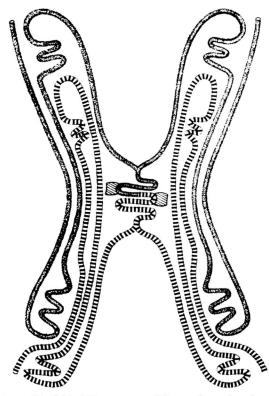

Fig. 18-12. (A) A possible folded fiber pattern different from that shown in Fig. 18-11C. The cytological telomeres include interstitial loops in addition to genetic telomeres. The two granulelike spindle attachments (kinetochores) are distinct from the centromere chromatin, which includes both replicated and unreplicated fractions. (B) A metaphase chromatid pair (group 17–18) from human liver culture cells, showing many of the features diagrammed in (A). Electron scattering measurements indicate a mass of 11.1×10^{-13} gm for these two chromatids, with a minimum of 9 to 14 type B fiber equivalents in each short arm. 29,800×. Micrograph from DuPraw (1966a), mass determinations by DuPraw and Bahr (1968). (C) Separation of sister chromatids involves final replication of centromere chromatin, permitting the two kinetochore granules to move apart.

ments to the newly formed nuclear envelope (Fig. 17-4). Finally, during the transcription and replication events of interphase, each chromatin fiber is thought to function as an independent unit, with specific parts of the DNA code being read at characteristic sites and at characteristic rates.

A great many observations, which have already been presented in previous sections, are most readily understood in terms of this folded fiber model. In particular, the random-looking, fibrous ultrastructure

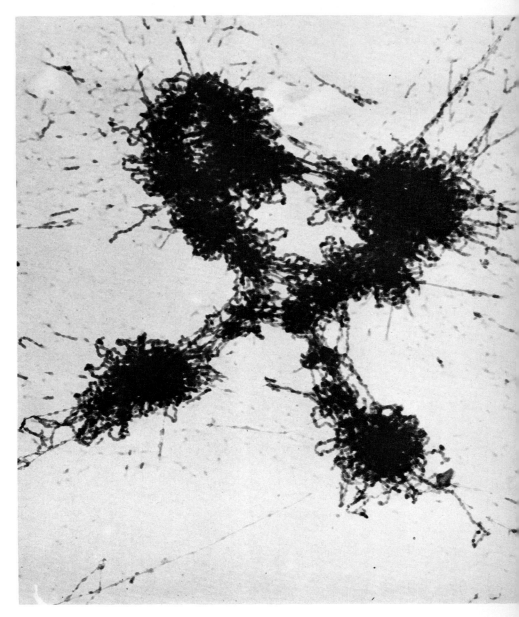

Fig. 18-12. (B) For legend see opposite page.

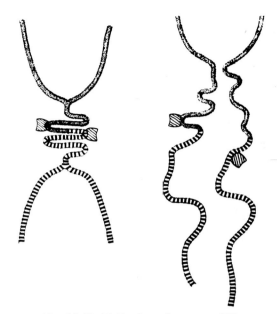

Fig. 18-12. (C) For legend see page 560.

of intact metaphase chromosomes reveals that they are composed primarily of 200–300 Å chromatin fibers that loop back on themselves in the telomeres and elsewhere (Figs. 18-4, 18-5, 18-6, and 18-7). Evidence from X-ray diffraction data for the existence of DNA supercoiling in native nucleohistone has also been discussed at length in Chapter 12. After the folded-fiber model had been proposed, Huberman and Riggs (1966) demonstrated the existence of continuous DNA molecules sometimes exceeding 1600 μ long in Chinese hamster cells; since Chinese hamster chromosomes at metaphase do not exceed 10 μ in length, it is clear that these molecules must be folded up in the chromosomes. DuPraw (1966a) has also shown that chromatin fibers occur in the centromere regions of human chromatids, that they are continuous with the chromatin fibers of the arms, and that they seem to hold the two sister chromatids together at metaphase (Fig. 18-12B).

Though it may seem surprising at first that the genetic material should be packed by irregular folding, rather than in some geometrically precise linear arrangement, this possibility has been accepted as probable for the much better-understood chromosomes of bacteria (Chapter 15). The genetic properties of DNA apparently depend on intact linear sequences of nucleotide pairs, but neither replication nor transcription seems to require DNA crystallinity. Likewise functional linearity, as reflected in meiotic crossing-over or in mitotic sister-strand exchanges, reflects an intrinsic capacity of DNA itself for linear recombination (to be discussed in the next section). While it is true that some chromosomes display linear structure at a gross microscopic level, such structure is most apparent in exceptional cases, such as the giant salivary and lampbrush chromosomes; in general, visible linearity may be regarded as a function of the linear chromatin fibers, and is expected to be more apparent when the unit chromatids are in relatively extended states (e.g., at prophase). At metaphase, when the chromatin is most tightly folded, a linear structure is often undetectable either at the level of light or electron microscopy. That the metaphase pattern of folding is really irregular *in vivo* is supported by the fact that mitotic chromosomes do not exhibit negative intrinsic birefringence, but only a weak positive form birefringence (Inoue ́ and Bajer, 1961). In larger metaphase chromosomes a pattern of regular quaternary coiling sometimes occurs (Fig. 18-6), which is resolvable at the light microscope level and which is believed to be superimposed on a cylindrical folded-fiber unit (Fig. 18-19).

The folded-fiber model draws a necessary distinction between simple and compound chromosomes, and provides a precise definition of a unit chromatid as "a single copy of any continuous DNA helix, together with

A

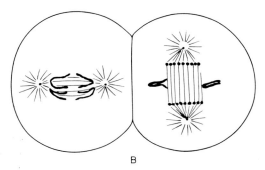

B

Fig. 18-13. Compound chromosomes composed of multiple unit chromatids in two different arrangements. (A) Parallel arrangement in giant salivary chromosomes. From DuPraw and Rae (1966). (B) Series arrangement in *Ascaris* cleavage chromosomes. From Sager and Ryan (1961).

its attached non-DNA components, which is required for the structural integrity of a cytologically-recognizable chromosome." In terms of this concept, a given chromosome may contain either one unit chromatid (simple chromosome) or several (compound chromosome); if it contains only one, the configuration of the unit chromatid can be folded or unfolded (linear); if it contains several, they may be genetic duplicates (polytene chromosomes) or not; in either case, the unit chromatids of a given chromosome can be arranged either in series (— —), in parallel (=), or both (= =). Evidence that giant salivary chromosomes consist of many hundred unit chromatids in parallel array has been discussed earlier in this chapter. A series arrangement of unit chromatids is also believed to occur in the large cleavage chromosomes of *Ascaris* (Fig. 18-13).

It has not yet been demonstrated that metaphase-anaphase chromatids really correspond to single "unit chromatids" as defined above. At least in some species, light microscope observations suggest that anaphase chromosomes may contain two or four parallel substrands, and metaphase autoradiographs sometimes indicate that thymidine-^{3}H can be incorporated into DNA simultaneously at two or more sites along a single chromosome arm. Such observations may mean that some anaphase chromosomes are compound in structure. However DuPraw (1965a,c, 1966a) has emphasized that electron micrographs of unsectioned metaphase-anaphase chromatids from human and honey bee cells do not show a duplex or quadriplex structure (Figs. 18-4, 18-5, 18-6); neither do the telomeres show the two or four free ends expected for such substrands (Fig. 18-7). Although many side-by-side lengths of chromatin fiber are present in the body of each chromatid, these appear to be continuous with one another through loops at the telomeres and elsewhere. Furthermore, typical anaphase chromosomes observed *in vivo* by phase contrast or interference microscopy do not show a duplex or quadriplex structure, although such structure is readily detectable in giant salivary chromosomes or tetraploid "diplochromosomes" produced by colchicine treatment (Walen, 1965).

If it is accepted that each 230 Å chromatin fiber of a *Drosophila* polytene chromosome corresponds to a unit chromatid (Fig. 18-8C), then it follows as well that each *Drosophila* anaphase chromosome corresponds to a single unit chromatid. Such a conclusion is required by the relative amounts of DNA in haploid, diploid, and polytene *Drosophila* tissues, as well as from Rae's observation that the chromatin fibers of polytene chromosomes and *Drosophila* mitotic chromosomes are similar in diameters and electron density (Fig. 18.8). The proposition that anaphase chromatids are fundamentally single-stranded is also strongly supported by Gall's and Callan's analysis of oocyte giant lampbrush chromosomes. In this material, the central axis of the chromosome corresponds to two chromatids, and correspondingly it has been shown to contain two fibers, each with a diameter of about 100–150 Å (Guyenot and Danon, 1953). DNase digestion of the axis proceeds at the rate expected if it contains only two Watson-Crick molecules (Gall, 1963a). Further data regarding the possible number of replication sites in a unit chromatid, and the question whether morphological "half-chromatids" really correspond to multiple unit chromatids in parallel, will be presented in later sections.

As proposed in the folded-fiber model, the protein components of the unit chromatids are regarded as including not only histones but also various DNA-linked nonhistone proteins, including such enzymes as RNA polymerase, NAD synthetase, nucleoside triphosphatase, phosphoproteins recently isolated by Langan and Lipmann, histone acetylases, and possibly DNA polymerase and the enzymes of nuclear oxidative phosphorylation (Chapter 17). DuPraw (1965a) has suggested that these molecules may be arranged on the DNA filaments in very orderly functional arrays. Presumably the histones are able to account for DNA secondary coiling, since Allfrey and Mirsky (1964) have shown that arginine-rich histones induce retraction of lampbrush chromosome loops. Studies with specific enzymes and metabolic inhibitors confirm that, whereas DNA itself is responsible for the linear continuity of a chromosome, it is the DNA-linked proteins which mediate chromosome condensation (Stubblefield, 1964; Stern and Hotta, 1963). In the folded-fiber model, irreversible folding by whatever mechanism is regarded as identical with a heterochromatic state, either in entire chromosomes or in specific chromosomal regions.

As illustrated in Fig. 18-12, several new distinctions in the classic concepts of telomere and centromere are suggested by the folded-fiber model. For instance, it seems necessary to distinguish a genetic telomere (corresponding to one end of a genetic linkage group) from a cytological telomere (corresponding to the morphological end of a metaphase chromatid). Whereas genetic telomeres probably correspond to the true ends of single DNA-protein fibers, cytological telomeres include multiple looped segments of chromatin fiber (Fig. 18-7), and are likely to contain genetic loci from widely separate parts of the linkage map. Genetic telomeres may or may not form parts of cytological telomeres, depending on the folding pattern at each stage of condensation. As one among many possibilities, the cytological telomeres drawn in Fig. 18-12 each contains a genetic telomere plus an interstitial loop.

With respect to the centromere, three separate components are distinguished in Fig. 18-12: (1) chromatin fibers specific to the kinetochore regions, which are woven between the sister chromatids and hold them together until metaphase; (2) granule- or platelike elements (kineto-chores) which serve as attachment sites for spindle tubules; and (3) chromatin fibers not specific to the kinetochores, which form parts of the centromere already in duplicate at metaphase. Consequently in Fig. 18-12 the two classic functions of the centromere, i.e., to hold the sister chromatids together and to attach the chromatids to the spindle, are assigned to entirely different components which presumably could not be resolved from one another by ordinary light microscopy. In Fig. 18-12C, anaphase separation of the two unit chromatids with their respective spindle tubule attachments is visualized as the result of replication in the kinetochore chromatin, which for a metacentric chro-matid pair implies the presence of at least one DNA swivel in the kineto-chore region; in fact, late replication in the centomere region has been reported by several authors studying autoradiographs of thymidine-^{3}H labeled metaphase chromosomes (discussed in a later section). It is likely that in some chromosomes and at some stages, *several* unreplicated fiber segments serve to hold sister chromatids together, including segments in chromosome regions other than the centromere (Fig. 18-12B). Conse-quently the scheme illustrated in Fig. 18-12 should be regarded as the simplest case. The possibility that the spindle tubule attachments may develop from material that is actually synthesized or assembled by the kinetochore chromatin, possibly in a DNA-dependent reaction, will be discussed in Chapter 19.

MULTISTRANDED VS. SINGLE-STRANDED CHROMOSOMES

It is an irony of cytological history that models of chromosome structure based on long single DNA molecules have been advocated largely by students of giant chromosomes (Gall, Callan, Beermann), whereas models postulating two or four replicate subunits per chromatid have been supported by students of much smaller metaphase-anaphase chromosomes (Ris; Osgood; Trosko and Wolff; Sparvoli, Gay, and Kaufmann). The idea that anaphase chromosomes already contain two or four identical half- or quarter-chromatids was first urged by Kaufmann (1936), Nebel (1939), Kuwada (1939) and others, largely on morpho-logical evidence; after digestion in acids, bases, or proteases, metaphase-anaphase chromatids frequently exhibit very orderly, light-resolvable substrands, which appear to be tightly coiled around one another. As a result of such studies, Schrader concluded in 1953 that "the great majority of cytologists is now convinced" that each anaphase chromo-some possesses at least two replicate subunits. Nevertheless, this ac-ceptance on morphological grounds ignored such functional problems as the difficulty of separating the intertwined quarter-chromatids, and the absence of genetic segregation during mitotic divisions (which would be expected as a consequence of mutation in only one of several replicate DNA molecules). An even more critical objection is the fact that typical anaphase chromosomes, in the *absence* of predigestion, do not show a visible duplex structure either in well-fixed light microscope preparations after staining or *in vivo* by phase contrast microscopy.

With the application of electron microscopy to chromosomal substructure, the question of chromatid strandedness has been reopened. For instance, Sparvoli *et al.* (1965), using models reconstructed from serial thin sections, claim to have confirmed a 4-partite condition in chromatids of *Tradescantia*, the classic material originally studied by Kaufmann (1925). Osgood *et al.* (1964) have also interpreted their electron micrographs of unsectioned human leukocyte chromosomes as showing 16-stranded chromatids. On the other hand, Barnicot and Huxley (1961, 1965) were unable to find any indication of a duplex structure in human metaphase chromatids prepared either as electron microscope whole mounts or as thin sections. DuPraw (1966a) has also studied unsectioned human and honey bee chromosomes, which after surface spreading and critical point drying still retain the typical *in vivo* karyotypes; the chromatin fibers of these chromosomes are not organized into half- or quarter-chromatids (Figs. 18-5 and 19-1C). With regard to human chromosomes, the opposite conclusions of different investigators cannot be reconciled except by considering them the result of differences in chromosome preservation after significantly different preparative steps.

It is certainly true that after harsh treatment, larger anaphase chromatids produce two or more *morphological* substrands; however, the evidence that these substrands actually represent genetic replicates (i.e., separate and parallel unit chromatids) has always been circumstantial at best. *Genetic* multistrandedness has been advocated or excluded for the same species examined by different techniques [e.g., Zweidler (1964) *vs.* Trosko and Wolff (1965) for *Vicia*], for different species examined by the same technique [e.g., Zweidler (1964) for *Vicia* and *Allium*], and sometimes for the same species examined with similar methods by different investigators (e.g., the human chromosomes discussed in the preceding paragraph). Yet such supposedly multistranded chromosomes as those of *Tradescantia* and *Vicia* exhibit near-linear X-ray dose-response curves for mutation and chromosomal aberrations that are nearly identical to the curves for much smaller *Drosophila* and human chromosomes (Wolff, 1963). Furthermore the DNA of *Tradescantia* and *Vicia* chromatids is distributed semiconservatively from one mitosis to the next in the same manner as the DNA of human and Chinese hamster chromatids.

The co-occurrence of morphological subchromatid strands with

single-hit mutagenesis and a semiconservative DNA distribution becomes understandable if each chromatid contains its DNA as a single
copy but this copy is folded into multiple parallel segments; this is the
type of structure that has been postulated for typical mitotic chromosomes in the folded-fiber model (Fig. 18-12). The formation of an apparent duplex or quadriplex structure in large chromatids after acid or
enzyme digestion is an artifact, at least in many cases, caused by orderly
secondary aggregation of the 230 Å chromatin fibers to form much
larger strands resolvable at the light microscope level. Such aggregation
has been demonstrated by Barnicot (1967) in negatively stained newt
chromosomes and is often seen in badly preserved chromosomes with
the electron microscope. Unfortunately the aggregation process cannot
be resolved with the light microscope and continues to lead light microscopists astray. Other indirect evidence for multistranded anaphase
chromosomes, such as the isolabeling phenomenon and the occurrence
of half-chromatid gaps, will be discussed in the next section.

Genes and DNA Molecules in Macroorganisms

In plant and animal cells as in microorganisms, several fundamental
properties are exhibited in common both at the level of intact chromosomes and at the level of individual DNA molecules. As described in
Chapter 15, the correspondence between the properties of DNA and
of bacterial and viral chromosomes has led to an unequivocal demonstration that the two are identical in microorganisms, i.e., that one chromosome is one Watson-Crick double helix. In plant and animal chromosomes as well, it may be said that the general trend of research in recent
years has been toward a similar conclusion. For instance, Djordjevic and
Szybalski (1960) demonstrated by bromodeoxyuridine labeling and density centrifugation that DNA itself replicates semiconservatively in
human cells (Chapter 13), while Prescott and Bender (1963a) used autoradiography to show that DNA is distributed semiconservatively during
replication of intact human chromosomes. Although for macroorganisms an identity between one chromosome and one DNA molecule has
not yet been established, and various alternative possibilities are still
being explored, it is already clear that both objects display not only semiconservative replication, but also linear genetic recombination, sequential synthesis of new DNA at focalized sites, fragmentation under the
influence of both X-irradiation and inhibitors of DNA synthesis, and the
capacity to cause specific amino acid substitutions as a consequence of
a single genetic event. These similarities have led DuPraw (1965c, 1966a)

and others to postulate that in plant and animal cells as in microorganisms, one long, folded DNA helix corresponds to a "unit chromatid."

RECOMBINATION IN CHROMOSOMES AND IN CHROMOSOMAL DNA

In microorganisms, the fact that genetic recombination is associated with an interchromosomal exchange of DNA segments could not be demonstrated except by isotopic labeling experiments (Chapter 15). In macroorganisms, however, such exchanges could be detected very early by visible cytological phenomena, such as chiasma formation and exchange of parts between nonidentical homologs. Attention was first called to the chiasmata of meiotic prophase by Janssens (1909), who came to the conclusion that one chromatid of each homolog pair breaks and rejoins with the other in a reciprocal fashion. This interpretation was later questioned, but various studies have since demonstrated that chiasma formation is correlated with a physical exchange between two of the four chromatids present during prophase. For example, Brown and Zohary (1955) studied *Lilium* plants heterozygous for a terminal deficiency, which made one homolog shorter than the other; they found that the formation of a single chiasma in this chromosome arm results in separation of the two short sister arms from one another at anaphase I, whereas in the absence of a chiasma the two short arms move to the same pole. Similar morphological evidence for an exchange of chromatin between homologs was presented earlier by Stern (1931) in *Drosophila* and by Creighton and McClintock (1931) in maize.

The first investigator to present evidence that the time of genetic crossing-over actually coincides with the time of chiasma formation was Plough (1917), who found that when *Drosophila* females are exposed briefly to a high temperature, crossing-over is increased specifically in those eggs that are at the zygotene stage of meiotic prophase. At about the same time, Bridges (1916) demonstrated genetically that the crossing-over event must involve four copies of each gene affected; this genetic four-strandedness is based on two chromatids in each of two homologs, and it provides further evidence that each chromatid contains but a single copy of any given genetic locus. The fact that crossing-over between homologs occurs *after* the interphase replication of DNA, and that it usually occurs reciprocally between nonsister chromatids, implies a special, orderly mechanism for accomplishing the process. The visible manifestation of this mechanism is undoubtedly the synaptinemal complex (page 545), which appears in the prophase nuclei just before chiasma formation and is absent in organisms that lack chiasma or genetic crossing-over (Coleman and Moses, 1964). However the mode of action of the synaptinemal complex is not yet understood. Whatever the mechanism it apparently operates more vigorously at elevated temperatures, as confirmed recently in *Neurospora* by Perkins (1962).

Genetic recombination between homologs is also known to occur in somatic cells, where chiasmata and synaptinemal complexes are not observed but where the homologs sometimes exhibit "somatic pairing." Recently Holliday (1965) has found that the frequency of mitotic crossing-over in the smut fungus *Ustilago* is increased by ultraviolet irradiation during interphase; by exposing synchronized cells to UV at different stages of the cell cycle, he was able to show that somatic crossing-over takes place during the interphase S period (in contrast to the prophase recombination during meiosis). Holliday further observed that different genes are affected at different times in the S period, and that genes near the telomeres respond early in the S phase, while genes near the centromere respond later. These experiments provide direct evidence that replication in *Ustilago* chromosomes proceeds from the telomeres to the centromere.

In addition to crossing-over between homologs, Taylor *et al.* (1957) discovered by autoradiography that reciprocal exchanges of DNA occur between sister-chromatids during or after the interphase S-period preceding mitosis. Although such sister-chromatid exchanges are not detectable genetically, they are clearly visible after autoradiography of thymidine-^{3}H labeled chromatids (Fig. 18-5). As noted previously, the major pattern of DNA distribution for whole chromosomes is a semiconservative one, in which radioactive DNA is divided equally between chromatids at the first division after labeling, and at the second division one member of each chromatid pair receives labeled DNA while the other does not. This fundamental semiconservative pattern requires that each chromatid must possess two DNA-containing units, which extend the length of the chromatid and which remain intact in subsequent generations. Sister chromatid exchanges, however, lead to a limited dispersal of labeled DNA between the second generation chromatids (Fig. 18-5). As shown by Taylor (1958a), some exchanges occur during the first generation and some during the second generation, but none can be detected until the second metaphase; at that time, the first generation exchanges are recognizable because they can be found as an identical pattern in two separate chromatid pairs (twin exchanges), representing sister chromatids of the first generation kept together in the tetraploid cells. By contrast, second generation exchanges affect only one chromatid pair.

In order to determine whether the two conserved DNA units of each chromatid are identical or complementary, Taylor (1958a) analyzed the behavior of the one labeled and one unlabeled strand in each sister chromatid during sister chromatid exchanges in the first generation (twin exchanges) and in the second generation (single exchanges). His data showed that the labeled strands in sister chromatids cannot exchange with one another in the first generation, but that unlabeled strands can exchange with labeled strands; furthermore, an exchange between one labeled and one unlabeled strand is always accompanied by a reciprocal exchange at the same site between the other labeled and unlabeled strands. Thus sister chromatid exchange is a four-strand event, but unlike meiotic crossing-over the four strands occur in only two chromatids; furthermore, the two strands in one chromatid are unlike one another. All these relationships coincide with those expected if the two unlike strands are the two complementary polynucleotide chains of a single Watson-Crick molecule. Taylor's data exclude the possibility that the two DNA-containing units of one chromatid are two identical DNA molecules (e.g., two unit chromatids in parallel).

Empirically speaking, sister chromatid exchanges represent an exception in the semiconservative pattern of DNA distribution for plant and animal chromosomes; in this particular type of exception, both of the second-metaphase chromatids contain labeled DNA, but in a strictly complementary pattern—where one chromatid is labeled the other is not. However, a second kind of exception was noted by Taylor (1958a) in which both of the second-metaphase chromatids contain labeled DNA, and the patterns are noncomplementary. This phenomenon seriously violates the expectations of the semiconservative distribution, since homologous parts of sister chromatids at second metaphase should not be alike either in labeling (isolabeling) or nonlabeling (isounlabeling). Isolabeling has now been reported for: (1) restricted segments of exceptional chromatid pairs (Taylor, 1958a; Peacock, 1963); (2) the entire lengths of exceptional chromatid pairs (the rest of the metaphase plate following a semiconservative pattern; Peacock, 1963; LaCour and Pelc, 1958); and (3) entire metaphase plates with only exceptional "semiconservative" segments (Zweidler, 1964). At present many authors regard these isolabeling patterns as evidence that duplicate parallel strands are present in some chromosome segments, or in some individual chromosomes, or in all the chromosomes of some species (Ris, 1966a; Zweidler, 1964).

However such an interpretation is not the only one that can be advanced for the isolabeling phenomenon. Even a chromosome which consists of a single folded unit chromatid would show isolabeling as a necessary consequence of sister-chromatid exchanges localized at the telomeres. Such telomeric exchanges have not been considered by

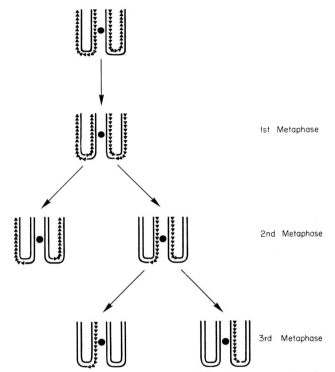

Fig. 18-14. The consequences of a sister chromatid exchange occurring in a telomeric loop of a folded-fiber chromatid. At second metaphase labeled DNA appears in homologous regions of both sister chromatids (isolabeling), but this DNA segregates to one sister chromatid at third metaphase. In this diagram the labeled strand of each DNA molecule is marked by arrow heads corresponding to the 3′–5′ polarity. See text for additional explanation.

previous authors because the telomeres are usually imagined as equivalent to the ends of the genetic map; to the contrary, recent electron microscope studies have shown that the telomeres of human mitotic chromosomes are sites where emerging chromatin fibers loop back into the body of the chromatid (Fig. 18-7). Figure 18-14 shows diagrammatically that a sister chromatid exchange occurring in or near a telomeric loop may result in the transfer of a DNA segment extending the entire length of the chromatid; the consequence of such an exchange, at least in the simplest case, is an equal isolabeling of both sister chromatids at second metaphase. More complex patterns of transverse and longitudinal folding would be expected to produce isolabeling patterns that involve only restricted segments of sister chromatids. From one point of view these anomalies in the usual semiconservative pattern provide a significant confirmation for a folded-fiber chromosome structure, and the observed patterns of isolabeling may in future provide important insights about the folding configurations of specific chromosomes.

It is of interest that a folded-fiber model not only predicts isolabeling as a consequence of telomeric exchanges, but it also predicts that iso-labeled segments should segregate to different sister chromatids at the third instead of the second metaphase (Fig. 18-14). Zweidler (1964) has reported exactly this result for isolabeled chromatids in the onion *Allium cepa*. Zweidler himself regards his data as showing that the meta-phase chromosomes of *Allium* are "cryptotetraploid," i.e., that each anaphase chromosome contains two unit chromatids in parallel. Never-theless his own experiments with *Vicia* chromosomes do not reveal this type of isolabeling, although *Vicia* chromosomes are regarded as crypto-tetraploid by other authors (e.g., Trosko and Wolff, 1965). Furthermore his experiments with *Allium* included a high incidence of conventional sister chromatid exchanges (0.91 exchange per chromosome), sug-gesting the possibility of unrecognized telomeric exchanges. His rare examples of third-metaphase isolabeling, though not expected for cryp-totetraploid chromosomes, would also be predicted for a folded-fiber chromosome as the effect of two successive exchanges in the same fiber region.

The banded, giant polytene chromosomes of *Drosophila* have provided the most successful material for correlating linear recombination fre-quencies with a visibly linear chromosomal structure. Painter (1933) used visible deficiencies and inversions among the linear bands of the X-chromosome to correlate these with a number of gene loci previously mapped according to their recombination frequencies. Soon after, Bridges (1936) discovered a duplication among the X-chromosome bands, which he showed to be associated with the "bar eye" mutation. De-letions, duplications and inversions have since been found to occur also in bacterial and viral chromosomes, establishing that such rearrange-ments may be accounted for by events occurring in single Watson-Crick DNA molecules. An early estimate of the ratio between "chromo-some distance" and "recombination distance" was made by Pontecorvo (1952), who noted that the genes "y" and "f" are separated by 334 μ in salivary chromosome 1, and by 56.7 genetic map units in recombination experiments; this represents an average of about 6 μ of chromosome length per recombination unit. Since recombination frequencies as low as 10^{-3} units had been measured, Pontecorvo estimated that these would correspond to no more than 100 Å of chromosome length. More re-cently it has become possible to estimate the average recombination fre-quency per nucleotide pair in *Drosophila,* by comparing the haploid DNA content (16 cm) with the total number of chromosome map units (about 288 units according to Burnham, 1962); this gives an average of about

556 μ of DNA per recombination unit, or 6.1×10^{-7} recombination units per nucleotide pair. A similar calculation for the X-chromosome in man (containing about 4.4 cm of DNA and estimated to be 150 map units long; McKusick, 1964), gives a value of 1.17×10^{-6} recombination units per nucleotide pair. It is apparent that the values in these organisms are much lower than the corresponding amounts of recombination per nucleotide pair in *E. coli* (5×10^{-4}), and this again is much lower than the value in T4 bacteriophage (1.7×10^{-2}). Possibly these low frequencies of recombination are related to the presence of DNA-linked proteins, which in plant and animal cells sheath and protect each DNA molecule (Fig. 17-5). Whatever the reason, the lower frequency of recombination in higher organisms is combined with less sensitive methods for detecting genetic recombinants, and these two circumstances together delayed the demonstration of intragenic crossing-over for some decades (see discussion of the gene concept in Chapter 15).

Recently however, Chovnick *et al.* (1962, 1964) have devised a technique which is sufficiently sensitive to detect crossing-over in *Drosophila* between mutants no more than 2.6×10^{-4} map units apart. Using this technique, they have been able to show that the *Drosophila* gene "rosy," like the genes of bacteria and viruses, is subdivisible into several linearly arranged mutation and recombination sites. So far, a group of 16 complementing "rosy" mutants have been analyzed and shown to occupy at least 6 linearly arranged intragenic sites. The two closest sites detected (2.6×10^{-4} map units) can be estimated as about 400 nucleotide pairs apart (6.1×10^{-7} map units per nucleotide pair); Chovnick *et al.* (1962) have also speculated that their data could represent recombination between as few as 40 nucleotide pairs. Such high resolution recombination experiments in macroorganisms have not yet reached the single nucleotide level of fine structure, but they have carried genetic analysis rapidly from the level of the whole chromosome to that of the polynucleotide "cistron." Though recombination models are still occasionally proposed which postulate special protein cross-over sites (Uhl, 1965), both genetic and cytological evidence favor the concept that linear recombination is essentially a function of the linear DNA molecule.

THE EFFECTS OF HIGH-ENERGY RADIATION ON CHROMOSOMES AND CHROMOSOMAL DNA

Important clues regarding the structure of interphase and metaphase chromosomes have been obtained by analysis of breaks induced after ultraviolet or X-irradiation. Mather (1937) was the first to contrast "whole-chromosome" breaks, which affect both metaphase chromatids symmetrically, with "single chromatid" breaks. In *Tradescantia* whole-chromosome breaks tend to result after irradiation early in interphase, single chromatid breaks result from irradiation during later interphase, and there is an appreciable intermediate time when the frequency of whole-chromosome breaks gradually decreases as single chromatid breaks increase. Mather correctly interpreted this to mean that chromosome replication takes place during interphase (a daring idea at the time), and that a single electron "hit" prior to replication breaks the entire chromosome whereas the same hit after replication breaks only one chromatid. Mather's plot of percentage of chromatid breaks *vs.* interphase time gives a curve that is essentially identical to the DNA synthesis curves later discovered by Pasteels and Lison (1950) using Feulgen microspectrophotometry. Later Taylor (1953) confirmed autoradiographically that the period of DNA synthesis in *Tradescantia* coincides with the time when whole-chromosome breaks undergo a transition to chromatid breaks.

For many years a major theoretical problem in interpreting radiation effects has been the fact that the paths of X-ray excited electrons are much shorter than the visible diameters of the metaphase chromatids. Since some earlier authors believed that the chromosomes actually swell up during interphase, it seemed impossible that these enlarged chromosomes could be fractured directly by a single electron hit. Even more difficult to believe was evidence that a single hit could sometimes fracture two chromosomes simultaneously. However, Neary *et al.* (1964) have recently reinvestigated the relationship between mean electron path length and frequency of chromatid breaks in *Tradescantia;* using monochromatic X-rays at carefully controlled, low energy levels, they found that chromatid breaks are produced with good efficiency *in vivo* even by electrons with mean path lengths as low as 500 Å. Since double-chromatid breaks were also found, they suggested that the diameter of the interphase chromatid may actually be less than half the 500 Å electron range. This dimension corresponds remarkably to the observed diameters of type B chromatin fibers (230 Å) as seen by electron microscopy; consequently Neary's results tend to confirm that the 230 Å fibers exist as such *in vivo*, and that one such fiber corresponds to one chromatid in *Tradescantia*.

With respect to chromosome and chromatid breaks produced by X-irradiation at interphase, Sax (1941) and others were able to quantify the effects, showing that "single-hit" breaks increase linearly with dosage while "double-hit" breaks increase as the square of the dosage. This sophisticated approach revealed that X-ray-induced breaks regularly reunite within 26–60 minutes in *Tradescantia,* thereby becoming undetectable if the original connections are reestablished. Significantly, healing of broken chromosomes does not occur in *Drosophila* sperm nuclei (which are metabolically inactive and lack DNA polymerase), but does occur in the sperm chromosomes after they enter the egg cytoplasm. More recently Taylor *et al.* (1962) have investigated the mechanism of reunion for chromosome breaks induced by fluorodeoxyuridine treatment or X-irradiation in *Vicia faba.* They were able to show that healing depends on DNA synthesis, since inhibition of thymidylate synthetase by fluorodeoxyuridine prevents reunion of X-ray-induced breaks. Furthermore, if the fluorodeoxyuridine block is removed by addition of thymidine, reunion of strands occurs up to an hour before anaphase. These results are readily understandable if the chromatid axis is based on a single DNA chain, and if the reunion of broken chains occurs by rematching of short single-stranded segments at the broken ends; such a mechanism would resemble the process by which a linear phage λ chromosome is transformed into its circular configuration (Chapter 15). In phage λ, union of the single-stranded chromosome ends is prevented if DNA polymerase is permitted to synthesize complementary terminal strands (Strack and Kaiser, 1965); it may therefore be significant that in higher cells broken chromosome ends are sometimes described as "sticky" but lose their stickiness (and ability to reunite) during interphase. The overall picture implies that very efficient repair mechanisms operate in the nuclei of macroorganisms, and that more often than not an accidentally broken chromatin fiber is successfully repaired. Occasionally, however, an anomalous reunion of multiple broken ends may give rise to an inversion or translocation.

Complex chromosomal rearrangements such as inversions, deletions and translocations usually result from X-irradiation by two-hit kinetics; however some investigators have found it necessary to postulate a combination of one-hit and two-hit mechanisms (Wolff, 1963), and it has also been found that neutron irradiation produces even the most complex chromosomal rearrangements as single-hit events both in *Drosophila* and in *Tradescantia.* The origin of an inversion as a single-hit event implies that the pattern of DNA packing in typical chromosomes is such that widely separated genetic loci are brought into close proximity, i.e., that the DNA is folded. Figure 18-15 demonstrates how a single break-rejoin event within a folded-fiber chromosome, such as that diagrammed in Fig. 18-12, can generate a paracentric inversion of the type commonly observed in *Drosophila* salivary chromosomes; similarly Fig. 18-16 illustrates the possible origin of a pericentric inversion from the same type of break-rejoin event. In terms of a folded-fiber model, single-hit kinetics will be realized for such rearrangements if the irradiation particles have energies high enough to break two chromatin fibers at once (e.g., neutrons); lower energy irradiation (e.g., X-rays) would be expected to

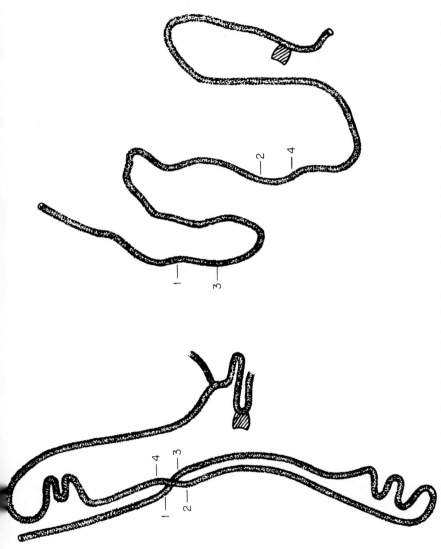

Fig. 18-15. Diagram based on Fig. 18-12, showing how a single break-rejoin event in a folded-fiber chromatid can give rise to a *paracentric* inversion. The numbered regions along the fiber designate Mendelian gene loci, which change from a sequence of 1-2-3-4-C to 1-3-2-4-C.

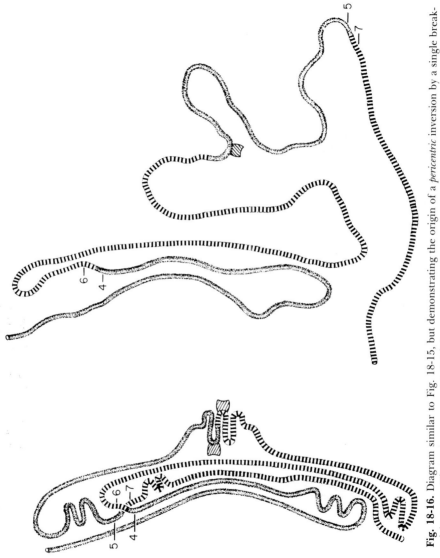

Fig. 18-16. Diagram similar to Fig. 18-15, but demonstrating the origin of a *pericentric* inversion by a single break-rejoin event. The gene sequence 4-5-C-6-7 becomes 4-6-C-5-7.

yield a mixture of one-hit and two-hit events, depending on the energy level and the proximity of the fibers *in vivo*.

In both human and *Tradescantia* chromosomes, X-irradiation at metaphase (rather than at interphase) tends to produce visible gaps which frequently extend only part way across the chromatid as a "half-chromatid break." Such gaps, which are produced with single-hit kinetics, have often been cited as evidence for the existence of replicate half-chromatids in anaphase chromosomes. Similar subchromatid breaks, gaps and fusion figures have been reported by Peacock (1961) in *Vicia*, by Crouse (1961) in *Lilium,* by Wilson and Sparrow (1960) in *Trillium,* and by LaCour and Rutishauser (1954) in *Scilla*. However as Mather (1937) noted long ago, these morphological images are difficult to interpret with certainty since they occur at the very limits of resolution of the light microscope; the critical test of half-chromatid breaks is a demonstration that they give rise to single chromatid breaks after an intervening replication. Exactly this experiment was carried out by Östergren and Wakonig (1954), who induced apparent half-chromatid breaks in *Allium* chromosomes both with X-rays and with the chemical agent coumarin. They found that in the second generation these subchromatid anomalies give rise, not to chromatid breaks but to twin-chromatid breaks, and they concluded that the apparent half-chromatid breaks are really full-chromatid breaks. Such a result is understandable for a folded fiber chromatid, in which the true structural axis has a diameter much less than the chromatid as a whole, but is folded back on itself one or more times; a break at only one point in such a folded chromatin fiber will not extend across the entire diameter of the cytological chromatid, and consequently will appear as a subchromatid break or gap at metaphase. Recently Kihlman and Hartley (1967) have re-confirmed the experiments of Östergren and Wakonig (1954), and have concluded that their results support the folded fiber model proposed by DuPraw (1965c).

REPLICATION PATTERNS IN CHROMOSOMES AND IN CHROMOSOMAL DNA

During early speculation about chromosome models based on one long, (differentially coiled) DNA molecule, a frequent objection was that such a long double helix would be unable to unwind, or would require an impossibly long time to unwind, in order to carry out the replication process. This objection has been partially answered by the discovery that a DNA helix 1.1 to 1.4 mm long constitutes the chromosome of the bacterium *E. coli*, and that this molecule is indeed able to replicate by a sequential, semiconservative mechanism evidently based on unwinding.

Because a typical plant or animal chromosome generally contains several *centimeters* of DNA, some question remains as to whether all this DNA can be in the form of one molecule or not. Although DNA filaments up to 2.2 *centimeters* long have recently been isolated from human nuclei (Sasaki and Norman, 1966), it is not yet certain that these correspond to single continuous helices. Analysis of DNA melting indicates that the time required for unwinding increases exponentially with the length of the helix, and becomes ridiculously long when the helix reaches one centimeter (Chapter 12). Nevertheless DNA replication (unlike melting) is an enzymatically catalyzed process, which might be expected to proceed with very different kinetics. There is also a distinct possibility that long double helices may undergo replication from two or more separate sites simultaneously; in this case, the unwinding problem may be solved by temporary single-strand breaks in the double helix, permitting free rotation around one chain.

That DNA synthesis in plants and animals proceeds by a semiconservative mechanism has been confirmed by Djordjevic and Szybalski (1960) for human cells and by Filner (1965) for tobacco cells. Their experiments involved heavy labeling of the DNA with bromodeoxyuridine or ^{15}N, followed by density gradient centrifugation according to the classic experiment first carried out with microorganisms by Meselson and Stahl (1958). The demonstration of a semiconservative replication mechanism at the molecular level should not be confused with the semiconservative *distribution* of DNA at the chromosomal level, as demonstrated by Taylor et al. (1957). Further evidence that DNA synthesis is sequential, in the sense that DNA replicated early in one S period is replicated early again in the next S period, has been obtained for the slime mold *Physarum* by Braun et al. (1965) and for human cells by Mueller and Kajiwara (1966). These authors performed double-labeling experiments with nuclei that were synchronized, either naturally (in the slime mold) or artificially (in cultured HeLa cells). In the experiments of Braun et al. the nuclei were labeled with thymidine-^{3}H in late S of one generation and with bromodeoxyuridine in early S of the next generation; it was found that none of the (late) thymidine-^{3}H labeled DNA incorporated the (early) bromodeoxyuridine label, showing that DNA which replicates early in one generation must replicate early again in the next generation.

Efforts to determine the rate at which replication proceeds at any one site have been made by Cairns (1966) for HeLa cells and by Taylor (1968) for Chinese hamster cells. Cairns' technique involved pulse labeling the nuclei with thymidine-^{3}H, then isolating the DNA by gentle methods and determining the lengths of labeled segments by autoradiography. He found that a pulse of 45 minutes labels DNA segments only 10–30 μ

long, indicating a replication rate of about 0.5 μ per minute; Taylor's estimate, based on bromodeoxyuridine incorporation, is in the order of 2 μ per minute. These values are much lower than the rate of 20–30 μ per minute found by Cairns (1963a) in E. coli, and they may reflect the supercoiling and protein linkages which characterize DNA in plant and animal chromatin. By comparing the rate of replication at one site with the total length of helix in a nucleus and the total time required for the S period, Taylor has estimated that the number of replication sites in a Chinese hamster nucleus must be in the order of 5000. The term "replicon" has recently been introduced to designate each separately replicated segment of DNA.

Originally it was thought that each replicon would correspond to a separate DNA molecule, but newer evidence strongly suggests that the DNA of plants and animals is arranged in very long helices that can replicate at several sites simultaneously. In Cairns' autoradiograph experiments, for instance, different labeled segments of DNA were seen to lie in long chains separated by unlabeled regions; although the material holding the labeled segments together was not proved to be DNA, this seemed to be the most likely possibility. It can also be estimated that, at 2 μ per minute, a DNA helix 1800 μ long (Huberman and Riggs, 1966) would require 15 hours to replicate at a single moving site; this is much longer than the usual S period in Chinese hamster cells. In Drosophila, the same DNA complement that requires 8–14 hours for a replication cycle in salivary cells replicates repeatedly at 10-minute intervals in embryonic nuclei; since about 30 cm of Watson-Crick helix are involved, such rapid embryonic replications must involve simultaneous synthesis at many sites, possibly by a special mechanism that incorporates preformed cytoplasmic oligonucleotide chains (Chapter 17). Replication at more than one site in the same DNA molecule requires one or more internal swivel points to permit local unwinding of the double helix. Theoretically such swivel points can be provided by single-strand breaks, i.e., by temporary ruptures in one strand of the double helix which may be introduced enzymatically by an endonuclease. Vinograd and Lebowitz (1966) have confirmed that single-strand breaks caused by pancreatic DNase are able to act as swivel sites for unwinding of supercoils in circular DNA molecules. It is therefore possible that the same DNA helix can replicate either sequentially at a single site or synchronously at multiple sites, depending on local endonuclease and DNA polymerase activities. The overall rate of nuclear DNA synthesis and the length of the S period in various tissues could be controlled in this fashion.

Almost all the information currently available about the timing of replication in different chromosomes and chromosomal segments is

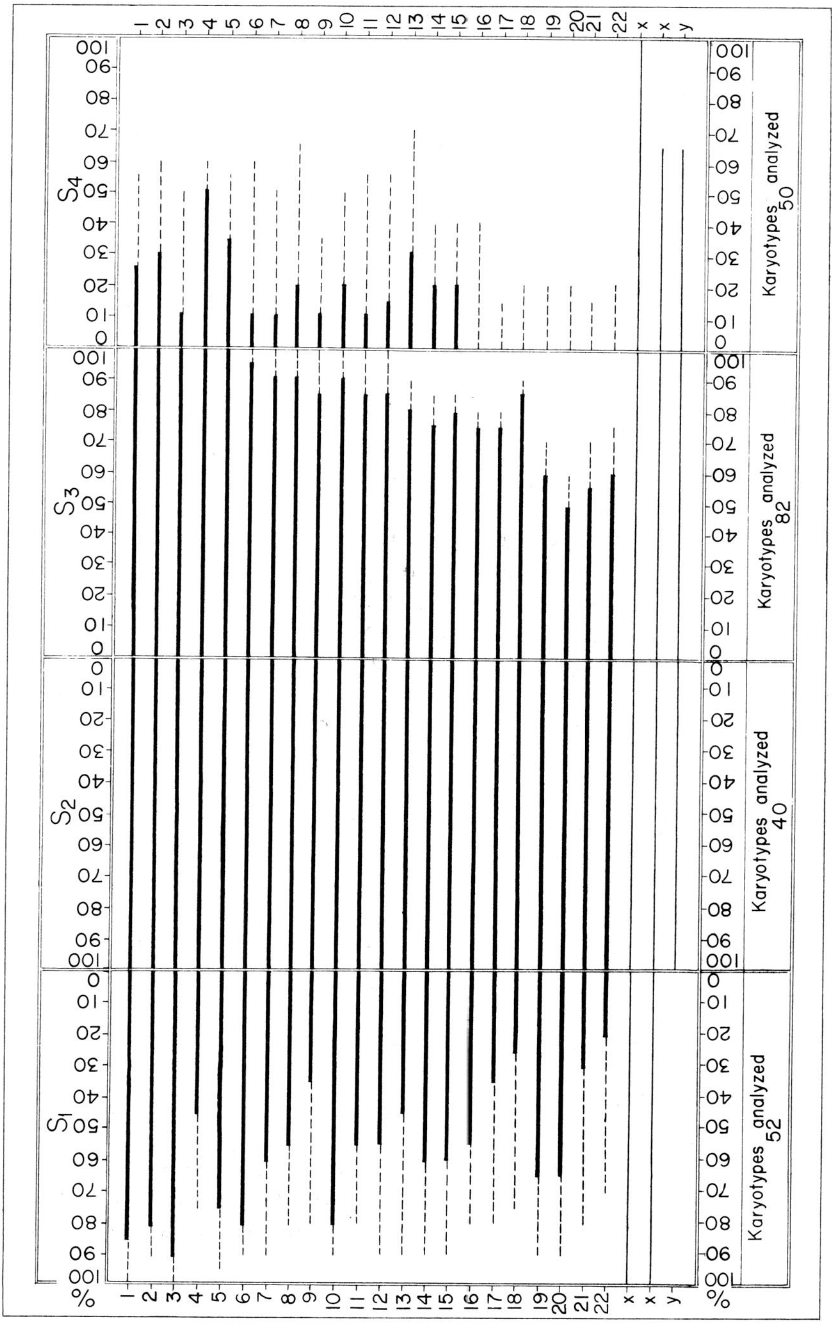
S1
Karyotypes analyzed 52
S2
Karyotypes analyzed 40
S3
Karyotypes analyzed 82
S4
Karyotypes analyzed 50
%

derived from light microscope autoradiography of metaphase chromosomes; such experiments suffer from two difficulties: (1) the fact that synthesis actually occurs in interphase, although the localization of label is studied at metaphase; and (2) the inherently low resolution of light microscope autoradiographic techniques. Nevertheless it has been possible to establish some general principles; as first reported by LaCour and Pelc (1958) and Lima-de-Faria (1959), the pattern of metaphase labeling varies according to whether thymidine-^{3}H is administered early or late in the S-period, i.e., DNA synthesis is not simultaneous at all loci, but occurs in focalized locations which follow one another in a definite time sequence. Frequently some chromosomes begin DNA synthesis minutes or hours before others in the same nucleus, and the completion of replication also varies from one chromosome to another; according to Bianchi and deBianchi (1965), the smallest human chromosomes tend to begin later and finish earlier than any others (Fig. 18-17). Heterochromatic regions or chromosomes are also frequently the last to complete their replication, e.g., the pericentric heterochromatin in *Drosophila* salivary chromosomes, the Y chromosome in males, and the heterochromatic X chromosome in female mammals.

A number of authors have reported a tendency for the centromere region to replicate relatively late in the S period, and some investigators have also detected an early telomere incorporation. Taylor (1958b) was the first to detect a quantitative gradient from telomeres to centromere in chromosomes of the plant genus *Crepis*. A similar pattern was discovered in human chromosome 2 by Stubblefield and Mueller (1962) and in human chromosomes 1 and 3 by Moorhead and Defendi (1963; Fig. 18-18). These "early telomere-late centromere" patterns appear most clearly in cells labeled at the very end of the S period, when frequently no label is found near the telomeres but incorporation still occurs near the centromere; for example, Schmid (1963) observed that many chromosomes of the human complement terminate DNA synthesis in or near the centromeres, and that the first parts of a chromosome to stop incorporating are often the distal parts of the arms. In Chinese hamster cells as well, Hsu (1964) used a 5-minute pulse to label synchronized cells at different stages, and concluded that the telomeres often (but not always) are the first parts of a given chromosome to finish replication, while the centromere is frequently last. Although excep-

---

Fig. 18-17. The timing of DNA replication in the 23 chromosome pairs of the human karyotype, as determined from metaphase autoradiographs. The solid lines represent the percentage of labeling in each pair of homologs during four subdivisions of the S period. Dotted lines indicate percentage of asynchrony between homologs. From Bianchi and deBianchi (1965).

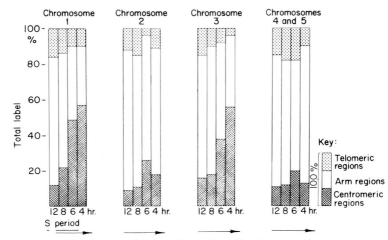

Fig. 18-18. The distribution of autoradiograph grains between telomeres, centromeres, and arms after pulse-labeling with thymidine-³H in various subdivisions of the S period. Human chromosomes 1 and 3 show a clear tendency toward an early telomere-late centromere pattern. From Moorhead and Defendi (1963).

tions to this rule are plentiful, there is no reason to doubt that it is a genuine principle of replication in many chromosomes.

Additional evidence for late centromere replication has recently been obtained by Walen (1965), who studied so-called "diplochromosomes" in colchicine-induced tetraploid cells of the marsupial *Potorous*. Diplochromosomes are complexes of four "granddaughter" chromatids which sometimes occur in tetraploid cells when the sister chromatids of one metaphase do not separate before replicating for a second metaphase. Walen found that if such chromosomes are labeled with thymidine-³H before the first metaphase, the label segregates into two of the four attached chromatids at second metaphase (in accord with a semiconservative pattern); however, the segregation is not random among the four chromatids, but tends to label the two *outermost* chromatids of the quartet. Since the four chromatids are held together at the centromere this result implies that the centromere determines a definite geometric relationship among all 8 arms, and such a relationship is most easily accounted for if the centromere has not replicated even though the arms have. In Chinese hamster chromosomes, Somers and Hsu (1962) noted that hydroxylamine tends to induce whole-chromosome breaks at the centromere, implying that there is a higher probability that hydroxylamine will encounter the centromere in an unreplicated state. In the ciliate *Euplotes* a remarkable type of sequential replication occurs in the large, ribbon-shaped macronucleus, very much resembling an early telomere-late centromere pattern; DNA synthesis is confined to two localized "reorganization bands," which appear first at the opposite ends of the macronucleus and move sequentially toward the center (Fig. 17-10).

These and other observations led DuPraw (1965c) to postulate in his folded-fiber model that each unit chromatid may replicate at two forks, which begin DNA synthesis at the genetic telomeres (i.e., the two ends

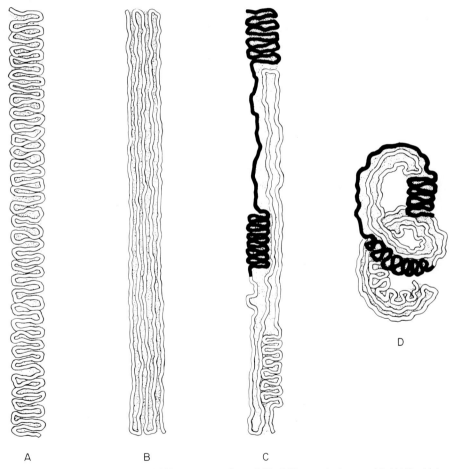

A   B   C   D

Fig. 18-19. Various possible folding patterns for a folded-fiber unit chromatid. (A) Entirely transverse; (B) Entirely longitudinal; (C) A combination of transverse and longitudinal folding; (D) Quaternary coiling superimposed on the folding pattern of (C). The blackened fiber segment shows that the distribution of autoradiograph grains at metaphase depends on the pattern of folding after fiber replication at interphase. From DuPraw (1966a).

of each nucleoprotein fiber) and move sequentially toward the center (i.e., toward the centromere; Fig. 18-11). In this concept, it is the unreplicated central part of each 230 A fiber which holds together the sister chromatids until the metaphase condensation. Although metaphase autoradiographs of interphase synthesis never reveal a simple sequential incorporation along a chromosome arm, it is expected that the complex, back-and-forth folding of the unit chromatid at metaphase will tend to mask whatever sequential incorporation occurs at interphase (Fig. 18-19). The model predicts that at metaphase, just before the sister chromatids of each pair separate, a small amount of DNA synthesis should occur in the centromere; although such synthesis has been looked for, it has not as yet been demonstrated. The reason may be that DNA synthesis is usually measured by the incorporation of thymidine-^{3}H, whereas Somers and Hsu (1962) have presented evidence that the centromere region is rich in G-C base pairs (Fig. 18-2).

Recent evidence that several replication sites may operate simultaneously in a single unit chromatid (i.e., in the same long DNA helix) serves to complicate this simplest-possible scheme, but does not fundamentally alter it. Only two replication sites occur in the macronucleus of *Euplotes;* if more replication sites occur in the chromosomes of plants and animals, this may mean that such chromosomes are compound structures (containing many unit chromatids in series), or that each unit chromatid replicates at several points simultaneously. In either case, it might be predicted that sister chromatids would be held together by unreplicated fiber segments along the arms as well as in the kinetochore region, and cytological evidence for such interchromatid attachments in arm regions is common. However, the exact distribution of sites along the chromatid and the direction in which synthesis proceeds remain to be determined.

THE EXPRESSION OF GENETIC INFORMATION IN MACROORGANISMS

Concurrently with the development of the amino acid-polynucleotide "code" (Table 14-3), a wide variety of cytochemical and experimental investigations have shown that an information transfer relationship exists between DNA, RNA, and protein synthesis in plant and animal cells as well as in microorganisms (Chapter 17). Although most data of this kind concern synthesis in interphase nuclei, two very fruitful lines of research have dealt specifically with synthesis mediated by chromosomes, i.e., the dipteran polytene chromosomes and the amphibian oocyte lampbrush chromosomes.

With regard to the polytene chromosomes, Balbiani (1881) noted very early that these contain occasional expanded or swollen, ringlike regions that are unusually basophilic. Later Beermann (1956) brought special attention to such "puffs" by showing that they are modified bands and by demonstrating that the particular bands which form puffs differ from one tissue to another in a highly specific manner. At any one time, only a few percent of the chromosome bands in a given nucleus show evidence of puffing, but autoradiographs indicate that these are sites of intensive RNA synthesis. Furthermore, under the influence of different metabolites new specific puffs can be caused to develop or to recede in a highly reproducible manner. Definitive proof that puff formation is an expression of genetic activity has been provided by Beermann (1961); he made genetic crosses between *Chironomus pallidivittatus*, which possesses characteristic salivary granules, and *C. tentans*, which does not. Beermann found that inability to produce salivary granules is inherited as a simple Mendelian recessive, and that the synthesis of granules is associated with the presence of a specific puff that occurs in the vicinity of the known gene locus. The "granule puff" is present in *C. pallidivittatus* but absent in *C. tentans*, and in the hybrids between them it occurs as a "half-puff" in only one of the paired homologs.

Several laboratories are intensively investigating the biochemical events that accompany puff formation. Swift (1962, 1964) and others have shown that there is usually no detectable change in the amount of DNA or histone in the band, but that RNA and nonhistone proteins accumulate markedly. Since the synthesis of puff RNA is inhibited by actinomycin D, it evidently represents a DNA-dependent process. The base composition of RNA from different specific puffs has been investigated by Edström and Beermann (1962); using a very sensitive microelectrophoresis procedure, they found that these RNA's differ significantly in base composition from one puff to another, and furthermore that the amount of adenine generally does not equal the amount of uracil nor does guanine equal cytosine. Assuming that each puff is a site for transcription of messenger RNA, these results provide direct evidence that different parts of the species' genetic information are transcribed in different puffs at different times, and also that only one strand of the Watson-Crick double helix is "read" in any one puff.

The structure of a puff as seen by light and electron microscopy is that of a region where the polytene fibers, normally tightly folded into chromosomal bands, become unfolded and "frayed" as separate fibers of extremely fine diameter. This fraying or loop formation was first deduced in sectioned salivary chromosomes by Beermann and Bahr (1954) and has since been seen by Rae (1966) in unsectioned preparations. It may be presumed that the chromatid fibers unwind to an extent that permits DNA to act as a template in an RNA polymerase reaction, but since histones are present in about the same amounts before and during puff formation it is not yet clear how the unfolding process is accomplished. Allfrey *et al.* (1968) have recently found evidence that histone acetylases are present in giant salivary chromosomes, suggesting the possibility that control may depend on the presence or absence of N-terminal acetyl in the histone molecules (see Chapter 17). It should also be noted that RNA synthesis, though more active in puffed regions, appears to go on at a lower rate in ordinary bands and interbands. Other experiments, which are concerned with the induction of specific puffs by various artificial stimulants, will be discussed in connection with cell differentiation (Chapter 20).

As first noted by Gall (1956a), the lampbrush "loops" of amphibian oocyte chromosomes show many fundamental similarities to the puffs of dipteran polytene chromosomes. These loops are sites of very active RNA and protein synthesis, their synthetic activity is sensitive to actinomycin D, and the initiation of synthesis seems to depend on an unfolding or spinning out process in which a DNase-sensitive strand emerges from a tightly packed chromomere. Edström and Gall (1963) investigated the base composition of chromosomal RNA in *Triturus* oocytes, showing that this differs from the nucleolar and cytoplasmic RNA's as well as from chromosomal DNA. Nevertheless, the *sums* of G + C and A + U in chromosomal RNA are the same as those in DNA, as would be expected if the DNA constitutes a template for the RNA. In the giant granular loops there is good evidence that RNA synthesis must precede protein synthesis, and that this RNA synthesis occurs very rapidly after spinning out of the DNA filament. That the loops can exhibit heterozygosity and are inherited according to simple Mendelian laws has been demonstrated by Callan and Lloyd (1960).

A potentially important line of investigation in both dipteran polytene chromosomes and lampbrush chromosomes is concerned with the existence of "metabolic DNA," i.e., DNA which is synthesized at local sites along the chromosome in a manner that may be independent of simple chromosomal replication. For example, certain puffs in *Sciara* (but not *Drosophila*) are sites of active thymidine-^{3}H incorporation accompanied by a localized increase in total DNA mass. In *Chironomus*, Keyl (1965) has compared the DNA content of homologous bands between two different species, and has found that the proportion varies independently from one band to another; however they usually show a geometric or "replicative" progression of 2, 4, 8, etc. Plaut *et al.* (1966) have also found that a 5- or 10-minute pulse of thymidine-^{3}H may be incorporated at about 50 separate sites in a single *Drosophila* salivary chromosome; this discontinuous labeling pattern is not directly correlated with the pattern of bands and interbands, since both these regions often show incorporation. It appears that a single dipteran chromosome may contain 50 or more replicons, and that each replicon may be able to synthesize DNA by geometric increases independently of the rest of the chromosome. In amphibian oocytes too, Izawa *et al.* (1963) found that the nucleoplasm contains approximately as much DNA as the lampbrush chromosomes, while the chromosomes themselves contain some 4 times as much DNA per haploid set as somatic nuclei. This excess DNA has been partially accounted for by Miller's (1964) discovery that each amphibian oocyte nucleolus contains a circular DNA filament; since there are many hundred nucleoli in a single nucleus at this stage, a large amount of extrachromosomal DNA is involved. Preliminary evidence indicates that the nucleolar DNA is synthesized initially along one or more of the lampbrush chromosome loops, and therefore represents a kind of "DNA transcription." However, it is not yet known how widespread this phenomenon may be, nor the manner in which synthesis is controlled and localized.

19

CELL DIVISION

. . . the role in mitosis of the chromosome arms, which carry most of the genetic material, may be compared with that of a corpse at a funeral: they provide the reason for the proceedings but do not take an active part in them.

D. MAZIA *1961*

Previous chapters have outlined the present understanding of genetic organization in interphase nuclei and in the condensed chromosomes of dividing cells; beyond this, the actual mechanisms by which the genetic and nongenetic materials of one mother cell are separated in an orderly fashion to two or more daughter cells remain to be considered.

Spontaneous division of one object to form two is not exclusively a cell property, since it occurs also at the level of individual organelles such as chloroplasts and mitochondria (Chapters 5 and 7). Furthermore, division as such is not the only way in which a cellular or subcellular structure may be duplicated. Daughter centrioles are assembled (duplicated) in association with mother centrioles, but evidently are not derived from them by division (Chapter 9). Neither do the sister cells of the insect blastoderm arise by division of entire cells, but rather by successive duplication of one cell part (the nucleus), followed by simultaneous partition of the duplicates into 1000 or more cells. Nevertheless the events of cell division are usually visualized in terms of a "typical" mitotic cycle, including: (1) replication of chromosomes and centrioles (or centrosomes) during interphase; (2) prophase condensation of chromosomes, disintegration of the nuclear envelope and nucleolus, and assembly of a mitotic spindle; (3) metaphase alignment of chromosomes, with the kinetochores of sister chromatids engaged to opposite poles of the spindle; (4) anaphase separation of sister chromatids to opposite poles, followed rapidly by cytoplasmic division; (5) telophase diassembly of the spindle and reassembly of a nuclear envelope and nucleolus.

Although earlier theories of cell division sometimes attempted to explain all these events in terms of some single hypothetical mechanism, comparative observations of division in different cell types and after experimental modification have now established that many separate processes operate in "typical" mitosis. For instance, chromosome replication does not occur during the division process itself, but represents a lengthy series of chemical events completed during interphase. Chromosomes may also replicate repeatedly without cell division, or cells may divide without chromosome replication (and even in the complete absence of a nucleus). In bacteria and dinoflagellates cell division is accomplished without the assistance of a mitotic spindle, while among macroorganisms development of a spindle sometimes depends on replication of the centrioles (as in most animals) and sometimes does not (as in higher plants, which lack centrioles). In many protozoans, fungi, and in eggs of the crustacean *Cyclops*, the nuclear envelope does not disintegrate during mitosis; in such instances, the spindle fibers either develop inside the nucleus, or alternatively the spindle may lie outside the envelope while establishing connections to the chromosomes inside the envelope. In some species the nucleolus persists during the whole of the mitotic cycle, demonstrating that its disintegration is not an absolute prerequisite for division. Finally, cytoplasmic division (cytokinesis) occurs by fundamentally different mechanisms in animal cells (which are constricted by a division furrow) and in plant cells (which synthesize a new transverse cell wall). These and other variations in the division process serve to emphasize that a "typical" cell division, if such an event ever occurs, must represent a coordinated marshaling of many overlapping mechanisms.

A number of authors have pointed out that in some respects a dividing cell represents a cell which is in a special state of differentiation. During mitosis a large part of the cellular protein is committed to the formation of the spindle; for example, Mazia and Roslansky (1956) calculated that 12% of the total protein in a sea urchin oocyte is included in the mitotic apparatus, and Mazia (1961) estimates that the spindle makes up as much as 50% of the cell volume in smaller cells. There is also a distinct tendency for other forms of differentiation to interfere with or eliminate cell division in a particular tissue, e.g., differentiated muscle fibers and neurons almost never divide. Nevertheless if cell division is a state of differentiation, it is a remarkably temporary one; many cells require less than an hour to pass from prophase to telophase, and a "mitotic time" of 10 hours is exceeded only in special instances (e.g., the long meiotic prophase in many oocytes). In a population of cells that is dividing repeatedly and at random, the ratio of mitotic time (prophase to telophase) to the total cell generation time (prophase to prophase) may be inferred from the mitotic index, i.e., the percentage of cells found in mitosis at any given instant. The fundamental relationship is given by the equation:

$$\frac{MT}{MT + IT} \times \log_e 2 = \log_e (1 + MI)$$

where MT is the mitotic time, (MT + IT) is the generation time, and MI is the mitotic index (Edwards et al., 1960).

Ultrastructure of the Mitotic Apparatus

During the early years of thin-section electron microscopy, the functional elements of the mitotic apparatus, including the centrioles, kinetochores, and spindle fibers, proved to be unusually difficult to preserve; consequently many descriptions dating from the 1950's are incomplete or

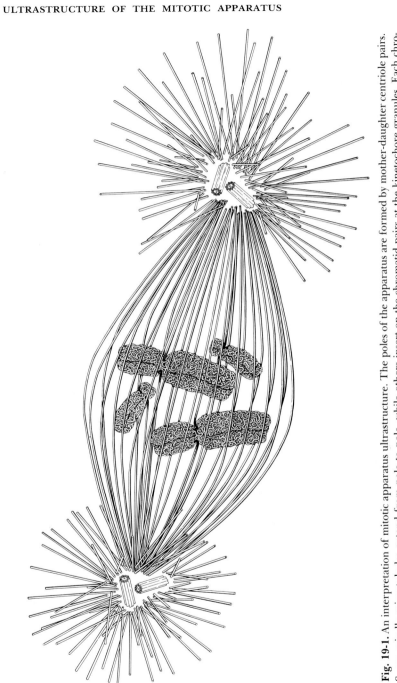

Fig. 19-1. An interpretation of mitotic apparatus ultrastructure. The poles of the apparatus are formed by mother-daughter centriole pairs. Some spindle microtubules extend from pole to pole, while others insert on the chromatid pairs at the kinetochore granules. Each chromosome consists of two sister chromatids, each made up of a folded chromatin fiber. Half- and quarter-chromatids do not occur.

partially erroneous. Even the reality of spindle fibers continued to be questioned until about 1953, when Inoue used a refined polarizing microscope to demonstrate these fibers in living cells of both plants and animals. In agreement with the "fixed" images of classical light micros-copy, Inoué was able to distinguish several classes of spindle fiber (Fig. 19-1): (1) the chromosomal fibers, which pass from the spindle poles to the kinetochores of the chromosomes; (2) the continuous fibers, which pass from one pole to the other without attaching to the chromosomes; (3) the astral fibers, which radiate in a spherelike configuration around each pole (or centrosphere); and (4) the interzonal fibers, which are seen at anaphase in the region between the two separating chromosome groups. As reported by Inoué, the birefringence of the spindle is pri-marily a positive form birefringence, indicating the presence of protein filaments oriented parallel to the spindle axis.

As early as 1957, Porter observed very fine filaments (ca. 300 Å in diameter) in electron micrographs of the spindle region in various rat cells; these filaments exhibited an electron dense circumference and a light center, suggesting tubular structures, and they tended to occur in pairs. Nevertheless, consistent success in preserving the spindle fibers depended on the addition of divalent cations (Ca^{++}, Mg^{++}) to the fixing reagents, an innovation that was developed by Harris (1961) when she used seawater to improve the preservation of the mitotic apparatus in sea urchin embryos (Fig. 18-3); later Roth and Jenkins (1962) systemati-cally demonstrated that spindle fibers are stabilized by Ca^{++} in *Amoeba* as well. These and subsequent investigations have now served to estab-lish that the mitotic apparatus in plants, animals and protozoans is always based on microtubular filaments, which converge at the spindle poles and which run in remarkably straight paths from the poles to the chro-mosomes (Fig. 19-2). The diameters of these microtubules are fairly constant within a tissue, but vary somewhat between species. Thus the spindle fibers of the giant amoeba *Pelomyxa* are only 140 Å in diameter, those of the sea urchin *Strongylocentrotus* are 150–200 Å, while those reported by Ledbetter and Porter (1963) in higher plants are 200–230 Å. The number of microtubules in a spindle varies from about 16 in yeast (Moor, 1967) to approximately 5000 in some higher plants (e.g., in *Haemanthus* according to A. Bajer).

Recently Kiefer *et al.* (1966) and Barnicot (1966) have observed the

---

Fig. 19-2. (A) Thin-section of a human (HeLa) cell at metaphase or early anaphase; note the fibrous substructure of the chromosomes. 9,260×. From Robbins and Gonatas (1964). (B) Attachment of spindle microtubules to a HeLa chromosome; the site of attachment is a dense granule or plate. 68,400×. From Robbins and Gonatas (1964). (C) A human chromosome 16 prepared as a whole-mount; the attachment sites for spindle microtubules are not preserved by this method. 20,200×. From DuPraw and Rae (1966).

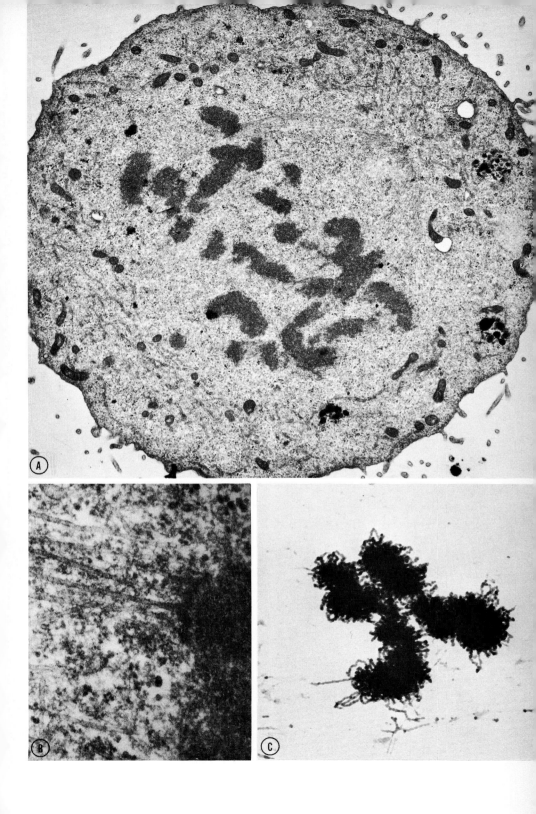

substructure of single, negatively stained spindle tubules isolated from sea urchin embryos and newt heart cells. These filaments appear to be true hollow cylinders, and are composed of globular protein subunits about 33 Å in diameter; the arrangement of these protein monomers is such that they form approximately 13 longitudinal "protofilaments" in the tubule wall, similar to the protofilaments described by André and Thiéry (1963) in the nine outer tubules of sperm flagella (Fig. 9-5). Moor (1967) has also described a similar arrangement of globular monomers in yeast spindle tubules prepared by freeze-etching (Fig. 19-3). In both sea urchin and yeast spindles the filament substructure is very similar to structures reported in other cells for cytoplasmic microtubules and for the nine outer tubules of cilia (Fig. 9-5); such structural similarities have suggested to several authors that the same protein monomers might assemble in slightly different ways to form microtubules of the spindle, of cilia or of the cytoplasm (Chapter 9). Although spindle and cytoplasmic microtubules usually have somewhat different diameters even within a single cell, several lines of evidence support an identity of subunits. For example in higher plants cytoplasmic microtubules are rare or absent at metaphase, suggesting that they are disassembled during the same period when the spindle is assembled. Ruby (1961) has also reported an immunological cross reaction between sea urchin cilia and sea urchin mitotic apparatus. In yeast, one intranuclear protein crystal seems to give rise to both spindle and cytoplasmic microtubules (Moor, 1967). In addition, flagellar and mitotic microtubules share a notable dependency on the presence of a centriole—a feature which is less obvious for cytoplasmic microtubules but sometimes occurs. For these and other reasons a fundamental similarity at the molecular level is expected, though not yet demonstrated.

As noted by Harris (1961), both pole-to-pole and pole-to-chromosome filaments can be found in thin sections, but the two types appear to be identical in diameter and other features. The most obvious difference is that the pole-to-chromosome filaments are inserted on individual chromatids at a dense, crescent-like granule in the kinetochore region (Fig. 19-2). One chromatid pair possesses two such kinetochore granules oriented in opposite directions, and each one receives several spindle tubules from its own pole (Fig. 18-3). Although there is rarely any sign of visible substructure within a single kinetochore granule, Robbins and Gonatas (1964) have observed that the crescentic granule in HeLa chromosomes is separated from the chromosome proper by an osmiophobic zone about 150 Å wide (Fig. 19-2B). By contrast with the chromosomal filaments, the continuous pole-to-pole filaments pass among the chromosomes without attaching; in HeLa cells these filaments sometimes

Fig. 19-3. Spindle microtubules in yeast prepared by freeze-etching; each tubule shows an oblique striation corresponding to a helical arrangement of protein monomers (arrow). The mitotic spindle in yeast develops inside the nuclear envelope (right). 99,000×. From Moor (1967).

extend directly *through* the chromosome arms. When the chromosome groups separate at anaphase, the continuous filaments are conspicuous in the interzonal region, where they eventually form the last connection between daughter cells at telophase. Most authors report that the diameters of the chromosomal and continuous filaments do not change noticeably during the chromosomal movements preceding metaphase or during anaphase.

Two centrioles oriented at right angles to each other are typically present at each pole in a dividing animal cell (Figs. 19-1 and 19-4). As described in Chapter 9, the centrioles are cylindrical bodies about 5000 Å long, 1500 Å in diameter and are composed of 9 tubular elements evenly spaced around the wall of the cylinder. Each of the 9 tubular elements, moreover, is actually triple in structure, being composed of three tubular subfibrils approximately 240 Å in diameter (Fig. 9-4E). The fine structure of the mitotic centrioles appears to be identical to that of the basal bodies (or kinetosomes) which give rise to

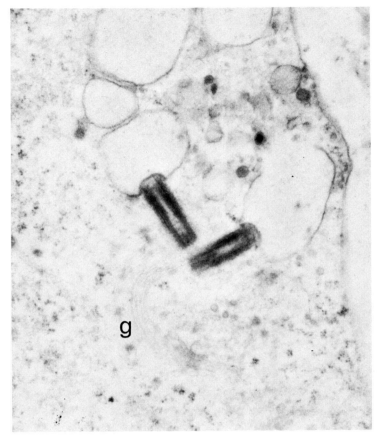

Fig. 19-4. A mother-daughter centriole pair, lying in typical positions at right angles to one another; Golgi membranes are also visible (g). 34,600×. From Friedländer and Wahrman (1966).

all functional cilia and flagella. In sea urchin embryos and other dividing cells, the spindle filaments converge toward the centrioles but apparently do not actually make contact with them. According to Harris (1961, 1965), the region around the centriole contains: (1) vacuole-like elements apparently derived from the endoplasmic reticulum; (2) radiating tubular "astral rays"; and (3) the termini of spindle filaments in folded or otherwise irregular configurations. The sum total of these structures make up the centrosphere (or aster), which increases progressively in volume during metaphase and anaphase. At late anaphase, some of the ER-like components from the asters accumulate around the chromosomes, eventually fusing to reconstitute a nuclear envelope. Observations very similar to these have been reported for human (HeLa) cells by Robbins and Gonatas (1964), who reported in addition a characteristic osmiophilic "cloud" surrounding each centriole. In plant cells studied by Porter and his collaborators, the spindle tubules converge toward the poles, but no centrioles are present; nevertheless, ER-like fragments accumulate around the poles at metaphase, and at late anaphase these migrate into the spindle among the chromosomes. Some of the fragments contribute to the developing nuclear envelopes, while others continue toward the mid-plate, where they apparently form part of the phragmoplast, which organizes a new transverse cell wall. Unusual centrioles are present in many protozoans; for example, in the flagellate *Barbulanympha* Cleveland (1963) has described the centrioles as including long polar appendages that grow up to 30 μ in length and 4–5 μ wide.

The confirmation by electron microscopy that spindle filaments from opposite poles really are attached to the kinetochores of sister chromatids (as postulated by some light microscopists and denied by others) now provides a fairly concrete framework for investigating the mechanisms of chromosomal movement during mitosis and meiosis. In addition, the discovery that these filaments are tubular elements oriented parallel to the direction of motion serves to place the mitotic movements in a class with various protoplasmic streaming phenomena, where similarly oriented cytoplasmic microtubules are prominently involved (Chapter 9). As in the other primitive types of motility, the exact mechanism of movement in mitosis is not yet adequately understood. Nevertheless, it seems increasingly clear that the tubular elements themselves are endowed with special properties which permit them to confer translational energies on much larger objects.

Chemistry of the Mitotic Apparatus

Earlier cytochemical investigations of the mitotic apparatus served to establish a fundamental involvement of protein sulfhydryl groups. There appears to be a complex equilibrium between soluble SH groups, soluble S—S, and protein SH, such that reciprocal shifts in concentration occur as the spindle is assembled in prophase and disassembled in anaphase. One of the first chemical studies was that of Rapkine (1931), who detected changes in the distribution of trichloroacetic acid-soluble sulfhydryl groups during mitosis. Although Rapkine attributed the soluble SH to glutathione, more refined procedures later indicated that a protein is responsible for sulfhydryl fluctuations (Sakai and Dan,

1959). Impressive cytochemical studies by Kawamura and Dan (1958) also demonstrated that protein SH is highly concentrated in the spindle until its disassembly. Stern's (1958) investigation of lily anthers further indicated that the soluble SH decreases during anaphase while soluble S—S increases. That SH hydrogen bonding and S—S covalent bonding play important roles in stabilizing the spindle is supported by the fact that the mitotic apparatus is preserved in dithiodiglycol, but is disorganized or dispersed by reagents that attack sulfur bonds (Zimmerman, 1963).

More recently the overall composition of the mitotic apparatus, including centrioles, astral rays, spindle, chromosomes, and ground plasm, has been analyzed in some detail by Mazia and his collaborators, who have developed techniques for isolating this structure in bulk from cleaving sea urchin eggs. In the earliest work, Mazia and Dan (1952) used 30% ethyl alcohol to stabilize the spindle, and detergent was employed to disrupt the cells; these harsh procedures led to some errors in estimates of spindle protein molecular weights. Subsequently however, Mazia's laboratory developed much more elegant isolation procedures, which employ dithiodiglycol to stabilize S—S bonds and which preserve some of the enzymatic activity of the spindle. They have established that the isolated mitotic apparatus is 90% protein (dry weight), and that it also contains 5–6% RNA together with polysaccharides and lipid; its water content is approximately the same as the surrounding cytoplasm.

One of the most remarkable discoveries to come out of this work is that the sea urchin mitotic apparatus is composed primarily of a single protein, which behaves as a homogeneous molecular species in the ultracentrifuge and during electrophoresis. Sakai (1966) has shown that this protein in its monomeric form sediments at 2.5 S, indicating a molecular weight of 34,700, and that each molecule possesses four SH groups. Upon oxidation the monomers react to form dimers held together by an S—S linkage (mol. wt. 68,700). Evidence has been presented by Kiefer *et al.* (1966) that the 2.5 S monomers correspond to the 33 Å subunits that are seen to compose the spindle microtubules. Amino acid analysis of the spindle proteins shows that they contain a preponderance of acid side chains, with an isoelectric point estimated at about pH 4.5 (Mazia, 1961); in fact, the amino acid composition is very similar to that of actin from mammalian muscle and also to the flagellar proteins of *Chlamydomonas*. According to Sakai (1966) the 3.5 S dimers contain 4.5% nucleotides, indicating that the RNA content of the mitotic apparatus is not entirely due to the presence of ribosomes (which can be seen among the spindle tubules in thin sections). A functional analysis of mitotic apparatus proteins is still in progress, but two preliminary facts have been established: (1) the isolated MA exhibits ATPase activity; and (2) the mitotic microtubule protein is capable of an electron transfer reaction with a contractile protein isolated from the egg cortex.

The Physiology of Cell Division

For the sake of precise analysis, the prophase to telophase events may be divided into the following separate processes: (1) assembly of the spindle–aster system; (2) engagement of sister chromatids to opposite poles of the spindle and movement of chromatid pairs to the metaphase plate; (3) anaphase separation of sister chromatids to opposite poles of the spindle; (4) elongation of the spindle, further separating the chromosome groups from one another; and (5) cytokinesis, involving formation and completion of the division furrow in animal cells or phragmoplast formation in plant cells.

ASSEMBLY OF THE SPINDLE–ASTER SYSTEM

In the normal physiology of mitosis, the assembly of the mitotic apparatus is clearly induced or controlled by the centrioles (except in higher plants). This fact was apparent to the classic light microscopists on descriptive grounds alone, since the "division" of the centriole and migration of daughter centrioles to opposite sides of the nucleus is typically the earliest event in a division cycle. As noted in Chapter 9, more precise investigations with the electron microscope have failed to confirm that centrioles divide, but such studies do indicate that a daughter centriole is usually assembled very close to a mother centriole, typically lying at right angles to it (Fig. 19-4). In nondividing cells a single mother-daughter pair is often found, which in light microscope preparations may appear as one granule; consequently, the process of centriole "division," as seen by light microscopy, is thought to involve separation of two pre-existing centrioles, followed by assembly of a new daughter for each original granule. A typical metaphase cell thus contains four centrioles, two at each pole (Harris, 1961; Robbins and Gonatas, 1964). According to Costello (1961) the presence of two centrioles at each pole of the spindle, and their orientation at right angles to one another, is visible with the *light* microscope in eggs of the acoel flatworm *Polychoerus*.

Direct confirmation for the presence of four functional centers at metaphase has been obtained in experiments by Mazia *et al.* (1960), following treatment of uncleaved sea urchin zygotes with mercaptoethanol. Cleavage is delayed by this reagent, but resumes when the mercaptoethanol is removed; if the block is maintained until control eggs are in their second division, then the experimental eggs on resuming mitosis form spindle figures with four poles, and the egg undergoes a direct division into four cells; at the next division, however, each of the four cells produces only a monopolar spindle, demonstrating that the formation of four poles at the first division is due to a *separation* of centers rather than a *duplication* of centers. The monopolar spindles are nonfunctional, but after an intervening interphase cycle the cells again enter prophase with normal bipolar spindles, indicating that a normal centriole duplication has occurred. By varying this experimental design, Mazia could investigate the time at which the centers normally are duplicated; he found that in sea urchin eggs this event occurs at late telophase or early interphase, making it the one step which precedes DNA synthesis in the next cycle of cell reproduction.

As seen in the light microscope, the migration of centrioles toward opposite sides of the nucleus is accompanied by the appearance of a fiberlike connective between the migrating granules. This connective is the first visible element of the spindle-to-be, and it is gradually joined by other fibrils to constitute a small primary spindle lying outside the nuclear envelope. In the flagellate *Barbulanympha* studied by Cleveland (1963) the nuclear envelope does not disintegrate during mitosis, and the extranuclear primary spindle with its pole-to-pole fibers remains distinct from the pole-to-chromosome fibers that later traverse the envelope. Influenced by these and other observations, Mazia (1961) has regarded the fully formed spindle as a compound structure which includes a primary or "central" spindle (composed of continuous fibers) together with a "chromosomal" spindle (composed of pole-to-kinetochore fibers). It has also been suggested that the growth of the central spindle per se may be responsible for "pushing" the two centrioles gradually apart. According to E. W. Taylor (1959), the velocity of this separation in newt fibroblasts is uniform in a given cell, varying between cells from 0.85 to 2.43 μ per minute, and the maximum distance attained by the centrioles is about 50 μ.

As noted in Chapter 9, there are good grounds for doubting the genetic continuity of the centrioles. During the growth of ciliate protozoans, new basal bodies seem to arise by a very rapid assembly process, rather than by division or budding. Furthermore the protozoan *Naegleria* evidently lacks centrioles during part of its life cycle, but develops two typical ones in conjunction with flagellar growth. The sea urchin egg is itself an excellent case in point, since Morgan (1896) discovered that artificial activation of the egg (parthenogenesis) results in formation of multiple "cytasters," including bipolar and multipolar spindles; these cytasters lack chromosomes but are nevertheless capable of center replication and division. Lorch *et al.* (1953) also showed that cytasters can develop in sea urchin blastomeres even after surgical removal of the normal mitotic apparatus, so that the appearance of multiple spindle centers in parthenogenetic eggs definitely implies a spontaneous or *de novo* origin. This conclusion has been hotly debated for some decades, and is still not settled (reviewed by Wilson, 1925; Mazia, 1961). The possibility has been suggested that the spontaneous asters may not contain true centrioles, but Dirksen has confirmed by electron micros-copy that they do. At present there is a distinct likelihood that these chromosome-less cytasters represent a spontaneous assembly of both centrioles and spindle tubules from precursor macromolecules stored in the egg plasm. Their close relationship to the normal spindle is shown by the fact that even a monopolar cytaster sometimes engages the egg chromosomes in a metaphase-like configuration (although no anaphase movement toward the single pole is observed to occur).

Went (1960) has confirmed by immunological techniques that the major protein components of the mitotic apparatus are present in un-fertilized sea urchin eggs, anticipating their assembly into a functional spindle. Rabbit antiserum was prepared against the *Strongylocentrotus* mitotic apparatus (isolated in bulk), and this antiserum was shown to react with extracts of the unfertilized eggs; the reciprocal experiment gave a positive cross-reaction between anti-egg serum and the isolated mitotic apparatus, and in fact no evidence could be found for any anti-gen in the mitotic apparatus which was not also present in the egg. These findings confirm the earlier inferences of Heilbrunn (1920), who ob-served that the viscosity of the cytoplasm outside the mitotic apparatus *decreases* as the spindle is assembled, increasing again when it is dis-assembled; thus he concluded that fibrous material for the spindle is recruited from the cytoplasm. It was suggested by Kawamura that the mitotic apparatus may be composed of SH proteins which are stored during interphase in the form of S—S proteins, and this possibility is supported by the properties of the microtubule monomer (Sakai, 1966). Gross and Cousineau (1963) also found that newly fertilized eggs of the sea urchin *Arbacia* incorporate leucine-^{3}H specifically into the mitotic apparatus, suggesting that some synthesis of spindle proteins occurs after fertilization.

ENGAGEMENT OF SISTER CHROMATIDS TO OPPOSITE POLES AND MOVEMENT TO THE METAPHASE PLATE

The events which lead to alignment of the chromosomes on the meta-phase plate are referred to as metakinesis, and insofar as they include an attachment of sister chromatids to opposite poles they are an essential prelude to the orderly separation of chromatids at anaphase. In purely descriptive terms, Harris (1965) has shown that at prophase, as soon as the nuclear envelope begins to disintegrate, the nucleus is rapidly invaded by the microtubules of the primary spindle; consequently pole-to-kinetochore attachments seem to be established *before* the chromosomes move to the metaphase plate. Similarly, a variety of experimental evidence shows that the kinetochores are involved in the metakinesis movements. Bajer and Molé-Bajer (1956) have plotted the paths of movement of the kinetochores and chromosome arms from time-lapse films; it appears that the kinetochores move to the metaphase plate in a much more direct manner than the arms. Also, as shown by Uretz *et al.* (1954), point UV irradiation of the kinetochore can inactivate the metakinesis movement of specific chromosomes in newt fibroblasts. Mazia and Zimmerman (1958) showed that treatment of the sea urchin mitotic apparatus with mercaptoethanol leads to a "relaxation" of the spindle which results in scattering of the metaphase chromosomes from their orderly configuration; after removal of the mercaptoethanol, the chromatid pairs are once more drawn back to the metaphase plate. These and other data clearly indicate that an attachment of spindle filaments to the appropriate kinetochores precedes and is essential to the alignment of the chromosomes on the metaphase plate.

The mechanism by which two sister kinetochores attach specifically to *opposite* poles has been investigated recently by Nicklas (1967). Using a micromanipulator he was able to detach meiotic bivalents from their metaphase plates, and discovered that such detached chromosomes can spontaneously reattach to the spindle. In more elaborate experiments he could turn the bivalents through 180° before allowing them to reattach; these experiments showed that the engagement of a particular kinetochore to a particular pole depends primarily on the position of the chromosome, i.e., the kinetochore attaches to that pole which is in its direct "line of sight" and not necessarily to the nearest pole. Consequently this study indicates that it is the normal structure of the chromatid pair itself, with sister kinetochores "facing" in opposite directions, (Fig. 18-3), which ensures engagement to opposite poles. Pease (1946) also disrupted the kinetochore-to-pole connections with high pressure and noted that the attachments sometimes re-form in anomalous ways, e.g., sister kinetochores engaged to the same pole or to each other.

It would appear that the alignment of chromosomes into a metaphase plate is a reflection of "equal action" by both poles on the respective members of each chromatid pair; thus even during unequal cell division, the chromatid pairs usually lie exactly midway between the two spindle poles (though the spindle itself may lie eccentrically in the cell). Further-more, in anomalous cases when the chromosomes come under the in-fluence of multipolar spindles, they tend to lie in positions equidistant from the various pairs of poles. The chromatid pairs also exhibit a considerable amount of "wandering" during metakinesis and metaphase, with occasional movements away from the metaphase plate toward one pole and back again (Bajer and Mole-Bajer, 1963). Various theories have postulated either that the chromosomes are pulled by the spindle filaments or else pushed by them; however, experiments by Takeda and Izutsu (1960) strongly indicate that the influence is a "pulling" action, which tends to move each chromatid toward the pole to which it is engaged. In their experiments, a UV microbeam was used to irradiate the kinetochore region of one chromatid but not its sister at metaphase; it was found that such irradiation results in a movement of the chroma-tid pair *toward* the pole to which the unirradiated chromatid is engaged. It would seem that the symmetrical positions and general behavior of chromatid pairs on the metaphase plate can largely be accounted for, provided that each chromatid is pulled with nearly equal force toward an opposite pole, and that sister chromatids remain physically attached to one another until the end of metaphase. Further investigation is necessary to determine how these conditions are created and controlled at a molecular level.

Once the chromatid pairs have lined up on the metaphase plate, there is usually a pause of very appreciable duration when little or no visible change is seen. Although no conspicuous morphological change occurs, it is certain that one or more events take place on a chemical level, since the duration of the metaphase pause becomes shorter as the temperature is increased. Many authors have suggested that this represents the time required to complete the separation of the chromatids, which until the end of metaphase remain physically bound together at their kineto-chore regions and sometimes along the arms. Although the separation of chromatids is nearly synchronous in all chromatid pairs, Upcott (1939) has reported asynchronous separations in tetraploid species of tulip.

To some extent a paradox is encountered in the behavior of the centromere at metaphase. In the era of light microscopy the centromere was assigned two separate functions which at the fine structural level are likely to be at least partly exclusive of one another. That is, insofar as the centromere is a site for spindle tubule attachments, it must be a double structure at metaphase (each sister chromatid has its own spindle attachment); on the other hand, insofar as the centromere is a site for holding together sister chromatids it behaves as a unit at metaphase. Electron micrographs by Harris (1965), Robbins and Gonatas (1964), and others clearly show that the spindle microtubules attach at two separate dense granules, one of which occurs in the centromere region of each sister chromatid (Figs. 18-3 and 19-1). At the same time, electron micrographs by DuPraw (1966a) indicate that human chromatid pairs are held together at metaphase by chromatin fibers in the centromere region; these fibers are identical in appearance and continuous with the chromatin fibers of the chromosome arms (Fig. 18-12B). In the folded-fiber model of chromosome structure, DuPraw has postulated that the centromere of the light microscopist includes two separate entities: (1) one or more unreplicated segments of chromatin fiber (i.e., DNA) which hold together the completely replicated parts of sister chromatids; and (2) a spindle attachment granule (or kinetochore), possibly consisting of an adhesive protein "coded" by the centromere chromatin (Chapter 18).

ANAPHASE: THE MOVEMENT OF CHROMOSOMES TO POLES, AND OF THE POLES AWAY FROM EACH OTHER

The anaphase separation of chromatids, when viewed *in vivo* or in time-lapse films, is surely one of the most exciting phenomena in all biology. This movement has been carefully analyzed in a number of species by different authors (reviewed by Mazia, 1961), and typically involves a highly direct translation of the kinetochores at almost uniform velocity toward their respective poles. The exact velocity of the movement differs somewhat in different cell types, but is in the order of 0.2–4 μ per minute (closely equivalent in magnitude to other linear tension movements, such as the movement of food granules in the arms of a suctorian; see Chapter 9). As noted by Nicklas (1965), the velocity of movement is independent of the masses of the individual chromosomes (another characteristic of linear tension movements); however, in grasshopper spermatocytes there is a tendency for the peripheral chromosomes to move about 25% faster than the central ones.

Bělař (1929) was the first to emphasize that the anaphase movement includes two distinct processes: first, a movement of the chromosomes toward their respective poles, during which the chromosomal fibers shorten to as little as one-fifth their metaphase lengths; and second, an elongation of the spindle during which the distance between the poles increases, thereby further drawing the two groups of chromosomes apart. In primary spermatocytes of the aphid *Tamalia,* only the spindle elongation occurs and the chromosomes do not approach their poles at all (Ris, 1943). On the other hand, spindle elongation itself is absent in newt fibroblasts, where E. W. Taylor found that the poles actually move closer together as the chromosomal fibers shorten. In grasshopper spermatocytes, Ris (1949) showed that exposure to chloral hydrate inhibits the spindle elongation but not the shortening of the chromosomal fibers. From these and similar experiments, it seems certain that two separate mechanisms are involved, which Mazia (1961) has suggested represent a pulling by the "chromosomal spindle" and a pushing by the "central spindle" (i.e., the pole-to-pole fibers). In typical cells there is a definite though overlapping sequence, beginning with the movement of chromosomes toward their poles, followed by movement of the poles away from one another, and completed by the appearance of a division furrow in animal cells or a phragmoplast in plants.

The movement of the chromosomes to their poles very clearly represents an oriented interaction between each kinetochore and the spindle pole to which it is engaged. The fact that the force responsible for moving the chromosomes is transmitted through the kinetochores has long been evident in the characteristic shapes and positions assumed by the chromosomes. For example the kinetochore almost always leads the chromosome arms, so that metacentric chromosomes form V shapes, submetacentrics form J's, and acrocentrics form rods. Furthermore in those genetic rearrangements which produce dicentric chromosomes, the two kinetochores of one chromatid often engage with opposite poles, stretching the chromosome body between them in a configuration known as an "anaphase bridge." In some cases the chromosome is actually broken by this "tug-of-war," whereas in other cases one kinetochore may prove stronger and draw the chromosome to its pole; frequently the spindle itself is bent or deformed by the unusual play of forces. Point UV irradiation of a kinetochore or of the spindle fibers near a kinetochore usually prevents the anaphase movement of the chromosome involved, showing that each chromosome is moved individually by its kinetochore. Generally speaking, the impression is one of simple mechanical action of the sort expected if the spindle fibers connecting each chromosome to its pole should simply contract, thereby drawing the chromosome and pole together. In fact, a contractile mechanism of anaphase movement was postulated as early as 1878 by Klein, but this class of hypothesis is almost certainly too simple. For one thing, it is well established that the spindle filaments do not become thicker as they shorten, but rather seem to melt into the centrosphere region. For another thing the extent of shortening, to one-fifth the original length, seems much too extreme to be accounted for by any elastic mechanism.

Östergren *et al.* (1960) have emphasized that the movements of the chromosomes to their poles during anaphase share the still-puzzling characteristics of many other linear tension movements (Chapter 9).

Bajer's (1967) elegant time-lapse films of mitosis in the plant *Haemanthus* show that many other objects besides kinetochores are commonly transported poleward by the spindle during prometaphase, metaphase, and anaphase. These objects include pieces of nucleoli, unidentified cytoplasmic granules, acentric chromosome fragments, and the long dangling arms of the metaphase chromosomes. Recently Forer (1965) has obtained direct experimental evidence that the spindle is a site of linear movement toward the poles whether or not the chromosomes themselves are free to move. A UV microbeam was used to create a small area of reduced birefringence on the spindle between the chromosomes and the poles; it was found that such "marked" areas immediately move at constant velocity toward the nearest pole, the rate being about the same as the movement of chromosomes during anaphase. Significantly, this movement in the spindle is observed both at metaphase, when the chromosomes remain in place, and at anaphase when the chromosomes move along with the marked spot. It would seem that the spindle has some of the aspects of an endless belt, which carries on a continuous movement at constant velocity and imparts movement to other objects when they engage the mechanism properly.

In accord with this endless belt analogy, there is a certain amount of evidence that the movement of the chromosomes from the mid-plate toward the poles is accompanied by a reciprocal movement of other materials from the poles toward the mid-plate. This was first noted in onion root tip cells by Porter and Machado (1960), who observed by electron microscopy that elements of the endoplasmic reticulum accumulate around the poles at metaphase, and that these elements enter the spindle at anaphase. The ER fragments seem to pass between the chromosomes, moving in the opposite direction, until eventually they reach the mid-plate, where they contribute to the development of the new transverse cell wall (phragmoplast). Mazia (1961) has also cited instances in which ribonucleoprotein seems to accumulate in the interzonal region (between the separating anaphase chromosomes) as the chromosomes approach the poles. It is not clear whether this RNA is derived from the chromosomes themselves or represents ribosomes previously trapped in the spindle (such ribosomes are usually conspicuous in thin sections of metaphase cells). In any case the chromosome-to-pole movement apparently requires the presence of at least two spindle centers since monopolar cytasters, though they may engage the chromosomes, do not transport them to the single pole.

With respect to spindle elongation, this component of the anaphase movement is quite distinct from the chromosome movement to the poles (since either one may occur without the other). In honey bee embryonic cells, the short thick metaphase spindle becomes rapidly long and narrow during anaphase, but interference microscopy indicates that this change does not involve an influx of water or other changes in mass concentration (DuPraw unpublished observation). Two major mechanisms have been proposed: in the first, the interzonal region is thought to undergo a general growth, possibly by recruitment of material from the spindle poles. Certainly the region between the separating anaphase chromosomes has a unique consistency since the matrix lacks birefringence, it is often a site of breakage to form two half-spindles during isolation of the mitotic apparatus, and it contains the region where the division furrow is completed or the mid-plate forms during cytokinesis. In the second hypothesis, emphasis is placed on the birefringent pole-to-pole filaments which still traverse the interzonal region until late telophase; these continuous filaments are postulated to grow in length, actively pushing the poles apart. An exciting approach to the problem was pioneered by Hoffmann-Berling (1954), who succeeded in inducing spindle elongation in anaphase fibroblasts that had been extracted in cold glycerol; such "glycerol models" are analogous to glycerol-extracted muscle fibers, which have the ability to contract on addition of ATP (Chapter 8). In Hoffmann-Berling's experiments ATP did not induce shortening of the chromosomal fibers, but spindle elongation did occur at high ATP concentrations, thereby causing the chromosomes to move apart; elongation was observed under conditions comparable to those that cause *relaxation* in muscle fibers, but the effect was apparently not ATP-specific.

CYTOKINESIS

By any strict definition, the process of cytokinesis must be considered the one *sine qua non* of cell division. Although it is true that the events of chromosomal replication and mitotic segregation generally precede cytokinesis, cells sometimes divide without benefit of mitosis. Many ciliates, for instance, undergo a rather haphazard distribution of nuclear material, while enjoying a very precise cell division (amitosis). In the case of multinucleate plasmodia (including the eggs of most insects), nuclear replication by mitosis can be an entirely separate process from cell replication by cytokinesis. Even in cells where cytoplasmic division is normally coordinated to a high degree with the anaphase movements of the chromosomes, it can often be demonstrated experimentally that cytokinesis proceeds very well without any chromosomes at all. However, relatively few laboratories have devoted serious effort to an analysis of cell division in its strict sense, while the mitotic events of chromosome replication and separation have generated an enormous literature.

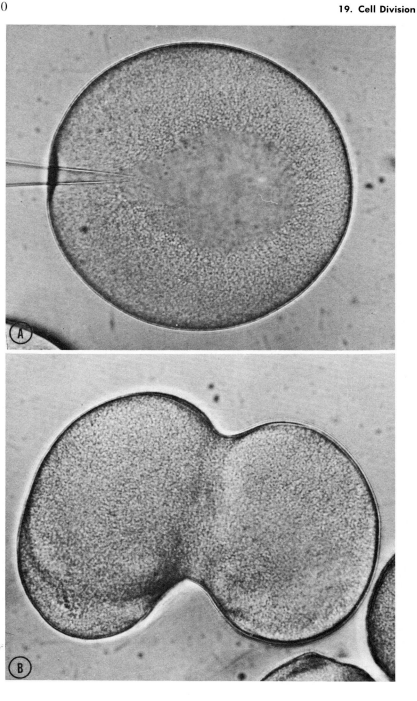

During a typical cell division, both the timing and orientation of cytokinesis are closely geared to the chromosomal movements; however, this adaptive coordination is not directed by the chromosomes themselves, as earlier cytologists suspected, but is mediated by the mitotic apparatus, which controls both the chromosomal movements and the position of the cleavage furrow (or mid-plate). That the chromosomes are unnecessary was first shown by E. B. Harvey (1936), who obtained enucleate fragments of sea urchin eggs by centrifugation; she observed that these fragments are able to carry out an impressive sequence of cleavages in the complete absence of any nuclear material, and in fact they often complete the normal cleavage pattern characteristic of the control (nucleated) eggs. A primary role for the spindle *centers* was later inferred by Roberts and Johnson (1956) from their study of multipolar spindles in beetle testes. They observed that a division furrow tends to form between each pair of centers, whether or not a spindle and chromosomes are present between them; thus if there are three centers and two spindles, the cell tends to divide into three rather than two. The close relationship between the spindle poles and the division furrow is most apparent in cells which divide unequally, such as oocytes and grasshopper neuroblasts, where the furrow appears between the poles even though both poles lie very far from the middle of the cell. Conklin (1917) showed that the relative size of the polar bodies produced in the oocyte divisions can be altered by stretching or displacing the spindle with centrifugal force. Moreover Kawamura (1960) was able to move the metaphase spindle to different positions with microneedles, permitting him to demonstrate that in grasshopper neuroblasts a division furrow can form at any place on the cell surface, but that its actual position is determined by the position of the spindle. Apparently the unequal division characteristic of insect neuroblasts is induced by an unequal growth of the asters, which causes the spindle to lie off-center in the cell.

This precise influence of the spindle centers on the position of the division furrow suggested to Dan (1943) and others that the centers might act to pull the cell surface down by means of the astral rays. However, Marsland (1951) and later investigators were led to an alternative concept, i.e., that the cell cortex itself is active, perhaps by forming a contractile ring in the furrow region. The latter concept is strongly supported by the demonstration that, after a given time point in ana-

---

Fig. 19-5. Cytokinesis in the absence of a mitotic apparatus. (A) Injection of sucrose solution dissolves the mitotic apparatus of a *Clypeaster* embryo just before first cleavage; (B) Cytokinesis proceeds despite the dissolution of the MA, and in a manner very suggestive of a contractile ring. 570×. From Hiramoto (1965).

phase, cytokinesis can begin and proceed to completion in the absence of the mitotic apparatus itself. For instance, Carlson (1952) showed that if the mid-anaphase spindle in a grasshopper neuroblast is pushed entirely to one end of the cell, the division furrow forms nevertheless in the original position of the spindle; if the spindle is displaced only slightly, however, then the furrow can be induced to shift (though not so freely as at metaphase). Later Hiramoto (1956) used a micropipette to remove the mitotic apparatus entirely from sea urchin eggs at different stages of mitosis; when the operation was performed before mid-anaphase no division occurred, but after mid-anaphase a normal cleavage furrow formed and divided the egg (Fig. 19-5). Various confirmatory experiments have also been carried out by dissolving the mitotic apparatus with colchicine or by displacing it with enormous droplets of oil or seawater just before cleavage (Hiramoto, 1965). It seems clear from these experiments that an active cell cortex is a reality, and that this activity is induced, or at least positioned, by some specific interaction between the spindle centers and the cell surface.

The "active cortex" may be described in operational terms as equivalent to a contractile ring, even though the mechanism may be dissimilar from muscle contraction. Wolpert (1960), for instance, has proposed an "astral relaxation" concept of cytokinesis, postulating that a reduction of surface tension at the poles could lead to *relatively* high surface tension in the furrow region, and that this surface tension differential might be sufficient to produce the observed indentation of the plasma membrane (division furrow). Reduction of surface tension at the poles is directly observable in many dividing cells as a peculiar bubbling or boiling effect at the polar surfaces during late anaphase and cytokinesis. On the other hand, a closer similarity between the division furrow and muscle contractility is supported by the experiments of Hoffman-Berling (1954, 1959) with glycerol-extracted fibroblasts; he found that in glycerol models of cells at early cytokinesis the division furrow is able to advance in the presence of ATP. By contrast with his "anaphase models," this reaction was observed only at specific ATP concentrations under conditions similar to those required for contraction of glycerol-extracted muscle fibers. Ohnishi (1962a) has also succeeded in isolating an actomyosin-like protein from the cortex and cytoplasm of sea urchin eggs; this protein is extractable in 0.6 M KCl, it shows a Mg^{++}-dependent ATPase activity, and it also responds to ATP with a reversible viscosity drop (all properties of actomyosin; see Chapter 8). More recently Sakai (1965) has reported that artificial fibers formed from the cortical contractile protein are able to shorten and elongate reversibly in an electron transfer reaction involving sulfhydryl groups. Mota (1959) actually photographed a bright, ring-shaped structure that occurs briefly in the cytoplasm of grasshopper spermatocytes when they fail to go through cytokinesis; this ring is visible by phase contrast *in vivo*, it constricts the mitochondrial mass at approximately the mid-plate position, and it is occasionally seen attached to an abortive division furrow at the cell surface.

With regard to the mechanism by which the spindle induces the division furrow to form at a specific position, there are as yet relatively few clues. A physical connection exists between the asters and the plasma membrane in *Crepidula* eggs (Conklin, 1917) and grasshopper neuroblasts (Carlson, 1952); furthermore, the middle of the spindle is attached to the division furrow at late anaphase in neuroblasts (Kawamura, 1960). Recently Sakai (1966) has demonstrated that the cortical contractile protein and the microtubule protein of the spindle are able to form complexes together *in vitro*, involving a reduction of the microtubule protein by the contractile protein and formation of an S—S bond.

In many types of dividing cell, there is evidence that cytokinesis includes a special mechanism that is necessary to complete the separation of sister cells *after* the contraction of the division furrow. For example, in grasshopper spermatocytes the mitochondria form long fibrous masses that lie parallel to the mitotic apparatus, and in telophase these seem to resist "pinching off"; sister spermatocytes are thus held together for a considerable time by the narrow residual neck (or *Zwischenkörper*). In HeLa cells, the telophase neck also persists for a time and contains intact pole-to-pole spindle filaments. Fawcett (1961) has shown by electron microscopy that thin telophase connections often persist between quartets of sister spermatids during the course of spermatogenesis in many mammals and during the differentiation of cnidoblasts in *Hydra*; such connections may be responsible for the notable synchrony of differentiation in these tissues. Presumably the complete separation of sister cells requires some synthesis of new cell membrane, which is analogous to the synthesis of a new transverse cell wall in plant cells. As summarized by Wolpert (1960), the first two blastomeres of the sea urchin egg possess about 28% more surface area than the original uncleaved egg (even though the volume remains constant through first cleavage). Dan and his students have carried out an elaborate analysis of the displacements of the surface membrane during cleavage, using the simple procedure of marking the egg surface with small particles, then tracking their movements during division (Fig. 19-6). These investigations have revealed that 80% of the new surface arises as an ex-

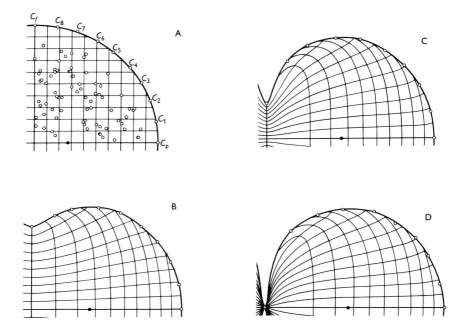

Fig. 19-6. Particles placed at specified positions on the surface of a *Clypeaster* egg before first cleavage can be tracked during the ensuing cytokinesis. By comparing C and D with A and B, it can be seen that the distance between particles increases most in the cleavage furrow itself; however the greatest increase in surface *area* occurs at the poles. From Hiramoto (1958).

pansion at the two poles, while some expansion also occurs in the furrow. The geometry of cleavage is such that there are two vertical contours (stationary rings) on either side of the cleavage furrow which do not change in diameter during division.

Attempts to detect changes in ultrastructure at the cell surface before and during cytokinesis have thus far provided little insight concerning the mechanism of furrowing (or of new membrane synthesis). Mercer and Wolpert (1958) were able to detect a fine, dense layer that appears under the plasma membrane during cleavage in sea urchin eggs; this layer was described as consisting of numerous fine tubules (apparently larger than cytoplasmic microtubules). On the other hand, in HeLa cells Robbins and Gonatas (1964) found only a generally increased cortical density or unstructured osmiophilia about 1000 Å thick, which underlies the plasma membrane at telophase. Mahowald (1963a) investigated the fine structure of superficial cleavage in *Drosophila* eggs, a process which involves the establishing of cell partitions simultaneously for about 4000 nuclei. In this system a flask-shaped furrow descends from the egg surface between each pair of nuclei, and adjacent furrows then fuse at their "deep" ends by lateral extension of the flasklike folds. The furrow is always lined by plasma membrane, beneath which visible filaments or vesicles about 500 Å in diameter occupy the cytoplasm at the growing end.

THE METABOLISM AND ENERGETICS OF DIVIDING CELLS

It appears that the time of cell division, at least in those cells which have been most carefully investigated, represents a metabolic low point in the overall cell cycle. For instance, Zeuthen found that no net increase in cell nitrogen occurs during the division of synchronized *Tetrahymena*, and in single protozoans the increase in respiratory enzymes shows a plateau at the time of division. Incorporation of isotopically labeled precursors into DNA, RNA and protein is also very generally reduced or nonexistent during mitosis in the tissue cells of macroorganisms. Mazia (1961) has likened the metabolic properties of cells in mitosis to those of enucleated cells, and indeed the consequences of mitosis may be even more drastic, since not only are the synthetic processes at a minimum but respiration itself is measurably reduced; possibly this effect reflects the specialized organization of the mitochondria at this time.

The general depression of metabolic activities during division suggests that the energy requirements for chromosomal movement and cyto-kinesis may be provided beforehand, and this concept has received a good deal of support from experiments with metabolic inhibitors and anoxia. It has often been observed that such respiratory poisons as car-bon monoxide, 2,4-dinitrophenol, cyanide or lack of oxygen are inef-fective in halting the mitotic process once it is underway; at the same time, they may delay the beginning of the next mitosis. Thus there seems to be a kind of "energy bank," in which the chemical energy necessary for a particular cell division is deposited before that division begins. This reservoir effect has made it difficult to identify the high energy compounds that are immediately involved in mitosis, or to establish the relative roles of respiration and glycolysis in supporting proliferation of cells. There also seem to be bewildering differences between similar cell types, such as frog eggs which divide under anaerobic conditions, and sea urchin eggs which do not. In pea root cells studied by Amoore (1961) an energy reservoir is apparently lacking, since absence of oxygen causes mitosis to stop at all stages. Such exceptional cases serve to con-firm that the processes of mitosis and cytokinesis do indeed require some continuous source of energy.

That the immediate source of energy may be ATP has been suggested by several investigations, including the glycerol model studies of anaphase and telophase fibroblasts by Hoffmann-Berling (1954). These cells, though extracted in cold glycerol, are still capable of responding to ATP by spindle elongation or equatorial contraction. Barnett (1953) also reported that addition of ATP permits mitosis to begin in cells previously inhibited with cyanide or anoxia. Refinement of techniques for isolating the mitotic apparatus in bulk from sea urchin eggs has permitted Mazia *et al.* (1961) to demonstrate that this structure possesses a very notable ATPase activity. Finally, Epel (1963) has demonstrated an admirable correlation between ATP levels and mitotic *rates* in sea urchin eggs. Using the firefly luciferin–luciferase assay for ATP, together with carbon monoxide as a respiratory inhibitor, Epel was able to show that a decline in ATP level during cleavage results in a slowing of mitosis, but does not halt division until ATP falls below 50% of the normal level. Once the ATP level declines sufficiently, however, mitosis stops regardless of stage; thus cells did not progress beyond early prophase, late prophase, metaphase, early anaphase, or late anaphase at low ATP levels.

The Initiation and Control of Cell Division

Before considering the initiation of cell division, it is well to recall the primitive role that division plays in the life cycle of such bacterial systems as *E. coli, Salmonella, B. subtilis* and similar microorganisms. In these simpler cells, reproduction is closely geared to the replication cycle of the single Watson-Crick DNA molecule that constitutes the species' nucleus-and-chromosome-in-one. Under optimum growth conditions the synthesis of DNA in these cells is virtually a continuous process, and two, four, or eight DNA replication cycles have significance only in terms of forming two, four, or eight individual cells. Synthesis leads naturally to division first at the DNA molecular level and then at the cell level; division itself is the built-in culmination of all those synthetic processes that *in toto* define the cell (and for that matter life).

In applying these concepts to eukaryotic cells, it must be recognized that a continuous synthesis of DNA with interspersed cell divisions is only rarely observed. Walker and Mitchison (1957), for instance, reported that DNA synthesis in the ciliate *Tetrahymena* is approximately linear during the 3–4 hours of the interphase growth period; however, in a closely-related ciliate (*Paramecium*), division is followed by a long period (G₁) during which no DNA synthesis occurs. It is the interpolation of such nonreplicative periods in higher cells that permits their specialization in processes such as embryonic differentiation, and it is likewise this phenomenon that raises the question of initiation and control in cell division. As pointed out by Mazia (1961), "control" of cell division means a slowing or blocking of a primitive life process, which in turn implies ultimate death for the cells concerned. These thoughts are in line with the fundamental insight of the great cytologist Weismann, who noted that only the germ cells of plants and animals have a future, while the somatic cells represent terminal specializations developed for the survival of the germ line; thus the famous aphorism, "A chicken is only an egg's way of making another egg."

In the cells of macroorganisms replication of a cell implies replication of many specialized structures other than the nucleus, e.g., mitochondria, chloroplasts, endoplasmic reticulum; the growth of these components may or may not exhibit a high degree of synchrony with nuclear replication. As a general rule, the S period (DNA synthesis) occupies only a fraction of interphase; the onset of cell division thus represents a symphonic culmination of many diverse growth processes, including the synthesis of molecules required for the mitotic apparatus and the high energy compounds required for chromosomal movement. We know that these growth processes are coordinated by intra- and intercellular feedback mechanisms of wonderful sensitivity. Even in so simple an organism as *Amoeba*, Prescott (1956) observed that division ensues only when the cell mass has exactly doubled, and division can be prevented indefinitely simply by cutting off pseudopods or bits of cytoplasm from time to time.

This adaptive coordination between cytoplasmic growth and nuclear replication has important implications for the control of cell division, i.e., mitosis under one set of conditions may appear to be under nuclear "control," but under other conditions can appear to be under cytoplasmic control. It is not uncommon to observe, for instance, that several nuclei in a common cytoplasm are "induced" to divide with perfect synchrony, yet this phenomenon means nothing more than that some necessary cytoplasmic event is rate limiting (Mazia, 1961). Similarly in nucleocytoplasmic hybrids produced by fertilizing egg fragments of one species with sperm of another, or by transplanting nuclei from embryos of one species to eggs of another, it is a rule that the rate of division is determined by the cytoplasmic parent; in all probability, however, this relationship reflects the fact that the mitotic apparatus itself is largely assembled from molecules already present in the cytoplasm of the unfertilized egg. Despite these and many other examples of cytoplasmic "control," an inhibition of nuclear DNA synthesis by appropriate metabolic blocks invariably prevents mitosis.

It seems clear that any natural or artificial impediment to the essential growth processes of the cell must be reflected in a slowing, stopping, or alteration in the apparent control of cell division; this principle has been supported by a wide range of observations. An excellent example is the transition in embryonic development from rapid, synchronous divisions during egg cleavage to slower, nonsynchronous divisions later on. Agrell (1964) has found that in the embryos of *Paracentrotus* and *Echinus* this transition corresponds to the time when the nuclei must initiate a *net* synthesis of DNA, i.e., when the stored cytoplasmic DNA has been exhausted. The same principle is evident in the effect of UV irradiation on the nucleolus in grasshopper neuroblasts, which Gaulden and Perry (1958) found would block mitosis if irradiation occurred between late telophase and mid-prophase. This experiment is readily understood in terms of nucleolar function in the synthesis of cytoplasmic ribosomes, an essential prerequisite for protein synthesis and interphase growth. Still another expression of this principle is the discovery that the mitotic index in many tissues exhibits one or more diurnal peaks, very likely reflecting daily fluctuations in energy metabolism (especially in plants).

In addition to these more generalized influences on cell division, it is clear that macroorganisms have developed a number of highly specific control devices, which are precisely directed toward preventing or enhancing the completion of mitotic replication in different tissues. The most patent control system of this type can be found in many metazoan eggs, which often await fertilization for days or weeks in an arrested metaphase or anaphase condition. Other more subtle but nonetheless specific control mechanisms certainly operate in somatic tissues, where long-term viability depends on a phenomenon Mazia has called "mitotic discipline." Even minor lapses or escapes from mitotic discipline can result in lethal disturbances in the proportions and interactions of tissue cells (i.e., cancer).

It would appear that one of the most frequent devices for preventing or controlling cell proliferation in somatic tissues involves partial or complete blockage of DNA replication. Thus the average DNA content per nucleus in many organs is close to the diploid DNA amount, indicating that no synthesis has occurred after the last division of each cell. In the naturally synchronized microspores of *Lilium*, Hotta and Stern (1963) have demonstrated that synthesis of the enzyme, thymidine kinase, appears to act as a "trigger" for initiating DNA synthesis. Their studies showed that thymidine kinase appears in these cells during a relatively brief part of interphase (amounting to a "pulse" of enzyme activity), and that its appearance can be prevented by inhibitors of RNA or protein synthesis; furthermore, elimination of thymidine kinase synthesis prevents both DNA synthesis and the subsequent nuclear divisions. It has been emphasized by Mazia and Hinegardner (1963) that a lack of DNA synthesis may reflect either an absence of necessary enzyme systems (including DNA polymerase) or some hindrance in the competence of the DNA to act as a template. Mazia was able to test these two alternatives in early sea urchin embryos by adding exogenous DNA to nuclei isolated at different developmental stages, after which the resulting DNA synthesis was monitored through incorporation of labeled precursors. During the earliest cleavage stages, when replication occurs every 2 hours, he found that the embryos contain a large overabundance of DNA polymerase activity, so that the addition of exogenous template DNA can stimulate synthesis by a factor of 10 times or more. On the other hand the rate of cell division slows down in older embryos, and at these stages Mazia found that the nuclei do not respond so markedly to added template DNA. The results indicate that the activity of DNA polymerase in a nucleus is a variably quantity, which can be rate limiting at one stage but not another. Artificially induced tetraploid cells were also found to exhibit twice the polymerase activity of diploids at the same stage, suggesting that the enzyme may actually constitute part of the DNA-linked chromosomal proteins.

The block in DNA synthesis and mitosis which usually characterizes tissue cells can frequently be reversed, especially under conditions of *in vitro* cell culture, when rapid proliferation is often observed. By this means, tissue culture cells can assume an "immortality" that is denied them in their normal somatic relationships. Carrel, for instance, maintained a line of chick heart cells for 33 years with no indication that the cultures could not go on indefinitely. A similar unblocking of DNA synthesis plays an important role in wound healing, as shown by the interesting experiments of Srinivasan (1964). In his technique a circular wound was caused by inserting a needle into the lens of a rabbit's eye; the circle of lens epithelium cells next to the wound then responded by initiating DNA synthesis within 12–14 hours and mitosis in about 24 hours. Interestingly, the stimulus to initiate DNA synthesis and mitosis travels out to more remote cells as a concentric "wave" with a velocity of about 17 μ per hour. In these and many other examples it appears that each cell is able to make a decision as to whether it will or will not replicate its DNA; depending on how the "switch" is thrown, the cell eventually enters mitosis or else commits its metabolic resources to some form of differentiation. In determining how the DNA synthesis switch will be set, there is increasing evidence that cell-to-cell contact plays a significant role. For example, Abbott and Holtzer (1966) have found that chondrocytes cultured *in vitro* can alternate between two distinct functional states—a stellate form that incorporates thymidine-^{3}H for DNA replication and a rounded form that incorporates ^{35}S for synthesis of cartilage; the cartilage-synthesizing state seems to be correlated with the "grouping" of cells in direct physical contact. Many other experiments are available to show that adherence between cells can inhibit mitotic replication.

It has been pointed out that, although the DNA content of a nucleus may double by mid-interphase, yet the growth rate supported by this nucleus does not double until the mitotic separation of chromosomes into two cells (or at least into two nuclei). This phenomenon seems to reflect a multitude of control steps that intervene in the relationship between a nucleus and its cytoplasm, e.g., the rate of ribosome synthesis, variations in the stability of messenger RNA's, passage of materials across the nuclear envelope, specific genetic regulatory mechanisms, interphase chromatin condensation, and so on. Although the details of such interactions are only poorly known, there are indications that they involve fundamental quantitative or semiquantitative restrictions. Thus Boveri noted long ago that some tissues maintain a strict ratio between nuclear and cytoplasmic volumes, and between the degree of ploidy and the size of the cell. More recently Commoner (1964) has pointed out that a linear proportionality between DNA content and cell mass is expected because the DNA mass itself represents a major investment in cellular metabolism by its demands on the nucleotide precursor pool and on oxidative phosphorylation; in fact, data are available to suggest that cells containing larger amounts of DNA tend to have higher total masses. This principle helps to account for the renewal of growth after nuclear replication, and also for certain lapses in the integration between DNA replication and cell division. Repeated replication of DNA in the absence of mitotic division, for example, leads either to endopolyploidy or to polyteny (as in dipteran giant chromosomes); such phenomena seem to meet a physiological requirement for larger cells with higher DNA content in the tissues concerned. The inverse effect, mitotic division without DNA replication, also occurs sometimes in polyploid and diploid cells, reconstituting a condition of somatic haploidy through "somatic reduction" (Blakely and Steward, 1961; Simantel *et al.*, 1962). It appears that, physiologically speaking, two sets of chromosomes in one nucleus are not equivalent to two sets of chromosomes in two nuclei.

Since DNA replication does not guarantee cell division, it seems evident that additional preparations must occur in the period between the end of DNA synthesis and the beginning of prophase (G_2). The completion of these preparations may be regarded as a kind of trigger for initiating division, although the actual events may represent nothing more exotic than the synthesis of components for the mitotic apparatus or for the specialized cortical functions in cytokinesis. In the ciliate *Stentor,* Weisz (1956) has provided direct experimental evidence that diffusible materials accumulate during interphase which are capable of initiating cell division. In his experiments, a small *Stentor* which had just completed fission was grafted to a larger *Stentor* soon to begin division; by virtue of the parabiotic association, fission was induced prematurely in the postdivision animal. Whatever the nature of the active agent (or state), it was shown that it disappears at the time of division. Diffusible agents capable of inducing mitosis also occur in rats during liver regeneration, since a parabiotic association between a normal rat and a rat with a regenerating liver leads to mitotic activity in the undamaged liver.

Potentially the most elegant method for analyzing the normal sequence of premitotic events depends on natural or experimental synchronization of all the cells in a mass culture (Zeuthen, 1964). This has been achieved experimentally with varying success for bacteria, protozoans, algae, yeast, and higher cells in tissue culture. Scherbaum and Zeuthen (1954) pioneered a method for synchronizing mitosis in mass cultures of *Tetrahymena* by repeated 30-minute cycles of alternate heat shock and normal temperature; this treatment has the effect of preventing division but not growth, and leads to the formation of large cells with high DNA content. Eighty minutes after the reestablishing of normal temperature, about 85% of the cells enter division together, and several more division cycles occur at 100-minute intervals. Since no increase in cell nitrogen occurs during the division period, the synchronization technique effectively disengages the processes of growth from those of cell division. Very similar effects have been induced by Tamiya (1964) in cultures of the green alga *Chlorella* by varying the incident light. The naturally synchronized microsporocyte divisions in lily and *Trillium* anthers have also been chemically investigated by H. Stern and his collaborators (1966).

Although the technique is promising, clear insights regarding the mechanisms of cell division have been slow to develop from artificial synchronization studies. In part the difficulty revolves around the peculiarities of fission in the more successfully synchronized organisms, such as *Tetrahymena*. It appears that these organisms complete most of the necessary steps for division during the heat shock treatment, including DNA replication and a doubling in the number of kinetosomes; however, some step necessary for the organization of the kinetosomes into a second functional mouth region is prevented or reversed by sublethal temperatures. There is evidence that this step involves the synthesis of one or more specific proteins (Zeuthen, 1964). Several synchronized cell systems have also provided confirmatory evidence for the importance of sulfur and sulfhydryl compounds in the fission process. In artificially synchronized *Chlorella*, Hase *et al.* (1959) detected an unusual, sulfur-containing peptide-nucleotide complex which increased in amount prior to division; recent work indicates that the nucleotide element is RNA-like and that most of the sulfur is in cysteine. Tamiya (1964) has also reported a sulfur-containing *DNA* fraction that seems to be associated with cell division in *Chlorella*. In addition, James (1964) has reported that addition of the sulfhydryl amino acids (cysteine and methionine) to synchronized cultures of the flagellate *Astasia* has the effect of reducing fission time and improving the synchronization. Autoradiographs of these cells show that they incorporate radioactive ^{35}S specifically near the anterior end, where longitudinal fission is initiated. All these findings are in accord with the general concept that the assembly and operation of the mitotic apparatus are heavily dependent on sulfhydryl and disulfide bonds; nevertheless, many more details remain to be elucidated.

Plainly, the deciphering of natural mitotic control mechanisms is an intricate undertaking, if for no other reason than that mitotic "control" can be simulated artificially by so many inhibitory agents. Although a variety of specific compounds are known which have the effect of initiating or enhancing cell division, it is uncertain to what extent they represent merely the inhibitors of inhibitors. The plant hormones gibberellin, kinetin, and indoleacetic acid, for instance, are able to induce cell division in various differentiated plant tissues (e.g., tobacco pith); the androgens and estrogens secreted by mammalian gonads also have mitogenic effects, which are more marked in some tissues than in others. In cultures of mammalian peripheral leukocytes, mitosis is commonly induced by the addition of phytohemagglutinin, a plant product. For the most part, the mode of action of these agents is still under investigation.

20

EGGS AND EMBRYOS AS CELL SYSTEMS

That a single cell can carry the total heritage of the complex adult, that it can in the course of a few days or weeks give rise to a mollusc or a man, is one of the great marvels of nature.

E. B. WILSON *1925*

Repeatedly in preceding chapters the discussions have been forced to stop at the fringes of available knowledge, leaving many a crucial question unanswered pending the publication of new observations and new interpretations. This awareness of unresolved ignorance is necessarily compounded in considering the problems of developmental biology, for in the embryo are encountered all the persistent problems of cell structure and function, magnified and illuminated by second-order phenomena such as cell differentiation and cell-to-cell recognition. If there is still uncertainty about the molecular architecture of a mitochondrion, how much more uncertainty must there be about the principles that dictate variations in mitochondrial structure from one tissue to another? If we do not entirely understand the mechanisms that impose specificity on cell membranes, how is it possible to understand the ability of cells to recognize and respond specifically to one another? Despite such compounding of difficulties, it is clear that the new concepts of molecular biology are successfully creating fresh insights for developmental biologists, and that the same flame of discovery that has illuminated the sciences of cell structure and function is spreading to the science of development.

In considering the special phenomena exhibited by cells in embryos, one encounters three characteristic processes: first, the origin of many cells from one cell with little or no increase in total mass (cleavage); next, the differentiation of sister cells in strikingly different ways, giving origin to such diverse cell types as muscle, nerve, spermatozoa, etc.; and third, the selective migration of specific cell types, establishing new cell positions and new tissue relationships in the developing organism. Application of molecular principles to these phenomena has led to several new categories of data, which must now be regarded as legitimate sub-areas of molecular biology. These include: the phenomena of genetic regulation, inescapably bound up with the differential capacities of various tissues to synthesize different proteins; the specific influences of one cell on another, as represented both in induction phenomena and in the capacity of cells to recognize and selectively adhere to one another; and finally, the ultimate question of biological reproduction—whether DNA nucleotide sequences in themselves contain all the information necessary to specify an organism?

Genetic Regulatory Mechanisms

The importance of differential protein synthesis for morphogenetic phenomena is one of the more obvious and long-standing principles of developmental biology. It requires an unusual synthesis of hemoglobin to make an erythrocyte, or an extraordinary amount of actomyosin to make a muscle fiber; numerous other, less conspicuous examples are known, including many types of specific enzyme synthesis. One of the major contributions of molecular biology in the last decade has been to establish that the specificity of proteins such as hemoglobin resides in the genes, that the genes are segments of Watson-Crick DNA molecules, and that one way to account for a cell that makes hemoglobin but not actomyosin is to suppose that its hemoglobin genes are turned on while its actomyosin genes are turned off. Furthermore, the switching mechanism for turning genes on and off can be visualized as a local activation or inhibition of the RNA polymerase reaction (i.e., genetic transcription)—a mechanism that is amenable to analysis in cell-free systems (Chapter 13).

The first instance in which differential genetic activity could be demonstrated directly was provided by the "puffs" of dipteran giant polytene chromosomes. These chromosomes, which occur in several different organs, exhibit a specific pattern of visible chromomere-like banding that is closely correlated with the linear positions of the genes (Chapter 18). Individual bands have the capacity to initiate activity, including the synthesis of RNA and the accumulation of proteins, which transforms the band into a visibly swollen or "puffed" condition. It was shown by Beermann (1956) that in different tissues of the same larva at any one time, different sets of bands become puffed; this effect is so reproducible that a tissue may be identified by the pattern of its "active" chromosomal sites. Careful cytochemical analysis of the puffing phenomenon by Rudkin and Woods (1959), Swift (1962), Edström and Beermann (1962) and others has shown that little change occurs in the amounts of DNA or histone, but that specific RNA's and nonhistone proteins accumulate markedly. Not only is the base ratio of the RNA specific and asymmetrical, as would be expected of messenger RNA, but in at least one case Beermann (1961) has been able to correlate the appearance of a specific puff with a Mendelian factor responsible for production of salivary granules (Chapter 18).

Artificial induction of specific puffs was first achieved by Clever and Karlson (1960), who discovered that larvae injected with insect prothoracic gland hormone (ecdysone) develop two new puffs within a matter of hours. Changes in puffing pattern were also obtained by Kroeger (1960) after transferring salivary gland nuclei into fresh egg cytoplasm, by Hadorn et al. (1963) after implanting whole larval salivary glands into adult female fruit flies, and by Ritossa and Von Borstel (1964) after RNase digestion. These experiments serve to establish that genetic activity in the polytene chromosomes is very sensitive to the nuclear environment, but they have not clarified why a given set of conditions activates some genes and not others. Clever (1964), for instance, has found that the two ecdysone-activated puffs differ in their responses to different hormone concentrations and in the duration of puff activity until spontaneous regression occurs. These response properties would seem to be inherent in the macromolecular organization of the chromatin.

An important clue to the nature of genetic control in higher organisms lies in the phenomenon of chromatin condensation. It has long been known that entire chromosomes or chromosome segments which remain condensed during interphase contain very few or no active loci. Such "heterochromatic" regions were originally considered to be a special type of chromatin, but electron microscopy has established that they are composed of chromatin fibers identical in appearance to "euchromatic" regions; the only obvious difference is that heterochromatic fibers are tightly folded up during interphase. In a number of instances, there is also evidence that euchromatin can undergo a transition to form heterochromatin, or vice versa; in mammals, for example, one of the two X chromosomes in the female regularly becomes heterochromatic while the other remains euchromatic. If the two X's differ in genetic composition, the female tends to show a mosaic phenotype, indicating that the heterochromatic X is genetically inactive, and that in different cells the heterochromatic member of the two X chromosomes is not the same one (Grumbach et al., 1963). Thus heterochromatin may be regarded as a state of chromatin in which tight folding is correlated with relative genetic inactivity, rather than as a special kind of chromatin. This insight is immediately supported by many other instances in which condensation, or tight folding of chromatin, is related to a reversible loss of synthetic activity. The most obvious example is the metaphase condensation of all chromosomes, which has effects likened by Mazia (1961) to enucleation. Konrad (1963) has shown that RNA synthesis drops precipitously during mitotic prophase, and protein synthesis is also greatly reduced during metaphase and anaphase. In the dipteran giant chromosomes, as well, the chromomere bands represent synthetically inactive regions where the chromatin is tightly folded (DuPraw and Rae, 1966); these become active only *after* a conspicuous unfolding or fraying of strands to form a puff (Berendes, 1967). Finally, in amphibian oocyte lampbrush chromosomes, Gall (1963a) and Callan (1963) have found evidence that the synthesis of RNA depends on a "spinning out" of DNA from a tightly folded chromomere into an extended lateral loop (Chapter 18). At present it is not entirely clear whether folding per se is responsible for chromatin repression, or whether folding is simply the normal accompaniment of more fundamental inhibitory events at the molecular level.

In investigating these questions, by far the greatest attention has been given the histone proteins, since these basic molecules are normally linked quantitatively to DNA in the cell nucleus (Chapters 12 and 17). X-ray diffraction and other physical analyses support the idea that an association of histones with DNA induces some form of folding and/or supercoiling in the DNA filaments (Chapter 12); in support of this concept, Allfrey and Mirsky (1964) have found that addition of arginine-rich histones to lampbrush chromosomes induces retraction of the DNA loops. At the same time, a number of laboratories have found that histones exert strong inhibitory effects on the RNA polymerase reaction (i.e., genetic transcription), largely through their capacity to complex with the template DNA. Some experiments of this type are open to the criticism that histones simply precipitate template DNA from solution; however Hurwitz *et al.* (1963) have shown that partial histone inhibition can alter the nearest-neighbor frequencies of messenger RNA transcribed, indicating some specificity in the mode of histone action (Chapter 13). Bonner (1965) also cites evidence that the different types of histone are not randomly associated with different DNA molecules in the native state, but that specific histones complex with specific DNA's. Thus electrophoresis of native nucleohistone leads to separation of many molecular species, each characterized by a slightly different charge, whereas electrophoresis of artificial nucleohistone (reconstituted by precipitation from a soluble histone mixture) gives but a single band. An attractive hypothesis is that chromatid condensation and genetic repression are both functions of specific linkages between histone fractions and DNA.

This hypothesis in its most elaborate form proposed that there might be a separate type of histone for every gene, and that each histone would be able to seek out its gene in the interphase nucleus, complex with it, and thereby turn it off. Unfortunately, attempts to demonstrate a large number of distinct histone species have been uniformly unsuccessful; it appears that a given nucleus contains no more than 20 to 50 different kinds of histone molecule, far too few to provide a specific molecule for each gene. Nevertheless, alternative possibilities exist and are under active investigation. For instance, Bonner *et al.* (1968) have isolated an unusual histone–RNA complex from pea seedling nuclei, which has led them to suggest that a combination of gene-specific RNA's with less specific histones might provide the diversity necessary for individual genetic control. A more likely alternative is based on the fact that, in any one cell, the great majority of the chromatin seems to be genetically inactive; thus Allfrey and Mirsky (1962) discovered that 80% of the DNA in isolated calf thymus nuclei could be removed with DNase without reducing the rate of messenger RNA synthesis. This fact suggests a model of genetic regulation in which most of the DNA is repressed by nonspecific linkages with histone, whereas a few genes are "activated" by some highly specific mechanism. Frenster (1965b) has detailed a model of this kind, in which intranuclear polyanions would complex with one strand of a DNA double helix, forcing histones off and permitting RNA polymerase to "read" the other strand; this model is supported by direct chemical comparison of repressed and active chromatin isolated in bulk from calf thymus nuclei, which shows that active chromatin is significantly richer in polyanions such as nonhistone proteins, RNA, phospholipid, and phosphoprotein. In an alternative hypothesis, Allfrey *et al.* (1964) have proposed that specific derepression of histone inhibition may be achieved by local acetylation of histones, enzymatically catalyzed by histone acetylases. They have reported direct evidence that acetylation reduces or eliminates histone inhibition of RNA polymerase reactions *in vitro.* A third concept has been advanced by DuPraw (1965a), who postulates that the histones may act as structural proteins to hold functional molecules such as RNA polymerase in a sheathlike array on the DNA filaments (Chapter 17); the position of the RNA polymerase itself would then determine which segments of DNA would be transcribed and which would not. This concept is consistent with the structure of individual chromatin filaments, as seen by electron microscopy (Fig. 17-5). However, the abundance of hypotheses in this area attests to the need for more hard information.

That genetic controls do operate *in vivo* through the interaction of DNA-linked proteins with DNA has been directly demonstrated by Bonner *et al.* (1963). They showed that native chromatin isolated from pea cotyledon nuclei will direct the *in vitro* synthesis of pea seed reserve globulin, a protein that normally constitutes about 4–10% of the total cotyledon protein. This effect is specific, since chromatin isolated in the same way from another pea tissue (apical bud) is inactive as a template for reserve globulin. After deproteinization, however, pure DNA's from both tissues (cotyledon and bud) are equally active as globulin templates. This elegant experiment serves to confirm that all tissues contain the same set of DNA "information," but that different parts of the genome are made unavailable in particular tissues by their specific associations with nuclear proteins. Whether the most significant nuclear proteins in this respect are the histones or the nonhistone DNA-linked proteins remains to be determined. Mirsky and Ris (1951) found notable inter-tissue differences in the nonhistone fraction, by contrast with a number of biochemical analyses that have revealed a remarkable lack of difference between tissues in their histone fractions (Chapter 12). On the other hand, cytochemical techniques by Bloch and Hew (1960a,b) have revealed significant alterations in the properties of histones during spermatogenesis and early cleavage in the snail *Helix;* Das *et al.* (1964) also detected histone transitions during early embryonic development in *Drosophila,* while Gifford and Tepper (1962) have reported histone changes during flowering in higher plants. This area of investigation is likely to become increasingly important for future concepts of genetic control.

In addition to genetic regulatory mechanisms that depend on DNA-protein linkages, evidence exists for another type of regulation that may be inherent in the genome itself. This type of control first received attention in bacteria such as *E. coli,* which have the capacity to produce an appropriate "adaptive enzyme" in response to specific substrates in the environment. For example, an *E. coli* culture which exhibits very little β-galactosidase activity when grown on glucose is able to synthesize β-galactosidase specifically when grown on lactose. A wide range of experiments indicate that lactose has the effect of inducing messenger RNA transcription from the gene responsible for β-galactosidase primary structure; this new messenger RNA then enters the cytoplasmic ribosome system where the enzyme itself is synthesized, and in the final step the enzyme catalyzes the hydrolysis of the lactose substrate. The induction effect is not absolutely specific, since a number of lactose analogs can also cause β-galactosidase synthesis, including some which are not susceptible to digestion by the enzyme. Jacob and Monod (1961) analyzed the adaptive enzyme effect in a series of brilliant experiments, which revealed the existence of a new functional genetic unit termed the "operon." An operon includes: (1) one or more structural genes which code for protein amino acid sequences; (2) an "operator" DNA segment which serves as an on-off switch for the structural genes; and (3) a regulator gene, the product of which keeps the operator turned off. In this model, the key event for enzyme induction is an interaction between the substrate molecule and the product of the regulator gene, such that the regulator product is removed from the system, permitting the operator to turn on transcription of the structural genes for enzyme synthesis (Fig. 15-4). In bacteria, there is now very impressive evidence that the operon type of genetic regulation is a reality; in fact, a protein which exhibits all the expected properties of the repressor for the β-galactosidase operon has recently been isolated by Gilbert and Müller-Hill (1966).

The success of the operon concept in bacterial genetics inspired the suggestion that similar controls might exist in the embryonic cells of macroorganisms. In fact, adaptive enzyme formation has actually been demonstrated in a few instances; for example, Knox (1956) discovered that tryptophan induces an increase in the tryptophan pyrrolase activity of (adult) mammalian liver, and Rizki and Rizki (1963) confirmed this effect for some larval tissues of *Drosophila*. Greengard *et al.* (1963) have now shown that the adaptive increase in tryptophan pyrrolase activity is inhibited by puromycin (which blocks protein synthesis) and by actinomycin (blocking mRNA synthesis); it seems clear, therefore, that the inducer produces its effect by turning on transcription of a structural gene for tryptophan pyrrolase. Cahn (1964) has also discovered adaptive changes in lactic dehydrogenase "isozyme" synthesis in response to alterations in O_2 tension in chick tissues, and according to Kato (1959), alkaline phosphatase activity increases in chick embryos as a response to injected phenyl phosphate. In plant embryos, Amherst has also reported that growth on a nitrate medium leads to the appearance of nitrate reductase activity, whereas this does not occur if the plants are grown on an ammonium nitrogen source. Although it seems likely that a type of operon control operates in these cases, it is still uncertain that adaptive enzyme synthesis has broad significance for cell differentiation as such. Unlike bacterial enzyme induction, the differentiation of a muscle fiber or a neuron is a relatively irreversible process; transplantation of whole nuclei from advanced embryonic tissues into unfertilized eggs also provides evidence that the nuclei sometimes maintain remarkably stable changes during embryonic differentiation (Briggs and King, 1959; Gurdon, 1964). It has been pointed out that special types of operon "circuit" could lead to highly stable genetic activation, e.g., if the product of one operon "A" should act as an inducer for another operon "B", while the product of B induces A; in that case, both units would be permanently turned on. However, it seems unlikely that this type of control could survive the isolation of the chromatin for *in vitro* RNA synthesis, as in the experiments of Bonner *et al.* (1963). Furthermore, attempts to induce differentiation in tissue cultures by providing likely precursor molecules (e.g., di-iodotyrosine for thyroid differentiation) have generally been unsuccessful. These facts are somewhat easier to understand if genetic regulation in higher organisms is mediated primarily by stable DNA-protein associations.

Whatever the mechanism of gene inhibition, it appears that this repression can often be reversed for specific genes by the action of relatively unspecific hormones. Bonner (1965) has assembled a large number of examples in which both plant and animal hormones are known to induce a tissue-specific increase in RNA synthesis, followed by more prolonged increases in the synthesis of specific enzymes. In many cases, there is direct evidence from actinomycin-sensitivity, sedimentation analysis, or cell free synthesis that the induced RNA is actually a messenger RNA for the enzymes concerned. One example that has been thoroughly analyzed by Greengard *et al.* (1963) is the effect of cortisone on mammalian liver, which leads to an increase in RNA synthesis within 1 hour, increased protein synthesis within 2 hours, and a long-term increase in the activities of tryptophan pyrrolase, two transaminases, glucose-6-phosphatase, fructose diphosphate phosphatase and aldolase. Other substances which act in a similar way are the mammalian hormones estrogen, testosterone, insulin, ACTH, thyroxine and "growth hormone"; the insect hormone ecdysone; the plant hormones indoleacetic acid, gibberellic acid and "flowering hormone"; and the carcinogen 3-methylcholanthrene (Bonner, 1965). In most cases, there is no direct evidence that the hormone acts by altering the structure of the chromatin itself. However, Tuan and Bonner (1964) have demonstrated that ethylene chlorohydrin (which mimics gibberellic acid) causes an intrinsic change in the chromatin of dormant potato tubers. Isolated chromatin from untreated tubers is inactive as a template in the RNA polymerase reaction, whereas chromatin from nondormant tubers that have been turned on with ethylene chlorohydrin is highly active. There is a possibility that some hormones act as substrate analogs to induce enzyme synthesis in a manner similar to substrate induction of adaptive enzymes (by activating an operon). Further analysis of these hormonal effects, especially in cell-free systems, should provide important insights regarding the fundamental mechanisms of genetic regulation in macroorganisms.

The Role of the Cytoplasm in Differentiation

As noted in the preceding section, there is direct evidence from studies of giant chromosomes, from nuclear transplant analysis and from comparative studies of template activity by native chromatin in cell-free systems that the genes of different tissues are controlled (or inhibited) by factors present in the chromatin itself. However, this immediate genetic control need not be the only factor operating in cell differentiation, and indeed it has long been recognized that cytoplasmic factors must be invoked at some level to account for the different fates of seemingly identical sister cells. In all embryogenic organisms, the somatic cells are derived from one another by successive mitotic divisions, and with certain conspicuous exceptions all the cells of the developing embryo receive equivalent sets of chromosomes. That the DNA itself is a constant factor during embryonic proliferation and differentiation has been clearly demonstrated in both plants and animals. For instance, in carrots Steward *et al.* (1958) have shown that a single secondary phloem cell, removed from the adult plant and cultured *in vitro*, can dedifferentiate, go through a process of growth and mitotic replication, and eventually give rise to an entire normal carrot plant; this would not be possible unless the phloem cell had received the entire set of DNA "information" necessary to produce roots, leaves, flowers, and other components of an intact plant. Similarly the transplantation of a nucleus from an amphibian blastula, or even from the gut of a swimming larva, back into an uncleaved egg regularly permits development of a complete, normal adult frog (Gurdon, 1964). If then the nuclei of the various presumptive tissue cells are interchangeable, it must follow that later variations in cell structure and function are the result of differences in extranuclear components. The principle that these differences are frequently expressed at the level of specific gene activation (or repression) does not alter the fact that they are determined in an extranuclear fashion; neither does it eliminate the possibility that some cytoplasmic mechanisms may operate in a manner that is permanently independent of the nucleus.

Modes of Plasmatic Variation

Sufficient information has accumulated at present to distinguish several classes of "plasmatic determiner." Although these classes are reasonably distinct, they cannot always be characterized in chemical terms and, in particular examples of cytoplasmic influence, it is not always possible to be sure which class is operating. Nevertheless, it is conceptually useful to recognize the following: (1) morphogenetic substances which are the direct precursors of some specific structure, or which direct the synthesis of specific structural molecules; (2) regulator substances, which operate by altering the functional state of pre-existing mechanisms, such as genetic transcription; (3) DNA-containing cytoplasmic particles, e.g., chloroplasts, mitochondria, and various "plasmagenes"; and (4) autonomous cytoplasmic assembly patterns, which are able to specify the structural assembly of various molecules in a manner that is more or less independent of the nucleus.

Perhaps the classic example of morphogenetic substances in the precursor sense is provided by the differentiation of the reproductive

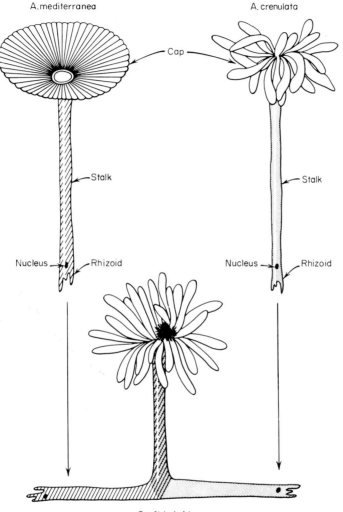

A.mediterranea

A. crenulata

Cap

Stalk

Stalk

Nucleus — Rhizoid

Nucleus — Rhizoid

Graft hybrid

Fig. 20-1. The unicellular alga *Acetabularia* develops a cap which is species specific in morphology. If nucleated cells of two species (*med* and *cren*) are grafted together, the resulting cap is intermediate in form. Experiments described in the text show that if the nucleus is removed, the species-specific influence persists for a time but eventually disappears. Cap form appears to depend on substances synthesized in a nucleus-dependent reaction, probably including specific RNA's and proteins. From Sager and Ryan (1961) after Hämmerling.

cap in the large, unicellular alga *Acetabularia*. These cells attain stalk lengths of 3–5 cm, and during the reproductive period they develop an elaborate "cap," the form of which is species specific (Fig. 20-1). Despite its large size each cell contains but a single nucleus, which is located at the opposite end from the cap and which can be eliminated by the simple technique of cutting off the basal end. Hämmerling and his collaborators (1934, 1963) discovered that even after removal of the nucleus, *Acetabularia* is able to synthesize protein for a period of weeks and can also form a species specific cap even 1–2 months after enucleation. Nevertheless, differentiation of the cap depends on diffusible substances synthesized by the nucleus. This is shown most strikingly by experiments in which a nucleus of *A. mediterranea* is transferred into an enucleate cell of *A. crenata;* in the first reproductive cycle the cap formed is the *A. crenata* type, but in the second cycle it is intermediate between *A. crenata* and *A. mediterranea,* and after the third cycle it is of the *A. mediterranea* type (corresponding to the new nucleus). Essentially similar results are obtained in the reciprocal experiment, when an *A. crenata* nucleus is transferred into an enucleate *A. mediterranea* cytoplasm. By varying the level of the enucleation transect, Hämmerling could show that the persistent cytoplasmic influence is due to diffusible substances that are concentrated at the "cap" end of the cell, are virtually absent from the opposite end, and vary in amount depending on the physiological state of the cell. It has also been shown that the elaboration and transport of these morphogenetic substances continues in the dark, even though cap formation and net protein synthesis do not take place under these circumstances. Although the exact nature of the determiners is not fully established, most evidence points to one or more species of messenger RNA. The structural specificity of these substances is most remarkable, since a mingling of two cytoplasms or of nuclei from two different species in the same cytoplasm, leads to precisely graded, intermediate cap forms (Fig. 20-1). No evidence for an independent cytoplasmic influence has been found.

In animal eggs and embryos, several laboratories have demonstrated that morphogenetic information is regularly stored in the form of messenger RNA. For example Malkin *et al.* (1964) examined the early protein synthesis which occurs in sea urchin eggs immediately after fertilization; they found that this synthesis is associated with polyribosomes, but that it is not inhibited when actinomycin D is used to block transcription of new messenger RNA. This suggests that the unfertilized egg already contains preformed messenger, which is somehow prevented from participating in protein synthesis until after fertilization. That an "on-off" control mechanism operates at the ribosomal level in unfertilized eggs has also been shown by experiments of Hultin and Bergstrand (1960), who found that cell-free "microsome" preparations from unfertilized eggs are inactive under the same conditions that permit protein synthesis by microsomes from fertilized eggs. More recently Humphreys *et al.* (1965) have demonstrated by ultracentrifugation that chick feather primordia contain polyribosomes which are synthetically inactive; the messenger RNA strand holding the ribosomes together (Chapter 14)

Fig. 20-2. A bacterial cell (*Bacillus megaterium*) which is developing a spore. Development of the spheroid spore represents a kind of cell differentiation, and involves two specific membranes of differing morphology. The inner membrane of the spore exhibits abundant globular particles of macromolecular dimensions; the outer membrane is relatively smooth, with infrequent large particles. Between the two membranes, a thick protective cortex is being deposited. 32,800×. Micrograph by DuPraw; freeze-etch preparation done collaboratively with D. Branton, D. Nelson, and S. Whytock.

seems to be in a special state which renders it resistant to RNase digestion. After a given time these polyribosomes are able to synthesize protein again, and at the same time the messenger RNA becomes RNase sensitive. A similar storage of preformed but inactive polyribosomes seems to occur in spores of the bacterium *Bacillus megaterium* (Chambon, DuPraw, and Kornberg, 1968; Fig. 20-2).

Wilt (1966) has demonstrated precise synthetic controls operating at the ribosome level during the synthesis of hemoglobin in explanted chick blastoderms; in this system, actinomycin prevents the onset of hemoglobin synthesis, but only if it is administered about 8–10 hours before hemoglobin normally appears. This indicates that the transcription of messenger RNA for hemoglobin has been completed in chick embryonic cells some hours before the cells begin "translating" the message for globin synthesis. Multigene messenger RNA's are known to occur in some systems (e.g., in RNA viruses), and Ohtaka and Spiegelman (1963) found that the ribosomal control mechanisms are such that one gene can be read more frequently than other genes in the same message. Although it is not yet known how the ribosome translation process is so precisely controlled, there may be physical restraints that prevent the ribosomes from contacting the messenger RNA strands; possibly the membranes of the endoplasmic reticulum contribute to this control process (Chapter 16). In any case, it seems likely that the storage of cytoplasmic information in the form of messenger RNA is logistically a more efficient cellular mechanism than storing large amounts of specific product protein (such as hemoglobin).

Plasmatic substances which act to control pre-existing mechanisms (such as the translation of messenger RNA) would seem to represent a distinct class of morphogenetic determiner. The existence of such substances was discovered by classical embryologists in various invertebrate eggs, where localized basophilic regions or granules seem to determine the differentiation of germ cells. This phenomenon has been carefully reinvestigated by Geyer-Duszynska (1959) and Nicklas (1959) in cecidomyid flies, where a remarkable elimination of chromosomes occurs in the somatic nuclei but not in the presumptive germ cell nuclei. Of approximately 40 chromosomes present in the zygote nucleus, all but 8 are eliminated from the somatic nuclei at the fourth division (owing to a failure in the anaphase movement of the chromosomes to the poles); in males, two additional chromosomes are eliminated at the seventh division. This chromosome elimination does not occur in nuclei which enter the pole plasm, an egg region characterized by the presence of a homogeneous substance staining deeply with hematoxylin; eventually these intact polar nuclei give rise to the primordial germ cells. If the hematoxylin-positive material is displaced by centrifugation, it prevents chromosome elimination in any somatic nuclei that lie in its vicinity; conversely if the substance is eliminated entirely by microcautery, chromosome elimination occurs in the presumptive germ cells, leading eventually to sterile flies with ovaries containing the reduced somatic chromosome number. Several similar examples have been studied in other invertebrates; in the crustacean *Cyclops*, visible basophilic granules cluster around one pole of the spindle during the early cleavage of the egg, and the cells which eventually receive these granules become the primordial germ cells.

In the nematode *Ascaris* "chromatin diminution" seems to be *induced* by a substance which is cytologically invisible, but which can be demonstrated by appropriate centrifugation or irradiation experiments. In the somatic cleavage cells of *Ascaris* embryos, each of the two large zygote chromosomes breaks up into about 30 small chromosomes plus two larger terminal segments that lack kinetochores and are lost to the cytoplasm (Fig. 18-13). Normally this chromatin diminution fails to occur in one daughter cell of each cleavage, so that after the fifth cleavage there are 31 "reduced" cells and one with complete chromosomes (which gives rise to the germ cells). However King and Beams (1938) showed that eggs which initiate cleavage while they are being centrifuged at 150,000 g pass through a deferred cytokinesis, after which *all* the blastomere nuclei (which have shared a common cytoplasm) exhibit chromatin diminution. Moritz (1967) has recently demonstrated differences in the basic proteins of *Ascaris* chromosomes depending on whether or not they will undergo diminution. In this and previous examples, the plasmatic substances responsible for inducing or preventing the elimination of chromatin would seem to act as regulators of the mitotic process, rather than as morphogenetic precursors.

In other examples, although striking plasmatic effects have been discovered by classical embryologists, present knowledge does not permit a distinction between regulator substances and precursor substances. For instance, Conklin (1931) found that centrifugation alters the development of tunicate eggs in a manner that is largely independent of visible particles, and he concluded that the eggs contain three or four "potency regions" in which elements of the ground plasm are responsible for determining specific developmental fates. This and many similar phenomena await reinvestigation by more precise biochemical methods.

With respect to plasmatic regulation, it is a general principle that complex homeostatic mechanisms operate in all cells to maintain a physiological "steady state" of energy transfer compounds, nutrients, and specific precursor substances. Although such mechanisms are not confined to proliferating or differentiating tissues, alterations in "steady state" certainly operate either as causes or effects during morphogenesis. Lehninger (1964) has given an excellent example of the complex metabolic control involved in determining the concentration of just one Krebs cycle intermediate—oxaloacetic acid. This compound is produced in at least three different ways: by the oxidation of malic acid, by the carboxylation of pyruvic acid, and by the transamination of aspartic acid. Furthermore, it is used up in five different ways: by condensation with acetyl-CoA to form citric acid, by reduction to malic acid, by transamination with glutamic acid, by decarboxylation, and by transcarboxylation with acetyl-CoA. Consequently, the concentration of oxaloacetate in a cell at any given time represents a dynamic balance between the reactions that tend to produce it and the reactions that tend to remove it. The physiological importance of this concentration is apparent in the variety of effects oxaloacetate is known to produce, including: catalyzing the oxidations of acetyl-CoA, glutamic acid, and isocitric acid; catalyzing fatty acid synthesis; a precursor of phosphopyruvate for glycogen synthesis; and inhibiting the oxidation of malic acid and succinic acid. All these reactions are mitochondrial and to that extent cytoplasmic (Chapter 7); their immediate relevance for differentiation is shown by the fact that succinyl-CoA, a Krebs cycle intermediate, is a precursor for the synthesis of δ-aminolevulinic acid, which is a precursor for hemoglobin. Hell (1964) has shown, in fact, that the addition of δ-aminolevulinic acid to an explanted chick blastoderm significantly advances the time when hemoglobin synthesis becomes detectable.

Since the physiological state of each cell is sensitive to various factors in that cell's environment, it is not surprising that agents as unspecific as temperature and pH can lead to significant morphogenetic changes. Such effects are very marked in plants, to the extent that even the recognition of species can become difficult. In animals, the classic example of direct environmental effects is the phenomenon of cyclomorphosis in the crustacean *Daphnia*. Entire populations of these tiny freshwater creatures exhibit seasonal changes in size and shape, particularly evident in the relative lengths of their "helmets." These changes can be imitated in the laboratory, and have been shown to depend on slight differences in growth by successive generations of *Daphnia* developing under slightly different temperature, food, and turbidity conditions (Jacobs, 1962). Essentially similar effects operate during embryonic differentiation, and the morphogenesis of individual cells can often be shown to reflect the microenvironment in which each cell finds itself. Thus gradients in yolk concentration, changes in circulating hormones

(Williams, 1963), waste products from surrounding cells, diffusion barriers reducing the oxygen tension, ion pump alterations in osmotic concentrations, all are capable of influencing the outcome of a morphogenetic process. The classic example is the distribution of yolk in many types of egg, which tends to become more concentrated near one pole (the vegetal pole) and is sometimes distributed according to gravity alone (e.g., in the seaweed *Fucus*). The yolk gradient in turn influences the position of the spindle and the cleavage planes, so that large yolk-filled cells are formed at the vegetal pole, and small yolk-deficient cells at the opposite (animal) pole. Typically the large vegetal cells differentiate as parts of the gut or its derivatives (endoderm), while the small "animal" cells form epidermis and neural tissues. The importance of such animal-vegetal gradients for normal differentiation was demonstrated by Hörstadius (1937, 1939) in a classic analysis of development in sea urchin embryos. His experiments consisted of separating different layers of blastomeres along the animal-vegetal axis, then recombining the layers in different sets to observe the altered patterns of development. For example, an "artificial embryo" made up of one-quarter of an animal hemisphere together with one-quarter of an endoderm layer developed as a small but almost normally proportioned larva. On the other hand, if an entire animal hemisphere was combined with the same endoderm component the larva was badly malformed in a manner suggesting disproportionate "animal" influence. The same animal hemisphere without endoderm but developing in the presence of lithium ions could produce a normal larva, demonstrating that the "vegetal influence" is mimicked by a simple ion gradient.

Many other examples could be given. A particularly remarkable one is the regeneration exhibited by the flatworm *Planaria* after an individual is cut in two; usually the original tail end develops a new head while the head end develops a new tail, and it has been shown that this process is accompanied by a gradient in the rate of protein synthesis along the anterior-posterior axis (the presumptive head end exhibiting the most rapid amino acid incorporation). Flickinger (1959) designed an experiment in which the head of a planarian was removed, after which the cut end was exposed to chloramphenicol, an inhibitor of protein synthesis. As a result of the depressed protein synthesis at the cut end, the regeneration process gave rise to a tail instead of a head, while the uncut tail end of the animal reorganized itself to form a new head. Although it is not known how the gradients in protein synthesis (and $^{14}CO_2$ incorporation) are established and regulated in *Planaria*, they apparently play a causal role in directing head-tail differentiation. In plants too, the differentiation of a bud into either a flower or a leaf is evidently controlled by axial gradients along the stem; the substances involved have been extensively analyzed and include the plant hormones in-doleacetic acid and kinetin.

Both the precursor and regulator types of plasmatic influence, as discussed in preceding paragraphs, can be assumed to operate under nuclear "control." This is especially evident in the case of stored mes-senger RNA, which is likely to be transmitted directly from nuclear DNA into the cytoplasm. In other examples, nuclear control may be much less direct, e.g., by dictating the synthesis of enzymes necessary to produce hormones which then function by regulating genetic activity in the nucleus. Very long sequences of feedback control—nucleus trans-mitting to cytoplasm, cytoplasm to nucleus, nucleus to cytoplasm, etc., undoubtedly occur within differentiating cells, and are further compli-cated by branch reactions initiated from the nuclei or cytoplasms of neighboring cells. When such nuclear-cytoplasmic interactions become sufficiently complex, a point is reached when it is no longer possible to decide whether the nucleus is controlling the cytoplasm or the cyto-plasm is controlling the nucleus. Though geneticists are prone to assign all specificity "ultimately" to DNA, the point has been made in Chapter 14 that nucleotide sequences in themselves contain information only in the sense that a series of dots and dashes contains information; the meaning is conferred when the code is translated—when specific (cyto-plasmic) enzymes catalyze the synthesis of specific amino acyl-sRNA molecules, and when these amino acyl-sRNA's are called up in a par-ticular sequence by a (cytoplasmic) ribosome–messenger RNA–enzyme complex. In one sense, molecular biology has made questions of "nuclear" versus "cytoplasmic" influence ultimately meaningless, simply because many cytoplasmic molecules are synthesized in the nucleus, and many nuclear molecules are synthesized in the cytoplasm. However it remains entirely meaningful to ask whether the specific properties of an organism (and variations between organisms) are always referable to the specific properties of DNA (i.e., to a single "hereditary material"), or whether an organism can be fully described only by including in-formation that is quite independent of DNA.

In earlier years when it was believed that all DNA is confined to the nucleus, the sense of this question was often raised by students of "extra-nuclear" or "nonchromosomal" inheritance; some of the clearest ex-amples depended on non-Mendelian inheritance of chloroplast or mito-chondrial characteristics. However the recent discovery that chloroplasts and mitochondria contain not only unique kinds of DNA, but also the enzymatic machinery required to synthesize RNA and proteins (Chap-ters 5 and 7), has tended to bring such phenomena under an all-unifying "DNA theory of inheritance." Additional intriguing questions are raised, of course: for example, is the RNA polymerase of a chloroplast specified by the chloroplast's own DNA or by the nuclear DNA? How are the metabolic resources of the cell coordinated among many semi-autonomous organelles? What regulates all the genetic regulatory mechanisms of the nucleus, chloroplasts, and mitochondria? These questions are immediately pertinent for the differentiation process in higher plants, where an important feature of morphogenesis is the appearance of chloroplasts in some tissues (leaf palisade cells) but not others (many stem tissues). Beyond these problems, however, it is still legitimate to ask whether any *bona fide* examples of "non-DNA" inheritance remain.

One hereditary mechanism that seems to involve more than DNA replication is the influence of the cell cortex during morphogenesis in ciliate protozoans. The *patterns* of cilia and certain other organelles in these creatures are closely linked with the arrangement of kinetosomes (or basal bodies) lying in the cell cortex. Tartar (1961) and Sonneborn (1963) have each carried out very detailed investigations of fission and morphogenesis in the ciliates *Stentor* and *Paramecium*, where by appropriate methods the nuclear and cortical components can be varied independently of one another. Such experiments have revealed a phenomenon Sonneborn calls "cytotaxis"—the capacity of pre-existing structures to pattern the assembly of new molecules into other structures with identical characteristics. What this concept implies is that DNA may determine the specificity of individual protein molecules, but that the manner in which these molecules are assembled to form functional organelles is partly determined and inherited through the organelles themselves (and presumably independently of DNA). Sonneborn has studied a number of spontaneous variants, including double cells which contain all the cytoplasmic organelles in duplicate, and a unique ciliate with two oral regions (produced by spontaneous exchange of a small cortical area during the mating of a double cell with a normal one). Such structural variations are inherited quite independently of the nucleus, and they remain stable during hundreds of successive fission and growth cycles. One of the most fascinating cortical variants is a "reversed kinety," i.e., a longitudinal row of kinetosomes and cilia in which the normal anterior-posterior polarity is exactly reversed. Generation after generation, this reversed kinety gives rise to other reversed kineties, while in the course of 400 fission cycles the single anterior-posterior row is gradually displaced laterally, moving in a consistent direction around the circumference of the cell. Thus inheritance of the "reversed" characteristic is a function of one highly localized cortical region.

Tartar's (1961) analysis of morphogenesis in the large ciliate *Stentor* has employed very clever micrurgical rearrangements of cortical regions and nuclei. By dividing a cell into quarters or smaller fragments (mincing) and recombining these in abnormal ways, he has been able to demonstrate that bits of ectoderm have a remarkable capacity to reorient in relation to one another, achieving the best approximation of an intact cell and then regenerating those parts that may be missing. Such reconstitution proceeds even in the absence of a nucleus, although the capacity for regeneration is reduced. In an earlier study, Tartar (1956) found evidence that the development of the "mouth" region is induced by a juxtaposition of ectoplasm with wide pigment stripes to ectoplasm with narrow pigment stripes, i.e., by a discontinuity in an otherwise graded cortical pattern. That the nucleus does contribute to the regeneration process is shown by recombining cytoplasmic elements and nuclear "nodes" from two species, *S. coeruleus* and *S. polymorphus;* in this case, a quantitative interdependence is found, such that successful regeneration occurs only in organisms containing a preponderance of nuclear elements from one species with cytoplasmic elements from the same species. A similar subtle interdependence of cytoplasm and nucleus has been revealed at the level of specific protein synthesis in *Paramecium aurelia;* Beale (1954) found that the specificity of surface antigens in this species is under the influence of at least three different gene loci, only one of which is expressed at any given time. By altering the temperature of a culture over the course of several cell generations, he was able to switch one gene off and another gene on, but the "switch" mechanism appeared to be cytoplasmic. Thus when a nucleus operating on one antigen "setting" was transferred through the mating process into the cytoplasm of a cell that was "set" for a different antigen, the cytoplasmic setting was adopted. Inasmuch as temperature can alter the antigen characteristics again after a few cell generations, this phenomenon does not represent a permanently heritable characteristic.

Valid examples of "non-DNA inheritance" must be shown to be not only independent of DNA, but persistent through many reproductive cycles; in macroorganisms the latter requirement can seldom be met under experimental conditions. Yet there has always been a minor but persistent school of thought in developmental biology, which has rejected the concept of an all-powerful Master Molecule (in Nanney's phrase), and has attempted to demonstrate that chromosomes, genes, and indeed DNA are simply the most noticeable components of an integrated system, the true reproductive unit of which is the living cell. Potentially the type of experiment required to demonstrate this is similar to that employed by Sonneborn and Tartar in ciliates: the DNA component must be held constant, while variations in the non-DNA components must be shown to perpetuate themselves indefinitely. Numerous attempts to carry out such an experiment have been made; some of the earliest were performed by Boveri (1889), Baltzer (1917), Loeb (1916), and others, who were able to fertilize anucleate egg fragments from one species of sea urchin with sperm from another species (producing so-called androgenetic merogons); the resulting larvae exhibit a heavy influence from the cytoplasmic parent, but it is not possible to rear successive generations from such hybrids in order to determine whether the cytoplasmic influence can persist autonomously. Much more refined experiments of this type became possible after Briggs and King (1955) showed that it is micrurgically feasible to transplant an intact diploid nucleus from a blastula cell of one (amphibian) species to the enucleate egg of another species. Moore (1960, 1962) first employed this method to recombine nuclear and extranuclear elements between the two frog species, *R. pipiens* and *R. sylvatica;* he found that nucleocytoplasmic *pipsyl* "hybrids" are able to develop normally to a late blastula or gastrula stage, after which development becomes blocked or abnormal (as in fertilization hybrids between these species). However, Moore (1960) was able to test the persistence of nuclear and cytoplasmic influences in this developmental block by means of "serial nuclear transfers" (Fig. 17-13). A *pipiens* daughter nucleus, after having replicated 10–12 times in *sylvatica* cytoplasm, could be removed from the hybrid embryo at a stage before any developmental block was evident, and then transferred back to an enucleate *pipiens* egg. In this experiment it was found that the *pipiens* nucleus can still support the early stages of cleavage in a *pipiens* cytoplasm, but it is no longer able to function normally through the whole course of development (which stops at a gastrula stage). The experiment could be continued by transplanting daughter nuclei from such an altered *pipiens* nucleus back to other enucleated *pipiens* eggs, letting them develop to a blastula stage, then again transplanting daughter nuclei back to *pipiens* eggs, for five or more "generations"; despite such prolonged "washing" in native cytoplasm, the *pipiens* nuclei showed no improvement in their capacity to support normal development. It seems clear from this experiment that *sylvatica* egg cytoplasm is able to produce an irreversible change in *pipiens* nuclei, of a type which does not interfere with chromosomal replication, but which tends to be perpetuated through the replication process. Whatever the nature of this nuclear change, it is associated with severe anomalies in chromosome number and morphology (Moore, 1962). This example also demonstrates the conceptual difficulties that ensue when a "cytoplasmic effect" is expressed by an irreversible change in the nucleus.

Micrurgical transplantation of nuclei between species, while potentially a very important technique for revealing the roles of cytoplasmic elements in heredity, has so far been limited to relatively few macroorganisms (reviewed by Gurdon, 1964); in these species, the experimental results fall into one of two categories: either (1) the new combination of nucleus and cytoplasm is a compatible one, in which case the hybrid shows exclusively nuclear characteristics; or (2) the new combination is incompatible (as in Moore's *pip-syl* hybrids), in which case it is not possible to test the autonomy of cytoplasmic influences through successive generations. These results do not necessarily demonstrate that all biological information is transmitted through DNA; they do show, however, that the techniques available for detecting a non-DNA inheritance in macroorganisms, if such a phenomenon occurs, are very few and subject to multiple interpretations. Many examples can be found of cytoplasmic influence in the morphogenesis of plants and animals (e.g., involving the cortex of the insect egg; Seidel, 1961), but in single-generation experiments these can always be accounted for on a hypothesis of precursor or regulator substances stored in the plasm at an earlier time (i.e., maternal influence). The recent discovery of unique chloroplast and mitochondrial DNA's raises the entire problem to a new level of complexity. Instances of hereditary transmission through the chloroplasts and through the mitochondria had previously been carefully established as examples of extranuclear inheritance (reviewed by Sager and Ryan, 1961); now, although such examples are no less "extranuclear," they cannot be regarded as representing cytotaxis in the sense defined by Sonneborn. In fact, the mere ubiquity of extranuclear DNA makes it difficult to design an experiment which could unequivocally demonstrate whether or not a non-DNA dependent cytotaxis occurs in macroorganisms.

Despite these problems, there remains a residuum of facts which are not easily accounted for by the information contained in polynucleotide sequences alone, and which promise an exciting new era of genetic research if the proper analytical techniques can be found. The best examples are derived from interspecies genetic crosses in which the hybrids are fertile and can be backcrossed repeatedly to the paternal parent; in this manner, the entire chromosomal complement of one species can be transferred into the cells of another species, with continued analysis of the effects through successive generations. Such experiments have been successfully achieved in maize by Rhoades (1933), in *Epilobium* by Michaelis (1954), in the moss *Funaria* by Von Wettstein (1937), and in mosquitoes by Laven (1959); in all cases, though the influence of the chromosomes is evident, some maternal characteristics cannot be eliminated by the paternal chromosomes even after many years. Although most examples are drawn from plant species, the characteristics studied were not exclusively those of the plastids, and in fact Von Wettstein's analysis led him to distinguish three compartments in the hereditary apparatus: (1) that of the chromosomes; (2) extrachromosomal inheritance through the plastids, and (3) a persistent, heritable influence associated with the nonplastid cytoplasmic elements. The latter is often detectable through phenomena such as gamete sterility in nucleocytoplasmic hybrids. These examples of cytoplasmic inheritance deserve reexamination in the light of newly discovered, extranuclear DNA components. At the very least, they raise the question of whether plastid DNA can influence nonplastid characteristics at the species level; from a more extreme point of view, they permit us to ask again whether all biological information is really a function of DNA alone.

Classical Problems in Differentiation and Morphogenesis

The history of developmental biology is characterized by an exuberant cataloguing of mysterious phenomena, such as Driesch's (1891) discovery that the first two blastomeres of an echinoderm embryo produce one larva when they remain together, but two complete larvae if they are separated. Much of the mystery in these phenomena can be diminished or eliminated by the application of newer molecular concepts in biology; that is to say, such effects can now be approached in terms of theoretical questions that are likely to be answered by one or another of several limited possibilities. The exact mechanisms that operate in any specific case, e.g., during regulative development of an echinoderm embryo, are likely to be quite different from those that operate in other cases, such as induction of the neural tube in a vertebrate embryo. In any particular case, only an intensive investigation at the molecular level can lead to satisfactory answers, and such investigations are still relatively limited in number.

Nevertheless, the general approach is clear-cut. The investigator inquires first whether some type of differential genetic control is operating in his system, and if so whether the "active" genes can be specified, for example by identifying the crucial enzymes (or other proteins) that appear in some cells but not others (and by determining the time or sequence of their appearance). The investigator may also inquire whether cytoplasmic elements function either to initiate differential gene activity or in some manner that does not involve the genetic apparatus. Possible modes of cytoplasmic activity, as discussed in preceding paragraphs, include the assembly of precursor molecules; the manipulation of regulator substances (including gradients of simple ions, nutrients, or hormones); the activity of DNA-containing cytoplasmic particles; and the possibility of effects dependent on a supramolecular cytoplasmic organization (i.e., cytotaxis). An example may serve to clarify the relationship between these molecular concepts and the classical approach of experimental embryology. When a section of ectodermal tissue is transplanted from a frog embryo to the future mouth region of a salamander embryo, it is found that some factor in the salamander "induces" the frog tissue to form labial palps. These palps would not form if the ectoderm were isolated by itself, yet even when they are induced by the salamander tissues they develop with the species-specific shape and pattern of the frog larva. In molecular terms, the fact that the palps are froglike indicates that their formation depends on species-specific macromolecules, which must be synthesized locally under genetic control by the frog DNA. The induction of this synthesis by the salamander embryo suggests that the genetic activity is initiated by a relatively unspecific extranuclear substance of the "regulator" type. Future experimental questions may be directed to the nature of the regulator substance on the one hand, and of the species-specific frog macromolecules on the other hand. This is an approach which emphasizes the science rather than the mystery in such developmental effects, and which can hope ultimately to resolve them in molecular terms.

Most of the difficulties peculiar to developmental biology are not owing to a lack of agents that can induce changes in embryonic cells, but to the fact that these cells are altered unpredictably by *many* kinds of environmental change. The experimental conditions themselves often lead to juxtaposition of tissues not usually found together, or to abnormal ionic environments, which can touch off effects that are interesting but may have little relationship to events in the intact embryo. An excellent example is provided by the discovery of Barth and Barth (1959) that amphibian epithelial cells, isolated in pure saline solution with added serum globulin, spontaneously differentiate as striated muscle cells, ciliated epithelial cells, functional neurons, or pigment cells. Treatment of such cells with lithium chloride is sufficient to direct most of them into differentiation as pigment cells; however it does not follow that lithium ions function as genetic regulators in the intact embryo. From these and many similar observations it is clear that the spectrum of physical and chemical variables in the embryo is more than sufficient to account in a formal way for the origin of tissue variations. What is remarkable about "native" developmental systems is the extreme reproducibility of their differentiations both in space and time; this reproducibility implies formidable homeostatic control mechanisms which must operate at a supracellular level, and which confer on the tissues a general resistance to random environmental fluctuations.

UNEQUAL CELL DIVISION AND THE CONTROL OF DIFFERENTIATION

The process of mitosis ensures that all the cells of a typical embryo will receive the full DNA complement of the species; the process of differentiation, on the other hand, implies that sister cells often receive different non-DNA complements, and it further implies that the unequal distribution of such elements is a controlled and orderly process. Many examples are now known in which the sister cells of a mitotic division are visibly different in size or other characteristics, and in a way that is directly related to their subsequent differentiations. For instance, the neuroblasts of insects go through a series of unequal divisions, the smaller daughter each time terminating mitosis and differentiating as a ganglion cell, whereas the larger daughter continues to divide as an "undifferentiated" neuroblast (or stem cell). Similar unequal divisions are especially common in higher plants, where the relative positions of the cells tend to be determined once and for all by the plane of cleavage (individual cells being unable to migrate to new positions). In woody plants, for example, a layer of permanently "undifferentiated" cells (the stem cambium) actively divides throughout the life of the plant, separating presumptive xylem to one side and presumptive phloem to the other. In mosses and ferns, all the cells of the stem may be produced by the successive divisions of a single apical cell, which represents the undifferentiated daughter of a very long series of (unequal) mitotic divisions. The occurrence of these visibly unequal divisions suggests that in other instances, sister cells which look identical may differ in ways that are cytologically undetectable. It is therefore a matter of some theoretical importance to determine how far unequal mitosis can account for the events of normal differentiation, and to elucidate the underlying mechanisms that regulate visible or invisible segregation of cytoplasmic components.

It seems fairly clear that an unequal partitioning of cytoplasmic elements is of much greater significance in the embryos of some species than in others. Many invertebrates exhibit a "mosaic" type of development, such that isolated blastomeres cannot develop regulatively to produce intact larvae but differentiate primarily in the same ways that would have occurred in the intact embryo. Although these cells can still be made to alter their patterns of differentiation by appropriate experimental treatment, the evidence shows that their fates *in vivo* are correlated with a mitotic partitioning of yolk and other cytoplasmic particles. For example in the eggs of *Tubifex*, a polychaete worm, Lehmann (1958) used electron microscopy to demonstrate unequal populations of mitochondria, lipid droplets, yolk spheres, and other particulates in the early cleavage cells. Similarly, Berg and Humphrey (1960) found three times as many mitochondria and eight times as many lipid droplets in the posterior as compared with anterior blastomeres of ascidian embryos. There is no reason to doubt that such inequalities in the distribution of nutrients and ATP-generating organelles has functional significance for the fates of these cells *in vivo*. In fact, Conklin (1931) demonstrated that a displacement of cytoplasmic components by centrifugation leads to altered patterns of development in ascidian and other eggs. Although he could not detect a correlation between the pattern of development and the visible localization of particles, his light microscope observations were too limited in resolution to conclude that differentiation is not influenced by the distributions of mitochondria and yolk.

In insect embryos, Seidel and his students (1961) have carried out many careful experiments, employing ligatures, microcautery, ultraviolet irradiation, and other techniques, which have established that the uncleaved egg contains special plasmatic areas specifically required for the differentiation of particular structures. Eliminating a certain region of egg cortex by microcautery leads to a defective embryo, in contrast to the elimination of specific cleavage nuclei, which has little or no effect. In these embryos, cytoplasmic division is deferred until a stage when the egg contains about 4000 nuclei, at which time the cortex is rapidly divided up into typical uninucleate cells (superficial cleavage). That these cells receive unequal complements of mitochondria and other cytoplasmic inclusions has been directly demonstrated by Mahowald (1963b) in an electron microscope study of the *Drosophila* blastoderm. There is as yet almost no information to account for the unequal distribution of cytoplasmic inclusions in the egg, the chemical nature of those components that are active in differentiation, or the manner in which they specify morphogenetic events.

A general tendency for mitosis to be reduced or absent in differentiated tissues has been noted by many authors (Chapter 19). This apparent mutual exclusiveness between differentiation and replication is nowhere more evident than in those cases when one sister cell continues mitosis but does not differentiate, while the other sister cell differentiates but no longer carries on mitosis. As mentioned previously, the "stem cell" mode of development is characteristic of insect neuroblasts, plant meristematic tissues, and many other systems. Quastler and Sherman

(1959) carried out an autoradiographic study of mouse intestinal epithelium, which led them to conclude that each cell reaches a decision point shortly after mitosis: either it will continue to proliferate or it will stop proliferating and become a functional epithelial cell. The decision is made before DNA synthesis begins, and it depends in part on the position of the cell relative to other cells in the same villus. Stockdale and Holzer (1962) also found cytochemical evidence that chick cells which synthesize myosin do not synthesize DNA. More recently Abbott and Holzer (1966) have shown by autoradiography that chondrocytes in tissue culture include two populations of cells: a given chondrocyte incorporates either ^{35}S for the synthesis of chondroitin sulfate (a component of cartilage) or thymidine-^{3}H for the synthesis of DNA, but not both. Although the molecular basis for this "switch" phenomenon is not entirely understood, it may reflect the alternative modes of DNA template activity, i.e., for transcription by RNA polymerase or for replication by DNA polymerase (Chapter 13).

Whatever the mechanism, evidence has accumulated that a choice between replication and differentiation is not always necessary and that when it does occur it is subject to later reversal. The first clear example a "dedifferentiation" was demonstrated by Steward et al. (1958) in wild carrots; they found that factors present in coconut milk can initiate proliferation by single phloem cells in tissue culture. These cells first give rise to a mass of "clonal" tissue, which then differentiates to form stem, root, leaves, and ultimately all the components of a mature carrot plant. The proliferating phloem cells actually "cleave" in the characteristic pattern of the zygote, indicating that these tissue cells are behaving like gametes. In animals, the experiments of Abbott and Holzer (1966) with chick chondrocytes also demonstrate that an individual cartilage cell can stop the synthesis of chondroitin sulfate in order to initiate DNA synthesis and mitosis. Nuclear transplantation experiments by Gurdon (1964) have demonstrated that a few nuclei from the differentiated gut epithelium of swimming tadpoles, when transferred back to an enucleate egg, are able to support the full course of embryogenesis. In some instances, one tissue type can give rise directly to another, as indicated by the lens regeneration experiments of Yamada (1966); in this work, removal of the lens from the eye of an adult newt caused alterations in the neighboring iris cells, which eventually regenerated a new lens. Yamada employed autoradiography to follow the sequence of biochemical changes, which include: (1) RNA synthesis in iris cell nuclei; (2) protein synthesis and initiation of DNA synthesis; (3) discharge of iris pigment granules, cell proliferation, and accumulation of ribosomes; (4) cessation of DNA synthesis; and (5) appearance of specific lens proteins, including α, β, and γ-crystallins. Grobstein (1966) has suggested that DNA replication may be required before a new mode of differentiation can be established; this would fit well with the finding that turnover in DNA-linked proteins increases during replication, as though the proteins are forced out of their nucleoprotein complex to permit DNA unwinding. It would also accord with the developing suspicion that those molecular relationships responsible for tissue differentiation cannot be replicated in the mitotic process. Such relationships presumably consist of specific linkages between DNA and proteins.

EMBRYONIC INDUCTION

That differentiation involves more than just an orderly segregation of cytoplasmic determiners was established by Driesch (1891), when he observed that each of the early cleavage cells of a sea urchin embryo is able to develop into a complete larva. In many species this extreme type of regulative development cannot be demonstrated, but most embryos do exhibit some form of induction, i.e., an influence by one tissue on the morphogenetic fate of another tissue. The classic demonstration of embryonic induction was reported by Spemann (1918), who showed that the amphibian blastula possesses a special "organizer" region corresponding to the dorsal lip of the blastopore (the presumptive notochord-mesoderm tissue); if the dorsal lip is removed from one embryo and implanted in the gastrula cavity (archenteron) of another embryo, it induces the ectoderm to form a second neural tube, leading ultimately to development of a double, "Siamese twin" embryo. However, when a layer of cellophane is interposed between the chorda-mesoderm and the overlying ectoderm no induction takes place, indicating that the effect depends on one or more diffusible agents which must pass from one tissue to the other. Since Spemann's pioneer work, many other examples of embryonic induction have been described both in the amphibian embryo and in the embryos of the chicken, mouse, insects, etc. In the best-known examples the inductions form long sequences, which have been described as "cascading" reactions, e.g., the chorda-mesoderm induces the neural tube with its optic cups, each optic cup then induces the development of a lens, each lens induces the formation of a cornea, and so on. In other examples there is a feedback relationship through time, such that mesoderm induces one change in the overlying ectoderm, after which the ectoderm induces another change in the underlying mesoderm; reactions of this kind might better be described as "reverberating" than "cascading." Although the many systems of embryonic induction possess some features in common, it is likely that the "inducing agent" in each case is a different material; consequently, at a molecular level the differences may eventually prove to be more impressive than the similarities. At present it is difficult to decide this, since in no system has the mechanism of induction been fully elucidated at a molecular level.

Perhaps the most conspicuous property which induction systems have in common is a remarkably gradual transition to the "determined" state. At an early developmental stage the inducible tissue may be "competent" to respond to any of several possible inducers, exhibiting an appropriately specific differentiation in each case. However as induction proceeds there is a progressive restriction in "potencies," which can be mapped in space (i.e., as diminishing potency fields) as well as in time. The remarkable stepwise loss in potency is well illustrated by experiments with limb bud primordia, nodelike regions of the body wall, that give rise to the four appendages of vertebrate embryos. It is possible to interchange the left and right anterior limb buds, as well as to reverse the dorsal-ventral or anterior-posterior axes of one limb bud. Provided that the operation is done early enough, all three axes of the limb bud are able to readjust themselves to produce a normally oriented limb. However, older limb buds gradually lose this developmental plasticity, in such a way that the three axes become determined at somewhat different times. For instance, at an intermediate time the limb bud can adjust its anterior-posterior axis, but not the right-left axis; somewhat later it can still adjust the dorsal-ventral axis but not the anterior-posterior axis. Finally it loses the capacity to regulate on any axis. It is tempting to postulate that this restriction in regulative capacity corresponds to the formation of new DNA-protein linkages, removing specific genes from the list of those that can still be activated. Sirlin and Brahma (1959) have shown, in fact, that substances labeled with radioactive phenylalanine move from the optic cup cells into the nuclei of lens cells as the latter are induced to differentiate. However, it has not yet been demonstrated that any inducer ever acts directly on DNA, and many alternative mechanisms are conceivable.

The general plasticity of embryonic cells has imposed serious obstacles on the many attempts to isolate and chemically define specific inducing materials. Each given type of induction can often be mimicked by tissues that do not normally act as inducers, and inducing activity may also be exhibited by dead tissues or by a wide range of inorganic chemicals. Early chemical analyses were largely directed toward isolating an active inducer from the amphibian organizer, but Okada (1938) found that neural induction could be achieved in *Triturus* simply by injecting Fuller's earth, silica, or calcium carbonate. These observations made it necessary to distinguish clearly between substances that are *able* to induce and substances that do induce in the intact embryo. The reality and diffusion characteristics of such "natural" inducers have been investigated by Grobstein (1956), who interposed filters of known thickness and pore size between the inducer (mouse spinal cord) and the inducible tissue (metanephrogenic mesenchyme); he found that in this system the inducing principle can traverse a distance of 60 μ through pores 0.4–0.8 μ in diameter, and 20 μ through pores 0.1 μ in diameter (1000 Å). These experiments established that direct contact between cells is not a prerequisite for induction. More recently Lash *et al.* (1962) succeeded in isolating a low molecular weight substance which appears to be the natural inducer of cartilage in chick embryos. In the intact embryo, the ventral spinal cord and notochord induce cartilage formation in the neighboring mesodermal somites, which then become the primordia of the vertebrae. Lash was able to extract and purify a single, nucleotide-containing component, which occurs only in chick ventral spinal cord and notochord and which induces embryonic somites to produce cartilage *in vitro*. According to Hommes *et al.* (1962), this compound contains cytidine and guanosine nucleotides, a hexosamine, and the amino acids aspartic acid, threonine, serine, glutamic acid, glycine, alanine, and valine.

That a transfer of proteins and RNA accompanies neural induction by the amphibian organizer was strongly supported by experiments of Rounds and Flickinger (1958) and Flickinger *et al.* (1959). In the first series of experiments, recombinations were made between (1) radioactive dorsal mesoderm and nonradioactive ectoderm; (2) radioactive ectoderm and nonradioactive dorsal mesoderm; and (3) a control series of radioactive ventral mesoderm (which lacks inducing activity) and nonradioactive ectoderm. After induction, the RNA fraction in the nonradioactive member of each pair was tested for the presence of isotope. It was found that transfer of radioactive RNA is highest from the inducing dorsal mesoderm to the ectoderm, and lowest from the noninducing ventral mesoderm to the ectoderm; an intermediate amount of RNA transfer occurs in a reverse direction, from the ectoderm to the mesoderm, during induction. Evidence for a transfer of protein as well as RNA was obtained by combining salamander ectoderm with frog dorsal mesoderm, then testing the induced ectoderm for frog antigens by immunological techniques; a significant positive reaction was observed.

Despite these direct contacts with the natural chordamesoderm inducer(s), much of the present understanding of amphibian "organizer" activity is based on extensive analysis of neural induction as mimicked by heterologous tissues such as guinea pig kidney, bone marrow, chick

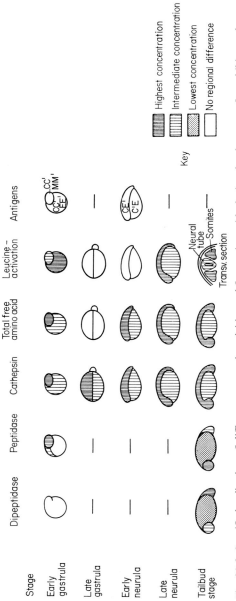

Fig. 20-3. Specific localization of different enzymatic activities and free amino acids during development of amphibian embryos. From Deuchar (1965).

proteins, and HeLa cells (reviewed by Yamada, 1961). There appear to be two distinct influences: one is a mesoderm inducer which is heat labile, exhibits an anterior-posterior gradient in the chordamesoderm, and is believed to be a protein; the other is a forebrain inducer which is relatively heat stable and exhibits a mediolateral gradient. The existence of two principles accounts for the fact that tissues killed by heat or alcohol treatment do not entirely lose their inducing activity, although the quality of induction generally changes in the direction of forebrain development. Further characterization of the natural inducers and their mode of action can be expected in future. Various possibilities are suggested by Deuchar's (1965) studies, which show that cathepsin and peptidase activity are both concentrated in the organizer region during gastrulation, and which also indicate that this region is rich in free amino acids (Fig. 20-3).

Cell Migration, Recognition, and Aggregation

In animal embryos, some of the most conspicuous morphogenetic events involve selective movements of cells, either individually or *en masse*, from one part of the embryo to another. These migrations are very critically timed and result in new juxtapositions of tissues, which in many cases appear to control the initiation of specific tissue-to-tissue inductions. Of all the cell phenomena peculiar to "molecular embryology," these directed mass cell movements touch most immediately on the capacities of cells to interact specifically, and thereby to generate a unique supracellular organization. As noted by Moscona (1962), cell migration implies several distinct problems, including: (1) what initiates the movement of some cells but not others; (2) what is the mechanism of locomotion; (3) what determines the path of movement; and (4) what terminates the migration, i.e., how do the cells recognize their new cell neighbors?

Descriptively, some of the most remarkable examples of embryonic cell migration involve the movements of the primordial germ cells into the developing gonads. It seems to be a general rule in animal embryos that the germ cells originate in a locale that is more or less distant from the other gonad tissues; this principle reaches an extreme in the avian embryo, where the germ cells actually arise from the extra-embryonic endoderm, while the rest of the gonad develops within the

Fig. 20-4. Amoeboid movement in honey bee embryonic cells, detectable at a developmental stage when sheets of ectoderm normally migrate over a mesoderm layer. Note that the cells are progressing in the direction of the inert debris to the upper right. From DuPraw (1965b).

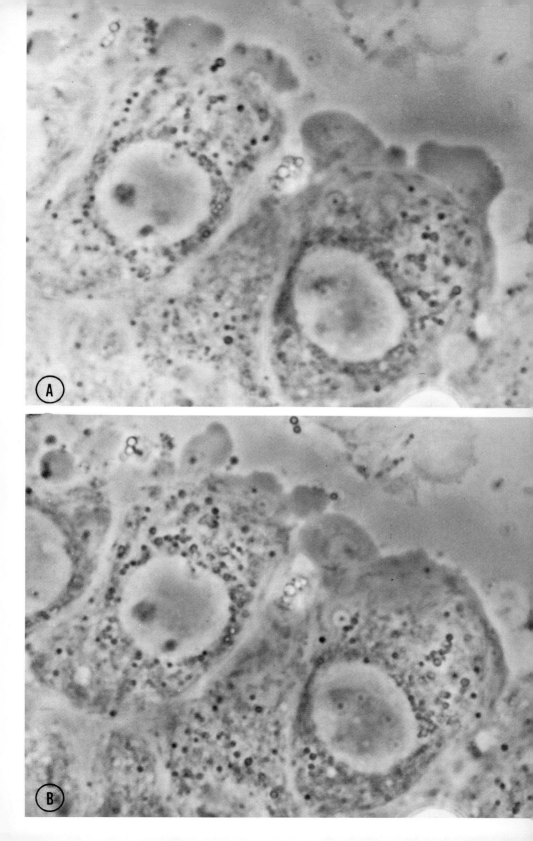

embryo from a mesodermal germinal ridge. Somewhat later in development, the extra-embryonic germ cells enter the circulating blood system and are carried through all parts of the embryo, but it is only in the germinal ridge that they selectively adhere and accumulate. This process has been demonstrated most startlingly by Simon (1960), who linked chick and duck embryos parabiotically and showed that the germ cells of one genus can selectively populate the germinal ridge of the other. In accomplishing their migration the germ cells exhibit a specific recognition of the germinal ridge cells, which is not a self-recognition but an interaction between differentiated cell types that have not previously encountered one another. Similar specific cell recognitions occur when the sperm of a given species selectively fertilize eggs of their own species, and when a developing nerve axon establishes contact with a specific effector organ.

Except in instances when the cells are carried passively through the blood system, the mode of locomotion in typical embryonic migrations seems to be amoeboid. For example, in sea urchin embryos Dan and Okazaki (1956) found that gastrulation is dependent on the extension and contraction of pseudopods by the secondary mesenchyme cells; Gustafson and Wolpert (1961) also observed pseudopod activity during the movement of primary mesenchyme cells. In honey bee embryos, DuPraw (1965b) has shown that cells isolated *in vitro* at a stage when lateral ectoderm sheets are migrating down over a mid-ventral mesoderm plate, typically exhibit pseudopod formation and amoeboid configurations along their free edges (Fig. 20-4). Amoeboid movement is also commonly observed when embryonic or adult tissues are cultured *in vitro*, which has permitted a number of revealing experiments. For instance, Abercrombie and Heaysman (1954) found that fibroblasts tend to move continuously over their glass substratum until they come into direct cell-to-cell contact, after which their movements are restricted in a phenomenon Abercrombie has called "contact inhibition." It has also been demonstrated that the random movements of fibroblasts in culture can be oriented by providing grooves or other textural patterns in the substratum. Evidence that both random and oriented cell movements occur during the development of chick embryos has been obtained by DeHaan (1963), who mapped the migration of precardiac mesoderm cells into the heart region of the chick embryo; at first the movements seem to be randomly dispersive, but later they appear to follow a textural "path" provided by a substratum of special endoderm cells.

The nearly universal capacity of tissue cells to migrate *in vitro* led Weiss to suggest that the ultimate problem of histogenesis is not what makes cells move but what makes them stop moving. Implicit in this concept is the idea that tissues and indeed organisms, are formed by a selective adhesion of individual cells to one another, and that this adhesion is brought about by special surface interactions that are either identical to or closely coupled with the recognition mechanisms. Very strong support for this hypothesis has now been accumulated through experiments involving experimental dissociation of cells, followed by specific cell reaggregation.

The first experimental system for dissociation and reaggregation of tissue cells was discovered by Wilson (1908), who separated living sponges into individual cells and cell groups by straining them through bolting cloth; he found that the strained cells could spontaneously reassociate into spheroid aggregates, which then proceeded to differentiate into complete sponges again. A remarkable specificity for this reaction was demonstrated by Spiegel (1954), who dissociated cells from two species of sponge differing in body color (one cream-white and the other orange); when these cells were mixed together in a random suspension the primary aggregates that formed were chimeric, i.e., they contained both types of cell side by side. However, the cells continued to move in the primary aggregates, and ultimately they formed secondary aggregates which contained either all white cells or all orange cells. The mechanism of "sorting out" has been further explored in a comparable sponge system by Humphreys (1963), who dissociated the cells chemically by removing divalent cations (Ca^{++} and Mg^{++}) at low temperature (5°C). He found that such chemically dissociated cells are unable to reaggregate if they are placed in fresh medium at low temperature, even if the medium contains divalent cations; however, they regain the ability to aggregate if the cell-free supernatant from their chemical dissociation is added back. This demonstrates that some material other than divalent cations is required for aggregation, and that this material tends to be removed from the cells by the dissociation process. If the cells are permitted to reincubate at 22° they are then able to regenerate the adhesion substances very rapidly. That these substances are genus-specific was demonstrated by dissociating *Haliclona* cells and *Microciona* cells separately, then suspending the cells together at low temperature; adding back the *Haliclona* factor resulted in bluish purple *Haliclona* aggregates, while the red-orange *Microciona* cells remained dispersed. Comparable results were observed in the reciprocal experiment with *Microciona* factor. Finally, if both factors were added back together, then both types of specific aggregate appeared. The adhesion materials are destroyed by brief boiling but not by treatment with DNase, RNase, or collagenase, a result indicating that they are specific proteins.

Application of experimental dissociation-reaggregation techniques to vertebrate embryos was first achieved by Holtfreter (1939) and Townes and Holtfreter (1955), who isolated various embryonic layers of the amphibian embryo *in vitro*, disaggregated the cells, and observed their developmental responses to one another. For example, a mixture of presumptive epidermal cells with presumptive neural cells produced a blastula-like sphere in which the epidermal cells eventually migrated to the surface while the neural cells remained in the interior; eventually this combination developed a recognizable neural tube surrounded by a double layer of epidermis (Fig. 20-5). From the results of many such experiments, Townes and Holtfreter proposed that the morphogenetic movements observed in the intact embryo may be accounted for by migratory tendencies inherent in the tissue cells, i.e., some tissues tend to migrate inward and others outward.

A successful extension of this approach to chick and mouse embryos was begun by Moscona (1952), who dissociated the cells by removing divalent cations and digesting briefly with trypsin. Later Moscona developed an elegant rotating culture technique which eliminated variables due to adhesion of the cells to the glass substratum and permitted an exact quantification of the reaggregation phenomenon. In this procedure the suspended cells are swirled together in a rotating vortex at the center of the culture flask, and their tendency to adhere can be measured by the rate and size of the aggregates formed. Even selective adhesion by dead cells can be investigated in this way. Moscona's earlier experiments showed that the cells of many embryonic tissues are able to "recognize" other cells of the same tissue type, aggregating specifically with these in mixed suspensions; for example, cartilage cells aggregate with cartilage and liver cells with liver when both are suspended together. Frequently the secondary aggregates formed in this way advance to a tertiary stage in which functional differentiations are evident, e.g., the cartilage aggregates begin to deposit a characteristic extracellular matrix. Two features of the aggregation phenomenon investigated in this way are especially significant: (1) cells from adult tissues often lack the capacity to aggregate; and (2) aggregation is prevented by low temperatures, suggesting that it is energy dependent. Since the rotating vortex is sufficient to bring the cells together, this energy dependence cannot be explained by a requirement for locomotor activity.

The development of these refined techniques made it possible for Moscona (1957) to investigate the specificity of aggregation in mixtures of chick and mouse embryonic cells. Contrary to the species-specific sorting out observed in sponges, the chick and mouse cells form chimeric aggregates, in which both types of cell are mingled side by side. Never-

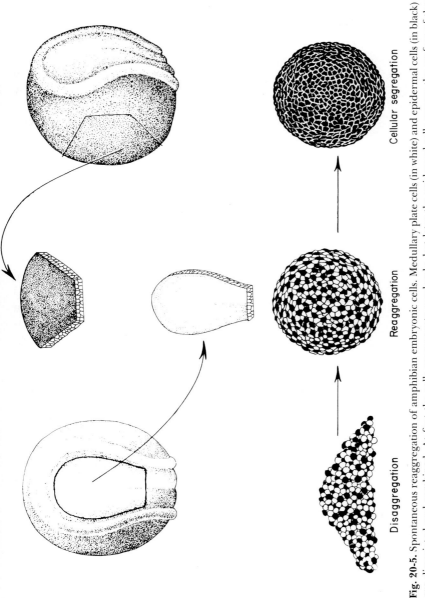

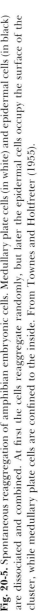

Disaggregation   Reaggregation   Cellular segregation

Fig. 20-5. Spontaneous reaggregation of amphibian embryonic cells. Medullary plate cells (in white) and epidermal cells (in black) are dissociated and combined. At first the cells reaggregate randomly, but later the epidermal cells occupy the surface of the cluster, while medullary plate cells are confined to the inside. From Townes and Holtfreter (1955).

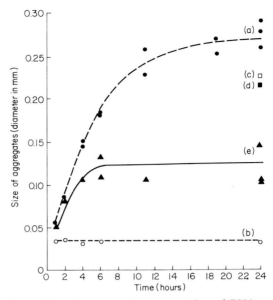

Fig. 20-6. Dependence of *in vitro* aggregation on protein and RNA synthesis. Curve (a) plots the size of control aggregates formed by chick neural retina cells; curve (b) shows that no aggregation occurs in a medium with puromycin, an inhibitor of protein synthesis. In the presence of actinomycin, an inhibitor of RNA synthesis, aggregation begins but plateaus at an early stage [curve (e)]. From Moscona and Moscona (1963).

theless, the same cells are able to sort out according to tissue specificities. Thus in a suspension of mouse kidney, mouse cartilage, chick kidney, and chick cartilage cells, only two types of aggregate form: chimeric chick-mouse kidney and chimeric chick-mouse cartilage. The avian and mammalian cells are able to interact to an amazing extent, forming recognizable kidney tubules together or even inducing one another to differentiate in specific ways. For example in mixtures of chick spinal cord cells with embryonic mouse kidney cells, the neural and kidney tissues first sort out into separate rudiments, after which the chick tissue induces the formation of kidney tubules in the mouse tissue.

The effectiveness of trypsin in separating these tissue cells suggests that a protein is involved in their adhesion. Direct evidence for this supposition has been obtained by Moscona and Moscona (1963), who showed that the reaggregation of chick retinal cells is rapidly but reversibly suppressed by puromycin (an inhibitor of RNA-dependent protein synthesis). Treatment of the cells with actinomycin D also inhibited aggregation, but more slowly and irreversibly, suggesting that a continuous production of messenger RNA is required (Fig. 20-6). As in sponge reaggregation, there is a requirement for divalent cations in the cohesion of embryonic cells, but the temperature sensitivity of the aggregation phenomenon shows that ionic charges alone are not responsible. Although the ultimate mechanisms of recognition and cohesion between tissue cells are not yet known, a comparison of mechanisms that have been found to operate in simpler systems leads to three general hypotheses.

1. Reaggregation may depend on a specific antibody-antigen type reaction. This is the mechanism responsible for the recognition between egg and sperm in various marine invertebrates; in these species the egg produces a specific mucopolysaccharide called "fertilizin" (Lillie, 1919), which has been purified and shown to react *in vitro* with a specific sperm protein (antifertilizin). Fertilizin is a molecule of about 300,000 molecular weight, fibrous in form, containing galactose and some 14 different amino acids (Tyler, 1965).

2. Tissue aggregation may also involve special chemotactic substances of the type shown to occur during the fruiting aggregation in slime molds. These species ordinarily exist as independent amoeboid cells (myxamoebae), but during sexual reproduction the separate cells migrate back from their dispersed positions to form a central, multicellular fruiting body. Bonner (1947) was able to demonstrate that this natural reaggregation is induced by a diffusible substance that attracts the individual cells and stimulates them to follow its gradient of increasing concentration. Disruption of the chemical gradient by artificial currents disrupts the symmetrical pattern of migration. The active principle (named "acrasin" by Bonner) has been isolated by Shaffer (1956) and Sussman *et al.* (1956), who found it to be a fairly small molecule (dialyzable) and stable to boiling as well as to high and low pH. Acrasin could be fractionated into two separate components, neither of which induced aggregation by itself; however these components have not been chemically characterized. Another interesting property of acrasin is that it not only causes oriented movement by the myxamoebae, but it also induces the individual cells to begin synthesizing more acrasin.

3. Steinberg (1962, 1963) has proposed, partly on theoretical grounds, that the sorting out of tissues from mixed suspensions and the movement of one tissue to the interior as the other moves to the exterior, can be accounted for entirely by quantitative differences in the forces of cohesion rather than by qualitative differences involving specific macromolecules. He compares the coaggregation of cells to the condensation of molecules when two immiscible liquids are interdispersed; the liquid with the highest surface tension (cohesiveness) forms the internal or

discontinuous phase, while the other forms the external, continuous phase. This interesting concept has been supported by accurate predictions of the kinetics of cell aggregation in specific mixtures, e.g., between chick heart cells and chick retinal cells.

Undoubtedly, the analysis of surface interactions between cells has been hindered by lack of information concerning the molecular structure of the plasma membrane and the mode of its synthesis (Chapter 10). Additional investigations devoted to these important problems should help to narrow the range of practical hypotheses about tissue cell cohesion and recognition.

REFERENCES

1. Abbo, F. E., and Pardee, A. B. (1960). *Biochim. Biophys. Acta* **39:** 478. [XV]
2. Abbott, J., and Holtzer, H. (1966). *J. Cell Biol.* **28:** 473. [XIX, XX]
3. Abercrombie, M., and Heaysman, J. E. M. (1954). *Exptl. Cell Res.* **6:** 293. [XX]
4. Abetti, G. (1957). "The Sun." Macmillan, New York. [IV]
5. Abram, D., and Koffler, H. (1964). *J. Mol. Biol.* **9:** 168. [IX]
6. Adams, G. (1787). "Essays on the Microscope." Hindmarsh, London. [I]
7. Adelberg, E. A., and Pittard, J. (1965). *Bacteriol. Rev.* **29:** 161. [XV]
8. Afzelius, B. A. (1955). *Exptl. Cell Res.* **8:** 147. [XVI, XVII]
9. Afzelius, B. A. (1963a). *J. Ultrastruct. Res.* **9:** 381. [IX]
10. Afzelius, B. A. (1963b). *J. Cell Biol.* **19:** 229. [XVII]
11. Agrell, I. (1964). *In* "Synchrony in Cell Division and Growth" (E. Zeuthen, ed.), p. 39. Wiley (Interscience), New York. [XIX]
12. Akinrimisi, E. O., Bonner, J., and Ts'o, P. O. P. (1965). *J. Mol. Biol.* **11:** 128. [XII]
13. Albrecht, G., and Corey, R. B. (1939). *J. Am. Chem. Soc.* **61:** 1087. [XII]
14. Alfert, M. (1956). *J. Biophys. Biochem. Cytol.* **2:** 109. [XII]
15. Alfert, M., Bern, H. A., and Kahn, R. H. (1955). *Acta Anat.* **23:** 185. [XVII]
16. Allen, R. D. (1955). *Biol. Bull.* **109:** 339. [IX]
17. Allen, R. D. (1961). *In* "The Cell" (J. Brachet and A. E. Mirsky, eds.), Vol. II, p. 136. Academic Press, New York. [IX]
18. Allen, R. D. (1964). *In* "Primitive Motile Systems in Cell Biology" (R. D. Allen and N. Kamiya, eds.), p. 407. Academic Press, New York. [IX]
19. Allen, R. D., and Roslansky, J. D. (1959). *J. Biophys. Biochem. Cytol.* **6:** 437. [IX]
20. Allen, R. D., Cooledge, J. W., and Hall, P. J. (1960). *Nature* **187:** 896. [IX]
21. Allen, R. D., and Cowden, R. R. (1962). *J. Cell Biol.* **12:** 185. [IX]
22. Allfrey, V. G. (1954). *Proc. Natl. Acad. Sci. U.S.* **40:** 881. [XVII]
23. Allfrey, V. G., and Mirsky, A. E. (1962). *Proc. Natl. Acad. Sci. U.S.* **48:** 1590. [XVII, XX]
24. Allfrey, V. G., and Mirsky, A. E. (1964). *In* "The Nucleohistones" (J. Bonner and P. O. P. Ts'o, eds.), p. 267. Holden-Day, San Francisco, California. [XII, XVIII, XX]
25. Allfrey, V. G., Stern, H., Mirsky, A. E., and Saetren, H. (1952). *J. Gen. Physiol.* **35:** 529. [XVII]
26. Allfrey, V. G., Daly, M. M., and Mirsky, A. E. (1953). *J. Gen. Physiol.* **37:** 157. [XIV]
27. Allfrey, V. G., Daly, M. M., and Mirsky, A. E. (1955). *J. Gen. Physiol.* **38:** 415. [XVII]
28. Allfrey, V. G., Littau, V. C., and Mirsky, A. E. (1963). *Proc. Natl. Acad. Sci. U.S.* **49:** 414. [XVII]
29. Allfrey, V. G., Faulkner, R., and Mirsky, A. E. (1964). *Proc. Natl. Acad. Sci. U.S.* **51:** 786. [XIII, XVII, XX]
29a. Allfrey, V. G., Pogo, B., Littau, V., Gershey, E., and Mirsky, A. E. (1968). *Science* **159:** 314. [XVII]
30. Amberson, W. R. (1958). *Am. Scientist.* **46:** 33. [I]
31. Ames, B. N., and Dubin, D. T. (1960). *J. Biol. Chem.* **235:** 769. [XV]
32. Ames, B. N., and Hartman, P. E. (1963). *Cold Spring Harbor Sym. Quant. Biol.* **28:** 349. [XV]
33. Amoore, J. E. (1961) *Proc. Roy. Soc.* **B154:** 95. [XIX]
34. Andersen, B. and Ussing, H. H. (1960). *In* "Comparative Biochemistry" (M. Florkin and H. S. Mason, eds.), Vol. II. p. 371. Academic Press, New York. [XI]

Roman numerals refer to chapters in which each article is mentioned.

35. Anderson, E., and Beams, H. W. (1956). *J. Biophys. Biochem. Cytol.* **2**(Suppl.): 439. [XVII]
36. Anderson, T. (1951). *Trans. N.Y. Acad. Sci.* [2] **13**: 130. [XVII]
37. Andersson-Cedergren, E. (1959). *J. Ultrastruct. Res.* **1** (Suppl.): 97. [VII]
38. André, J. (1962). *J. Ultrastruct. Res.* **3** (Suppl.): 1. [VII]
39. André, J., and Thiéry, J. (1963). *J. Microscopie* **2**: 71. [IX]
40. Anfinsen, C. B. (1956). *J. Biol. Chem.* **221**: 405. [XII]
41. Anfinsen, C. B., Haber, E., Sela, M., and White, F. H. (1961). *Proc. Natl. Acad. Sci. U.S.* **47**: 1309. [XII]
42. Aposhian, H. V., and Kornberg, A. (1962). *J. Biol. Chem.* **237**: 519. [XIII, XV]
43. App, A. A., and Jagendorf, A. T. (1963). *Biochim. Biophys. Acta* **76**: 286. [V]
44. Arlinghaus, R., Shaeffer, J., and Schweet, R. (1964). *Proc. Natl. Acad. Sci. U.S.* **51**: 1291. [XIV]
45. Arnon, D. I., and Horton, A. A. (1963). *Acta Chem. Scand.* **17** (Suppl.): 135. [III]
46. Arnon, D. I., Allen, M. B., and Whatley, F. R. (1954). *Nature* **174**: 394. [I, IV, VII]
47. Arnon, D. I., Whatley, F. R., and Allen, M. B. (1958). *Science* **127**: 1026. [IV]
48. Arnon, D. I., Whatley, F. R., and Horton, A. A. (1962). *Federation Proc.* **21**: 91. [IV]
49. Arnon, D. I., Tsujimoto, H. Y., and McSwain, B. D. (1964). *Proc. Nat. Acad. Sci. U.S.* **51**: 1274. [IV]
50. Arnon, D. I., Tsujimoto, H. Y., and McSwain, B. D. (1965). *Nature* **207**: 1367. [IV]
51. Aronson, A. (1965). *J. Mol. Biol.* **13**: 92. [XVI]
52. Arrighi, F. E., and Hsu, T. C. (1965). *Exptl. Cell Res.* **39**: 305. [XVIII]
53. Astbury, W. T. (1947). *Symp. Soc. Exptl. Biol.* **1**: 66. [XII]
54. Astbury, W. T., Beighton, E., and Weibull, C. (1955). *Symp. Soc. Exptl. Biol.* **9**: 282. [IX]
55. Atkinson, M. R., and Morton, R. K. (1960). *In* "Comparative Biochemistry" (M. Florkin and H. S. Mason, eds.), Vol. II, p. 1. Academic Press, New York. [III]
56. Atkinson, M. R., Johnson, E., and Morton, R. K. (1959). *Nature* **184**: 1925. [III]
57. Avery, O. T., Macleod, C. M., and McCarty, M. (1944). *J. Exptl. Med.* **79**: 137. [I, XV, XVII]
58. Bahr, G. F., and Zeitler, E., eds. (1965). *In* "Symposium on Quantitative Electron Microscopy," p. 217. Williams & Wilkins, Baltimore, Maryland. [XII, XVIII]
58a. Bailey, K. (1948). *Biochem. J.* **43**: 271. [VIII]
59. Bainton, D. F., and Farquhar, M. G. (1966). *J. Cell Biol.* **28**: 277. [XVI]
60. Baïrati, A., and Lehmann, F. E. (1953). *Exptl. Cell Res.* **5**: 220. [X]
61. Bajer, A. (1967). *J. Cell Biol.* **33**: 713 [XIX]
62. Bajer, A., and Molé-Bajer, J. (1956). *Chromosoma* **7**: 558. [XIX]
62a. Bajer, A., and Molé-Bajer, J. (1963). *In* "Cinemicrography in Cell Biology" (G. G. Rose, ed.), p. 357. Academic Press, New York. [XIX]
63. Baker, P. F., Hodgkin, A. L., and Shaw, T. I. (1962). *J. Physiol. (London)* **164**: 330, 355. [XI]
64. Balbiani, E. G. (1881). *Zool. Anz.* **4**: 637. [XVIII]
65. Ball, E. G. (1938). *Biochem. Z.* **295**: 262. [III, VI]
66. Ball, E. G. (1939). *Cold Spring Harbor Symp. Quant. Biol.* **7**: 100. [III]
67. Ball, E. G., and Ramsdell, P. A. (1939). *J. Biol. Chem.* **131**: 767. [III]
68. Baltzer, F. (1917). "Über Entwicklung und Vererbung bei Bastarden," Verhandl. Schweiz. Naturforsch. Ges., Zurich. [XX]
69. Barer, R., Joseph, S., and Meek, G. A. (1959). *Exptl. Cell Res.* **18**: 179. [XVII]
70. Barnard, E. A. (1960). *In* "The Cell Nucleus" (J. S. Mitchell, ed.), p. 222. Butterworths, London and Washington, D.C. [XII]

Roman numerals refer to chapters in which each article is mentioned.

71. Barnett, R. C. (1953). *Biol. Bull.* **104:** 263. [XIX]
72. Barnicot, N. A. (1966). *J. Cell Sci.* **1:** 217. [IX, XIX]
72a. Barnicot, N. A. (1967). *J. Cell Biol.* **32:** 585. [XVIII]
73. Barnicot, N. A., and Huxley, H. E. (1961). *Ann. Human Genet.* **25:** 253. [XVIII]
74. Barnicot, N. A., and Huxley, H. E. (1965). *Quart. J. Microscop. Sci.* **106:** 197. [XVIII]
75. Barr, G. C., and Butler, J. A. V. (1963). *Nature* **199:** 1170. [XIII]
76. Barrnett, R. J., and Palade, G. E. (1957). *J. Biophys. Biochem. Cytol.* **3:** 577. [VII]
77. Barth, L., and Barth, L. (1959). *J. Embryol. Exptl. Morph.* **7:** 210. [XX]
78. Barton, A. A. (1961). *Cancer Res.* **21:** 198. [XVII]
79. Bauer, H. (1938). *Naturwissenschaften.* **26:** 77. [XVIII]
80. Bayley, S. T. (1964). *J. Mol. Biol.* **8:** 231. [XIV]
81. Beadle, G. W., and Tatum, E. L. (1941). *Proc. Natl. Acad. Sci. U.S.* **27:** 499. [XV]
82. Beale, G. H. (1954). "The Genetics of *Paramecium aurelia*." Cambridge Univ. Press, London and New York. [XX]
83. Beermann, W. (1956). *Cold Spring Harbor Symp. Quant. Biol.* **21:** 217. [XVIII, XX]
84. Beermann, W. (1960). *Chromosoma* **11:** 263. [XVII]
85. Beermann, W. (1961). *Chromosoma* **12:** 1. [XX]
86. Beermann, W. (1966). *In* "Cell Differentiation and Morphogenesis" (W. Beermann, ed.), p. 24. North-Holland Publ., Amsterdam. [XVIII]
87. Beermann, W., and Bahr, G. (1954). *Exptl. Cell Res.* **6:** 195. [XVIII]
88. Beermann, W., and Pelling, C. (1965). *Chromosoma* **16:** 1. [XVIII]
89. Beers, C. D. (1963). *Trans. Am. Microscop. Soc.* **82:** 131. [XVII]
89a. Bělǎr, K. (1929). *Arch. Entwicklungsmech. Organ.* **118:** 359. [XIX]
90. Belitzer, V. A., and Tsibakowa, E. T. (1939). *Biokhimiya* **4:** 516. [III, VI]
91. Benda, C. (1897). "Über die Spermatogenese der Vertebraten und hoherer Evertebraten," Verhandl. Physiol. Ges. Berlin. [VII]
92. Bendall, J. R. (1953). *J. Physiol. (London)* **121:** 232. [VIII]
93. Ben Geren, B. (1954). *Exptl. Cell Res.* **7:** 558. [X]
94. Bennett, H. S. (1956). *J. Biophys. Biochem. Cytol.* **2** (Suppl.): 99. [X]
95. Bennett, H. S. (1960). *Proc. 10th Cong. Soc. Cell Biol., Paris.* [X]
96. Bennett, T. P., Goldstein, J., and Lipmann, F. (1965). *Proc. Natl. Acad. Sci. U.S.* **53:** 385. [XIV]
97. Ben-Shaul, Y. (1964). *Plant Physiol.* **39:** 231. [V]
98. Bensley, R. R., and Hoerr, N. L. (1934). *Anat. Record* **60:** 251, 449. [VII]
99. Benzer, S. (1955). *Proc. Natl. Acad. Sci. U.S.* **41:** 344. [XV]
99a. Benzer, S., and Weisblum, B. (1961). *Proc. Natl. Acad. Sci. U.S.* **47:** 1149. [XIV]
100. Berendes, H. D. (1967). *Chromosoma* **22:** 274. [XX]
101. Berg, P. (1956). *J. Biol. Chem.* **222:** 1025. [XIV]
102. Berg, P., and Ofengand, E. J. (1958). *Proc. Natl. Acad. Sci. U.S.* **44:** 78. [XIV]
103. Berg, P., Fancher, H., and Chamberlin, M. (1963). *In* "Informational Macromolecules" (H. J. Vogel, V. Bryson, and J. O. Lampen, eds.), p. 467. Academic Press, New York. [XII, XIII]
104. Berg, W. (1920). *Arch. Mikr. Anat.* **94:** 518. [XVI]
105. Berg, W. E., and Humphreys, W. J. (1960). *Develop. Biol.* **2:** 42. [XX]
106. Bernfield, M. R., and Nirenberg, M. W. (1965). *Science* **147:** 479. [XIV]
107. Bhaskaran, S., and Swaminathan, M. S. (1960). *Exptl. Cell Res.* **20:** 598. [XVIII]
108. Bianchi, N. O., and deBianchi, M. S. A. (1965). *Chromosoma* **17:** 273. [XVIII]
109. Billen, D. (1962). *Biochem. Biophys. Res. Commun.* **7:** 179. [XII, XIII]
110. Billen, D., and Hnilica, L. S. (1964). *In* "The Nucleohistones" (J. Bonner and P. Ts'o, eds.), p. 289. Holden-Day, San Franciso, California. [XIII]
111. Birnstiel, M. L., and Flamm, W. G. (1964). *Science* **145:** 1435. [XVII]

112. Birnstiel, M. L., and Hyde, B. B. (1963). *J. Cell Biol.* **18:** 41. [XVII]
112a. Birnstiel, M. L., Chipchase, M. I. H., and Hayes, R. J. (1962). *Biochim. Biophys. Acta* **55:** 728, 734. [XVII]
113. Bishop, D., Pace, N., and Spiegelman, S. (1967). *Proc. Natl. Acad. Sci. U.S.* **58:** 1790. [XIII]
114. Bishop, J., Leahy, J., and Schweet, R. (1960). *Proc. Natl. Acad. Sci. U.S.* **46:** 1030. [XIV]
115. Bitler, B., and McElroy, W. D. (1957). *Arch. Biochem. Biophys.* **72:** 358. [VI]
116. Blair, P. V., Perdue, J. F., and Green, D. E. (1964). *Science* **144:** 560. [VII]
117. Blake, C., Koenig, D., Mair, G., North, A., Phillips, D., and Sarma, V. (1965). *Nature* **206:** 757. [XII]
118. Blakely, L. M., and Steward, F. C. (1961). *Am. J. Botany* **48:** 351, 358. [XIX]
119. Blinks, L. R. (1940). *Cold Spring Harbor Symp. Quant. Biol.* **8:** 204. [XI]
120. Blinzinger, K., Rewcastle, N. B., and Hager, H. (1965). *J. Cell Biol.* **25:** 293. [VII]
121. Bloch, D. P., and Godman, G. C. (1955). *J. Biophys. Biochem. Cytol.* **1:** 17. [XVII]
122. Bloch, D. P., and Hew, H. Y. C. (1960a). *J. Biophys. Biochem. Cytol.* **7:** 515. [XX]
122a. Bloch, D. P., and Hew, H. Y. C. (1960b). *J. Biophys. Biochem. Cytol.* **8:** 69. [XX]
123. Boardman, N. K., Francki, R., and Wildman, S. G. (1966). *J. Mol. Biol.* **17:** 470. [XIV]
124. Bode, V. C., and MacHattie, L. A. (1968). *J. Mol. Biol.* **32:** 673. [XII, XV]
125. Boivin, A., Vendrely, R., and Vendrely, C. (1948). *Compt. Rend. Acad. Sci.* **226:** 1061. [XVII]
126. Bollum, F. J. (1960). *J. Biol. Chem.* **235:** 2399. [XII, XIII]
127. Bollum, F. J., and Houts, G. E. (1963). *Federation Proc.* **22:** 462. [XIII]
128. Bollum, F. J., and Potter, V. R. (1957). *J. Am. Chem. Soc.* **79:** 3603. [XIII]
129. Bonhoeffer, F., and Gierer, A. (1963). *J. Mol. Biol.* **7:** 534. [XV]
130. Bonner, J. (1965). "The Molecular Biology of Development." Oxford Univ. Press, London and New York. [XII, XIII, XX]
131. Bonner, J., and Huang, R. C. (1963). *J. Mol. Biol.* **6:** 169. [XIII]
132. Bonner, J., Huang, R. C., and Maheshwari, N. (1961). *Proc. Natl. Acad. Sci. U.S.* **47:** 1548. [XII, XIII]
132a. Bonner, J., Huang, R. C., and Gilden, R. V. (1963). *Proc. Natl. Acad. Sci. U.S.* **50:** 893. [XVII, XX]
132b. Bonner, J., Dahmus, M., Fambrough, D., Huang, R. C., Marushige, K., and Tuan, D. (1968). *Science* **159:** 47. [XII, XVII, XX]
133. Bonner, J. T. (1947). *J. Exptl. Zool.* **106:** 1. [XX]
134. Bonnett, H., and Newcomb, E. (1965). *J. Cell Biol.* **27:** 423. [XVI]
135. Bornstein, P., and Piez, K. A. (1965). *Science* **148:** 1353. [XII]
136. Bovee, E. C. (1964). *In* "Primitive Motile Systems in Cell Biology" (R. D. Allen and N. Kamiya, eds.), p. 189. Academic Press, New York. [IX]
137. Boveri, T. (1888). "Zellen-studien," Vol. 2. Fischer, Jena. [XVIII]
138. Boveri, T. (1889). *Sitzber. Physk.-Med. Ges. Wurzburg.* [XX]
139. Boveri, T. (1905). "Zellen-studien," Vol. 5. Fischer, Jena. [XVII]
140. Boveri, T. (1910). "Die Potenzen der Ascaris-Blastomeren," Festschr. R. Hertwig 3. [XVII]
141. Bowen, R. H. (1929). *Quart. Rev. Biol.* **4:** 299, 484. [XVI]
142. Boyle, P. J., and Conway, E. J. (1941). *J. Physiol. (London)* **100:** 1. [XI]
143. Brachet, J. (1940). *Compt. Rend. Soc. Biol.* **133:** 90. [XVI, XVII]
144. Brachet, J. (1942). *Arch. Biol. (Liege)* **53:** 207. [XVIII]
145. Brachet, J. (1950). "Chemical Embryology." Wiley (Interscience), New York. [XIII]
146. Brachet, J., and Chantrenne, H. (1951). *Nature* **168:** 950. [XVII]

Roman numerals refer to chapters in which each article is mentioned.

147. Bradbury, E. M., and Crane-Robinson, C. (1964). *In* "The Nucleohistones" (J. Bonner and P. Ts'o, eds.), p. 117. Holden-Day, San Francisco, California. [XII]

148. Bradbury, E. M., Price, W. C., Wilkinson, G. R., and Zubay, G. (1962). *J. Mol. Biol.* **4:** 39, 50. [XII]

149. Bradfield, J. R. G. (1955). *Symp. Soc. Exptl. Biol.* **9:** 306. [IX]

150. Brandt, P. W. (1958). *Exptl. Cell Res.* **15:** 300. [X]

151. Brandt, P. W., and Pappas, G. D. (1960). *J. Biophys. Biochem. Cytol.* **8:** 675. [X]

152. Brante, G. (1949). *Acta Physiol. Scand. Suppl.* **63:** 1. [X]

153. Branton, D. (1966). *Proc. Natl. Acad. Sci. U.S.* **55:** 1048. [X]

154. Branton, D. (1967). *Exptl. Cell Res.* **45:** 703. [X]

155. Branton, D., and Park, R. (1967). *J. Ultrastruct. Res.* **19:** 283. [V]

156. Braun, R., Mittermayer, C., and Rusch, H. (1965). *Proc. Natl. Acad. Sci. U.S.* **53:** 924. [XVII, XVIII]

157. Brawerman, G. (1966). *In* "Biochemistry of Chloroplasts" (T. W. Goodwin, ed.), Vol. I, p. 301. Academic Press, New York. [V]

158. Brawerman, G., and Chargaff, E. (1960). *Biochim. Biophys. Acta* **37:** 221. [V]

159. Brenner, S. (1953). *Exptl. Cell Res.* **5:** 257. [XVII]

160. Brenner, S. (1957). *Proc. Natl. Acad. Sci. U.S.* **43:** 687. [XIV]

161. Brenner, S., Streisinger, G., Horne, R. W., Champe, S., Barnett, L., Benzer, S., and Rees, M. (1959). *J. Mol. Biol.* **1:** 281. [IX, XV]

162. Brenner, S., Jacob, F., and Meselson, M. (1961). *Nature* **190:** 576. [XIV, XV]

163. Brenner, S., Stretton, A., and Kaplan, S. (1965). *Nature* **206:** 994. [XIV, XV]

164. Bretschneider, L. H. (1952). *Intern. Rev. Cytol.* **1:** 305. [XVII]

165. Bridges, C. B. (1916). *Genetics* **1:** 107. [XVIII]

166. Bridges, C. B. (1936). *Science* **83:** 210. [XV, XVIII]

167. Bridges, P. N. (1942). *J. Heredity* **33:** 403. [XVIII]

168. Brierley, G. P., Bachmann, E., and Green, D. E. (1962). *Proc. Natl. Acad. Sci. U.S.* **48:** 1928. [VII]

169. Briggs, R., and King, T. (1952). *Proc. Natl. Acad. Sci. U.S.* **38:** 455. [XVII]

170. Briggs, R., and King, T. J. (1955). *In* "Biological Specificity and Growth," 12th Growth Symp. (E. G. Butler, ed.), p. 207. Princeton Univ. Press, Princeton, New Jersey. [XVII, XX]

171. Briggs, R., and King, T. J. (1959). *In* "The Cell" (J. Brachet and A. E. Mirsky, eds.), Vol. I, p. 538. Academic Press, New York. [XVII, XX]

172. Bril-Petersen, E., and Westenbrink, H. G. K. (1963). *Biochim. Biophys. Acta* **76:** 152. [XVIII]

173. Brody, S., and Yanofsky, C. (1963). *Proc. Natl. Acad. Sci. U.S.* **50:** 9. [XV]

174. Brokaw, C. J. (1961). *Exptl. Cell Res.* **22:** 151. [IX]

175. Bronowski, J. (1965). "Science and Human Values," 119 pp. Harper Row, New York. [I]

176. Brown, A. (1902). *J. Chem. Soc.* **81:** 373. [XII]

177. Brown, D. D., and Gurdon, J. B. (1964). *Proc. Natl. Acad. Sci. U.S.* **51:** 139. [XVII]

178. Brown, G. L. (1963). *Progr. Nucleic Acid Res.* **2:** 259. [XIV]

179. Brown, R. (1833). *Trans. Linn. Soc.* **16:** 685. [I, XVII]

180. Brown, S. W. (1966). *Science* **151:** 417. [XVIII]

181. Brown, S. W., and Nur, U. (1964). *Science* **145:** 130. [XVIII]

181a. Brown, S. W., and Zohary, D. (1955). *Genetics* **40:** 850. [XVIII]

182. Brownlee, G., Sanger, F., and Barrell, B. (1967). *Nature* **215:** 735. [XIV]

183. Buchner, E. (1897). *Ber. Deut. Chem. Ges.* **30:** 117. Translation in "Great Experiments in Biology" (M. Gabriel and S. Fogel, eds.), p. 27. Prentice-Hall, Englewood Cliffs, New Jersey. [I, III, VI]

184. Burgos, M. H., and Fawcett, D. W. (1955). *J. Biophys. Biochem. Cytol.* **1:** 287. [XVI]
185. Burnham, C. R. (1962). "Discussions in Cytogenetics." Burgess, Minneapolis, Minnesota. [XVIII]
186. Burton, K. (1959). *Biochem. J.* **71:** 388. [III]
187. Busch, H. (1965). "Histones and Other Nuclear Proteins." Academic Press, New York. [XII, XVII]
188. Busch, H., Steele, W., Hnilica, L., Taylor, C., and Mavioglu, H. (1963). *J. Cell. Comp. Physiol.* **62** (Suppl.): 95. [XII]
189. Butler, J. A. V. (1964). *In* "The Nucleohistones" (J. Bonner and P. Ts'o, eds.), p. 36. Holden-Day, San Francisco, California. [XII]
190. Butler, J. A. V., Cohn, P., and Simson, P. (1960). *Biochim. Biophys. Acta* **38:** 386. [XIV]
191. Cahn, R. D. (1964). *Develop. Biol.* **9:** 327. [XX]
192. Cain, D. F., Infante, A. A., and Davies, R. E. (1962). *Nature* **196:** 214. [VIII]
193. Cairns, J. (1961). *J. Mol. Biol.* **3:** 756. [XV]
194. Cairns, J. (1963a). *J. Mol. Biol.* **6:** 208. [XII, XIII, XV, XVII]
195. Cairns, J. (1963b). *Cold Spring Harbor Symp. Quant. Biol.* **28:** 43. [XII, XV, XVIII]
196. Cairns, J. (1963c). *Proc. 16th Intern. Cong. Zool.* **4:** 271. [XII, XVII]
197. Cairns, J. (1966). *J. Mol. Biol.* **15:** 372. [XVII, XVIII]
198. Cajal, S. R. (1888). *Rev. Trim. Histol. Normal Pathol.* [XI]
199. Caldwell, P. C., Hodgkin, A. L., Keynes, R. D., and Shaw, T. I. (1960). *J. Physiol. (London)* **152:** 561. [XI]
200. Callan, H. G. (1952). *Symp. Soc. Exptl. Biol.* **6:** 243. [XVIII]
201. Callan, H. G. (1955). *In* "Symposium on Fine Structure of Cells," p. 89. Noordhoff, Groningen, Netherlands. [XVIII]
202. Callan, H. G. (1963). *Intern. Rev. Cytol.* **15:** 1 [XVIII, XX]
203. Callan, H. G. (1966). *J. Cell Sci.* **1:** 85. [XVII]
204. Callan, H. G., and Lloyd, L. (1960). *Phil. Trans. Roy. Soc. London* **B243:** 135. [XVIII]
205. Callan, H. G., and MacGregor, H. C. (1958). *Nature* **181:** 1479. [XVIII]
206. Callan, H. G., and Tomlin, S. G. (1950). *Proc. Roy. Soc.* **B137:** 367. [XVII]
207. Callanan, M. J., Carroll, W., and Mitchell, E. (1957). *J. Biol. Chem.* **229:** 279. [XII]
208. Calvin, M. (1959). *Science* **130:** 1170. [IV]
209. Calvin, M. (1963). *In* "The Nature of Biological Diversity" (J. M. Allen, ed.), p. 15. McGraw-Hill, New York. [IV, VI]
210. Calvin, M., and Benson, A. A. (1948). *Science* **109:** 140. [IV]
211. Cantor, K. P., and Hearst, J. E. (1966). *Proc. Natl. Acad. Sci. U.S.* **55:** 642. [XVIII]
212. Carlsen, F., Knappeis, G., and Buchthal, F. (1961). *J. Biophys. Biochem. Cytol.* **11:** 95. [VIII]
213. Carlson, J. G. (1952). *Chromosoma* **5:** 199. [XIX]
214. Carlson, L., Caspersson, T., Foley, G. E., Kudynowski, J., Lomakka, G., Simonsson, E., and Soren, L. (1963). *Exptl. Cell Res.* **31:** 589. [XVIII]
215. Caspersson, T. O. (1950). "Cell Growth and Cell Function." Norton, New York. [XIII, XVII]
216. Caspersson, T. O., and Schultz, J. (1939). *Nature* **143:** 602. [XVI]
217. Chamberlin, M., and Berg, P. (1962). *Proc. Natl. Acad. Sci. U.S.* **48:** 81. [XIII]
218. Chamberlin, M., and Berg, P. (1964). *J. Mol. Biol.* **8:** 297. [XIII]
219. Chamberlin, M., Baldwin, R. L., and Berg, P. (1963). *J. Mol. Biol.* **7:** 334. [XIII]
220. Chambon, P., DuPraw, E., and Kornberg, A. (1968). *J. Biol. Chem.* **243:** 5101. [XIII, XX]

Roman numerals refer to chapters in which each article is mentioned.

221. Champe, S. P., and Benzer, S. (1962). *Proc. Natl. Acad. Sci. U.S.* **48:** 532. [XV]
222. Chance, B. (1943). *J. Biol. Chem.* **151:** 553. [XII]
223. Chance, B., and Hess, B. (1959). *Science* **129:** 700. [VII]
224. Chance, B., and Parsons, D. F. (1963). *Science* **142:** 1176. [VII]
225. Chance, B., and Williams, G. R. (1955). *Nature* **176:** 250. [III, VI]
226. Chance, B., and Williams, G. R. (1956). *Advan. Enzymol.* **17:** 65. [VI]
227. Chance, B., Estabrook, R. W., and Lee, C. (1963). *Science* **140:** 379. [VII]
228. Chapeville, F., Lipmann, F., Ehrenstein, G., Weisblum, B., Ray, W., and Benzer, S. (1962). *Proc. Natl. Acad. Sci. U.S.* **48:** 1086. [XIV]
229. Chapman-Andresen, C. (1963). *Compt. Rend. Trav. Lab. Carlsberg* **33:** 73. [X]
230. Chapman-Andresen, C., and Holter, H. (1955). *Exptl. Cell Res.* **3** (Suppl.): 52. [X]
231. Chapman-Andresen, C., and Holter, H. (1964). *Compt. Rend. Trav. Lab. Carlsberg* **34:** 211. [X]
232. Chaproniere-Rickenberg, D. M., Mahler, H., and Fraser, D. (1964). *Virology* **23:** 96 [XV]
233. Chargaff, E. (1950). *Experientia* **6:** 201. [XII]
234. Chesterton, G. K. (1925). "The Everlasting Man." Dodd, Mead, London. [I]
235. Chorazy, M., Bendich, A., Borenfreund, E., and Hutchison, D. (1963). *J. Cell Biol.* **19:** 59. [XVIII]
236. Chovnick, A., Schalet, A., Kernaghan, R., and Talsma, J. (1962). *Am. Naturalist* **96:** 281. [XVIII]
236a. Chovnick, A., Schalet, A., Kernaghan, R., and Krauss, M. (1964). *Genetics* **50:** 1245. [XVIII]
237. Christensen, A. K., and Fawcett, D. W. (1961). *J. Biophys. Biochem. Cytol.* **9:** 653. [XVI]
238. Chun, E. H. L., Vaughan, M. H., and Rich, A. (1963). *J. Mol. Biol.* **7:** 130. [V]
239. Clark, M. F., Matthews, R. E. F., and Ralph, R. K. (1964). *Biochim. Biophys. Acta* **91:** 289. [V, XIV]
240. Claude, A. (1938). *Science* **87:** 467. [XVI]
241. Claude, A. (1941). *Cold Spring Harbor Symp. Quant. Biol.* **9:** 263. [XIV, XVI]
242. Claude, A. (1948). *Harvey Lectures Ser.* **43:** 121. [VII, XIV, XVI]
243. Clayton, R. K., and Sistrom, W. R. (1964). *Proc. Natl. Acad. Sci. U.S.* **52:** 67. [III]
244. Cleland, J. (1873). *Quart. J. Microscop. Soc.* [N.S.] **13:** 255. [I]
245. Cleveland, L. R. (1963). *In* "The Cell in Mitosis" (L. Levine, ed.), p. 3. Academic Press, New York. [XIX]
246. Clever, Ü. (1964). *In* "The Nucleohistones" (J. Bonner and P. Ts'o, eds.), p. 317. Holden-Day, San Francisco, California. [XX]
246a. Clever, Ü., and Karlson, P. (1960). *Exptl. Cell Res.* **20:** 623. [XX]
247. Clowes, R. C. (1964). *In* "The Bacteria" (I. Gunsalus and R. Stanier, eds.), Vol. V, p. 253. Academic Press, New York. [XV]
248. Cohen, G. N., and Monod, J. (1957). *Bacteriol. Rev.* **21:** 169. [XI]
249. Cohen, M., and Bowler, E. (1953). *Protoplasma* **42:** 414. [V]
250. Cohn, M. (1953). *J. Biol. Chem.* **201:** 735. [VI]
251. Cohn, Z. A., and Hirsch, J. G. (1960). *J. Exptl. Med.* **112:** 983, 1015. [X]
252. Cole, K. S., and Curtis, H. J. (1936). *Cold Spring Harbor Symp. Quant. Biol.* **4:** 73. [X]
253. Coleman, J. R., and Moses, M. J. (1964). *J. Cell Biol.* **23:** 63. [XVIII]
254. Coleman, L. C. (1943). *Genetics* **28:** 2. [XVIII]
255. Colman, R. F., and Frieden, C. (1966). *J. Biol. Chem.* **241:** 3652, 3661. [XII]
256. Collander, R. (1949). *Physiol. Plantarum* **2:** 300. [X]
257. Commoner, B. (1962). *In* "Horizons in Biochemistry" (M. Kasha and B. Pullman, eds.), p. 319. Academic Press, New York. [XIII]
258. Commoner, B. (1964). *Nature* **202:** 960. [XIX]

259. Conklin, E. G. (1917). *J. Exptl. Zool.* **22:** 311. [XIX]
260. Conklin, E. G. (1931). *J. Exptl. Zool.* **60:** 1. [XX]
261. Conklin, E. G. (1951). *Ann. N.Y. Acad. Sci.* **51:** 1281. [IX]
262. Cooper, C., and Lehninger, A. L. (1956). *J. Biol. Chem.* **219:** 489, 519. [VII]
263. Corey, R. B., and Donohue, J. (1950). *J. Am. Chem. Soc.* **72:** 2899. [XII]
264. Cormier, M. J., and Totter, J. R. (1957). *Biochim. Biophys. Acta* **25:** 229. [VI]
265. Corneo, G., Moore, C., Sanadi, D., Grossman, L., and Marmur, J. (1966). *Science* **151:** 687. [VII]
266. Corti, B. (1774). *"Osservazioni microscopiche sulla Tremella e sulla Circolazione del Fluido in una Planta acquajuola."* Lucca. [IX]
267. Costello, D. P. (1961). *Biol. Bull.* **120:** 285. [XIX]
268. Cowan, P. M., and McGavin, S. (1955). *Nature* **176:** 501. [XII]
269. Crampton, C. F. (1957). *J. Biol. Chem.* **227:** 495. [XII, XIII]
270. Crampton, C. F., and Petermann, M. L. (1959). *J. Biol. Chem.* **234:** 2642. [XIV]
271. Crampton, C. F., Stein, W. H., and Moore, S. (1957). *J. Biol. Chem.* **225:** 363. [XII, XVII]
272. Crane, F., Glenn, J., and Green, D. E. (1956). *Biochim. Biophys. Acta* **22:** 475. [VII]
273. Creighton, H. B., and McClintock, B. (1931). *Proc. Natl. Acad. Sci. U.S.* **17:** 492. [XVIII]
274. Crestfield, A. M. (1963). *Federation Proc.* **22:** 419. [XII]
275. Crick, F. H. C. (1963). *Science* **139:** 461. [XIV]
276. Crick, F. H. C. (1966). *J. Mol. Biol.* **19:** 548. [XIV]
277. Crick, F. H. C., Griffith, J., and Orgel, L. (1957). *Proc. Natl. Acad. Sci. U.S.* **43:** 416. [XIV]
278. Crick, F. H. C., Barnett, L., Brenner, S., and Watts-Tobin, R. (1961). *Nature* **192:** 1227. [XIV, XV]
279. Criddle, R. S. (1966). *In* "Biochemistry of Chloroplasts" (T. W. Goodwin, ed.), Vol. I, p. 203. Academic Press, New York. [V]
280. Criddle, R. S., and Park, L. (1964). *Biochem. Biophys. Res. Commun.* **17:** 74. [V]
281. Criddle, R. S., Bock, R. M., Green, D. E., and Tisdale, H. (1962). *Biochemistry* **1:** 827 [III, VII]
282. Crouse, H. V. (1961). *Chromosoma* **12:** 190. [XVIII]
283. Cruft, H. J., and Leaver, J. L. (1961). *Nature* **192:** 556. [XII]
284. Csapo, A. (1960). *In* "Structure and Function of Muscle" (G. H. Bourne, ed.), Vol. I, p. 229. Academic Press, New York. [VIII]
285. Cunningham, W. P., Morré, D. J., and Mollenhauer, H. H. (1966). *J. Cell Biol.* **28:** 169. [XVI]
286. Curtis, H. H., and Cole, K. S. (1942). *J. Cellular Comp. Physiol.* **19:** 135. [XI]
287. Dainty, M., Kleinzeller, A., Lawrence, A. S. C., Miall, M., Needham, J., Needham, D., and Shen, S.-C. (1944). *J. Gen. Physiol.* **27:** 355. [VIII]
288. Dale, H. H. (1914). *J. Physiol. (London)* **48:** 111. [XI]
289. Dallam, R. D., and Thomas, L. E. (1953). *Biochim. Biophys. Acta* **11:** 79. [XVIII]
290. Dalton, A. J., and Felix, M. D. (1953). *Am. J. Anat.* **92:** 277. [XVI]
291. Dalton, A. J., Kahler, H., Streibich, M., and Lloyd, B. (1950). *J. Natl. Cancer Inst.* **11:** 439. [XVI]
292. Daly, M. M., and Mirsky, A. E. (1954). *J. Gen. Physiol.* **38:** 405. [XII]
293. Daly, M. M., Mirsky, A. E., and Ris, H. (1951). *J. Gen. Physiol.* **34:** 439. [XII]
294. Dan, K. (1943). *J. Fac. Sci. Univ. Tokyo, Sect. IV.* **4:** 323. [XIX]
295. Dan, K., and Okazaki, K. (1956). *Biol. Bull.* **110:** 29. [XX]
296. Danielli, J. F. (1958). *Proc. Roy. Soc.* **B148:** 321. [XVII]

Roman numerals refer to chapters in which each article is mentioned.

297. Danielli, J. F., and Davson, H. (1935). *J. Cellular Comp. Physiol.* **5:** 495. [VII, X]
298. Darwin, C. (1868). "Animals and Plants under Domestication," 2 vols. London. [I]
299. Das, C., Kaufmann, B. P., and Gay, H. (1964). *J. Cell Biol.* **23:** 423. [XX]
300. Davenport, H. E. (1952). *Nature* **170:** 1112. [III]
301. Davenport, H. E., and Hill, R. (1952). *Proc. Roy. Soc.* **B139:** 327. [III]
302. Davidson, N. (1964). *In* "The Nucleohistones" (J. Bonner and P. Ts'o, eds.), p. 134. Holden-Day, San Francisco, California. [XII]
303. Davie, E. W., Koningsberger, V. V., and Lipmann, F. (1956). *Arch. Biochem. Biophys.* **65:** 21. [XIV]
304. Davies, H. G., and Tooze, J. (1964). *Nature* **203:** 990. [XVIII]
305. Davies, R. E. (1963). *Nature* **199:** 1068. [VIII, XII]
306. Davison, P. F., and Butler, J. A. V. (1956). *Biochim. Biophys. Acta* **21:** 568. [XII, XVII]
307. Davson, H., and Danielli, J. F. (1943). "The Permeability of Natural Membranes." Macmillan, New York. [X]
307a. Dawid, I. B., and Wolstenholme, D. R. (1967). *J. Mol. Biol.* **28:** 233. [VII]
308. De, D. N. (1961). *Nucleus* **4:** 1. [XVII]
308a. Deamer, D., and Branton, D. (1967). *Science* **158:** 655. [X]
309. Dean, R. B. (1941). *Biol. Symp.* **3:** 331. [XI]
310. DeDuve, C. (1964). *Federation Proc.* **23:** 1045. [X]
311. DeDuve, C., Appelmans, F., and Wattiaux, R. (1952). *2nd Intern. Congr. Biochem., Paris, Abstr. Commun.* p. 278. [X]
312. DeDuve, C., Pressman, B. C., Gianetto, R., Wattiaux, R., and Appelmans, F. (1955). *Biochem. J.* **60:** 604. [X]
313. DeGier, J., and Van Deenen, L. L. M. (1961). *Biochim. Biophys. Acta* **49:** 286. [X]
314. DeHaan, R. L. (1963). *In* "Biological Organization at the Cellular and Supercellular Level" (R. J. C. Harris, ed.), p. 147. Academic Press, New York. [XX]
315. Demerec, M. (1955). *Proc. Natl. Acad. Sci. U.S.* **41:** 359. [XV]
316. Demerec, M. (1964). *Proc. Natl. Acad. Sci. U.S.* **51:** 1057. [XV]
317. DeMoss, J. A., Genuth, S. M., and Novelli, G. D. (1956). *Proc. Natl. Acad. Sci. U.S.* **42:** 325. [XIV]
318. DeRobertis, E. (1954). *J. Histochem. Cytochem.* **2:** 341. [XVII]
319. DeRobertis, E. (1964). "Histophysiology of Synapses and Neurosecretion." Macmillan, New York. [XI]
320. DeRobertis, E., and Bennett, H. S. (1954). *Federation Proc.* **13:** 35. [XI]
321. DeRobertis, E., Rodriguez de Lores Arnaiz, G., Salganicoff, L., Pellegrino de Iraldi, A., and Zieher, L. M. (1963). *J. Neurochem.* **10:** 225. [XI]
322. DeSa, R., Hastings, J. W., and Vatter, A. E. (1963). *Science* **141:** 1269. [VI]
323. Deuchar, E. M. (1965). *In* "The Biochemistry of Animal Development" (R. Weber, ed.), Vol. I, p. 245. Academic Press, New York. [XX]
324. Devlin, T. M., and Lehninger, A. L. (1956). *J. Biol. Chem.* **219:** 507. [VII]
325. DiBerardino, M., and King, T. J. (1965). *Develop. Biol.* **11:** 217. [XVII]
326. Dingle, A. D., and Fulton, C. (1966). *J. Cell Biol.* **31:** 43. [IX]
327. Dintzis, H. M. (1961). *Proc. Natl. Acad. Sci. U.S.* **47:** 247. [XIV]
328. Dirksen, E. R., and Crocker, T. T. (1966). *J. Cell Biol.* **31:** 28A. [IX]
329. Dixon, M., and Webb, E. C. (1964). "Enzymes," 2nd ed. Academic Press, New York. [XII]
330. Djordjevic, B., and Szybalski, W. (1960). *J. Exptl. Med.* **112:** 509. [XVIII]
331. Donnan, F. G. (1911). *Z. Elektrochem.* **17:** 572. [XI]
332. Doty, P. (1962). *Biochem. Soc. Symp.* **21:** 8. [XIV]
333. Doty, P., Boedtker, H., Fresco, J. R., Haselkorn, R., and Litt, M. (1959). *Proc. Natl. Acad. Sci. U.S.* **45:** 482. [XII]

334. Doty, P., Marmur, J., Eigner, J., and Schildkraut, C. (1960). *Proc. Natl. Acad. Sci. U.S.* **46:** 461. [XII]
335. Driesch, H. (1891). *Z. Wiss. Zool.* **53:** 160. [XX]
336. Dubois, R. (1887). *Compt. Rend. Acad. Sci.* **105:** 690. [VI]
337. DuPraw, E. J. (1965a). *Proc. Natl. Acad. Sci. U.S.* **53:** 161. [XIII, XVII, XVIII]
338. DuPraw, E. J. (1965b). *Develop. Biol.* **12:** 53. [IX, XX]
339. DuPraw, E. J. (1965c). *Nature* **206:** 338. [XVII, XVIII]
340. DuPraw, E. J. (1965d). *Am. Zool.* **5:** 648. [XVIII]
341. DuPraw, E. J. (1966a). *Nature* **209:** 577. [XVIII, XIX]
342. DuPraw, E. J. (1966b). *J. Cell Biol.* **31:** 30A. [XVIII]
343. DuPraw, E. J., and Bahr, G. F. (1968). *J. Cell Biol.* **39:** 38A. [XII, XVII, XVIII]
344. DuPraw, E. J., and Rae, P. M. M. (1966). *Nature* **212:** 598. [XVIII, XX]
345. Dutrochet, R. H. (1824). "Recherches anatomiques et physiologiques sur la structure intime des animaux." Paris. [I]
346. Dutrochet, R. (1837). "Memoirs pour servir a l'histoire anatomique et physiologique des vegetaux et des animaux." Brussels. [IV]
347. Dutton, H. J., and Manning, W. M. (1941). *Am. J. Botany* **28:** 516. [IV]
348. DuVigneaud, V., Ressler, C., and Trippett, S. (1953). *J. Biol. Chem.* **205:** 949. [XII]
349. Duysens, L. N. M. (1954). *Nature* **173:** 692. [III]
350. Eccles, J. C. (1964). *Science* **145:** 1140. [X]
351. Eck, R. V. (1963). *Science* **140:** 477. [XIV]
352. Ecker, A. (1849). *Z. Wiss. Zool. Abt. A* **1:** 218. [IX]
353. Edgar, R. S., and Lielausis, I. (1964). *Genetics* **49:** 649. [XV]
354. Edgar, R. S., and Wood, W. B. (1966). *Proc. Natl. Acad. Sci. U.S.* **55:** 498. [XV]
355. Edgar, R. S., Denhardt, G. H., and Epstein, R. H. (1964). *Genetics* **49:** 635. [XV]
356. Edström, J. E. (1960). *J. Biophys. Biochem. Cytol.* **8:** 47. [XVII]
357. Edström, J. E., and Beermann, W. (1962). *J. Cell Biol.* **14:** 371. [XVIII, XX]
358. Edström, J. E., and Gall, J. G. (1963). *J. Cell Biol.* **19:** 279. [XVIII]
359. Edwards, G. J. (1925). *Biol. Bull.* **48:** 236. [X]
360. Edwards, J., Koch, A., Youcis, P., Freese, H., Laite, M., and Donalson, J. (1960). *J. Biophys. Biochem. Cytol.* **7:** 243. [XIX]
361. Ege, R., Gottlieb, E., and Rakestraw, N. W. (1925). *Am. J. Physiol.* **72:** 76. [XI]
362. Ehrenstein, G., Weisblum, B., and Benzer, S. (1963). *Proc. Natl. Acad. Sci. U.S.* **49:** 669. [XIV]
363. Ehret, C. F., and DeHaller, G. (1963). *J. Ultrastruct. Res.* **6** (Suppl.): 1. [IX]
364. Eisenstadt, J., and Brawerman, G. (1964). *J. Mol. Biol.* **10:** 392. [XIV]
365. Emerson, R., and Arnold, W. (1932). *J. Gen. Physiol.* **16:** 191. [IV]
366. Emerson, R., and Lewis, C. M. (1943). *Am. J. Botany* **30:** 165. [IV]
367. Engelhardt, W. A., and Ljubimova, M. N. (1939). *Nature* **144:** 668. [VIII]
368. Englander, S. W., and Englander, J. J. (1965). *Proc. Natl. Acad. Sci. U.S.* **53:** 370. [XIV]
369. Epel, D. (1963). *J. Cell Biol.* **17:** 315. [XIX]
370. Ephrussi, B. (1950). *Harvey Lectures Ser.* **46:** 45. [VII]
371. Epstein, M., and Holt, S. (1963). *J. Cell. Biol.* **19:** 325 [X]
372. Epstein, R. H., Bolle, A., Steinberg, C. M., Kellenberger, E., Boy de la Tour, E., and Chevalley, R. (1963). *Cold Spring Harbor Symp. Quant. Biol.* **28:** 375. [XV]
373. Ernster, L., Siekevitz, P., and Palade, G. E. (1962). *J. Cell. Biol.* **15:** 541. [XVI]
374. Essner, E., and Novikoff, A. (1962). *J. Cell Biol.* **15:** 289. [XVI, XVII]

Roman numerals refer to chapters in which each article is mentioned.

375. Estabrook, R. W., and Sacktor, B. (1958). *J. Biol. Chem.* **233:** 1014. [VII]
376. Faludi-Dániel, A., and Galmiche, J. (1963). *Hereditas* **50:** 136. [V]
377. Fast, J. D. (1962). "Entropy." McGraw-Hill, New York. [II]
378. Fatt, P., and Katz, B. (1952). *J. Physiol. (London)* **117:** 109. [XI]
379. Fawcett, D. W. (1955). *J. Natl. Cancer Inst.* **15:** 1475. [XVI]
380. Fawcett, D. W. (1956). *J. Biophys. Biochem. Cytol.* **2:** 403. [XVIII]
381. Fawcett, D. W. (1961). *Exptl. Cell Res.* **8** (Suppl.): 174. [XIX]
382. Fawcett, D. W. (1964). *In* "Modern Developments in Electron Microscopy" (B. M. Siegel, ed.), p. 257. Academic Press, New York. [XVI]
382a. Fawcett, D. W. (1966). *Am. J. Anat.* **119:** 129. [XVII]
383. Fawcett, D. W., and Ito, S. (1958). *J. Biophys. Biochem. Cytol.* **4:** 135. [XVI]
384. Fawcett, D. W., and Porter, K. R. (1954). *J. Morphol.* **94:** 221. [IX]
385. Feldherr, C. M. (1962). *J. Cell Biol.* **14:** 65. [XVII]
386. Feldherr, C. M. (1964). *J. Cell Biol.* **20:** 188. [XVII]
387. Feldherr, C. M. (1965). *Exptl. Cell Res.* **38:** 670. [XVII]
388. Feldherr, C. M., and Feldherr, A. B. (1960). *Nature* **185:** 250. [XVII]
389. Felix, K., Fischer, H., and Krekels, A. (1956). *Progr. Biophys. Biophys. Chem.* **6:** 1. [XII]
390. Felsenfeld, G., and Cantoni, G. (1964). *Proc. Natl. Acad. Sci. U.S.* **51:** 818. [XIV]
391. Felsenfeld, G., and Rich, A. (1957). *Biochim. Biophys. Acta* **26:** 457. [XII]
392. Feughelman, M., Langridge, R., Seeds, W. E., Stokes, A. R., Wilson, H. R., Hooper, C. W., Wilkins, M. H. F., Barclay, R. K., and Hamilton, L. D. (1955). *Nature* **175:** 834. [XII, XVIII]
393. Feulgen, R., and Rossenbeck, H. (1924). *Z. Physiol. Chem.* **135:** 203. [XII, XVI]
394. Fiers, W., and Sinsheimer, R. L. (1962). *J. Mol. Biol.* **5:** 424. [XV]
395. Filner, P. (1965). *Exptl. Cell Res.* **39:** 33. [XVIII]
396. Finch, J. T. (1964). *J. Mol. Biol.* **8:** 872. [XII]
397. Finch, J. T., Klug, A., and Stretton, A. O. W. (1964). *J. Mol. Biol.* **10:** 570. [XV]
398. Fischberg, M., Gurdon, J. B., and Elsdale, T. R. (1958). *Exptl. Cell Res.* **6** (Suppl.): 161. [XVII]
399. Fischer, E. (1902). *Chem. Zentr.* **26:** 939. [XII]
400. Fischer, H. (1934). *Planta* **22:** 767. [XVII]
401. Fisher, H. F., Conn, E. E., Vennesland, B., and Westheimer, F. H. (1953). *J. Biol. Chem.* **202:** 687. [III]
402. Fiske, C. H., and SubbaRow, Y. (1927). *Science* **65:** 401. [III]
403. Flamm, W. G., and Birnstiel, M. L. (1964). *Exptl. Cell Res.* **33:** 616. [XVII]
404. Fleischer, S., Fleischer, B., and Stoeckenius, W. (1967). *J. Cell Biol.* **32:** 193. [VII]
405. Flemming, W. (1880). Translation (1965). *J. Cell Biol.* **25** (Suppl.): 3. [I, XVIII]
406. Fletcher, W. M., and Hopkins, F. G. (1907). *J. Physiol. (London)* **35:** 247. [VI, VIII]
407. Flickinger, R. A. (1959). *Growth* **23:** 251. [XX]
408. Flickinger, R. A., Hatton, E., and Rounds, D. (1959). *Exptl. Cell Res.* **17:** 30. [XX]
409. Fol, H. (1879). *Mem. Soc. Phys. Nat. Geneve* **26:** 89. [I]
410. Forer, A. (1965). *J. Cell Biol.* **25** (Suppl.): 95. [XIX]
411. Forro, F. (1965). *Biophys. J.* **5:** 629. [XV]
412. Foss, H. M., and Stahl, F. W. (1963). *Genetics* **48:** 1659. [XV]
413. Franklin, N. C. (1961). *Virology* **14:** 417. [XV]
414. Franklin, R. M., and Granboulan, N. (1965). *J. Mol. Biol.* **14:** 623. [XV]
415. Frédéric, J. (1958). *Arch. Biol. (Liege)* **69:** 167. [VII]
416. Frenkel, A. W. (1954). *J. Am. Chem. Soc.* **76:** 5568. [V]
417. Frenster, J. H. (1965a). *Nature* **205:** 1341. [XVII]

418. Frenster, J. H. (1965b). *Nature* **206**: 680. [XX]
419. Frenster, J. H. (1965c). *Nature* **208**: 894. [XVII, XVIII]
420. Frenster, J. H., Allfrey, V. G., and Mirsky, A. E. (1960). *Proc. Natl. Acad. Sci. U.S.* **46**: 432. [XIV, XVII]
421. Frenster, J. H., Allfrey, V. G., and Mirsky, A. E. (1963). *Proc. Nat. Acad. Sci. U.S.* **50**: 1026. [XVII]
422. Fresco, J. R., Alberts, B. M., and Doty, P. (1960). *Nature* **188**: 98. [XII]
423. Friedkin, M., and Wood, H. (1956). *J. Biol. Chem.* **220**: 639. [XVII]
424. Friedländer, M., and Wahrman, J. (1966). *J. Cell Sci.* **1**: 129. [XIX]
425. Fuchs, E., Zillig, W., Hofschneider, P., and Preuss, A. (1964). *J. Mol. Biol.* **10**: 546. [XIII]
426. Fuhs, G. W. (1965). *Bacteriol. Rev.* **29**: 277. [XV]
427. Fuller, R. C. (1963). *In* "General Physiology of Cell Specialization" (D. Mazia and A. Tyler, eds.), p. 223. McGraw-Hill, New York. [V]
428. Furth, J., Hurwitz, J., and Goldmann, M. (1961). *Biochem. Biophys. Res. Commun.* **4**: 362. [XIII]
429. Galibert, F., Lelong, J., Larsen, C., and Boiron, M. (1966). *J. Mol. Biol.* **21**: 385. [XIV]
430. Gall, J. G. (1952). *Exptl. Cell Res.* **2** (Suppl.): 95. [XVIII]
431. Gall, J. G. (1954). *Exptl. Cell Res.* **7**: 197. [XVII]
432. Gall, J. G. (1956a). *Brookhaven Symp. Biol.* **8**: 17. [XVIII]
433. Gall, J. G. (1956b). *J. Biophys. Biochem. Cytol.* **2**: 393. [XVII]
434. Gall, J. G. (1958). *In* "The Chemical Basis of Development" (W. D. McElroy and B. Glass, eds.), p. 103. Johns Hopkins Press, Baltimore, Maryland.
435. Gall, J. G. (1959). *J. Biophys. Biochem. Cytol.* **5**: 295. [XVII]
436. Gall, J. G. (1961). *J. Biophys. Biochem. Cytol.* **10**: 163. [IX]
437. Gall, J. G. (1963a). *In* "Cytodifferentiation and Macromolecular Synthesis" (M. Locke, ed.), p. 119. Academic Press, New York. [XVIII]
438. Gall, J. G. (1963b). *Science* **139**: 120. [XVII]
439. Gall, J. G. (1966a). *J. Cell Biol.* **31**: 639. [IX]
440. Gall, J. G. (1966b). *Natl. Cancer Inst. Monogr.* **23**: 475. [XVII]
441. Gall, J. G. (1966c). *Chromosoma* **20**: 221. [XVII]
441a. Gall, J. G. (1967). *J. Cell Biol.* **32**: 391. [XVII]
442. Gall. J. G., and Callan, H. G. (1962). *Proc. Natl. Acad. Sci. U.S.* **48**: 562. [XVIII]
443. Galvani, L. (1791). "Commentary on the Effects of Electricity on Muscular Motion," 176 pp. Translated by M. G. Foley (1953). Burndy Library, Norwalk, Connecticut. [XI]
444. Gamow, G. (1954). *Nature* **173**: 318. [XIV]
445. Ganesan, A. T., and Lederberg, J. (1965). *Biochem. Biophys. Res. Commun.* **18**: 824. [XV]
446. Gardos, G. (1954). *Acta. Physiol. Acad. Sci. Hung.* **6**: 191. [XI]
447. Garnier, Ch. (1897). *Bibliographie Anat.* **5**: 278. [XVI]
448. Gasser, H. S., and Erlanger, J. (1922). *Am. J. Physiol.* **62**: 496. [XI]
449. Gaulden, M. E., and Perry, R. P. (1958). *Proc. Natl. Acad. Sci. U.S.* **44**: 553. [XIX]
450. Gay, H. (1956). *J. Biophys. Biochem. Cytol.* **2** (Suppl): 407. [XVII, XVIII]
451. Geiduschek, E. P., Nakamoto, T., and Weiss, S. B. (1961). *Proc. Natl. Acad. Sci. U.S.* **47**: 1405. [XIII]
452. Gellert, M., and Davies, D. R. (1964). *J. Mol. Biol.* **8**: 341. [XV]
453. German, J. (1964). *J. Cell Biol.* **20**: 37. [XVII]

Roman numerals refer to chapters in which each article is mentioned.

454. Geyer-Duszyńska, I. (1959). *J. Exptl. Zool.* **141:** 391. [XVII, XX]
455. Gibbons, I. R. (1961). *Nature* **190:** 1128. [IX]
456. Gibbons, I. R. (1963). *Proc. Natl. Acad. Sci. U.S.* **50:** 1002. [IX]
457. Gibbons, I. R. (1967). *In* "Molecular Organization and Biological Function" (J. M. Allen, ed.), p. 211. Harper, New York. [IX]
458. Gibbons, I. R., and Grimstone, A. V. (1960). *J. Biophys. Biochem. Cytol.* **7:** 697. [IX]
459. Gibor, A., and Granick, S. (1962). *J. Cell Biol.* **15:** 599. [V]
460. Gierer, A. (1963). *J. Mol. Biol.* **6:** 148. [XIV]
461. Gifford, E. M., and Tepper, H. B. (1962). *Am. J. Botany* **49:** 902. [XX]
462. Gilbert, W. (1963). *J. Mol. Biol.* **6:** 389. [XIV]
462a. Gilbert, W., and Müller-Hill, B. (1966). *Proc. Natl. Acad. Sci. U.S.* **56:** 1891. [XV, XX]
463. Gillespie, R. J., Maw, G. A., and Vernon, C. A. (1953). *Nature* **171:** 1147. [III]
464. Girard, M., Latham, H., Penman, S., and Darnell, J. E. (1965). *J. Mol. Biol.* **11:** 187. [XIV, XVII]
465. Glynn, I. M. (1957). *Progr. Biophys. Biophys. Chem.* **8:** 241. [XI]
466. Glynn, I. M. (1962). *J. Physiol. (London)* **160:** 18P. [XI]
467. Goldacre, R. J., and Lorch, I. J. (1950). *Nature* **166:** 497. [IX]
468. Goldstein, L. (1958). *Exptl. Cell Res.* **15:** 635. [XVII]
469. Goldstein, L. (1963). *In* "Cell Growth and Cell Division" (R. J. Harris, ed.), p. 129. Academic Press, New York. [XVII]
470. Goldstein, L., and Plaut, W. (1955). *Proc. Natl. Acad. Sci. U.S.* **41:** 874. [XVII]
471. Golgi, C. (1898). *Arch. Ital. Biol.* **30:** 60. [XI, XVI]
472. Gorter, E., and Grendel, F. (1925). *J. Exptl. Med.* **41:** 439. [X]
473. Goulian, M., and Kornberg, A. (1967). *Proc. Natl. Acad. Sci. U.S.* **58:** 1723. [XIII]
473a. Goulian, M., Lucas, Z., and Kornberg, A. (1968). *J. Biol. Chem.* **243:** 627. [XIII]
474. Granboulan, N., and Granboulan, P. (1964). *Exptl. Cell Res.* **34:** 71. [XVII]
475. Granick, S. (1961). *In* "The Cell" (J. Brachet and A. E. Mirsky, eds.), Vol. II, p. 490. Academic Press, New York. [V]
475a. Granick, S., and Gibor, A. (1967). *Progr. Nucleic Acid Res. Mol. Biol.* **6:** 143. [V, VII, IX]
476. Grant, P. (1958). *J. Cellular Comp. Physiol.* **52:** 227, 249. [XVII]
477. Green, A. A., and McElroy, W. D. (1956). *Biochim. Biophys. Acta* **20:** 170. [VI]
478. Green, D. E., Loomis, W. F. and Auerbach, V. H. (1948). *J. Biol. Chem.* **172:** 389. [VII]
479. Green, M. M., and Green, K. C. (1949). *Proc. Natl. Acad. Sci. U.S.* **35:** 586. [XV]
480. Green, P. (1964). *Am. J. Botany* **51:** 334. [V]
481. Greenawalt, J. W., Rossi, C. S., and Lehninger, A. L. (1964). *J. Cell Biol.* **23:** 21. [VII]
482. Greengard, O., Smith, M. A., and Acs, G. (1963). *J. Biol. Chem.* **238:** 1548. [XX]
483. Greider, M. H., Kostir, W., and Frajola, W. (1956). *J. Biophys. Biochem. Cytol.* **2** (Suppl.): 445. [XVII]
484. Griffiths, D. E., and Chaplain, R. A. (1962). *Biochem. Biophys. Res. Commun.* **8:** 497, 501. [VI]
485. Griffiths, D. E., Morrison, J. F., and Ennor, A. H. (1957). *Biochem. J.* **65:** 153. [III]
486. Grimstone, A. V., and Klug, A. (1966). *J. Cell Sci.* **1:** 351. [IX]
487. Grobstein, C. (1956). *Exptl. Cell Res.* **10:** 424. [XX]
488. Grobstein, C. (1966). *Am. Zool.* **6:** 89. [XX]
489. Gropp, A. (1963). *In* "Cinemicrography in Cell Biology" (G. G. Rose, ed.), p. 279. Academic Press, New York. [X]
490. Gross, J., Highberger, J., and Schmitt, F. O. (1954). *Proc. Natl. Acad. Sci. U.S.* **40:** 679. [XII]
491. Gross, P. R., and Cousineau, G. H. (1963). *J. Cell Biol.* **19:** 260. [XIX]

492. Grumbach, M., Morishima, A., and Taylor, J. H. (1963). *Proc. Natl. Acad. Sci. U.S.* **49:** 581. [XX]

493. Grunberg-Manago, M., Ortiz, P. J., and Ochoa, S. (1955). *Science* **122:** 907. [XIII]

494. Grundfest, H. (1957). *J. Neurophysiol.* **20:** 516. [XI]

495. Guest, J. R., and Yanofsky, C. (1966). *Nature* **210:** 799. [XIV, XV]

496. Guild, W. R., and Robison, M. (1963). *Proc. Natl. Acad. Sci. U.S.* **50:** 106. [XV]

497. Gunning, B. E. S. (1965). *J. Cell Biol.* **24:** 79. [V]

498. Gurdon, J. B. (1962). *Develop. Biol.* **4:** 256. [XVII]

499. Gurdon, J. B. (1964). *Advan. Morphogenesis* **4:** 1. [XVII, XX]

500. Gurley, L., Irvin, J., and Holbrook, D. (1964). *Biochem. Biophys. Res. Commun.* **14:** 527. [XIII]

501. Gustafson, T., and Wolpert. L. (1961). *Exptl. Cell Res.* **24:** 64. [XX]

502. Guyénot, E., and Danon, M. (1953). *Rev. Suisse Zool.* **60:** 1. [XVIII]

502a. Hackenbrock, C. R. (1966). *J. Cell Biol.* **30:** 269. [VII]

503. Hadorn, E., Gehring, W., and Staub, M. (1963). *Experientia* **19:** 530. [XX]

504. Hagopian, M. (1966). *J. Cell Biol.* **28:** 545. [VIII]

505. Hall, B. D., and Spiegelman, S. (1961). *Proc. Natl. Acad. Sci. U.S.* **47:** 137. [XIV, XV]

506. Hall, C. E., and Doty, P. (1958). *J. Am. Chem. Soc.* **80:** 1269. [XII]

507. Hämmerling, J. (1934). *Arch. Entwicklungsmech. Organ.* **132:** 424. [XVII]

508. Hämmerling, J. (1943). *Z. Vererbungslehre* **81:** 84, 114. [XVII]

509. Hämmerling, J. (1953). *Intern. Rev. Cytol.* **2:** 475. [XVII]

510. Hämmerling, J. (1959). *Biol. Zentr.* **78:** 703. [XVII]

511. Hämmerling, J. (1963). *Symp. Soc. Exptl. Biol.* **17:** 127. [XX]

512. Hampton, J. C. (1958). *Acta Anat.* **32:** 262. [X]

513. Hanawalt, P., and Wax, R. (1964). *Science* **145:** 1061. [XV]

514. Hanson, J., and Huxley, H. E. (1955). *Symp. Soc. Exptl. Biol.* **9:** 228. [VIII]

515. Hanson, J., and Lowy, J. (1960). *In* "Structure and Function of Muscle" (G. H. Bourne, ed.), Vol. I, p. 265. Academic Press, New York. [VIII]

516. Hanson, J., and Lowy, J. (1961). *Proc. Roy. Soc.* **B154:** 173. [VIII]

517. Hanson, J., and Lowy, J. (1963). *J. Mol. Biol.* **6:** 46. [VIII]

518. Harden, A., and Young, W. (1906). *Proc. Roy. Soc.* **B78:** 369. [III]

519. Hardesty, B., Miller, R., and Schweet, R. (1963a). *Proc. Natl. Acad. Sci. U.S.* **50:** 924. [XIV]

520. Hardesty, B., Hutton, J., Arlinghaus, R., and Schweet, R. (1963b). *Proc. Natl. Acad. Sci. U.S.* **50:** 1078. [XIV]

521. Harris, E. J., and Maizels, M. (1951). *J. Physiol. (London)* **113:** 506. [XI]

522. Harris, J. E. (1941). *J. Biol. Chem.* **141:** 579. [XI]

523. Harris, P. (1961). *J. Biophys. Biochem. Cytol.* **11:** 419. [XIX]

524. Harris, P. (1965). *J. Cell Biol.* **25** (Suppl.): 73. [XIX]

525. Hart, R. G. (1965). *Proc. Natl. Acad. Sci. U.S.* **53:** 1415. [XIV]

526. Harting-Park, J., Meriwether, B., Clodfelder, P., and Cunningham, L. (1961). *J. Biol. Chem.* **236:** 136. [XII]

527. Hartmann, J. F. (1953). *J. Comp. Neurol.* **99:** 201. [XVII]

528. Haruna, I., and Spiegelman, S. (1965). *Proc. Natl. Acad. Sci. U.S.* **54:** 579. [XIII]

529. Haruna, I., Nozu, K., Ohtaka, Y., and Spiegelman, S. (1963). *Proc. Natl. Acad. Sci. U.S.* **50:** 905. [XIII]

530. Harvey, E. B. (1936). *Biol. Bull.* **71:** 101. [XIX]

531. Harvey, E. B. (1946). *J. Exptl. Zool.* **102:** 253. [I, VII]

Roman numerals refer to chapters in which each article is mentioned.

532. Hase, E., Mihara, S., Otsuka, H., and Tamiya, H. (1959). *Arch. Biochem. Biophys.* **83:** 170. [XIX]

533. Hasselbach, W. (1953). *Z. Naturforsch.* **8b:** 449. [VIII]

534. Hasselbach, W., and Makinose, M. (1962). *Biochem. Biophys. Res. Commun.* **7:** 132. [VIII, XVI]

535. Hastings, J. W., and Gibson, Q. H. (1963). *J. Biol. Chem.* **238:** 2537. [VI]

536. Haupt, W. (1964). *Ber. Deut. Botan. Ges.* **76:** 313. [V]

537. Haxo, F. T., and Blinks, L. R. (1950). *J. Gen. Physiol.* **33:** 389. [IV]

538. Hay, E. D., and Revel, J. P. (1963). *J. Cell Biol.* **16:** 29. [XVII, XVIII]

539. Hayashi, M. (1965). *Proc. Natl. Acad. Sci. U.S.* **54:** 1736. [XIII]

540. Hayashi, M., Hayashi, M. N., and Spiegelman, S. (1963). *Proc. Natl. Acad. Sci. U.S.* **50:** 664. [XIII]

541. Hayashi, M., Hayashi, M. N., and Spiegelman, S. (1964). *Proc. Natl. Acad. Sci. U.S.* **51:** 351. [XIII]

542. Hayashi, T. (1952). *J. Gen. Physiol.* **36:** 139. [VIII]

543. Hayashi, T., Holtzman, E., and Lamont, H. C. (1962). *Arch. Biochem. Biophys.* **97:** 551. [XII]

544. Heber, U. (1962). *Nature* **195:** 91. [V]

545. Heilbrunn, L. V. (1920). *J. Exptl. Zool.* **30:** 211. [XIX]

546. Heitz, E. (1928). *Jahrb. Wiss. Botan.* **69:** 762. [XVII, XVIII]

547. Heitz, E. (1931). *Planta* **12:** 775. [XVII]

548. Heitz, E. (1932). *Planta* **18:** 616. [V]

549. Hell, A. (1964). *J. Embryol. Exptl. Morphol.* **12:** 621. [XX]

550. Henking, H. (1891). *Z. Wiss. Zool.* **51:** 685. [XVIII]

551. Henning, U., and Yanofsky, C. (1962). *Proc. Natl. Acad. Sci. U.S.* **48:** 183. [XV]

552. Henri, V. (1903). "Lois Générales de l'Action des Diastases." Hermann, Paris. [XII]

553. Hershey, A. D. (1946). *Genetics* **31:** 620. [XV]

554. Hershey, A. D., and Burgi, E. (1956). *Cold Spring Harbor Symp. Quant. Biol.* **21:** 91. [XV]

555. Hershey, A. D., and Burgi, E. (1960). *J. Mol. Biol.* **2:** 143. [XV]

556. Hershey, A. D., and Burgi, E. (1965). *Proc. Natl. Acad. Sci. U.S.* **53:** 325. [XV]

557. Hershey, A. D., and Chase, M. J. (1952). *J. Gen. Physiol.* **36:** 39. [XV]

558. Hertwig, O. (1876). *Morphol. Jahrb.* **1:** 347. [I]

559. Hess, O. (1967). *Genetics* **56:** 283. [XVIII]

560. Highberger, J. H., Gross, J., and Schmitt, F. O. (1951). *Proc. Natl. Acad. Sci. U.S.* **37:** 286. [XII]

561. Hill, A. V. (1938). *Proc. Roy. Soc.* **B126:** 136. [VIII]

562. Hill, R. (1937). *Nature* **139:** 881. [IV]

563. Hill, R., and Scarisbrick, R. (1951). *New Phytologist* **50:** 98. [III]

564. Hill, R. L., and Smith, E. L. (1956). *Biochim. Biophys. Acta* **19:** 376. [XII]

565. Hind, G., and Jagendorf, A. T. (1963). *Proc. Natl. Acad. Sci. U.S.* **49:** 715. [IV, VI]

566. Hiramoto, Y. (1956). *Exptl. Cell Res.* **11:** 630. [XIX]

567. Hiramoto, Y. (1958). *J. Exptl. Biol.* **35:** 407. [XIX]

568. Hiramoto, Y. (1965). *J. Cell Biol.* **25** (Suppl.): 161. [XIX]

569. Hirata, Y., Shimomura, O., and Eguchi, S. (1959). *Tetrahedron Letters* **5:** 4. [VI]

570. Hirs, C., Moore, S., and Stein, W. (1960). *J. Biol. Chem.* **235:** 633. [XII]

571. Hirs, C. H., Halmann, M., and Kycia, j. H. (1961). In "Biological Structure and Function" (T. W. Goodwin and O. Lindberg, eds.), Vol. I, p. 41. Academic Press, New York. [XII]

572. Hirsch, J. G. (1962). *J. Exptl. Med.* **116:** 827. [X]

573. Hirsch, J. G., and Cohn, Z. A. (1960). *J. Exptl. Med.* **112:** 1005. [X]
574. His, W. (1886). *Abhandl. Saechs Akad. Wiss. Leipsig, Math. Naturw. Kl.* **13:** 477. [XI]
575. Hoagland, M. B. (1955). *Biochim. Biophys. Acta* **16:** 288. [XIV]
576. Hoagland, M. B., Keller, E. B., and Zamecnik, P. C. (1956). *J. Biol. Chem.* **218:** 345. [XIV]
577. Hoagland, M. B., Zamecnik, P. C., and Stephenson, M. L. (1957). *Biochim. Biophys. Acta* **24:** 215. [XIV]
578. Hoagland, M. B., Stephenson, M. L., Scott, J. F., Hecht, L. I., and Zamecnik, P. C. (1958). *J. Biol. Chem.* **231:** 241. [XIV]
579. Hodge, A. J. (1959). *Rev. Mod. Phys.* **31:** 331. [V]
580. Hodge, A. J., and Schmitt, F. O. (1960). *Proc. Natl. Acad. Sci. U.S.* **46:** 186. [XII]
581. Hodgkin, A. L. (1951). *Biol. Rev.* **26:** 339. [XI]
582. Hodgkin, A. L., and Huxley, A. F. (1939). *Nature* **144:** 710. [XI]
583. Hodgkin, A. L., and Huxley, A. F. (1952). *J. Physiol. (London)* **116:** 449, 473. [XI]
584. Hodgkin, A. L., and Keynes, R. D. (1955). *J. Physiol. (London)* **128:** 28. [XI]
585. Hodgkin, A. L., Huxley, A. F. and Katz, B. (1952). *J. Physiol. (London)* **116:** 424. [XI]
586. Hoff-Jorgensen, E., and Zeuthen, E. (1952). *Nature* **169:** 245. [XVII]
587. Hoffman, J. F. (1960). *Federation Proc.* **19:** 127. [XI]
588. Hoffmann-Berling, H. (1954). *Biochim. Biophys. Acta* **15:** 226, 332. [XIX]
589. Hoffmann-Berling, H. (1955). *Biochim. Biophys. Acta* **16:** 146. [IX]
590. Hoffmann-Berling, H. (1958). *Biochim. Biophys. Acta* **27:** 247. [IX]
591. Hoffmann-Berling, H. (1959). *In* "Cell, Organism and Milieu" (D. Rudnick, ed.), p. 45. Ronald Press, New York. [XIX]
592. Hoffmann-Berling, H. (1960). *In* "Comparative Biochemistry" (M. Florkin and H. S. Mason, eds.), Vol. II, p. 342. Academic Press, New York. [IX]
593. Hofmeister, F. (1901). "Die chemische Organization der Zelle." F. Vieweg und Sohn, Braunschweig. [V]
594. Hogeboom, G. H. (1949). *J. Biol. Chem.* **177:** 847. [XVI]
595. Hogeboom, G. H., Schneider, W., and Palade, G. (1948). *J. Biol. Chem.* **172:** 619. [VII]
596. Holley, R. W., Apgar, J., Everett, G., Madison, J., Marquisee, M., Merrill, S., Penswick, J., and Zamir, A. (1965). *Science* **147:** 1462. [XIV]
597. Holliday, R. (1965). *Genet. Res., England* **6:** 104. [XVII, XVIII]
598. Holter, H., and Marshall, J. M. (1954). *Compt. Rend. Trav. Lab. Carlsberg. Ser. Chim.* **29:** 7. [X]
599. Holtfreter, J. (1939). *Arch. Exptl. Zellforsch.* **23:** 169. [XX]
600. Holtfreter, J. (1954). *Exptl. Cell Res.* **7:** 95. [XVII]
601. Hommes, F. A., VanLeeuwen, G., and Zilliken, F. (1962). *Biochim. Biophys. Acta* **56:** 320. [XX]
602. Hooke, R. (1665). "Micrographia." London. [I]
603. Horowitz, N. (1956). *Sci. Am.* **195:** 78. [I]
604. Hörstadius, S. (1937). *Biol. Bull.* **73:** 295. [XX]
605. Hörstadius, S. (1939). *Biol. Rev.* **14:** 132. [XX]
606. Hoshino, M. (1961). *Exptl. Cell Res.* **24:** 606. [XVII]
607. Hotta, Y., and Stern, H. (1963). *Proc. Natl. Acad. Sci. U.S.* **49:** 648. [XIX]
608. Hotta, Y., Ito, M., and Stern, H. (1966). *Proc. Natl. Acad. Sci. U.S.* **56:** 1184. [XVIII, XIX]

Roman numerals refer to chapters in which each article is mentioned.

609. Howard, A., and Pelc, S. R. (1953). *Heredity* **6** (Suppl.): 261. [XVII]
610. Hsu, T. C. (1963). *Exptl. Cell Res. Suppl.* **9:** 73. [XVIII]
611. Hsu, T. C. (1964). *J. Cell Biol.* **23:** 53. [XVII, XVIII]
612. Hsu, T. C., and Somers, C. E. (1961). *Proc. Natl. Acad. Sci. U.S.* **47:** 396. [XVIII]
613. Huang, R. C., and Bonner, J. (1962). *Proc. Natl. Acad. Sci. U.S.* **48:** 1216. [XII, XIII, XVII, XX]
614. Huang, R. C., and Bonner, J. (1965). *Proc. Natl. Acad. Sci. U.S.* **54:** 960. [XII, XVII]
615. Huang, R. C., Maheshwari, N., and Bonner, J. (1960). *Biochem. Biophys. Res. Commun.* **3:** 689. [XIII, XVII]
616. Huang, R. C., Bonner, J., and Murray, K. (1964). *J. Mol. Biol.* **8:** 54. [XII, XIII]
617. Huberman, J. A., and Attardi, G. (1966). *J. Cell Biol.* **31:** 95. [XVIII]
617a. Huberman, J. A., and Attardi, G. (1967). *J. Mol. Biol.* **29:** 487. [XVIII]
618. Huberman, J. A., and Riggs, A. D. (1966). *Proc. Natl. Acad. Sci. U.S.* **55:** 599. [XVII, XVIII]
619. Huennekens, F. M., and Whiteley, H. R. (1960). *In* "Comparative Biochemistry" (M. Florkin and H. S. Mason, eds.), Vol. I, p. 107. Academic Press, New York. [III]
620. Huf, E. (1936). *Arch. Ges. Physiol.* **237:** 143, 240. [XI]
621. Hughes, A. (1959). "A History of Cytology." Abelard-Schuman, London. [I, XVII]
622. Hull, R. W. (1961). *J. Protozool.* **8:** 351. [IX]
623. Hultin, T. (1950). *Exptl. Cell Res.* **1:** 376. [XIV, XVI]
624. Hultin, T., and Bergstrand, A. (1960). *Develop. Biol.* **2:** 61. [XX]
625. Humphreys, T. (1963). *Develop. Biol.* **8:** 27. [XX]
626. Humphreys, T., Penman, S., and Bell, E. (1965). *In* "Molecular and Cellular Aspects of Development" (E. Bell, ed.), p. 410. Harper, New York. [XX]
627. Hurwitz, J., Bresler, A., and Diringer, R. (1960). *Biochem. Biophys. Res. Commun.* **3:** 15. [XIII]
628. Hurwitz, J., Furth, J., Anders, M., and Evans, A. (1962). *J. Biol. Chem.* **237:** 3752. [XIII]
629. Hurwitz, J., Evans, A., Babinet, C., and Skalka, A. (1963). *Cold Spring Harbor Symp. Quant. Biol.* **28:** 59. [XIII, XX]
630. Huxley, A. F. (1957). *Progr. Biophys. Biophys. Chem.* **7:** 255. [VIII]
631. Huxley, A. F., and Niedergerke, R. (1954). *Nature* **173:** 971. [VIII]
632. Huxley, H. E. (1953). *Biochim. Biophys. Acta* **12:** 387. [VIII]
633. Huxley, H. E. (1960). *In* "The Cell" (J. Brachet and A. E. Mirsky, eds.), Vol. IV, p. 366. Academic Press, New York. [VIII]
634. Huxley, H. E. (1963). *J. Mol. Biol.* **7:** 281. [VIII, IX]
635. Huxley, H. E. (1966). *Harvey Lectures Ser.* **60:** 85. [VIII]
636. Huxley, H. E., and Hanson, J. (1954). *Nature* **173:** 973. [VIII]
637. Huxley, H. E., and Zubay, G. (1960). *J. Mol. Biol.* **2:** 10. [XIV]
638. Hydén, H. (1960). *In* "The Cell" (J. Brachet and A. E. Mirsky, eds.), Vol. IV, p. 216. Academic Press, New York. [XI]
639. Ingen-Housz, J. (1779). "Experiences sur Vegetables, etc." F. Didot le Jeune, Paris. Translation (1955) in "Great Experiments in Biology" (M. Gabriel and S. Fogel, eds.), p. 158. Prentice-Hall, Englewood Cliffs, New Jersey, [IV]
640. Ingram, V. M. (1963). "The Hemoglobins in Genetics and Evolution." Columbia Univ. Press, New York. [XII]
641. Ingram, V. M., and Stretton, A. O. W. (1962). *Biochim. Biophys. Acta* **62:** 456. [XII]
642. Inman, R. B. (1964). *J. Mol. Biol.* **10:** 137. [XII]
643. Inman, R. B., Schildkraut, C. L., and Kornberg, A. (1965). *J. Mol. Biol.* **11:** 285. [XIII]

644. Inoué, S. (1953). *Chromosoma* **5:** 487. [XIX]

645. Inoué, S., and Bajer, A. (1961). *Chromosoma* **12:** 48. [XVIII]

646. Inoué, S., and Sato, H. (1962). *Science* **136:** 1122. [XVIII]

646a. Inoué, S., and Sato, H. (1966). *In* "Molecular Architecture in Cell Physiology" (T. Hayashi and A. G. Szent-Györgyi, eds.), p. 209. Prentice-Hall, Englewood Cliffs, New Jersey. [XVIII]

647. Ishida, T., and Miura, K. (1965). *J. Mol. Biol.* **11:** 341. [XIV]

648. Ito, M., Hotta, Y., and Stern, H. (1967). *Develop. Biol.* **16:** 54. [XVIII]

649. Ito, M., Kostyuk, P. G., and Oshima, T. (1962). *J. Physiol.* **164:** 150. [X]

650. Ito, S. and Winchester, R. J. (1963). *J. Cell Biol.* **16:** 541. [XVI]

651. Itoh, M., Izawa, S., and Shibata, K. (1963). *Biochim. Biophys. Acta* **66:** 319. [V]

652. Iwai, K. (1964). *In* "The Nucleohistones" (J. Bonner and P. Ts'o, eds.), p. 59. Holden-Day, San Francisco, California. [XII]

653. Izawa, M., Allfrey, V. G., and Mirsky, A. E. (1963a). *Science* **140:** 382. [XVIII]

654. Izawa, M., Allfrey, V. G., and Mirsky, A. E. (1963b). *Proc. Natl. Acad. Sci. U.S.* **50:** 811. [XVIII]

655. Jacob, F., and Monod, J. (1961a). *J. Mol. Biol.* **3:** 318. [XV, XX]

656. Jacob, F., and Monod, J. (1961b). *Cold Spring Harbor Symp. Quant. Biol.* **26:** 193. [XV, XX]

657. Jacob, F., and Wollman, E. L. (1958). *Symp. Soc. Exptl. Biol.* **12:** 75. [XV]

658. Jacobs, J. (1962). *Intern. Rev. Ges. Hydrobiol.* **47:** 146. [XX]

659. Jacobson, W., and Webb, M. (1952). *Exptl. Cell Res.* **3:** 163. [XVIII]

660. Jahn, T., and Rinaldi, R. (1959). *Biol. Bull.* **117:** 100. [IX]

661. James, T. W. (1964). *In* "Synchrony in Cell Division and Growth" (E. Zeuthen, ed.), p. 323. Wiley (Interscience), New York. [XIX]

662. Janssens, F. A. (1909). *Cellule* **25:** 387. [XVIII]

663. Jarosch, R. (1956). *Protoplasma* **47:** 478. [IX]

664. Jarosch, R. (1964). *In* "Primitive Motile Systems in Cell Biology" (R. D. Allen and N. Kamiya, eds.), p. 599. Academic Press, New York. [VIII, IX]

665. Jehle, H. (1965). *Proc. Natl. Acad. Sci. U.S.* **53:** 1451. [XIII]

666. Johns, E. W., and Butler, J. A. V. (1962). *Biochem. J.* **82:** 15. [XII]

667. Johns, E. W., Phillips, D. M. P., Simson, P., and Butler, J. A. V. (1960). *Biochem. J.* **77:** 631. [XII]

668. Josse, J., Kaiser, A. D., and Kornberg, A. (1961). *J. Biol. Chem.* **236:** 864. [XIII]

669. Kaiser, A. D. (1962). *J. Mol. Biol.* **4:** 275. [XV]

670. Kaiser, A. D., and Hogness, D. S. (1960). *J. Mol. Biol.* **2:** 392. [XV]

671. Kaja, H. (1955). *Protoplasma* **44:** 136. [V]

672. Kalckar, H. (1937). *Enzymologia* **2:** 47. [VI]

673. Kamiya, N. (1959). *Protoplasmatologia* **8,** 3a: 1. [IX]

674. Kamiya, N. (1964). *In* "Primitive Motile Systems in Cell Biology" (R. D. Allen and N. Kamiya, eds.), p. 257. Academic Press, New York. [IX]

675. Kamiya, N., and Kuroda, K. (1956). *Botan. Mag. (Tokyo)* **69:** 544. [IX]

675a. Kamiya, N., and Kuroda, K. (1957). *Proc. Japan Acad.* **33:** 149, 201. [IX]

676. Kartha, G., Bello, J., and Harker, D. (1967). *Nature* **213:** 862. [XII]

677. Kato, Y. (1959). *Develop. Biol.* **1:** 477. [XX]

678. Kaufmann, B. P. (1925). *Am. Naturalist* **59:** 190. [XVIII]

679. Kaufmann, B. P. (1936). *Botan. Rev.* **2:** 529. [XVIII]

Roman numerals refer to chapters in which each article is mentioned.

680. Kaufmann, B. P., and McDonald, M. R. (1956). *Cold Spring Harbor Symp. Quant. Biol.* **21**: 233. [XVII, XVIII]

681. Kaufmann, B. P., McDonald, M. and Gay, H. (1948). *Nature* **162**: 814. [XVIII]

682. Kawamura, K. (1960). *Exptl. Cell Res.* **21**: 1. [XIX]

683. Kawamura, N., and Dan, K. (1958). *J. Biophys. Biochem. Cytol.* **4**: 615. [XIX]

684. Keck, K. (1963). *Proc. 16th Intern. Congr. Zool.* **3**: 203. [XVII]

685. Keilin, D. (1925). *Proc. Roy. Soc.* **B98**: 312. [III]

686. Keilin, D. (1966). "The History of Cell Respiration and Cytochrome." Cambridge Univ. Press, London and New York. [I, III, VII]

687. Keilin, D., and Hartree, E. F. (1938). *Proc. Roy. Soc.* **B125**: 171. [I, III, VII]

688. Keilin, D., and Hartree, E. F. (1939). *Proc. Roy. Soc.* **B127**: 167. [III]

689. Keir, H. M., Smellie, R., and Siebert, G. (1962). *Nature* **196**: 752. [XII, XIII]

690. Kellenberger, E. (1961). *Advan. Virus Res.* **8**: 1. [XV]

691. Kellenberger, E., Sechaud, J., and Ryter, A. (1959). *Virology* **8**: 478. [XV]

692. Kendrew, J. C., Dickerson, R. E., Strandberg, B., Hart, R., Davies, D., Phillips, D., and Shore, V. (1960). *Nature* **185**: 422. [XII]

693. Kennedy, E. P., Fox, C. F., and Carter, J. R. (1966). *J. Gen. Physiol.* **49**: 347. [XI]

694. Kepes, A. (1964). *In* "Cellular Functions of Membrane Transport" (J. F. Hoffman, ed.), p. 155. Prentice-Hall, Englewood Cliffs, New Jersey. [XI]

695. Kerridge, D. (1959). *Biochim. Biophys. Acta* **31**: 579. [IX]

696. Kerridge, D., Horne, R., and Glauert, A. (1962). *J. Mol. Biol.* **4**: 227. [IX]

697. Kessel, R. G. (1963). *J. Cell Biol.* **19**: 391. [XVI]

698. Keyl, H. (1965). *Chromosoma* **17**: 139. [XVIII]

699. Keynes, R. D. (1951). *J. Physiol. (London)* **114**: 119. [XI]

700. Keynes, R. D. (1954). *Proc. Roy. Soc.* **B142**: 359. [XI]

701. Kiefer, B., Sakai, H., Solari, A., and Mazia, D. (1966). *J. Mol. Biol.* **20**: 75. [XIX]

702. Kihlman, B. A. (1962). *Caryologia* **15**: 261. [XVIII]

703. Kihlman, B. A. (1966). "Actions of Chemicals on Dividing Cells." Prentice-Hall, Englewood Cliffs, New Jersey. [XVIII]

704. Kihlman, B. A., and Hartley, B. (1967). *Hereditas* **57**: 289. [XVIII]

704a. Kihlman, B. A., and Hartley, B. (1968). *Mutat. Res.* (in press). [XVII]

705. Kihlman, B. A., Nichols, W., and Levan, A. (1963). *Hereditas* **50**: 139. [XVIII]

706. Kilkson, R., and Maestre, M. F. (1962). *Nature* **195**: 494. [XV]

707. King, R. L., and Beams, H. W. (1938). *J. Exptl. Zool.* **77**: 425. [XX]

708. King, T. J., and Briggs, R. (1956). *Cold Spring Harbor Symp. Quant. Biol.* **21**: 271. [XVII]

709. King, T. J., and DiBerardino, M. A. (1965). *Ann. N.Y. Acad. Sci.* **126**: 115. [XVII]

710. Kingdon, H., Webster, L., and Davie, E. (1958). *Proc. Natl. Acad. Sci. U.S.* **44**: 757. [XIV]

711. Kingsbury, B. F. (1912). *Anat. Record* **6**: 39. [VII]

712. Kirk, J. T. O. (1966). *In* "Biochemistry of Chloroplasts" (T. W. Goodwin, ed.), Vol. I, p. 319. Academic Press, New York. [V]

712a. Kirk, J. T. O., and Tilney-Bassett, R. A. E. (1967). "The Plastids." W. H. Freeman, San Francisco. [V]

713. Kitching, J. A. (1964). *In* "Primitive Motile Systems in Cell Biology" (R. D. Allen, and N. Kamiya, eds.), p. 445. Academic Press, New York. [IX]

714. Klee, W. A., and Richards, F. M. (1957). *J. Biol. Chem.* **229**: 489. [XII]

715. Kleinschmidt, A. K., Lang, D., Jacherts, D., and Zahn, R. K. (1962). *Biochim. Biophys. Acta* **61**: 857. [XV, XVII]

715a. Kleinschmidt, A. K., Burton, A., and Sinsheimer, R. L. (1963). *Science* **142:** 961. [XV]

716. Kleinsmith, L. J., Allfrey, V. G., and Mirsky, A. E. (1966). *Proc. Natl. Acad. Sci. U.S.* **55:** 1182. [XVII]

717. Klingenberg, M., and Pette, D. (1962). *Biochem. Biophys. Res. Commun.* **7:** 430. [VII]

718. Klingenberg, M., Slenczka, W., and Ritt, E. (1959). *Biochem. Z.* **332:** 47. [III]

719. Klug, A., and Caspar, D. L. D. (1960). *Advan. Virus Res.* **7:** 225. [XII, XV]

720. Kluss, B. C. (1962). *J. Cell Biol.* **13:** 462. [XVII]

721. Knappeis, G. G., and Carlsen, F. (1962). *J. Cell Biol.* **13:** 323. [VIII]

721a. Knight, E., and Darnell, J. (1967). *J. Mol. Biol.* **28:** 491. [XIV]

722. Knox, W. E. (1956). *Physiol. Revs.* **36:** 164. [XX]

723. Koelle, G. B., and Friedenwald, J. S. (1949). *Proc. Soc. Exptl. Biol. Med.* **70:** 617. [XI]

724. Kofler, M. (1946). "Festschrift E. C. Barell." Hoffman-LaRoche, Basel. [III]

725. Kölliker, A. (1841). "Beitrage zur Kenntniss der Geschlechtsverhaltniss." Berlin. [I]

726. Konigsberg, W., Guidotti, G., and Hill, R. J. (1961). *J. Biol. Chem.* **236:** PC55. [XII]

727. Konrad, C. G. (1963). *J. Cell Biol.* **19:** 267. [XIX, XX]

728. Kornberg, A. (1957). *In* "The Chemical Basis of Heredity" (W. McElroy and B. Glass, eds.), p. 579. Johns Hopkins Press, Baltimore, Maryland. [XIII]

729. Kornberg, A. (1961). "Enzymatic Synthesis of DNA." Wiley, New York. [XIII]

730. Kornberg, A., Lehman, I., and Simms, E. (1956). *Federation Proc.* **15:** 291. [XIII]

731. Kornberg, A., Bertsch, L., Jackson, J., and Khorana, H. (1964). *Proc. Natl. Acad. Sci. U.S.* **51:** 315. [XIII]

732. Kossel, A. (1884). *Z. Physiol. Chem.* **8:** 511. [XII]

733. Krasnovsky, A. (1960). *Ann. Rev. Plant Physiol.* **11:** 363. [IV, V]

734. Krebs, H. A., and Johnson, W. A. (1937). *Enzymologia* **4:** 148. [VI]

735. Kroeger, H. (1960). *Chromosoma* **11:** 129. [XX]

736. Krogh, A. (1946). *Proc. Roy. Soc.* **B133:** 140. [XI]

737. Kroon, A. M. (1963). *Biochim. Biophys. Acta* **69:** 184. [VII]

738. Kuff, E. L., and Dalton, A. J. (1960). *In* "Subcellular Particles" (T. Hayashi, ed.), p. 114. Ronald Press, New York. [XVI]

739. Kunitz, M. (1940). *J. Gen. Physiol.* **24:** 15. [XVI]

740. Kurland, C. G. (1960). *J. Mol. Biol.* **2:** 83. [XIV]

741. Kuwada, Y. (1939). *Cytologia* **10:** 213. [XVIII]

742. Labaw, L. W., and Mosley, V. M. (1955). *Biochim. Biophys. Acta* **17:** 322 [IX]

743. LaCour, L. F. (1963). *Exptl. Cell Res.* **29:** 112. [XVIII]

744. LaCour, L. F., and Crawley, J. (1965). *Chromosoma* **16:** 124. [XVII]

745. LaCour, L. F., and Pelc, S. R. (1958). *Nature* **182:** 506. [XVIII]

746. LaCour, L. F., and Rutishauser, A. (1954). *Chromosoma* **6:** 696. [XVIII]

747. Lagerstedt, S. (1949). "Cytological Studies on the Protein Metabolism of the Liver in Rat." Hakan Ohlssons Boktrykeri, Lund. [XVII]

748. Langan, T. A., and Lipmann, F. (1965). Unpublished manuscript cited by Kleinsmith *et al.* (1966).

749. Langridge, R., Wilson, H. R., Hooper, C. W., Wilkins, M. H. F., and Hamilton, L. D. (1960). *J. Mol. Biol.* **2:** 19, 38. [XII]

750. Lansing, A. I. (1953). *J. Histochem. Cytochem.* **1:** 265. [I]

751. Lark, C., and Lark, K. G. (1964). *J. Mol. Biol.* **10:** 120. [XV]

752. Lark, K. G. (1966). *Bacteriol. Rev.* **30:** 3. [XV]

Roman numerals refer to chapters in which each article is mentioned.

753. Lark, K. G., and Bird, R. E. (1965). *Proc. Natl. Acad. Sci. U.S.* **54:** 1444. [XV]

754. Lark, K. G., and Lark, C. (1965). *J. Mol. Biol.* **13:** 105. [XV]

755. Lark, K. G., Repko, T., and Hoffman, E. J. (1963). *Biochim. Biophys. Acta* **76:** 9. [XV]

756. Lash, J. W., Hommes, F. A., and Zilliken, F. (1962). *Biochim. Biophys. Acta* **56:** 313, 320. [XX]

757. Laven, H. (1959). *Cold Spring Harbor Symp. Quant. Biol.* **24:** 166, 173. [XX]

758. Lavoisier, A. L., and Laplace, P. (1780). *Memoire sur la Chaleur. Memoires de l'Acad. des Sci. Paris.* Translation (1955) in "Great Experiments in Biology" (M. Gabriel and S. Fogel, eds.), p. 85. Prentice-Hall, Englewood Cliffs, New Jersey. [VI]

759. Ledbetter, M. C., and Porter, K. R. (1963). *J. Cell Biol.* **19:** 239. [IX, XIX]

760. Ledbetter, M. C., and Porter, K. R. (1964). *Science* **144:** 872. [IX]

761. Leder, P., and Bursztyn, H. (1967). *Cold Spring Harbor Symp. Quant. Biol.* **31:** 297. [XIV]

761a. Leder, P., and Nirenberg, M. (1964a). *Proc. Natl. Acad. Sci. U.S.* **52:** 420. [XIV]

762. Leder, P., and Nirenberg, M. (1964b). *Proc. Natl. Acad. Sci. U.S.* **52:** 1521. [XIV]

763. Lederberg, J. (1952). *Genetics* **37:** 720. [XV]

764. Lederberg, J. (1956). *Am. Scientist* **44:** 264. [XV]

765. Lederberg, J., and Tatum, E. L. (1946). *Nature* **158:** 558. [XV]

766. Lee-Huang, S., and Cavalieri, L. F. (1963). *Proc. Natl. Acad. Sci. U.S.* **50:** 1116. [XIII]

767. Leeuwenhoek, A. van (1677). *Phil. Trans. Roy. Soc. London* **11:** 821. Reprinted (1955) in "Great Experiments in Biology" (M. Gabriel and S. Fogel, eds.), p. 106. Prentice-Hall, Englewood Cliffs, New Jersey. [I]

768. Leeuwenhoek, A. van (1702). *Phil. Trans. Roy. Soc. London* **22:** 552. See "The Collected Letters of Antoni van Leeuwenhoek." Swets and Zeitlinger, Amsterdam (1941). [I]

769. Lehman, I. R., Zimmerman, S., Adler, J., Bessman, M., Simms, E., and Kornberg, A. (1958). *Proc. Natl. Acad. Sci. U.S.* **44:** 1191. [XIII]

770. Lehmann, F. E. (1958). *In* "The Chemical Basis of Development" (W. McElroy and B. Glass, eds.), p. 73. Johns Hopkins Press, Baltimore, Maryland. [XX]

771. Lehninger, A. L. (1951). *J. Biol. Chem.* **190:** 345. [VII]

772. Lehninger, A. L. (1959). *J. Biol. Chem.* **234:** 2465. [VII]

773. Lehninger, A. L. (1960). *Ann. N.Y. Acad. Sci.* **86:** 484. [VII]

774. Lehninger, A. L. (1964). "The Mitochondrion." Benjamin, New York. [III, VI, VII, XX]

775. Lehninger, A. L. (1965). "Bioenergetics." Benjamin, New York. [VI, VII]

776. Lehninger, A. L., and Kennedy, E. (1948a). *J. Biol. Chem.* **172:** 847. [VII]

777. Lehninger, A. L., and Kennedy, E. (1948b). *J. Biol. Chem.* **173:** 753. [VII]

778. Lehninger, A. L., Wadkins, C., Cooper, C., Devlin, T., and Gamble, J. (1958). *Science* **128:** 450. [VII]

779. Lehninger, A. L., Rossi, C. S., and Greenawalt, J. W. (1963). *Biochem. Biophys. Res. Commun.* **10:** 444. [VII]

780. Leuchtenberger, C., Leuchtenberger, R., and Davis, A. (1954). *Am. J. Pathol.* **30:** 65. [XVII]

781. Levene, P. A., and London, E. (1929). *J. Biol. Chem.* **83:** 793. [XII]

782. Levin, O. (1962). *Arch. Biochem. Biophys.* **1** (Suppl.): 301. [III]

783. Levinthal, C. (1956). *Proc. Natl. Acad. Sci. U.S.* **42:** 394. [XV]

784. Levinthal, C., and Crane, H. R. (1956). *Proc. Natl. Acad. Sci. U.S.* **42:** 436. [XII, XIII]

785. Levinthal, C. and Davison, P. F. (1961). *J. Mol. Biol.* **3:** 674. [XVII]

786. Levinthal, C., Keynan, A., and Higa, A. (1962). *Proc. Natl. Acad. Sci. U.S.* **48:** 1631. [XIV]

787. Lewin, R. A. (1953). *Ann. N.Y. Acad. Sci.* **56:** 1091. [IX]
788. Lewis, E. B. (1945). *Genetics* **30:** 137. [XV]
789. Lewis, G. N. (1930). *Science* **71:** 569. [II]
790. Lewis, M. R., and Lewis, W. H. (1914). *Am. J. Anat.* **17:** 339. [VII]
791. Lewis, W. H. (1931). *Bull. Johns Hopkins Hosp.* **49:** 17. [X]
792. Lichtenthaler, H. K., and Park, R. B. (1963). *Nature* **198:** 1070. [V]
793. Liebig, J. (1847). *Ann. Chem. Pharm.* **62:** 257. [XI]
794. Liebig, J. (1863). "The Natural Laws of Husbandry." Walton and Maberly, London. [III]
795. Lillie, F. R. (1919). "Problems of Fertilization." Univ. of Chicago Press, Chicago, Illinois. [XX]
796. Lima-de-Faria, A. (1958). *Intern. Rev. Cytol.* **7:** 123. [XVIII]
797. Lima-de-Faria, A. (1959). *J. Biophys. Biochem. Cytol.* **6:** 457. [XVII, XVIII]
798. Lindsay, D. T. (1964). *Science* **144:** 420. [XII]
799. Lineweaver, H., and Burk, D. (1934). *J. Am. Chem. Soc.* **56:** 658. [XII]
800. Ling, G., and Gerard, R. (1949). *J. Cellular Comp. Physiol.* **34:** 382. [XI]
801. Linnane, A. W., Vitols, E. and Nowland, P. G. (1962). *J. Cell Biol.* **13:** 345. [VII]
802. Lipmann, F. (1941). *Advan. Enzymol.* **1:** 99. [III]
803. Littau, V. C., Allfrey, V. G., Frenster, J. H., and Mirsky, A. E. (1964). *Proc. Natl. Acad. Sci. U.S.* **52:** 93. [XVII]
804. Littau, V. C., Burdick, C. J., Allfrey, V. G., and Mirsky, A. E. (1965). *Proc. Natl. Acad. Sci. U.S.* **54:** 1204. [XVII]
805. Littlefield, J., Keller, E., Gross, J., and Zamecnik, P. (1955). *J. Biol. Chem.* **217:** 111. [XIV]
806. Littlefield, J., McGovern, A., and Margeson, K. (1963). *Proc. Natl. Acad. Sci. U.S.* **49:** 102. [XVII]
807. Loeb, J. (1916). "The Organism as a Whole." Putnam, New York. [XX]
808. Loewi, O. (1921). *Arch. Ges. Physiol.* **189:** 239. [XI]
809. Loewy, A. (1952). *J. Cellular Comp. Physiol.* **40:** 127. [IX]
810. Lohmann, K. (1929). *Naturwissenschaften* **17:** 624. [III, VIII]
811. Lohmann, K. (1932). *Biochem. Z.* **254:** 381. [III]
812. Lohmann, K. (1934). *Biochem. Z.* **271:** 264. [VIII]
813. Lohmann, K. (1935). *Biochem. Z.* **282:** 120. [III]
814. Lohmann, K., and Meyerhof, O. (1934). *Biochem. Z.* **273:** 60. [III]
815. Lohmann, K., and Schuster, P. (1937). *Biochem. Z.* **294:** 188. [VI]
816. Longuet-Higgins, H., and Zimm, B. (1960). *J. Mol. Biol.* **2:** 1. [XII]
817. Lorch, I., and Danielli, J. (1950). *Nature* **166:** 329. [XVII]
818. Lorch, I., Danielli, J., and Hörstadius, S. (1953). *Exptl. Cell Res.* **4:** 253. [XIX]
819. Losada, M., Whatley, F. R., and Arnon, D. I. (1961). *Nature* **190:** 606. [IV]
820. Lowey, S., and Cohen, C. (1962). *J. Mol. Biol.* **4:** 293. [VIII]
821. Lowey, S., Kučera, J., and Holtzer, A. (1963). *J. Mol. Biol.* **7:** 234. [VIII]
822. Luck, D. J. L. (1963). *Proc. Natl. Acad. Sci. U.S.* **49:** 233. [VII, X]
823. Luck, D. J. L., and Reich, E. (1964). *Proc. Natl. Acad. Sci. U.S.* **52:** 931. [VII]
824. Lundegardh, H. (1954). *Nature* **173:** 939. [III]
825. Lundsgaard, E. (1930). *Biochem. Z.* **227:** 51. [VIII]
826. Lung, B. (1968). *J. Ultrastruct. Res.* **22:** 485. [XVIII]
827. Luzzati, V., and Nicolaieff, A. (1963). *J. Mol. Biol.* **7:** 142. [XII]

Roman numerals refer to chapters in which each article is mentioned.

828. Lwoff, A. (1950). *New Phytologist* **49:** 72. [V]
829. Lynen, F., and Reichert, E. (1951). *Angew. Chem.* **63:** 47. [III]
830. Lynn, W., and Brown, R. H. (1958). *J. Biol. Chem.* **232:** 1015. [XVI]
831. Lyttleton, J. W. (1962). *Exptl. Cell Res.* **26:** 312. [V]
832. Maaløe, O., and Hanawalt, P. (1961). *J. Mol. Biol.* **3:** 144. [XV]
833. McClintock, B. (1929). *Genetics* **14:** 180. [XVIII]
834. McClintock, B. (1934). *Z. Zellforsch. Mikroskop. Anat.* **21:** 294. [XVII]
835. McClintock, B. (1938). *Genetics* **23:** 315. [XVIII]
836. McConnell, D., Tzagoloff, A., MacLennan, D., and Green, D. E. (1966). *J. Biol. Chem.* **241:** 2373. [VII]
837. McEwen, B. S., Allfrey, V. G., and Mirsky, A. E. (1963). *J. Biol. Chem.* **238:** 758, 2571, 2579. [XVII]
837a. McEwen, B. S., Allfrey, V. G., and Mirsky, A. E. (1964). *Biochim. Biophys. Acta* **91:** 23. [XVII]
838. MacHattie, L., and Thomas, C. (1964). *Science* **144:** 1142. [XII, XV]
839. McKusick, V. A. (1964). "On the X Chromosome of Man." Am. Inst. Biol. Sci., Washington, D.C. [XVIII]
840. MacMunn, C. A. (1886). *Phil. Trans. Roy. Soc. London* **177:** 267. [I, III]
841. Madison, J., Everett, G., and Kung, H. (1967). *Cold Spring Harbor Symp. Quant. Biol.* **31:** 409. [XIV]
842. Maestre, M. F., and Kilkson, R. (1965). *Biophys. J.* **5:** 275. [XV]
843. Maggio, R., Siekevitz, P., and Palade, G. (1963). *J. Cell Biol.* **18:** 293. [XVII]
844. Mahler, H. R., Sarkar, N. K., Vernon, L. P., and Alberty, R. A. (1952). *J. Biol. Chem.* **199:** 585. [III]
845. Mahlberg, P. G. (1964). *In* "Primitive Motile Systems in Cell Biology" (R. D. Allen and N. Kamiya, eds.), p. 43. Academic Press, New York. [IX]
846. Mahowald, A. P. (1963a). *Exptl. Cell Res.* **32:** 457. [XIX]
846a. Mahowald, A. P. (1963b). *Develop. Biol.* **8:** 186. [XX]
847. Maitra, U., and Hurwitz, J. (1967). *J. Biol. Chem.* **242:** 4897. [XIII]
848. Makino, S. (1951). "An Atlas of the Chromosome Numbers in Animals." Iowa State College Press, Ames, Iowa. [XVIII]
849. Malkin, L., Gross, P., and Romanoff, P. (1964). *Develop. Biol.* **10:** 378. [XX]
850. Mann, T. (1945). *Biochem. J.* **39:** 451. [IX]
851. Manton, I. (1952). *Symp. Soc. Exptl. Biol.* **6:** 306. [IX]
851a. Manton, I., and Clarke, B. (1952). *J. Exptl. Bot.* **3:** 265. [IX]
852. Marcker, K., and Sanger, F. (1964). *J. Mol. Biol.* **8:** 835. [XIV]
852a. Marcker, K., Clark, B., and Anderson, J. (1967). *Cold Spring Harbor Symp. Quant. Biol.* **31:** 279. [XIV]
853. Margoliash, E., Smith, E., Kreil, G., and Tuppy, H. (1961). *Nature* **192:** 1121. [XII]
854. Marin, G., and Prescott, D. M. (1964). *J. Cell Biol.* **21:** 159. [XVII, XVIII]
855. Marinozzi, V., and Bernhard, W. (1963). *Exptl. Cell Res.* **32:** 595. [XVII]
856. Markert, C., and Ursprung, H. (1963). *Develop. Biol.* **7:** 560. [XVII]
857. Marks, P., Burka, E., and Schlessinger, D. (1962). *Proc. Natl. Acad. Sci. U.S.* **48:** 2163. [XIV]
858. Marks, P., Rifkind, R., and Danon, D. (1963). *Proc. Natl. Acad. Sci. U.S.* **50:** 336. [XIV]
859. Marsh, B. B. (1952). *Biochim. Biophys. Acta* **9:** 247. [VIII]
860. Marsland, D. (1951). *Ann. N.Y. Acad. Sci.* **51:** 1327. [XIX]
861. Martius, C., and Knoop, F. (1937). *Z. Physiol. Chem.* **246:** 1. [VI]

862. Mast, S. O. (1926). *J. Morphol. Physiol.* **41:** 347. [IX]

862a. Mast, S. O., and Doyle, W. C. (1934). *Protoplasma* **20:** 555. [X]

863. Masters, B., Kamin, H., Gibson, Q., and Williams, C. (1965). *J. Biol. Chem.* **240:** 921. [III]

864. Mather, K. (1937). *Proc. Roy. Soc.* **B124:** 97. [XVIII]

865. Matthaei, J., Jones, O., Martin, R., and Nirenberg, M. (1962). *Proc. Natl. Acad. Sci. U.S.* **48:** 666. [XIV]

866. Matthews, B. W., Sigler, P. B., Henderson, R., and Blow, D. M. (1967). *Nature* **214:** 652. [XII]

867. Maxfield, M. (1953). *J. Gen. Physiol.* **37:** 201. [XI]

868. Mayer, J. R. (1845). "Die organische Bewegung in ihrem Zusammenhang mit dem Stoffwechsel." Heilbronn. [IV]

869. Mazia, D. (1961). *In* "The Cell" (J. Brachet and A. E. Mirsky, eds.), Vol. III, p. 80. Academic Press, New York. [XIX]

870. Mazia, D. and Dan, K. (1952). *Proc. Nat. Acad. Sci. U.S.* **38:** 826. [XIX]

871. Mazia, D., and Hinegardner, R. (1963). *Proc. Natl. Acad. Sci. U.S.* **50:** 148. [XIII]

872. Mazia, D., and Roslansky, J. (1956). *Protoplasma* **46:** 528. [XIX]

873. Mazia, D., and Zimmerman, A. M. (1958). *Exptl. Cell Res.* **15:** 138. [XIX]

874. Mazia, D., Harris, P., and Bibring, T. (1960). *J. Biophys. Biochem. Cytol.* **7:** 1. [XIX]

875. Mazia, D., Chaffee, R., and Iverson, R. (1961). *Proc. Natl. Acad. Sci. U.S.* **47:** 788. [XIX]

876. Mendel, G. (1865). *Verh. Nat. Verein. Brunn* **4:** 3. Translation (1959) in "Classic Papers in Genetics" (J. A. Peters, ed.), p. 1. Prentice-Hall, Englewood Cliffs, New Jersey. [I]

877. Menke, W. (1966). *In* "Biochemistry of Chloroplasts" (T. W. Goodwin, ed.), Vol. I, p. 3. Academic Press, New York. [V]

878. Mercer, E., and Wolpert, L. (1958). *Exptl. Cell Res.* **14:** 629. [XIX]

879. Merriam, R. W. (1959a). *J. Biophys. Biochem. Cytol.* **5:** 117. [XVI]

880. Merriam, R. W. (1959b). *J. Biophys. Biochem. Cytol.* **6:** 353. [IX, XVII]

881. Merriam, R. W. (1961a). *J. Biophys. Biochem. Cytol.* **11:** 559. [XVII]

882. Merriam, R. W. (1961b). *Exptl. Cell Res.* **22:** 93. [XVII]

883. Merriam, R. W. (1962). *J. Cell Biol.* **12:** 79. [XVII]

884. Meselson, M., and Stahl, F. W. (1958). *Proc. Natl. Acad. Sci. U.S.* **44:** 671. [XV]

885. Metchnikoff, E. (1883). *Biol. Zentr.* **3:** 560. [X]

886. Metzner, P. (1920). *Jahrb. Wiss. Botan.* **59:** 325. [IX]

887. Meves, F. (1918). *Arch. Mikrobiol. Anat. Entwicklungsmech.* **92:** 41. [VII]

888. Meyer, A. (1883). "Das Chlorophyll Korn." Felix, Leipzig. [V]

889. Meyer, G. F. (1968). *Z. Zellforsch.* **84:** 141. [XVIII]

889a. Meyer, G. F., and Hess, O. (1965). *Chromosoma* **16:** 249. [XVIII]

890. Meyerhof, O. (1921). *Arch. Ges. Physiol.* **191:** 128. [VIII]

891. Meyerhof, O., and Lohmann, K. (1928). *Biochem. Z.* **196:** 22, 49. [III]

892. Meyerhof, O., and Lohmann, K. (1932). *Biochem. Z.* **253:** 431. [III]

893. Meyerhof, O., and Schultz, W. (1935). *Biochem. Z.* **281:** 292. [III]

894. Michaelis, L. (1900). *Arch. Mikrobiol. Anat. Entwicklungsmech.* **55:** 558. [VII]

895. Michaelis, L., and Menten, M. L. (1913). *Biochem. Z.* **49:** 333. [XII]

896. Michaelis, P. (1954). *Advan. Genetics* **6:** 287. [XX]

897. Michejda, J. (1964). *Bull. Soc. Amis Sci. Lettres Poznan.* [VII]

898. Miescher, F. (1871). *Hoppe-Seyler Med. Chem. Untersuch.* **4:** 441. Translation (1955)

Roman numerals refer to chapters in which each article is mentioned.

in "Great Experiments in Biology" (M. Gabriel and S. Fogel, eds.), p. 233. Prentice-Hall, Englewood Cliffs, New Jersey. [I, XII, XVII]

899. Miescher, F. (1874). *Verhandl. Naturforsch. Ges. Basel* **6:** 138. [XII]

900. Miller, F. (1960). *J. Biophys. Biochem. Cytol.* **8:** 689. [X]

901. Miller, O. J., Breg, W., Mukherjee, B., Van N. Gamble, A., and Christakos, A. (1963). *Cytogenetics* **2:** 152. [XVIII]

902. Miller, O. L. (1964). *J. Cell Biol.* **23:** 60A. [XVII, XVIII]

903. Miller, O. L. (1966). *Natl. Cancer Inst. Monogr.* **23:** 53. [XVII]

904. Minagawa, T. (1961). *Virology* **13:** 515. [XV]

905. Mirsky, A. E., and Pollister, A. (1942). *Proc. Natl. Acad. Sci. U.S.* **28:** 344. [XII, XVII]

906. Mirsky, A. E., and Pollister, A. (1946). *J. Gen. Physiol.* **30:** 117. [XII, XVII]

907. Mirsky, A. E., and Ris, H. (1948). *J. Gen. Physiol.* **31:** 1. [XVII]

908. Mirsky, A. E., and Ris, H. (1949). *Nature* **163:** 666. [XVII, XVIII]

908a. Mirsky, A. E., and Ris, H. (1951). *J. Gen. Physiol.* **34:** 475. [XII, XVII, XVIII, XX]

909. Mitchell, P. (1961). *Nature* **191:** 144. [VII, XI]

910. Mitra, S., and Kornberg, A. (1966). *J. Gen. Physiol.* **49:** 59. [XIII]

911. Miura, K. (1967). *Progr. Nucleic Acid Res. Mol. Biol.* **6:** 39. [XIV]

912. Mizukami, I., and Gall, J. (1966). *J. Cell Biol.* **29:** 97. [IX]

913. Monier, R., Stephenson, M., and Zamecnik, P. (1960). *Biochim. Biophys. Acta* **43:** 1. [XII]

914. Montague, M., and Morton, R. (1960). *Nature* **187:** 916. [III, XII]

915. Montgomery, T. H. (1898). *J. Morphol.* **15:** 265. [XVII]

916. Montgomery, T. H. (1904). *Biol. Bull* **6:** 137. [XVII, XVIII]

917. Moor, H. (1967). *Protoplasma* **64:** 89. [IX, XIX]

918. Moore, B. C. (1963). *Proc. Natl. Acad. Sci. U.S.* **50:** 1018. [XVII]

919. Moore, J. A. (1958). *Exptl. Cell Res.* **6** (Suppl.): 179. [XVII]

920. Moore, J. A. (1960). *Develop. Biol.* **2:** 535. [XVII]

921. Moore, J. A. (1962). *J. Cellular Comp. Physiol.* **1** (Suppl.): 19. [XX]

922. Moorhead, P. S., and Defendi, V. (1963). *J. Cell Biol.* **16:** 202. [XVII, XVIII]

923. Morgan, A. R., Wells, R. D., and Khorana, H. G. (1966). *Proc. Natl. Acad. Sci. U.S.* **56:** 1899. [XIV]

924. Morgan, T. H. (1896). *Arch. Entwicklungsmech. Organ.* **3:** 339. [XIX]

925. Moritz, K. B. (1967). *Arch. Entwicklungsmech. Organ.* **159:** 31, 203. [XX]

926. Mortenson, L. E., Valentine, R. C., and Carnahan, J. E. (1962). *Biochem. Biophys. Res. Commun.* **7:** 448. [III]

927. Moscona, A. (1952). *Exptl. Cell Res.* **3:** 535. [XX]

927a. Moscona, A. (1957). *Proc. Natl. Acad. Sci. U.S.* **43:** 184. [XX]

928. Moscona, A. (1962). *Intern. Rev. Exptl. Path.* **1:** 371. [XX]

929. Moscona, M., and Moscona, A. (1963). *Science* **142:** 1070. [XX]

930. Moses, M. J. (1956). *J. Biophys. Biochem. Cytol.* **2:** 215. [XVIII]

931. Moses, M. J., and Coleman, J. R. (1964). *In* "The Role of Chromosomes in Development" (M. Locke, ed.), p. 14. Academic Press, New York. [XVII, XVIII]

932. Mota, M. (1959). *Exptl. Cell Res.* **17:** 76. [XIX]

933. Mota, M. (1962). *Proc. 5th Intern. Congr. Electron Microscopy* **2: NN-11.** [XVIII]

934. Muhlethaler, K. (1966). *In* "Biochemistry of Chloroplasts" (T. W. Goodwin, ed.), Vol. I, p. 49. Academic Press, New York. [V]

935. Mueller, G. C., and Kajiwara, K. (1966). *Biochim. Biophys. Acta* **114:** 108. [XVIII]

936. Mueller, P., Rudin, D. O., Tien, H., and Wescott, W. (1962). *Nature* **194:** 979. [X, XI]

937. Muirhead, H., and Perutz, M. F. (1963). *Nature* **199:** 633. [XII]

938. Mulder, G. J. (1839). *Berzelius Jahresber.* **18:** 534. [XII]

939. Mullins, L. J. (1961). *Ann. N.Y. Acad. Sci.* **94:** 390. [X]

940. Mundry, K. W., and Gierer, A. (1958). *Z. Vererbungslehre* **89:** 614. [XV]

941. Nagai, T., Makinose, M., and Hasselbach, W. (1960). *Biochim. Biophys. Acta* **43:** 223. [VIII]

942. Nagata, T. (1963). *Proc. Natl. Acad. Sci. U.S.* **49:** 551. [XV]

943. Nägeli, C. (1884). "Mechanisch-Physiologische Theorie der Abstammungslehre." Munich. [I]

944. Nakamoto, T., and Weiss, S. B. (1962). *Proc. Natl. Acad. Sci. U.S.* **48:** 880. [XIII]

945. Nanninga, L., and Mommaerts, W. (1960). *Proc. Natl. Acad. Sci. U.S.* **46:** 1155, 1166. [VIII]

946. Naora, H., Naora, H., and Brachet, J. (1960). *J. Gen. Physiol.* **43:** 1083. [XVII]

947. Naora, H., Naora, H., Izawa, M., Allfrey, V. G., and Mirsky, A. E. (1962). *Proc. Natl. Acad. Sci. U.S.* **48:** 853. [XVII]

948. Nass, M. M. K. (1966). *Proc. Natl. Acad. Sci. U.S.* **56:** 1215. [VII]

949. Nass, M. M. K., and Nass, S. (1963). *J. Cell Biol.* **19:** 593. [VII]

950. Naughton, M., and Dintzis, H. (1962). *Proc. Natl. Acad. Sci. U.S.* **48:** 1822. [XIV]

951. Neary, G. J., Savage, J., and Evans, H. (1964). *Intern. J. Radiation Biol.* **8:** 1. [XVIII]

952. Nebel, B. R. (1939). *Botan. Rev.* **5:** 563. [XVIII]

953. Needham, J., Shen, S-C., Needham, D. M., and Lawrence, A. (1941). *Nature* **147:** 766. [VIII]

954. Neelin, J. M. (1964). *In* "The Nucleohistones" (J. Bonner and P. Ts'o, eds.), p. 66. Holden-Day, San Francisco, California. [XII]

955. Neelin, J. M., and Neelin, E. M. (1960). *Can. J. Biochem. Physiol.* **38:** 355. [XII]

956. Neidle, A., and Waelsch, H. (1964). *Science* **145:** 1059. [XII]

957. Nelson, L. (1954). *Biochim. Biophys. Acta* **14:** 312. [IX]

958. Nernst, W. (1908). *Arch. Ges. Physiol.* **122:** 275. [XI]

959. Neubert, D., Wojtczak, A., and Lehninger, A. L. (1962). *Proc. Natl. Acad. Sci. U.S.* **48:** 1651. [VII]

960. Neutra, M., and Leblond, C. (1966). *J. Cell Biol.* **30:** 119. [XVI]

961. Nicklas, R. B. (1959). *Chromosoma* **10:** 301. [XX]

962. Nicklas, R. B. (1965). *J. Cell Biol.* **25** (Suppl.): 119. [XIX]

963. Nicklas, R. B. (1967). *Chromosoma* **21:** 17. [XIX]

964. Nielsen, S. O., and Lehninger, A. L. (1954). *J. Am. Chem. Soc.* **76:** 3860. [VI]

965. Nirenberg, M., and Leder, P. (1964). *Science* **145:** 1399. [XIV]

966. Nirenberg, M., and Matthaei, J. (1961). *Proc. Natl. Acad. Sci. U.S.* **47:** 1588. [XIV]

967. Nirenberg, M., Leder, P., Bernfield, M., Brimacombe, R., Trupin, J., Rottman, F., and O'Neal, C. (1965). *Proc. Natl. Acad. Sci U.S.* **53:** 1161. [XIV]

968. Nirula, S., Bhaskaran, S., and Swaminathan, M. (1961). *Exptl. Cell Res.* **24:** 160. [XVIII]

968a. Nishimura, S., Jones, D., Ohtsuka, E., Hayatsu, H., Jacob, T., and Khorana, H. (1965). *J. Mol. Biol.* **13:** 283. [XIV]

969. Nobel, P. S., and Packer, L. (1965). *Plant Physiol.* **40:** 633. [V]

970. Noda, L., Kuby, S., and Lardy, H. (1954). *J. Biol. Chem.* **210:** 83. [III]

971. North, A. C. T., and Rich, A. (1961). *Nature* **191:** 1242. [XV]

972. Novikoff, A. B. (1957). *Symp. Soc. Exptl. Biol.* **10:** 92. [VII]

973. Novikoff, A. B., Beaufay, H., and DeDuve, C. (1956). *J. Biophys. Biochem. Cytol.* **2** (Suppl.): 179. [X]

Roman numerals refer to chapters in which each article is mentioned.

974. Novikoff, A. B., Essner, E., and Quintana, N. (1964). *Federation Proc.* **23:** 1010. [X, XVI]
975. Nylander, O., and Malmstrom, B. G. (1959). *Biochim. Biophys. Acta* **34:** 196. [XII]
976. Ochoa, S. (1943). *J. Biol. Chem.* **151:** 493. [VI]
977. Ochoa, S. (1956). *Federation Proc.* **15:** 832. [I, XII, XIII]
978. Oesper, P. (1950). *Arch. Biochem.* **27:** 255. [III]
979. Ohnishi, T. (1962a). *J. Biochem.* **52:** 145. [XIX]
980. Ohnishi, T. (1962b). *J. Biochem.* **52:** 307. [X]
981. Ohnishi, T. (1964). *J. Biochem.* **55:** 494. [V, VIII]
982. Ohnishi, T., and Kawamura, H. (1963). *J. Phys. Soc. Japan* **18:** 1559. [XI]
982a. Ohnishi, T., and Ohnishi, T. (1962). *J. Biochem. (Tokyo)* **51:** 380. [VII]
983. Ohnuki, Y. (1965). *Nature* **208:** 916. [XVIII]
984. Ohtaka, Y., and Spiegelman, S. (1963). *Science* **142:** 493. [XV, XX]
985. Okada, Y. K. (1938). *Growth* **2:** 49. [XX]
986. Okazaki, T., and Kornberg, A. (1964). *J. Biol. Chem.* **239:** 259. [XIII]
987. Olivera, B. M., and Lehman, I. R. (1967). *Proc. Natl. Acad. Sci. U.S.* **57:** 1426. [XVII, XVIII]
988. Osawa, S., Allfrey, V. G., and Mirsky, A. E. (1957). *J. Gen. Physiol.* **40:** 491. [XVII]
989. Osgood, E., Jenkins, D., Brooks, R., and Lawson, R. (1964). *Ann. N.Y. Acad. Sci.* **113:** 717. [XVIII]
990. Östergren, G., and Wakonig, T. (1954). *Botan. Notiser* **4:** 357. [XVIII]
991. Östergren, G., Molè-Bajer, J., and Bajer, A. (1960). *Ann. N.Y. Acad. Sci.* **90:** 381. [XIX]
992. Osterhout, W. J. V. (1931). *Biol. Rev.* **6:** 369. [XI]
993. Osterhout, W. J. V. (1933). *Ergeb. Physiol. Biol. Chem. Exptl. Pharmakol.* **35:** 967. [XI]
994. Packer, L. (1966). *In* "Biochemistry of Chloroplasts" (T. W. Goodwin, ed.), Vol. I, p. 233. Academic Press, New York. [V]
995. Packer, L., Marchant, R., and Mukohata, Y. (1963). *Biochim. Biophys. Acta* **75:** 12, 23. [V]
996. Page, G. G., and Huxley, H. E. (1963). *J. Cell Biol.* **19:** 369. [VIII]
997. Painter, T. S. (1933). *Science* **78:** 585. [XV, XVIII]
998. Palade, G. E. (1952). *Anat. Record* **114:** 427. [VII]
999. Palade, G. E. (1956). *J. Biophys. Biochem. Cytol.* **2** (Suppl.): 85. [XVII]
1000. Palade, G. E. (1961). *In* "Electron Microscopy in Anatomy" (J. Boyd, F. Johnson, and J. Levers, eds.), p. 176. Williams & Wilkins, Baltimore, Maryland. [XVI]
1001. Palade, G. E., and Porter, K. R. (1954). *J. Exptl. Med.* **100:** 641. [XVI]
1002. Palade, G. E., and Siekevitz, P. (1956). *J. Biophys. Biochem. Cytol.* **2:** 171. [XIV, XVI]
1003. Palay, S. L. (1960). *J. Biophys. Biochem. Cytol.* **7:** 391. [XVII]
1004. Palay, S. L., and Karlin, L. J. (1959). *J. Biophys. Biochem. Cytol.* **5:** 373. [XVI]
1005. Pappas, R. D. (1956). *J. Biophys. Biochem. Cytol.* **2** (Suppl.): 431. [XVII]
1006. Park, R. B. (1966). *In* "The Chlorophylls" (L. P. Vernon and G. R. Seely, eds.), p. 283. Academic Press, New York. [V]
1007. Park, R. B., and Biggins, J. (1964). *Science* **144:** 1009. [V, VII]
1008. Park, R. B., and Pon, N. G. (1961). *J. Mol. Biol.* **3:** 1. [V]
1009. Park, R. B., and Pon, N. G. (1963). *J. Mol. Biol.* **6:** 105. [V]
1010. Parpart, A. K. (1964). *In* "Primitive Motile Systems in Cell Biology" (R. D. Allen and N. Kamiya, eds.), p. 471. Academic Press, New York. [IX]
1011. Parpart, A. K., and Ballentine, R. (1952). *In* "Modern Trends in Physiology and Biochemistry" (E. Barron, ed.), p. 135. Academic Press, New York. [X]

1012. Parsons, D. F. (1963). *Science* **140:** 985. [VII]
1013. Pasteels, J. J. (1964). *Excerpta Med. Intern. Congr. Ser.* **77:** 35. [XVII]
1014. Pasteels, J., and Lison, L. (1950). *Arch. Biol.* **61:** 445. [XVII]
1015. Pasteur, L. (1862). *Ann. Chim. Phys.* **64:** 1. Translation (1955) in "Great Experiments in Biology" (M. Gabriel and S. Fogel, eds.), p. 110. Prentice-Hall, Englewood Cliffs, New Jersey. [I]
1016. Patton, A. R. (1965). "Biochemical Energetics and Kinetics." Saunders, Philadelphia, Pennsylvania. [XII]
1017. Pauling, L., Corey, R., and Branson, H. (1951). *Proc. Natl. Acad. Sci. U.S.* **37:** 205. [XII]
1018. Payen, M., and Persoz (1833). *Ann. Chim. Phys.* **53:** 73. Translation (1955) in "Great Experiments in Biology" (M. Gabriel and S. Fogel, eds.), p. 25. Prentice-Hall, Englewood Cliffs, New Jersey. [XII]
1019. Peacock, W. J. (1961). *Nature* **191:** 832. [XVIII]
1020. Peacock, W. J. (1963). *Proc. Natl. Acad. Sci. U.S.* **49:** 793. [XVIII]
1021. Pease, D. C. (1946). *Biol. Bull.* **91:** 145. [XIX]
1022. Pease, D. C. (1963). *J. Cell Biol.* **18:** 313. [IX]
1023. Pelc, S. R., and LaCour, F. L. (1960). *In* "The Cell Nucleus" (J. S. Mitchell, ed.), p. 232. Butterworths, London and Washington, D.C. [XVII]
1024. Penman, S., Smith, I., Holtzman, E., and Greenberg, H. (1966). *Natl. Cancer Inst. Monogr.* **23:** 489. [XVII]
1025. Perkins, D. D. (1962). *Genetics* **47:** 1253. [XVIII]
1026. Perutz, M. F., Rossmann, M., Cullis, A., Muirhead, H., Will, G., and North, A. (1960). *Nature* **185:** 416. [XII]
1026a. Pestka, S., and Nirenberg, M. (1967). *Cold Spring Harbor Symp. Quant. Biol.* **31:** 641. [XIV]
1027. Peters, V., Kelly, G., and Dembitzer, H. (1963). *Ann. N.Y. Acad. Sci.* **111:** 87. [XVI]
1028. Pette, D., Luh, W., and Bücher, T. (1962). *Biochem. Biophys. Res. Commun.* **7:** 419, 425. [VI]
1029. Phillips, D. C. (1963). *In* "Aspects of Protein Structure" (G. N. Ramachandran, ed.), p. 57. Academic Press, New York. [XII]
1030. Phillips, D. M. P. (1964). *In* "The Nucleohistones" (J. Bonner and P. Ts'o, eds.), p. 46. Holden-Day, San Francisco, California. [XII]
1031. Piez, K., Lewis, M., Martin, G., and Gross, J. (1961). *Biochim. Biophys. Acta* **53:** 596. [XII]
1032. Pinchot, G. B., and Hormanski, M. (1962). *Proc. Natl. Acad. Sci. U.S.* **48:** 1970. [VI]
1033. Pitelka, D. R., and Child, F. M. (1964). *In* "Biochemistry and Physiology of Protozoa" (S. H. Hutner, ed.), Vol. III, p. 131. Academic Press, New York. [IX]
1034. Platt, J. R. (1961). *J. Theoret. Biol.* **1:** 342. [VIII, IX]
1035. Plaut, W., Nash, D., and Fanning, T. (1966). *J. Mol. Biol.* **16:** 85. [XVIII]
1036. Plough, H. H. (1917). *J. Exptl. Zool.* **24:** 147. [XVIII]
1037. Podolsky, R. J. (1960). *In* "Structure and Function of Muscle" (G. H. Bourne, ed.), Vol. II, p. 359. Academic Press, New York. [VIII]
1038. Podolsky, R. J., and Morales, M. F. (1956). *J. Biol. Chem.* **218:** 945. [III]
1039. Poglazov, B., Borhsenius, S., and Belavlseva, E. (1965). *Virology* **25:** 650. [IX]
1040. Pogo, B., and Pogo, A. (1964). *J. Cell Biol.* **22:** 296. [V]
1040a. Pogo, A., Pogo, B., Littau, V., Allfrey, V. G., Mirsky, A. E., and Hamilton, M. (1962). *Biochim. Biophys. Acta* **55:** 849. [XIV, XVII]

Roman numerals refer to chapters in which each article is mentioned.

1041. Pollister, A. (1952). *Exptl. Cell Res.* **2** (Suppl.): 59. [XVII, XVIII]
1042. Pollister, A., and Mirsky, A. E. (1946). *J. Gen. Physiol.* **30:** 101. [XII]
1043. Pomerat, C. M. (1953). *Exptl. Cell Res.* **5:** 191. [IX]
1044. Pomerat, C. M. (1957). Film referred to by Weiss and Pillai (1965). [XI]
1045. Pontecorvo, G. (1952). *Advan. Enzymol.* **13:** 121. [XVIII]
1046. Poort, C. (1961). *Biochim. Biophys. Acta* **46:** 373. [XVII]
1047. Porter, K. R. (1957). *Harvey Lectures Ser.* **51:** 175. [XIX]
1048. Porter, K. R. (1964). *Biophys. J.* **4:** 167. [XVI]
1049. Porter, K. R., and Franzini-Armstrong, C. (1964). *Nature* **202:** 355. [VIII]
1050. Porter, K. R., and Machado, R. D. (1960). *J. Biophys. Biochem. Cytol.* **7:** 167. [XIX]
1051. Porter, K. R., and Palade, G. E. (1957). *J. Biophys. Biochem. Cytol.* **3:** 269. [VIII, XVI]
1052. Porter, K. R., and Thompson, H. P. (1948). *J. Exptl. Med.* **88:** 15. [XVI]
1053. Porter, K. R., Claude, A., and Fullam, E. (1945). *J. Exptl. Med.* **81:** 233. [XVI]
1054. Portzehl, H. (1957). *Biochim. Biophys. Acta* **26:** 373. [VIII]
1055. Post, R., Merritt, C., Kinsolving, C., and Albright, C. (1960). *J. Biol. Chem.* **235:** 1796. [XI]
1056. Prescott, D. M. (1956). *Exptl. Cell Res.* **11:** 86, 94. [XIX]
1057. Prescott, D. M. (1959). *J. Biophys. Biochem. Cytol.* **6:** 203. [XVII]
1058. Prescott, D. M. (1962). *J. Histochem. Cytochem.* **10:** 145. [XVII]
1059. Prescott, D. M. (1963). *In* "Cell Growth and Cell Division" (R. J. C. Harris, ed.), p. 111. Academic Press, New York. [XVII]
1060. Prescott, D. M. (1966). *J. Cell Biol.* **31:** 1. [XVII]
1061. Prescott, D. M., and Bender, M. A. (1963a). *Exptl. Cell Res.* **29:** 430. [XVIII]
1062. Prescott, D. M., and Bender, M. A. (1963b). *J. Cellular Comp. Physiol.* **62** (Suppl.): 175. [XVIII]
1063. Prévost, J. L., and Dumas, J. B (1824). *Ann. Sci. Nat.* **2:** 100. [I]
1064. Priestly, J. (1772). *Phil. Trans. Roy. Soc. London* **62:** 147. [IV]
1065. Printz, M., and Von Hippel, P. (1965). *Proc. Natl. Acad. Sci. U.S.* **53:** 363. [XII]
1066. Pritchard, R. H., and Lark, K. G. (1964). *J. Mol. Biol.* **9:** 288. [XV]
1067. Pullman, B., and Pullman, A. (1960). *Radiation Res.* **2** (Suppl.): 160. [III]
1068. Pullman, M., San Pietro, A., and Colowick, S. (1954). *J. Biol. Chem.* **206:** 129. [III]
1069. Quastler, H., and Sherman, F. (1959). *Exptl. Cell Res.* **17:** 420. [XX]
1070. Raaflaub, J. (1953). *Helv. Physiol. Pharmacol. Acta* **11:** 142. [VII]
1071. Rabinowitch, E. I. (1945). "Photosynthesis and Related Processes," Vol. I. Wiley (Interscience), New York. [IV, VI]
1072. Rabinowitch, E. I. (1951). "Photosynthesis and Related Processes," Vol. II. Wiley (Interscience), New York. [II, V]
1073. Rabinowitch, E., and Weiss, J. (1937). *Proc. Roy. Soc.* **A162:** 251. [IV]
1074. Racker, E. (1955). *Nature* **175:** 249. [IV]
1075. Racker, E. (1965). "Mechanisms in Bioenergetics." Academic Press, New York. [VI]
1076. Racker, E., Tyler, D., Estabrook, R., Conover, T., Parsons, D., and Chance, B. (1965). *In* "Oxidases and Related Redox Systems." (T. King, H. Mason, and M. Morrison, eds.), Vol. II, p. 1077. Wiley, New York. [VII]
1077. Rae, P. M. M. (1966). *Nature* **212:** 139. [XVIII]
1078. Ramachandran, G. N., and Kartha, G. (1955). *Nature* **176:** 593. [XII]
1078a. Ramachandran, G. N., Sasisekharan, V., and Thathachari, Y. (1962). *In* "Collagen" (N. Ramanathan, ed.), p. 81. Wiley, New York. [XII]
1079. Randall, J., and Disbrey, C. (1965). *Proc. Roy. Soc.* **B162:** 473. [IX]
1080. Rapkine, L. (1931). *Ann. Physiol. Physiochim. Biol.* **7:** 382. [XIX]
1081. Rasch, E., and Woodard, J. (1959). *J. Biophys. Biochem. Cytol.* **6:** 263. [XVII]

1082. Raut, C. (1954). *J. Cellular Comp. Physiol.* **44:** 463. [VII]

1083. Ray, D. S., and Hanawalt, P. C. (1965). *J. Mol. Biol.* **11:** 760. [V]

1084. Rebhun, L. I. (1956). *J. Biophys. Biochem. Cytol.* **2:** 93. [XVI]

1085. Redi, F. (1688). "Experiments on the Generation of Insects." Translation (1955) in "Great Experiments in Biology" (M. Gabriel and S. Fogel, eds.), p. 187. Prentice-Hall, Englewood Cliffs, New Jersey. [I]

1085a. Reedy. M. K. (1968). *J. Mol. Biol.* **31:** 155. [VIII]

1086. Reeke, G. N., Hartsuck, J. A., Ludwig, M. L., Quiocho, F., Steitz, T., and Lipscomb, W. (1967). *Proc. Natl. Sci. U.S.* **58:** 2220. [XII]

1087. Reich, E., and Luck, D. J. L. (1966). *Proc Natl. Acad. Sci. U.S.* **55:** 1600. [VII]

1088. Reid, B. R., and Cole, R. D. (1964). *Proc. Natl. Acad. Sci. U.S.* **51:** 1044. [XVII]

1089. Reinhard, H. (1933). *Protoplasma* **19:** 541. [V]

1090. Renner, O. (1936). *Flora (Jena)* **30:** 218. [V]

1091. Revel, M., and Hiatt, H. (1964). *Proc. Natl. Acad. Sci. U.S.* **51:** 810. [XVII]

1092. Rho, J., and Bonner, J. (1961). *Proc. Natl. Acad. Sci. U.S.* **47:** 1611. [XVII]

1093. Rhoades, M. M. (1933). *J. Genet.* **27:** 71. [XX]

1094. Rich, A. (1960). *Proc. Natl. Acad. Sci. U.S.* **46:** 1044. [XII, XIII]

1095. Rich, A., and Davies, D. R. (1956). *J. Am. Chem. Soc.* **78:** 3548. [XII, XIII]

1096. Richards, F. M. (1958). *Proc. Natl. Acad. Sci. U.S.* **44:** 162. [XII]

1097. Richardson, C. C., Schildkraut, C. L., and Kornberg, A. (1963a). *Cold Spring Harbor Symp. Quant. Biol.* **28:** 9. [XIII]

1098. Richardson, C. C., Schildkraut, C. L., Aposhian, H. V., Kornberg, A., Bodmer, W., and Lederberg, J. (1963b). *In* "Informational Macromolecules" (H. J. Vogel, V. Bryson, and J. O. Lampen, eds.), p. 13. Academic Press, New York. [XIII]

1099. Richardson, C. C., Inman, R. B., and Kornberg, A. (1964). *J. Mol. Biol.* **9:** 46. [XIII]

1099a. Richardson, J. P. (1966). *Proc. Natl. Acad. Sci. U.S.* **55:** 1616. [XIII]

1100. Richardson, S. H., Hultin, H., and Green, D. E. (1963). *Proc. Natl. Acad. Sci. U.S.* **50:** 821. [X, XIII]

1101. Rieske, J. S. (1965). *In* "Non-heme Iron Proteins: Role in Energy Conversion" (A. G. San Pietro, ed.), p 461. Antioch Press, Yellow Springs, Ohio. [III, VII]

1102. Ris, H. (1943). *Biol. Bull.* **85:** 164. [XIX]

1103. Ris, H. (1949). *Biol. Bull.* **96:** 90. [XIX]

1104. Ris, H. (1955). *In* "The Submicroscopic Structure of Chromosomes," Symposium on the Fine Structure of Cells, Leiden, Holland. p. 121. Wiley (Interscience), New York. [XVII, XVIII]

1105. Ris, H. (1956). *J. Biophys. Biochem. Cytol.* **2** (Suppl.): 385. [XII, XVII]

1106. Ris, H. (1959). *Colloq. Ges. Physiol. Chem.* **9:** 1. [XVII, XVIII]

1107. Ris, H. (1961). *Can. J. Genet. Cytol.* **3:** 95. [V, XVII, XVIII]

1108. Ris, H. (1966a). *Proc. Roy. Soc.* **B164:** 246. [XVII, XVIII]

1109. Ris, H. (1966b). *Proc. 6th Intern. Conf. Electron Microscopy, Kyoto.* p. 339.

1110. Ris, H., and Chandler, B. L. (1963). *Cold Spring Harbor Symp. Quant. Biol.* **28:** 1. [XVII]

1111. Ris, H., and Mirsky, A. E. (1949). *J. Gen. Physiol.* **32:** 489. [XVIII]

1112. Ris, H., and Plaut, W. (1962). *J. Cell Biol.* **13:** 383. [V]

1113. Ritossa, F. M., and Spiegelman, S. (1965). *Proc. Natl. Acad. Sci. U.S.* **53:** 737. [XVII]

1114. Ritossa, F. M., and Von Borstel, R. C. (1964). *Science* **145:** 513. [XX]

1115. Rizki, T. M., and Rizki, R. M. (1963). *J. Cell Biol.* **17:** 87. [XX]

1116. Ro, T. S., Muramatsu, M., and Busch, H. (1964). *Biochem. Biophys. Res. Commun.* **14:** 149. [XVII]

Roman numerals refer to chapters in which each article is mentioned.

1117. Robbins, E., and Gonatas, N. (1964). *J. Cell Biol.* **21:** 429. [XIX]
1118. Roberts, H., and Johnson, N. (1956). *Biol. Bull.* **110:** 334. [XIX]
1119. Robertson, J. D. (1959). *Biochem. Soc. Symp.* **16:** 3. [X, XVII]
1120. Robertson, J. D. (1963). *J. Cell Biol.* **19:** 201. [X]
1121. Robertson, J. D. (1964). *In* "Cellular Membranes in Development" (M. Locke, ed.), p. 1. Academic Press, New York. [X]
1122. Roodyn, D. B. (1962). *Biochem. J.* **85:** 177. [VII]
1123. Rosen, S. I. (1964). *J. Cell Biol.* **23:** 78A. [XVI]
1124. Rosset, R., and Monier, R. (1963). *Biochim. Biophys. Acta* **68:** 653. [XIV]
1125. Roth, L. E. (1957). *J. Biophys. Biochem. Cytol.* **3:** 985. [XVII]
1126. Roth, L. E. (1958). *J. Ultrastruct. Res.* **1:** 223. [IX]
1127. Roth, L. E. (1959). *Proc. 4th Intern. Conf. Electron Microscopy* **2:** 241. [IX]
1128. Roth, L. E. (1960). *J. Protozool.* **7:** 176. [X]
1129. Roth, L. E., and Daniels, E. W. (1962). *J. Cell Biol.* **12:** 57. [XIX]
1130. Roth, L. E., and Jenkins, R. A. (1962). *Proc. 5th Intern. Conf. Electron Microscopy* **2:** NN-3. [XIX]
1131. Rounds, D. and Flickinger, R. (1958). *J. Exptl. Zool.* **137:** 479. [XX]
1132. Ruben, S. (1943). *J. Am. Chem. Soc.* **65:** 279. [IV]
1133. Ruben, S., Hassid, W., and Kamen, M. D. (1939). *J. Am. Chem. Soc.* **61:** 661. [IV]
1134. Ruben, S., Randall, M., Kamen, M., and Hyde, J. (1941). *J. Am. Chem. Soc.* **63:** 877. [IV]
1135. Ruby, A. (1961). Ph.D. Thesis. Univ. of California, Berkeley, California. [XIX]
1136. Rückert, J. (1892). *Anat. Anz.* **7:** 107. [XVIII]
1137. Rudkin, G. T. (1965). *Genetics* **52:** 470. [XVIII]
1138. Rudkin, G. T. (1967). *In* "The Chromosome" (G. Yerganian, ed.), p. 12. Williams & Wilkins, Baltimore, Maryland. [XVIII]
1139. Rudkin, G. T., and Woods, P. (1959). *Proc. Natl. Acad. Sci. U.S.* **45:** 997. [XX]
1140. Ryter, A., and Jacob, F. (1963). *Compt. Rend. Acad. Sci.* **257:** 3060. [XV]
1141. Sager, R. (1964). *In* "Biochemistry and Physiology of Protozoa" (S. H. Hutner, ed.), Vol. III, p. 297. Academic Press, New York. [V, XX]
1142. Sager, R., and Ishida, M. (1963). *Proc. Natl. Acad. Sci. U.S.* **50:** 725. [V]
1143. Sager, R., and Ryan, F. J. (1961). "Cell Heredity." Wiley, New York. [XX]
1144. Sakai, H. (1965). *Biochim. Biophys. Acta* **102:** 235. [XIX]
1145. Sakai, H. (1966). *Biochim. Biophys. Acta* **112:** 132. [XIX]
1146. Sakai, H., and Dan, K. (1959). *Exptl. Cell Res.* **16:** 24. [XIX]
1147. Salzman, N., Moore, D., and Mendelsohn, J. (1966). *Proc. Natl. Acad. Sci. U.S.* **56:** 1449. [XVIII]
1148. Sandborn, E., Koen, P., McNabb, J., and Moore, G. (1964). *J. Ultrastruct. Res.* **11:** 123. [IX]
1149. Sanger, F., and Thompson, E. O. P. (1953). *Biochem. J.* **53:** 353, 366. [XII]
1150. Sano, Y., and Knoop, A. (1959). *Z. Zellforsch.* **49:** 464. [XI, XVI]
1151. Sarabhai, A., Stretton, A., Brenner, S., and Bolle, A. (1964). *Nature* **201:** 13. [XV]
1152. Sarkar, N., Sarkar, S., and Kozloff, L. (1964). *Biochemistry* **3:** 511, 517. [IX]
1152a. Sasaki, M. S., and Norman, A. (1966). *Exptl. Cell Res.* **44:** 642. [XVII, XVIII]
1153. Satir, P., and Child, F. (1963). *Biol. Bull.* **125:** 390. [IX]
1154. Sauer, K., and Calvin, M. (1962). *J. Mol. Biol.* **4:** 451. [V]
1155. Sax, K. (1941). *Cold Spring Harbor Symp. Quant. Biol.* **9:** 93. [XVIII]
1156. Scarpelli, D., Craig, E., and Rosa, C. (1962). *Proc. 5th Intern. Congr. Electron Microscopy* **2:** L-6. [VII]
1157. Schachman, H., Adler, J., Radding, C., Lehman, I., and Kornberg, A. (1960). *J. Biol. Chem.* **235:** 3242. [XIII]

1158. Scherbaum, O., and Zeuthen, E. (1954). *Exptl. Cell Res.* **6:** 221. [XIX]

1159. Scherrer, K., and Darnell, J. E. (1962). *Biochem. Biophys. Res. Commun.* **7:** 486. [XIV, XVII]

1160. Scherrer, K., Latham, H., and Darnell, J. E. (1963). *Proc. Natl. Acad. Sci. U.S.* **49:** 240. [XIV, XVII]

1161. Schin, K. S. (1965). *Chromosoma* **16:** 436. [XVIII]

1162. Schleiden, M. J., and Schwann, T. (1839). "Beitrage zur Phytogenesis." Translated with Schwann's "Mikroskopische Untersuchungen" by H. Smith for the Sydenham Society, London (1847). Excerpt of Schwann's monograph given (1955) in "Great Experiments in Biology" (M. Gabriel and S. Fogel, eds.), p. 12. Prentice-Hall, Englewood Cliffs, New Jersey. [I, XVII]

1163. Schmid, W. (1963). *Cytogenetics* **2:** 175. [XVIII]

1164. Schmidt, W. J. (1941). *Chromosoma* **2:** 86. [XVIII]

1165. Schmitt, F. O. (1936). *Cold Spring Harbor Symp. Quant. Biol.* **4:** 7. [X]

1166. Schmitt, F. O. (1959). *In* "Biophysical Science—A Study Program" (J. L. Oncley, ed.). Wiley, New York. [XII]

1167. Schmitt, F. O., and Bear, R. (1939). *Biol. Rev. Cambridge Phil. Soc.* **14:** 27. [X]

1168. Schmitt, F. O., and Palmer, K. (1940). *Cold Spring Harbor Symp. Quant. Biol.* **8:** 94. [X]

1169. Schrader, F. (1921). *Biol. Bull.* **40:** 259. [XVIII]

1170. Schrader, F. (1953). "Mitosis." Columbia Univ. Press, New York. [XVIII, XIX]

1171. Schrödinger, E. (1945). "What is Life?" Macmillan, New York. [XII]

1172. Schroeder, W., Shelton, J., Shelton, J., and Cormick, J. (1962). *Proc. Natl. Acad. Sci. U.S.* **48:** 284. [XII]

1173. Schulman, H. M., and Bonner, D. M. (1962). *Proc. Natl. Acad. Sci. U.S.* **48:** 53. [XII]

1174. Schumaker, V. N. (1958). *Exptl. Cell Res.* **15:** 314. [X]

1175. Schuster, F. (1963). *J. Protozool.* **10:** 297. [IX]

1176. Schweet, R., Lamfrom, H., and Allen, E. (1958). *Proc. Natl. Acad. Sci. U.S.* **44:** 1029. [XIV]

1177. Scott, R. B., and Bell, E. (1964). *Science* **145:** 711. [XIV]

1178. Seaman, G. R. (1960). *Exptl. Cell Res.* **21:** 292. [IX]

1179. Seidel, F. (1961). *Zool. Anz. Suppl.* **24:** 121. [XX]

1180. Sekuzi, I., and Okunuki, K. (1956). *J. Biochem. (Tokyo)* **43:** 107. [III]

1181. Seliger, H. H., and McElroy, W. D. (1960). *Arch. Biochem. Biophys.* **88:** 136. [VI]

1182. Seliger, H. H., and McElroy, W. D. (1962). *Science* **138:** 683. [VI]

1183. Seliger, H. H., and McElroy, W. D. (1964). *Proc. Natl. Acad. Sci. U.S.* **52:** 75. [VI]

1184. Senebier, J. (1782). "Mémoires Physico-chimiques sur l'Influence de la Lumiére solaire pour Modifier les etres de trois Régnes, surtout ceux du Régne végétal," 3 vols. Chirol, Geneva. [IV]

1185. Shaffer, B. M. (1956). *Science* **123:** 1172. [XX]

1186. Shibko, S., Pangborn, J., and Tappel, A. (1965). *J. Cell Biol.* **25:** 479. [X]

1187. Shimomura, O., Goto, T., and Hirata, Y. (1957). *Bull. Chem. Soc. Japan.* **30:** 929. [VI]

1188. Shimomura, O., Johnson, F., and Saiga, Y. (1961). *J. Cellular Comp. Physiol.* **58:** 113. [VI]

1189. Shimomura, O., Johnson, F., and Saiga, Y. (1963). *J. Cellular Comp. Physiol.* **62:** 1. [VI]

1190. Shin, M., Tagawa, K., and Arnon, D. (1963). *Biochem. Z.* **338:** 84. [III, IV]

1191. Shumway, L. K., and Weier, T. E. (1967). *Am. J. Botany* **54:** 773. [V]

Roman numerals refer to chapters in which each article is mentioned.

1192. Sibatani, A., DeKloet, S., Allfrey, V. G., and Mirsky, A. E. (1962). *Proc. Natl. Acad. Sci. U.S.* **48:** 471. [XVII]

1193. Siddiqi, O. H. (1963). *Proc. Natl. Acad. Sci. U.S.* **49:** 589. [XV]

1194. Sie, E., McElroy, W., Johnson, F., and Haneka, Y. (1961). *Arch. Biochem. Biophys.* **93:** 286. [VI]

1195. Siekevitz, P. (1952). *J. Biol. Chem.* **195:** 549. [I, XIV, XVI]

1196. Siekevitz, P. (1963). *Ann. Rev. Physiol.* **25:** 15. [XVI]

1197. Siekevitz, P., and Palade, G. (1958). *J. Biophys. Biochem. Cytol.* **4:** 203, 309, 557. [XIV, XVI]

1198. Siekevitz, P., and Potter, V. (1955). *J. Biol. Chem.* **215:** 237. [VII]

1199. Signer, R., Caspersson, T., and Hammarsten, E. (1938). *Nature* **141:** 122. [XII]

1200. Simantel, G., Ross, J., Huang, C. and Haensel, H. (1962). *Proc. S. Dakota Acad. Sci.* **41:** 204. [XVIII, XIX]

1201. Simard-Duquesne, N., and Couillard, P. (1962). *Exptl. Cell Res.* **28:** 85, 92. [IX]

1202. Simon, D. (1960). *Arch. Anat. Microscop. Morphol. Exptl.* **49:** 94. [XX]

1203. Singer, M. F., and Cantoni, G. L. (1960). *Biochim. Biophys. Acta* **39:** 182. [XII]

1204. Singer, T. P. (1963). *In* "The Enzymes" (P. Boyer, H. Lardy, and K. Myrbäck, eds.), 2nd ed., Vol. VII, p. 345. Academic Press, New York. [III]

1205. Singer, T. P. (1965). *In* "Non-heme Iron Proteins: Role in Energy Conversion" (A. G. San Pietro, ed.), p. 349. Antioch Press, Yellow Springs, Ohio. [III]

1206. Sinsheimer, R. L. (1962). *In* "The Molecular Control of Cellular Activity" (J. M. Allen, ed.), p. 221. McGraw-Hill, New York. [XII]

1207. Sirlin, J. L. (1960). *Exptl. Cell Res.* **19:** 177. [XVII]

1208. Sirlin, J. L., and Brahma, S. K. (1959). *Develop. Biol.* **1:** 234. [XX]

1209. Sirlin, J. L., Kato, K., and Jones, K. (1961). *Biochim. Biophys. Acta* **48:** 421. [XVII]

1210. Sirlin, J., Jacob, J., and Kato, K. (1962). *Exptl. Cell Res.* **27:** 355. [XVII]

1211. Sirlin, J. L. Jacob, J., and Birnstiel, M. (1965). *Biochim. Biophys. Acta* **108:** 716. [XVII]

1212. Sisken, J. E., and Kinosita, R. (1961). *J. Biophys. Biochem. Cytol.* **9:** 509. [XVII]

1213. Sjöstrand, F. S. (1963). *J. Ultrastruct. Res.* **9:** 340, 561. [VII, X]

1214. Sjöstrand, F. S., and Hanzon, V. (1954). *Exptl. Cell Res.* **7:** 393. [VII]

1215. Slater, E. C. (1962). *Comp. Biochem. Physiol.* **4:** 281. [VI]

1216. Slautterback, D. B. (1961). *In* "The Biology of *Hydra*" (H. M. Lenhoff and W. F. Loomis, eds.), p. 77. Univ. of Miami Press, Miami, Florida. [XVI]

1217. Slautterback, D. B. (1963). *J. Cell Biol.* **18:** 367. [IX]

1218. Slautterback, D. B., and Fawcett, D. W. (1959). *J. Biophys. Biochem. Cytol.* **5:** 441. [XVI]

1219. Slayter, H. S., and Hall, C. E. (1966). *J. Mol. Biol.* **21:** 113. [XIII]

1220. Slayter, H. S., Warner, J. R., Rich, A., and Hall, C. E. (1963). *J. Mol. Biol.* **7:** 652. [XIV]

1221. Smith, E. L. (1962). *Proc. Natl. Acad. Sci. U.S.* **48:** 677, 859. [XIV]

1222. Smith, L. D. (1965). *Proc. Natl. Acad. Sci. U.S.* **54:** 101. [XVII]

1223. Smyth, D. G., Stein, W., and Moore, S. (1963). *J. Biol. Chem.* **238:** 227. [XII]

1224. Solari, A. J. (1965). *Proc. Natl. Acad. Sci. U.S.* **53:** 503. [XII, XVII, XVIII]

1225. Soll, D., Ohtsuka, E., Jones, D., Lohrmann, R., Hayatsu, H., Nishimura, S., and Khorana, H. G. (1965). *Proc. Natl. Acad. Sci. U.S.* **54:** 1378. [XIV]

1226. Somers, C. E., and Hsu, T. C. (1962). *Proc. Natl. Acad. Sci. U.S.* **48:** 937. [XVIII]

1227. Somers, C. E., Cole, A., and Hsu, T. C. (1963). *Exptl. Cell Res.* **9** (Suppl.): 220. [XVIII]

1228. Sonneborn, T. (1963). *In* "The Nature of Biological Diversity" (J. M. Allen, ed.), p. 165. McGraw-Hill, New York. [XVII, XX]

1229. Sotelo, J. R., and Wettstein, R. (1966). *Chromosoma* **20:** 234. [XVIII]

1230. Soudek, D., and Koukalová, B. (1963). *Folia Biol.* (*Prague*) **9:** 444. [XVII]
1231. Spahr, P. F., and Tissières, A. (1959). *J. Mol. Biol.* **1:** 237. [XIV]
1232. Sparvoli, E., Gay, H., and Kaufmann, B. P. (1965). *Chromosoma* **16:** 415. [XVIII]
1233. Spemann, H. (1918). *Arch. Entwicklungsmech. Organ.* **43:** 448. [XX]
1234. Spencer, M., and Poole, F. (1965). *J. Mol. Biol.* **11:** 314. [XII, XIV]
1235. Spencer, M., Fuller, W., Wilkins, M. H. F., and Brown, G. L. (1962). *Nature* **194:** 1014. [XII, XIV]
1236. Speyer, J., Lengyel, P., Basilio, C., and Ochoa, S. (1962). *Proc. Natl. Acad. Sci. U.S.* **48:** 63, 441. [XIV]
1237. Spiegel, M. (1954). *Biol. Bull.* **107:** 130. [XX]
1238. Spiegelman, S. (1963). *In* "Informational Macromolecules" (H. J. Vogel, V. Bryson, and J. O. Lampen, eds.), p. 27. Academic Press, New York. [XV]
1239. Spiegelman, S., Hall, B., and Storck, R. (1961). *Proc. Natl. Acad. Sci. U.S.* **47:** 1135. [XII]
1240. Spirin, A. S. (1964). "Macromolecular Structure of Ribonucleic Acids." Reinhold, New York. [XIV]
1241. Spirin, A. S., Kisselev, N. A., Shakulov, R. S., and Bogdanov, A. A. (1963). *Biokhimiya* **28:** 920. [XIV]
1242. Srinivasan, B. D. (1964). *Nature* **203:** 100. [XIX]
1243. Stahl, F. W., Edgar, R. S., and Steinberg J. (1964). *Genetics* **50:** 539. [XV]
1244. Stanier, R. Y. (1963). *In* "General Physiology of Cell Specialization" (D. Mazia and A. Tyler, eds.), p. 242. McGraw-Hill, New York. [V]
1245. Stanley, W. M. (1935). *Science* **81:** 644. [XV]
1246. Stedman, E., and Stedman, E. (1943). *Nature* **152:** 267, 556. [XIII]
1247. Steele, W. J., and Busch, H. (1963). *Cancer Res.* **23:** 1153. [XII, XVII]
1248. Steffensen, D. (1959). *Brookhaven Symp. Biol.* **12:** 103. [XVIII]
1249. Steinberg, M. S. (1962). *Science* **137:** 762. [XX]
1250. Steinberg, M. S. (1963). *Science* **141:** 401. [XX]
1251. Steinmann, E. (1952). *Exptl. Cell Res.* **3:** 367. [V]
1252. Steinmann, E., and Sjöstrand, F. S. (1955). *Exptl. Cell Res.* **8:** 15. [V]
1253. Stelluti, F. (1625). Reproduced (1963) in *Bee World* **44:** 23, 43. [I]
1254. Stent, G. G. (1958). *Advan. Virus Res.* **5:** 95. [XIII]
1255. Stephens, R. E. (1965). *Abstr. 9th Meeting Biophys. Soc.* p. 129. [VIII]
1256. Stephenson, M. L., and Zamecnik, P. C. (1956). *Federation Proc.* **15:** 362. [V]
1257. Stern, C. (1931). *Biol. Zentr.* **51:** 547. [XVIII]
1258. Stern, H. (1958). *J. Biophys. Biochem. Cytol.* **4:** 157. [XIX]
1259. Stern, H., and Hotta, Y. (1963). *In* "Cell Growth and Cell Division" (R. J. C. Harris, ed.), p. 57. Academic Press, New York. [XVIII]
1260. Stern, H., and Mirsky, A. E. (1953). *J. Gen. Physiol.* **36:** 181. [XVII]
1261. Stern, H., Allfrey, V., Mirsky, A. E., and Saetren, H. (1952). *J. Gen. Physiol.* **35:** 559. [XVII]
1262. Stern, H., Johnston, F., and Setterfield, G. (1959). *J. Biophys. Biochem. Cytol.* **6:** 57. [XVII]
1263. Stern, J. R., and Ochoa, S. (1949). *J. Biol. Chem.* **179:** 491. [VI]
1264. Stevens, B. J., and Swift, H. (1966). *J. Cell Biol.* **31:** 55. [XVII]
1265. Steward, F. C., Mapes, M. O., and Mears, K. (1958). *Am. J. Botany* **45:** 705. [XX]
1266. Stich, H. (1954). *Chromosoma* **6:** 199. [IX]
1267. Stockdale, F. E., and Holtzer, H. (1962). *Exptl. Cell Res.* **24:** 508. [XX]

Roman numerals refer to chapters in which each article is mentioned.

1268. Stocking, C. R., and Gifford, E. M. (1959). *Biochem. Biophys. Res. Commun.* **1:** 159. [V]
1269. Strack, H. B., and Kaiser, A. D. (1965). *J. Mol. Biol.* **12:** 36. [XV, XVIII]
1270. Strain, H. H., and Svec, W. A. (1966). *In* "The Chlorophylls" (L. Vernon and G. Seely, eds.), p. 22. Academic Press, New York. [IV]
1271. Straub, F. B. (1942). *Studies Inst. Med. Chem. Univ. Szeged.* **2:** 3. [VIII]
1272. Straus, W. (1963). *Ciba Found. Symp. Lysosomes 1963* Little, Brown, Boston, Massachusetts. [X]
1273. Streisinger, G., Edgar, R. S., and Denhardt, G. H. (1964). *Proc. Natl. Acad. Sci. U.S.* **51:** 775 [XV]
1274. Stryer, L. (1968). *Ann. Rev. Biochem.* **37** (in press). [XII]
1275. Stubblefield, E. (1964). *In* "Cytogenetics of Cells in Culture" (R. J. C. Harris, ed.), p. 223. Academic Press, New York. [XVIII]
1275a. Stubblefield, E., and Mueller, G. C. (1962). *Cancer Res.* **22:** 1091. [XVII, XVIII]
1276. Sturtevant, A. H. (1965). "A History of Genetics." Harper, New York. [I]
1277. Sugimoto, K., Okazaki, T., and Okazaki, R. (1968). *Proc. Natl. Acad. Sci. U.S.* **60:** 1356. [XIII]
1278. Sussman, M., Lee, F., and Kerr, N. (1956). *Science* **123:** 1171. [XX]
1279. Sutton, W. S. (1903). *Biol. Bull.* **4:** 24, 231. [XVIII]
1280. Swanbeck, G., and Forslind, B. (1964). *Biochim. Biophys. Acta* **88:** 422. [IX]
1281. Swift, H. (1950a). *Proc. Natl. Acad. Sci. U.S.* **36:** 643. [XVII]
1282. Swift, H. (1950b). *Physiol. Zool.* **23:** 169. [XVII]
1283. Swift, H. (1956). *J. Biophys. Biochem. Cytol.* **2** (Suppl.): 415. [XVI]
1284. Swift, H. (1962). *In* "The Molecular Control of Cellular Activity" (J. M. Allen, ed.), p. 73. McGraw-Hill, New York. [XVIII, XX]
1285. Swift, H. (1964). *In* "The Nucleohistones" (J. Bonner and P. Ts'o, eds.), p. 169. Holden-Day, San Francisco, California. [XVIII]
1286. Szent-Györgyi, A. G. (1941–1942). *Studies Inst. Med. Chem. Univ. Szeged* **1:** 5. [I, VIII]
1287. Szent-Györgyi, A. G. (1949). *Biol. Bull.* **96:** 140. [VIII, IX]
1288. Szent-Györgyi, A. G. (1953). *Arch. Biochem. Biophys.* **42:** 305. [VIII]
1289. Szent-Györgyi, A. G. (1960a). *In* "Structure and Function of Muscle" (G. H. Bourne, ed.). Vol. II, p. 1; Vol. III, p. 445. Academic Press, New York. [VIII]
1290. Szent-Györgyi, A. G. (1960b). "Introduction to a Submolecular Biology." Academic Press, New York. [I, II]
1291. Tagawa, K., and Arnon, D. I. (1962). *Nature* **195:** 537. [III, IV]
1292. Tagawa, K., Tsujimoto, H., and Arnon, D. I. (1963). *Proc. Natl. Acad. Sci. U.S.* **50:** 544. [IV]
1293. Takanami, M. (1967). *J. Mol. Biol.* **29:** 323. [XIV]
1293a. Takanami, M., and Okamoto, T. (1963). *J. Mol. Biol.* **7:** 323. [XIV]
1294. Takanami, M., and Yan, Y. (1965). *Proc. Natl. Acad. Sci. U.S.* **54:** 1450. [XIV]
1295. Takanami, M., Yan, Y., and Jukes, T. H. (1965). *J. Mol. Biol.* **12:** 761. [XIV]
1296. Takata, M. (1958). *Kagaku (Tokyo)* **28:** 142. [IX]
1297. Takeda, S., and Izutsu, K. (1960). *Symp. Cell Chem. (Japan)* **10:** 245. [XIX]
1298. Tamiya, H. (1964). *In* "Synchrony in Cell Division and Growth" (E. Zeuthen, ed.), p. 247. Wiley (Interscience), New York. [XIX]
1299. Tanaka, M., Benson, A., Mower, H., and Yasunobu, K. (1965). *In* "Non-heme Iron Proteins: Role in Energy Conversion" (A. G. San Pietro, ed.), p. 221. Antioch Press, Yellow Springs, Ohio. [III]
1300. Tartar, V. (1953). *J. Exptl. Zool.* **124:** 63. [XVII]
1301. Tartar, V. (1956). *J. Exptl. Zool.* **132:** 269. [XX]
1302. Tartar, V. (1961). "The Biology of *Stentor*," 413 pp. Pergamon, New York. [XVII, XX]

1303. Tashiro, Y., and Siekevitz, P. (1965). *J. Mol. Biol.* **11:** 149. [XIV]
1304. Tashiro, Y., and Yphantis, D. A. (1965). *J. Mol. Biol.* **11:** 174. [XIV]
1305. Taylor, E. W. (1959). *J. Biophys. Biochem. Cytol.* **6:** 193. [XIX]
1306. Taylor, J. H. (1953). *Exptl. Cell Res.* **4:** 164. [XVIII]
1307. Taylor, J. H. (1957). *Am. Naturalist* **91:** 209. [XVIII]
1308. Taylor, J. H. (1958a). *Genetics* **43:** 515. [XVIII]
1309. Taylor, J. H. (1958b). *Exptl. Cell Res.* **15:** 350. [XVII, XVIII]
1310. Taylor, J. H. (1963). *In* "Molecular Genetics" (J. H. Taylor, ed.), Part 1, p. 65. Academic Press, New York. [XVIII]
1311. Taylor, J. H. (1964). *J. Cell Biol.* **21:** 286. [XVIII]
1311a. Taylor, J. H. (1968). *J. Mol. Biol.* **31:** 579. [XVII, XVIII]
1312. Taylor, J. H., Woods, P., and Hughes, W. (1957). *Proc. Natl. Acad. Sci. U.S.* **43:** 122. [XVIII]
1313. Taylor, J. H., Haut, W., and Tung, J. (1962). *Proc. Natl. Acad. Sci. U.S.* **48:** 190. [XVIII]
1314. Telfer, W. H. (1963). *In* "Insect Physiology" (V. J. Brookes, ed.), p. 13. Oregon State Univ. Press, Corvallis, Oregon. [X]
1315. Theorell, H. (1934). *Biochem. Z.* **272:** 155. [III]
1316. Theorell, H. (1936). *Biochem. Z.* **288:** 317. [III]
1317. Thomas, J. B., and Bartels, C. T. (1966). *In* "Biochemistry of Chloroplasts" (T. W. Goodwin, ed.), Vol. I, p. 257. Academic Press, New York. [IV]
1318. Thompson, T. E. (1964). *In* "Cellular Membranes in Development" (M. Locke, ed.), p. 85. Academic Press, New York. [X, XI]
1319. Thunberg, T. (1923). *Z. Physik. Chem. (Leipzig)* **106:** 305. [IV]
1320. Tibbs, J. (1958). *Biochim. Biophys. Acta* **28:** 636. [IX]
1321. Tice, L. W., and Smith, D. S. (1965). *J. Cell Biol.* **25:** 121. [VIII]
1322. Tissières, A. (1959). *J. Mol. Biol.* **1:** 365. [XIV]
1323. Tissières, A., and Watson, J. D. (1958). *Nature* **182:** 778. [XIV]
1324. Tollin, G. (1960). *Radiation Res. Suppl.* **2:** 387. [V]
1325. Tomlin, S. G., and Callan, H. G. (1951). *Quart. J. Microscop. Sci.* **92:** 221. [XVIII]
1326. Tosteson, D. C. (1964). *In* "The Cellular Functions of Membrane Transport" (J. F. Hoffman, ed.), p. 3. Prentice-Hall, Englewood Cliffs, New Jersey. [XI]
1327. Tosteson, D. C., and Hoffman, J. F. (1960). *J. Gen. Physiol.* **44:** 169. [X]
1328. Townes, P. L., and Holtfreter, J. (1955). *J. Exptl. Zool.* **128:** 53. [XX]
1329. Trebst, A. V., Tsujimoto, H. Y., and Arnon, D. I. (1958). *Nature* **182:** 351. [V]
1330. Trosko, J. E., and Wolff, S. (1965). *J. Cell Biol.* **26:** 125. [XVIII]
1331. Truman, D. E. S., and Korner, A. (1962). *Biochem. J.* **85:** 154. [VII]
1332. Tsao, T. C. (1953). *Biochim. Biophys. Acta* **11:** 236. [VIII]
1333. Tschachotin, S. (1907). *Arch. Ges. Physiol.* **120:** 565. [XI]
1334. Ts'o, P., Bonner, J., Eggman, L., and Vinograd, J. (1956). *J. Gen. Physiol.* **39:** 325. [IX]
1335. Ts'o, P., Bonner, J., and Dintzis, H. (1958). *Arch. Biochem. Biophys.* **76:** 225. [XIV]
1336. Tsugita, A. (1962). *J. Mol. Biol.* **5:** 284. [XV]
1337. Tsugita, A., Gish, D., Young, J., Fraenkel-Conrat, H., Knight, C., and Stanley, W. (1960). *Proc. Natl. Acad. Sci. U.S.* **46:** 1463. [XII]
1338. Tuan, D., and Bonner, J. (1964). *Plant Physiol.* **39:** 768. [XX]
1339. Tyler, A. (1965). *Am. Naturalist* **99:** 309. [XX]
1340. Uhl, C. H. (1965). *Genetics* **51:** 191. [XVIII]
1341. Upcott, M. (1939). *Chromosoma* **1:** 178. [XIX]

Roman numerals refer to chapters in which each article is mentioned.

1342. Uretz, R. B., Bloom, W., and Zirkle, R. E. (1954). *Science* **120:** 197. [XVIII, XIX]

1343. Ussing, H. H., and Zerahn, K. (1951). *Acta Physiol. Scand.* **23:** 110. [XI]

1344. Vallentin, A. (1954). "The Drama of Albert Einstein," 312 pp. Doubleday, New York. [I]

1345. Van Beneden, E. (1883). *Arch. Biol.* **4:** 1. [XVIII]

1346. Van den Bergh, S. G., and Slater, E. C. (1962). *Biochem. J.* **82:** 362. [VII]

1347. Van Helmont, J. (1648). Translation (1955) in "Great Experiments in Biology" (M. Gabriel and S. Fogel, eds.), p. 155. Prentice-Hall, Englewood Cliffs, New Jersey. [IV]

1348. Van Niel, C. B. (1931). *Arch. Mikrobiol.* **3:** 1. [IV]

1349. Van't Hof, J., and Sparrow, A. H. (1963). *Proc. Natl. Acad. Sci. U.S.* **49:** 897. [XVII]

1350. Van Vunakis, H., Baker, W., and Brown, R. (1958). *Virology* **5:** 327. [XV]

1351. Vasington, F. D., and Murphy, J. V. (1962). *J. Biol. Chem.* **237:** 2670. [VII]

1352. Vendrely, R. (1955). *In* "The Nucleic Acids" (E. Chargaff and J. Davidson, eds.). Vol. II. p. 155. Academic Press, New York. [XVII]

1353. Vendrely, R., Knobloch, A., and Matsudaira, H. (1958). *Nature* **181:** 343. [XII]

1354. Vendrely, R., Knobloch-Mazen, A. and Vendrely, C. (1960). *Biochem. Pharmacol.* **4:** 19. [XII, XVIII]

1355. Vignais, P. M., Vignais, P. V., and Lehninger, A. L. (1963). *Biochem. Biophys. Res. Commun.* **11:** 313. [VII]

1356. Villegas, R., and Barnda, F. V. (1961). *J. Gen. Physiol.* **44:** 963. [X]

1357. Villegas, R., Caputo, C., and Villegas, L. (1962). *J. Gen. Physiol.* **46:** 245. [X]

1358. Vincent, W. S. (1952). *Proc. Natl. Acad. Sci. U.S.* **38:** 139. [XVII]

1359. Vincent, W. S. (1958). *In* "The Chemical Basis of Development" (W. McElroy and B. Glass, eds.), p. 152. Johns Hopkins Press, Baltimore, Maryland. [XVII]

1360. Vincent, W. S., and Baltus, E. (1960). *Biol. Bull.* **119:** 299. [XVII]

1361. Vinograd, J., and Lebowitz, J. (1966). *J. Gen. Physiol.* **49** (Suppl. II): 103. [XV, XVII, XVIII]

1361a. Virchow, R. (1855). *Arch. Pathol. Anat. Physiol.* **8:** 23. [I]

1362. Vishniac, W., and Ochoa, S. (1952). *J. Biol. Chem.* **195:** 75. [IV]

1363. Volkin, E., and Astrachan, L. (1957). *In* "The Chemical Basis of Heredity" (W. McElroy and B. Glass, eds.), p. 686. Johns Hopkins Press, Baltimore, Maryland. [XIII]

1364. Von Baer, K. E. (1828). "Über Entwicklungsgeschichte der Thiere. I." Konigsberg. [I]

1365. Von Euler, U. S. (1946). *Acta Physiol. Scand.* **12:** 73. [XI]

1366. Von Wettstein, D. (1959). *In* "Developmental Cytology" (D. Rudnick, ed.), p. 123. Ronald Press, New York. [V]

1367. Von Wettstein, D. (1961). *Can. J. Botany* **39:** 1537. [V]

1368. Von Wettstein, F. (1937). *Z. Vererbungslehre* **73:** 349. [XX]

1369. Wachstein, M., and Fernandez, C. (1964). *J. Histochem. Cytochem.* **12:** 40. [XVI]

1370. Wahl, R., and Kozloff, L. (1962). *J. Biol. Chem.* **237:** 1953. [IX]

1371. Wake, R. G., and Baldwin, R. L. (1962). *J. Mol. Biol.* **5:** 201. [XIII]

1372. Waldeyer, N. W. G. (1891). *Deut. Med. Wochschr.* **17:** 1213. [XI]

1373. Walen, K. H. (1965). *Genetics* **51:** 915. [XVIII]

1374. Walker, P. G. (1952). *Biochem. J.* **51:** 223. [X]

1375. Walker, P. M. B., and Mitchison, J. M. (1957). *Exptl. Cell Res.* **13:** 167. [XIX]

1376. Wallace, H., and Birnstiel, M. L. (1966). *Biochim. Biophys. Acta* **114:** 296. [XVII]

1377. Waller, J. P. (1964). *J. Mol. Biol.* **10:** 319. [XIV]

1378. Wang, T.-Y. (1963). *Exptl. Cell Res.* **9** (Suppl.): 213. [XIV, XVII]

1379. Wang, T.-Y. (1965). *Proc. Natl. Acad. Sci. U.S.* **54:** 800. [XVII]

1380. Warburg, O. (1913). *Arch. Ges. Physiol.* **154:** 599. [VII]
1381. Warburg, O., and Christian, W. (1931). *Biochem. Z.* **242:** 206. [III]
1382. Warburg, O., and Christian, W. (1932). *Biochem. Z.* **254:** 438. [III]
1383. Warburg, O., and Christian, W. (1936). *Biochem. Z.* **287:** 291. [VI]
1384. Warburg, O., and Christian, W. (1939). *Biochem. Z.* **303:** 40. [VI]
1385. Warburg, O., and Ostendorf, P. (1963). *Z. Naturforsch.* **18b:** 933. [IV]
1386. Ward, R. T. (1962). *J. Cell Biol.* **14:** 309. [VII]
1387. Warner, J. R., and Rich, A. (1964). *J. Mol. Biol.* **10:** 202. [XIV]
1388. Warner, J. R., Rich, A., and Hall, C. E. (1962). *Science* **138:** 1399. [XIV]
1389. Warner, J. R., Knopf, P. M., and Rich, A. (1963). *Proc. Natl. Acad. Sci. U.S.* **49:** 122. [XIV]
1390. Warner, R. C. (1956). *Federation Proc.* **15:** 379. [XII]
1391. Watson, H. C., and Kendrew, J. C. (1961). *Nature* **190:** 670. [XII]
1392. Watson, J. D., and Crick, F. H. C. (1953). *Nature* **171:** 737, 964. [XII, XIII, XIV]
1393. Watson, M. R., and Hopkins, J. M. (1962). *Exptl. Cell Res.* **28:** 280. [IX]
1394. Waugh, D. F., and Schmitt, F. O. (1940). *Cold Spring Harbor Symp. Quant. Biol.* **8:** 233. [X]
1395. Weaver, N. (1957). *Ann. Entomol. Soc. Am.* **50:** 283. [XX]
1396. Weber, A. (1956). *Biochim. Biophys. Acta* **19:** 345. [VIII]
1397. Weber, A., Herz, R., and Reiss, I. (1963). *J. Gen. Physiol.* **46:** 679. [VIII]
1398. Weber, H. H. (1935). *Arch. Ges. Physiol.* **235:** 205. [VIII]
1399. Weibull, C. (1953). *Acta Chem. Scand.* **7:** 335. [IX]
1400. Weibull, C., Beckman, H., and Bergström, L. (1959). *J. Gen. Microbiol.* **20:** 519. [VII]
1401. Weier, T. E., and Benson, A. A. (1966). *In* "Biochemistry of Chloroplasts" (T. W. Goodwin, ed.), Vol. I, p. 91. Academic Press, New York. [V]
1402. Weier, T. E., and Thomson, W. W. (1962). *J. Cell Biol.* **13:** 89. [V]
1403. Weier, T. E., Stocking, C. R., Thomson, W. W., and Drever, H. J. (1963). *J. Ultrastruct. Res.* **8:** 122. [V]
1404. Weier, T. E., Engelbrecht, A., Harrison, A., and Risley, E. (1965). *J. Ultrastruct. Res.* **13:** 92. [V, VII, X]
1405. Weier, T. E., Stocking, C. R., and Shumway, L. K. (1966). *Brookhaven Symp. Biol.* **19:** 353. [V]
1406. Weil, R., and Vinograd, J. (1963). *Proc. Natl. Acad. Sci. U.S.* **50:** 730. [XV]
1407. Weiss, P., and Hiscoe, H. B. (1948). *J. Exptl. Zool.* **107:** 315. [XI]
1408. Weiss, P., and Pillai, A. (1965). *Proc. Natl. Acad. Sci. U.S.* **54:** 48. [VII]
1409. Weiss, S. B. (1960). *Proc. Natl. Acad. Sci. U.S.* **46:** 1020. [XIII, XVII]
1410. Weiss, S. B., and Fox, C. F. (1964). *In* "The Nucleohistones" (J. Bonner and P. Ts'o, eds.), p. 298. Holden-Day, San Francisco, California. [XIII]
1411. Weissmann, C. (1965). *Proc. Natl. Acad. Sci. U.S.* **54:** 202. [XIII]
1412. Weisz, P. B. (1956). *J. Exptl. Zool.* **131:** 137. [XIX]
1413. Went, H. A. (1960). *Ann. N.Y. Acad. Sci.* **90:** 422. [XIX]
1414. Werz, G., and Zetsche, K. (1963). *Planta* **59:** 563. [XVII]
1415. Wettstein, F. O., and Noll, H. (1965). *J. Mol. Biol.* **11:** 35. [XIV]
1416. Wettstein, R., and Sotelo, J. R. (1965). *J. Ultrastruct. Res.* **13:** 367. [XVIII]
1417. Whaley, W. G., Mollenhauer, H., and Leech, J. (1960). *J. Biophys. Biochem. Cytol.* **8:** 233. [XVII]
1418. Whaley, W. G., Kephart, J. E., and Mollenhauer, H. H. (1964). *In* "Cellular Membranes in Development" (M. Locke, ed.), p. 141. Academic Press, New York. [XVI]

Roman numerals refer to chapters in which each article is mentioned.

1419. Whatley, F. R., and Horton, A. A. (1963). *Acta Chem. Scand.* **17** (Suppl.): 140. [IV]
1420. White, E., McCapra, F., Field, G., and McElroy, W. (1961). *J. Am. Chem. Soc.* **83:** 2402. [VI]
1421. Whittam, R. (1964). *In* "The Cellular Functions of Membrane Transport" (J. F. Hoffman, ed.), p. 139. Prentice-Hall, Englewood Cliffs, New Jersey. [XI]
1422. Wieland, T., and Pattermann, F. (1959). *Chem. Ber.* **92:** 2917. [VI]
1423. Wiener, J., Spiro, D., and Loewenstein, W. (1963). *J. Cell Biol.* **19:** 75A. [XVII]
1424. Wilbrandt, W., and Laszt, L. (1933). *Biochem. Z.* **259:** 398. [XI]
1425. Wilde, C. E. (1958). *Anat. Record* **132:** 517. [VIII]
1426. Wilkins, M. H. F. (1956). *Cold Spring Harbor Symp. Quant. Biol.* **21:** 75. [XII]
1427. Wilkins, M. H. F. (1960). *In* "Nucleoproteins" (R. Stoops, ed.), p. 45. Wiley (Interscience), New York. [XII]
1428. Wilkins, M. H. F. (1963a). *Science* **140:** 941. [XII]
1429. Wilkins, M. H. F. (1963b). *In* "Aspects of Protein Structure" (G. N. Ramachandran, ed.), p. 23. Academic Press, New York. [XII]
1430. Wilkins, M. H. F., and Randall, J. T. (1953). *Biochim. Biophys. Acta* **10:** 192. [XVIII]
1431. Wilkins, M. H. F., and Zubay, G. (1959). *J. Biophys. Biochem. Cytol.* **5:** 55. [XV]
1432. Wilkins, M. H. F., Stokes, A. R., and Wilson, H. R. (1953). *Nature* **171:** 738. [XII]
1433. Wilkins, M. H. F., Zubay, G., and Wilson, H. R. (1959). *J. Mol. Biol.* **1:** 179. [XII, XVII]
1434. Williams, C. (1963). *In* "The Nature of Biological Diversity" (J. M. Allen, ed.), p. 243. McGraw-Hill, New York. [XX]
1435. Williamson, A. R., and Schweet, R. (1965). *J. Mol. Biol.* **11:** 358. [XIV]
1436. Willstätter, R., and Stoll, A. (1913). "Untersuchungen über das Chlorophyll." Springer, Berlin. [IV]
1437. Wilson, E. B. (1909). *J. Exptl. Zool.* **6:** 147. [XVIII]
1438. Wilson, E. B. (1896, 1925). "The Cell in Development and Heredity," 1st and 3rd eds. Macmillan, New York. [I, V, VII, XVII, XVIII, XIX]
1439. Wilson, G. B., and Sparrow, A. H. (1960). *Chromosoma* **11:** 229. [XVIII]
1440. Wilson, H. V. (1908). *J. Exptl. Zool.* **5:** 245. [XX]
1441. Wilson, T. H. (1964). *In* "The Cellular Functions of Membrane Transport" (J. F. Hoffman, ed.), p. 215. Prentice-Hall, Englewood Cliffs, New Jersey. [XI]
1442. Wilt, F. H. (1966). *Am. Zool.* **6:** 67. [XX]
1443. Wintersberger, E. (1966). *Biochem. Biophys. Res. Commun* **25:** 1. [VII]
1444. Wohlfarth-Bottermann, K. E. (1961). *Protoplasma* **54:** 1. [IX]
1445. Wohlfarth-Bottermann, K. E. (1964). *In* "Primitive Motile Systems in Cell Biology" (R. D. Allen and N. Kamiya, eds.), p. 79. Academic Press, New York. [IX]
1446. Wolff, S. (1963). "Radiation-Induced Chromosome Aberrations." Columbia Univ. Press, New York. [XVIII]
1447. Wolken, J. J., and Palade, G. E. (1952). *Nature* **170:** 114. [V]
1448. Wollman, E. L., and Jacob, F. (1955). *Compt. Rend. Acad. Sci.* **240:** 2449. [XV]
1449. Wolpert, L. (1960). *Intern. Rev. Cytol.* **10:** 164. [XIX]
1450. Wolstenholme, D. R. (1965). *Chromosoma* **17:** 219. [XVIII]
1450a. Wood, W. B., and Edgar, R. S. (1967). *Sci. Am.* **217** (1): 60. [XV]
1451. Woodward, D. O., and Munkres, K. D. (1966). *Proc. Natl. Acad. Sci. U.S.* **55:** 872. [VII]
1452. Woodward, R. B. (1960). *J. Am. Chem. Soc.* **82:** 3800. [IV]
1453. Wu, R., and Kaiser, A. D. (1968). *J. Mol. Biol.* **35:** 523. [XV]
1454. Yakushiji, E., and Okunuki, K. (1940). *Proc. Imp. Acad. Tokyo* **16:** 299. [III]
1455. Yamada, T. (1961). *Advan. Morphogenesis* **1:** 1. [XX]

1455a. Yamada, T. (1966). *Am. Zool.* **6:** 21. [XX]

1456. Yankofsky, S. A., and Spiegelman, S. (1963). *Proc. Natl. Acad. Sci. U.S.* **49:** 538. [XIV]

1457. Yanofsky, C. (1963). *Cold Spring Harbor Symp. Quant. Biol.* **28:** 581. [XV]

1457a. Yanofsky, C. (1964). *In* "The Bacteria" (I. Gunsalus and R. Stanier, eds.), Vol. V, p. 373. Academic Press, New York. [XV]

1458. Yanofsky, C., Carlton, B., Guest, J., Helinski, D., and Henning, U. (1964). *Proc. Natl. Acad. Sci. U.S.* **51:** 266. [XV]

1459. Yoo, B. Y., and Bayley, S. T. (1967). *J. Ultrastruct. Res.* **18:** 651. [XVII]

1460. Yoshikawa, H., and Sueoka, N. (1963). *Proc. Natl. Acad. Sci. U.S.* **49:** 559, 806. [XV]

1461. Young, J. Z. (1951). "Doubt and Certainty in Science." Oxford Univ. Press, London and New York. [I]

1462. Zachau, H., Acs, G., and Lipmann, F. (1958). *Proc. Natl. Acad. Sci. U.S.* **44:** 885. [XIV]

1462a. Zachau, H., Dutting, D., Feldmann, H., Melchers, F., and Karau, W. (1967). *Cold Spring Harbor Symp. Quant. Biol.* **31:** 417. [XIV]

1463. Zeuthen, E. (1964). "Synchrony in Cell Division and Growth." Wiley (Interscience), New York. [XIX]

1464. Zimmerman, A. M. (1960). *Exptl. Cell Res.* **20:** 529. [XIX]

1465. Zimmerman, A. M. (1963). *In* "The Cell in Mitosis" (L. Levine, ed.), p. 159. Academic Press, New York. [XIX]

1466. Zinder, N. D., and Lederberg, J. (1952). *J. Bacteriol.* **64:** 679. [XV]

1467. Zipser, D. (1963). *J. Mol. Biol.* **7:** 739. [XV]

1468. Zobel, C. R., and Carlson, F. D. (1963). *J. Mol. Biol.* **7:** 78. [VIII]

1469. Zubay, G. (1958). *Nature* **182:** 388. [XII]

1470. Zubay, G. (1962). *Proc. Natl. Acad. Sci. U.S.* **48:** 457. [XIII]

1471. Zubay, G. (1964). *In* "The Nucleohistones" (J. Bonner and P. Ts'o, eds.), p. 95. Holden-Day, San Francisco, California. [XII]

1472. Zubay, G., and Doty, P. (1959). *J. Mol. Biol.* **1:** 1. [XII]

1473. Zubay, G., and Watson, M. (1959). *J. Biophys. Biochem. Cytol.* **5:** 51. [XII]

1474. Zubay, G., and Wilkins, M. H. F. (1960). *J. Mol. Biol.* **2:** 105. [XIV]

1475. Zubay, G., and Wilkins, M. H. F. (1962). *J. Mol. Biol.* **4:** 444. [XII]

1476. Zubay, G., and Wilkins, M. H. F. (1964). *J. Mol. Biol.* **9:** 246. [XII]

1477. Zweidler, A. (1964). *Arch. Julius Klaus-Stift. Vererbungsforsch. Sozialanthropol. Rassenhyg.* **39:** 54. [XVIII]

Roman numerals refer to chapters in which each article is mentioned.

SUBJECT INDEX

A

Acetabularia
  cap form, nucleus and, 633–634
  cytoplasmic streaming in, 218
  enucleate
    protein synthesis in, 504, 505
    ribonucleic acid synthesis in, 504, 505
    survival of, 504
  grafting experiments with, 510
Acetaldehyde
  glycolysis and, 104, 107
  pyruvate oxidase and, 108–110
Acetylalanine, histones and, 333
β-Acetylamino-deoxyglucosidase, 255
Acetylcholine, myoneural junction and, 282–284
Acetyl coenzyme A
  energy level of, 34
  energy transfer and, 41–42
  fatty acid oxidation and, 111
  formation, 108–110
    free energy change and, 35, 36
  malate formation and, 113
N-Acetylglucosamine, lysozyme and, 304
N-Acetylmuramic acid, lysozyme and, 304
Acetyl phosphate, energy and, 38
Acetyl serine, tobacco mosaic virus protein and, 327
Acid phosphatase
  Golgi vacuoles and, 455, 456
  homogenate fractions and, 253
  lysosomes and, 254–257
  nucleoli and, 487
  synthesis, nucleus and, 505
Aconitase, citric acid cycle and, 111
cis-Aconitate, citric acid cycle and, 110, 111
Acrasin, cell aggregation and, 661
Acridine
  giant polytene chromosomes and, 540
  phage mutants, 394
    reversions and, 437–438
Acridine orange, kinetosomes and, 204

Acrosome, Golgi apparatus and, 453, 455
Actin
  chloroplast protein and, 81
  electron microscopy of, 166, 169–171
  extraction of, 169
  α-helical content of, 308
  localization of, 180
  mitotic apparatus and, 600
  muscle and, 167
  myosin and, 168
  properties of, 169
  screw-action, contraction and, 187
Actinomycin(s)
  enzyme induction and, 630
  hemoglobin synthesis and, 636
  nucleolar labeling and, 496, 497
Actinomycin D
  cell aggregation and, 660
  chloroplasts and, 99
  chromosomes and, 527
  lampbrush chromosomes and, 551
  messenger stability and, 390
  ribnucleic acid polymerase and, 367, 369
  ribonucleic acid replicase and, 365
  ribosome synthesis and, 484
  sea urchin eggs and, 634
Action potential
  membrane models and, 276–277
  plasma membrane and, 272–278
  velocity of propagation, 277
Active transport
  inhibitors of, 266
  large molecules and, 270–272
  model of, 269
  plasma membrane and, 264–272
  small molecules and, 266–270
Actomyosin
  adenosine triphosphate and, 175–177
  cyclosis and, 217
  electron microscopy of, 171, 172
  properties of, 172–173
Actomyosin-like protein
  amoebas and, 223

703

Myosin
    bridges to actin filaments, 180–182
        movement of, 185–186
    chloroplast protein and, 81
    extraction of, 168, 169
    localization of, 180
    molecules, electron microscopy of, 166–168
    muscle and, 167
    properties of, 168–169
    structure of, 308
    synthesis, differentiation and, 649
Myxomyosin, protoplasmic streaming and, 215

N

Naegleria, centrioles of, 204, 602
Neoxanthin, quantasomes and, 92
Nernst equation, membrane potential and, 261–262
Neural retina
    cells, aggregation of, 660
Neural tube, induction of, 650
Neuroblasts
    cytokinesis, spindle and, 611
    ganglion cell formation and, 647
Neuron
    action potential of, 273–274
    electrochemical gradient of, 262
    fine structure of, 279–281
    functional organization of, 278–286
    membrane depolarization, ions and, 232
    mitochondria, 153
        structure of, 132
    nuclear envelope of, 465, 468
    sodium ions in, 264
    structure of, 279
Neurospora
    crossing-over in, 570
    hybrid nucleic acid in, 324
    mitochondria, 129, 137
        deoxyribonucleic acid of, 152, 512–513
        origin of, 150–151
    mutants of, 404
Neutrons, chromosomes and, 576
Newt
    chromosomes, strandedness of, 568
Nicotinamide adenine dinucleotide
    biosynthesis of, 45

    citric acid cycle and, 112–113
    coupled phosphorylation and, 117–118
    energy level of, 34
    extra mitochondrial reduction of, 139
    fatty acid oxidation and, 111
    glycolysis and, 103–107
    α-ketoglutarate dehydrogenase and, 111
    luminescence and, 124, 125
    mitochondrial
        concentration of, 136
        permeability and, 137
        protein and, 137
    oxidation
        coenzyme Q and, 137
        coupled with phosphorylation, 113–116
    phosphoglyceraldehyde dehydrogenase and, 305
Nicotinamide adenine dinucleotide-cytochrome *c* reductase, microsomes and, 449
Nicotinamide adenine dinucleotide dehydrogenase
    localization of, 136
    pyruvate oxidase and, 108
Nicotinamide adenine dinucleotide diaphorase, microsomes and, 449
Nicotinamide adenine dinucleotide phosphate
    biosynthesis of, 45
    extramitochondrial reduction of, 139
    pentose shunt and, 113
    photophosphorylation and, 68–71
    photosynthesis and, 73–75
Nicotinamide adenine dinucleotide phosphate-cytochrome *c* reductase, electron cycling in, 48–49
Nicotinamide adenine dinucleotide synthetase
    nucleus and, 463, 478–479
    nucleoli and, 487
Nitella
    action potential of, 273
    cyclosis in, 216–218
    internal negative charge of, 261, 263
    plastids, division of, 95
Nitrate reductase, induction of, 630
Nitrous acid, mutations and, 438–439
Noctiluca
    luminescence of, 121